THE BOOK OF FUNGI

PETER ROBERTS AND SHELLEY EVANS

THE BOOK OF FUNGI

A LIFE-SIZE GUIDE TO SIX HUNDRED
SPECIES FROM AROUND THE WORLD

Ivy Press

DR. PETER ROBERTS was a senior mycologist at the Royal Botanic Gardens, Kew. He is the coauthor of *New Naturalist: Fungi*, *Checklist of the British and Irish Basidiomycota* and *British Chanterelles and Tooth Fungi*. He is also on the editorial boards of *Field Mycology*, *Mycological Progress*, *Czech Mycology* and *Persoonia*.

SHELLEY EVANS was conservation officer for the British Mycological Society for ten years and is on the executive committee of the European Council for the Conservation of Fungi and the IUCN world specialist group for fungi. She is coauthor of *Pocket Nature: Fungi* and the author of numerous survey reports on British fungi. She is also on the editorial board of the journal *Field Mycology*.

First published in Great Britain in 2013 by
Ivy Press
210 High Street, Lewes
East Sussex BN7 2NS
United Kingdom
www.ivypress.co.uk

Copyright © 2011 The Ivy Press Limited

British Library Cataloguing-in-Publication Data
A CIP catalogue record for this book is available from the British Library.

ISBN 978-1-908005-85-4

DISCLAIMER
This book is not a field guide. The authors and publisher strongly advise anyone foraying for fungi to enlist the help of an experienced mycologist. Never eat any fungus, raw or cooked, unless you are 100 percent certain it is safe to do so. The authors and publisher cannot accept any legal responsibility or liability for personal injury, illness or possible death arising from reading the information contained in this book, or from failure to accurately follow any instructions or warning it contains.

LITHOCASE IMAGE iStockphoto/tenback

Colour origination by Ivy Press Reprographics
Printed in China

Distributed worldwide (except North America) by
Thames & Hudson Ltd., 181A High Holborn,
London WC1V 7QX, United Kingdom

This book was conceived,
designed and produced by

Ivy Press
210 High Street, Lewes
East Sussex BN7 2NS
United Kingdom
www.ivypress.co.uk

Creative Director PETER BRIDGEWATER
Publisher JASON HOOK
Art Director MICHAEL WHITEHEAD
Editorial Director CAROLINE EARLE
Senior Editor STEPHANIE EVANS
Project Editor JAMIE PUMFREY
Commissioning Editor KATE SHANAHAN
Designer GLYN BRIDGEWATER
Consultant Reader GEOFFREY KIBBY
Picture Manager KATIE GREENWOOD
Illustrators ADAM HOOK, CORAL MULA
Map Artwork RICHARD PETERS

CONTENTS

RIGHT **The Beefsteak Fungus** (*Fistulina hepatica*) slowly rots away the heartwood of living oaks and chestnuts, gradually hollowing out their trunks.

FOREWORD

Colorful, bizarre, mysterious—fungi have evolved an extraordinary range of weird and wonderful shapes and forms in every part of the globe, from the tropics to the poles. Titanic toadstools erupt from termite mounds, evil-smelling stinkhorns attract flies to spread their spores, flamboyantly colored corals emerge in the depths of forests, giant brackets slowly hollow out ancient trees… fungi are hard at work all around us, yet all too often they go unnoticed and unappreciated.

This book celebrates the kingdom of the fungi with a worldwide selection of 600 different species, each one of interest not just for its appearance, but also for the role it plays in the great chain of life.

Everyone knows that some fungi are edible and that mushrooms are cultivated for food. But did you know that most trees and flowering plants also depend on fungal partners for their nutrition? Or that all the wood in the world is rotted down and recycled by fungi—helping to create the fertile soils that plants need to grow? Or that many of the pharmaceuticals we depend upon today were originally derived from fungi?

Every species featured in this book has its own particular lifestyle and this lifestyle often dictates its form. There are fungi described that look like miniature bird's nests and use raindrops to catapult their spores into the air, fungi that grow on their neighbors and sprout fruitbodies out of their caps, fungi from arid deserts that are tough enough to withstand sun and sand, fungi that catch leaves from the rainforest before they hit the ground, fungi that set traps for eelworms, fungi that entice foraging sows with the pheromones of wild boars.

Edible fungi are featured, including some of the less familiar species that are now finding their way onto supermarket shelves. Poisonous fungi are also here, as well as several that are hallucinogenic, and others that have been found to possess potentially useful properties—particularly in the search for new and better pharmaceuticals.

More than 75,000 species of fungi have been described worldwide and the numbers keep growing, year by year. Even if the microscopic species are discounted, that still leaves far too many species to include in any single volume. What this book aims to do, therefore, is to provide an illustrated snapshot of the astonishing diversity of fungi—not only rarities and oddities from distant lands, but many common and conspicuous fungi that are just as interesting and are certain to occur in local woodlands, public parks, or your own backyard.

This book is not a field guide, but it may encourage you to take a closer look at the fungal life that surrounds us. You do not have to remember all the names or pin down everything you find to a particular species. But if this book helps you to recognize some of the shapes and forms—and also provides some insight into what fungi are all about—then it will have more than served its purpose.

7

BELOW **Fungi are the primary recyclers** of fallen leaves and wood, naturally composting them into a rich, fertile humus.

INTRODUCTION

Modern systematics, based on analysis of DNA sequences, divides the kingdom Fungi into at least seven different groups or phyla. Although they are all of interest (fungi in the phylum Neocallimastigomycota, for example, live in the stomachs of ruminants, helping to break down plant material), most are microscopic and beyond the scope of this book. All the selected species, therefore, belong either to the Ascomycota or to the Basidiomycota—the two fungal phyla that produce large, visible fruitbodies.

THE ASCOMYCOTA

The Ascomycota contains at least 40,000 different species worldwide, many of them rather inconspicuous, but including such familiar groups as the morels and truffles, the cup fungi, and most of the lichens, as well as many microscopic molds and yeasts. They all produce their spores within microscopic cells called asci, which typically open under pressure when mature, shooting the spores out into the air currents.

ABOVE **Microscopic spores** (stained red) developing within tubelike asci are a diagnostic feature of fungi in the phylum Ascomycota.

THE BASIDIOMYCOTA

The Basidiomycota contains at least 30,000 different species worldwide and includes many of our most familiar fungi, including all the agarics (mushrooms and toadstools), puffballs and stinkhorns, bracket fungi, chanterelles, club and coral fungi, as well as the plant-parasitic rusts and smuts. All of them produce their spores on the external surface of microscopic cells called basidia (hence their name) and their fruitbodies have evolved in many ingenious ways in order to liberate these spores.

HOW THIS BOOK IS ARRANGED

Not so long ago, the scientific classification of the larger fungi was based on the macroscopic and microscopic features of the fruitbodies and was fairly straightforward and intuitive. DNA research, however, has shown that not all these intuitions are correct. Some species that look very different are actually quite closely related, while some of the look-alikes are far apart. Puffballs (*Lycoperdon* species), for example, belong in the same family as the Cultivated Mushroom (*Agaricus bisporus*), but you would never guess that by looking at the fruitbodies (see below)—even with a microscope.

In this book, to make things easier, the species have been arranged in a similar way to most practical field guides, with the agarics (gilled mushrooms and toadstools) first, and the boletes or ceps second. Other non-gilled relatives—including chanterelles, brackets, and puffballs—follow in their various groups, while the larger ascomycetes—including the morels and truffles – complete the selection. The species are arranged alphabetically within each group and the picture key on pages 24–27 will help you find your way around. For those who are interested, a more formal, scientific classification is provided on pages 648–49.

Each of the 600 featured species is illustrated with a life-size photograph and accompanied by a summary of its known distribution, typical habitat, association (with particular kinds of tree, for example), and growth form (whether it usually grows clustered on trunks or singly on the ground). The guide to frequency is on a global scale, so may be less meaningful locally. Location maps give a quick indication of each species' global distribution, and engravings offer different views of a fruitbody or its immature form, together with the vital statistics of height and diameter. Following common botanical practice, each species' author is cited (for an explanation of this convention, see page 649).

9

Cultivated Mushroom (*Agaricus bisporus*)

Spiny Puffball (*Lycoperdon echinatum*)

LEFT **Appearances are not necessarily a good** guide to identifying members of the same family: mushrooms produce their spores externally, puffballs internally but DNA sequencing shows that both are quite closely related.

WHAT ARE FUNGI?

A hundred years or more ago, fungi were thought of as lower plants or cryptogams, on a par with mosses and liverworts. They did not produce flowers and their seeds were very small, but they were still plants of a sort. However, it gradually became clear that fungi had little or nothing to do with plants. They were not made of cellulose, like plants, but of chitin (a substance more usually associated with insects). They did not contain chlorophyll and could not use sunlight to convert carbon dioxide into sugars. As a result, in the 1960s, they were placed in their own grouping—the kingdom Fungi. Curiously, modern DNA research puts the fungi even further from plants. Fungi are part of the opisthokonts—a group that also includes the animals. It seems animals and fungi once had a common ancestor, some time after plants went their separate way.

ABOVE **Plants can photosynthesize**, using sunlight to convert carbon dioxide into food, but fungi and animals obtain their nutrients by digesting organic matter.

HOW DO THEY WORK?

While animals and plants are made up of cells, fungi are made up of microscopically thin, tubelike hyphae. When they clump together, these hyphae can often be seen as cobwebby threads in damp leaf litter, in compost, or even on the surface of moldy food.

Fungi "eat" by absorbing food through their hyphal walls, mostly in the form of simple sugars and amino acids. If these are not immediately available, they can extract them from more complex substances by secreting enzymes. Animals, including ourselves, use similar enzymes in the stomach to digest food. Fungi do the same—only their digestive system is external.

FINDING YOUR WAY ROUND A MUSHROOM

When we look at a fungus, we are generally looking at a sporocarp—the spore-producing fruitbody that may be called a mushroom, a toadstool, a puffball, and so on. The real fungus—the cobwebby mycelium made up of hyphae—is generally beneath the soil, or spreading through the leaf litter, or running through a fallen log. It is rather as if oak trees grew hidden underground and all we saw were acorns periodically forming on the surface.

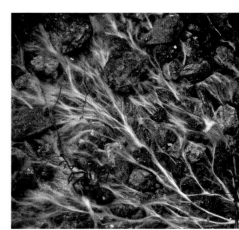

ABOVE **The mycelium** is the main "body" of the fungus that grows through soil, wood, or leaf litter, absorbing nutrients.

Take the Death Cap (*Amanita phalloides*, see below) as a classic example of a fungal fruitbody. It takes several weeks to develop on the mycelium, but once developed it expands quite rapidly from the button stage to maturity. It is this expansion that gave rise to the old idea of mushrooms and toadstools "growing" overnight.

The fruitbody has a distinct stem that lifts the cap and gills off the soil surface, the better to release spores into the air. The spores themselves (the fungal equivalent of seeds) are microscopic and are formed in their millions on the gills, which are covered by the cap. In the Death Cap, the immature gills are protected by a veil (membrane) that ruptures as the cap expands, leaving a ring on the stem. A second, universal veil encloses the whole fruitbody when young, the remains of which are left as detachable patches on the cap and as a sack-like volva at the stem base.

Other fruitbodies—of bracket fungi, stinkhorns, or morels—vary enormously in shape and in their methods of spore liberation, but the basic spore-bearing principle is the same.

11

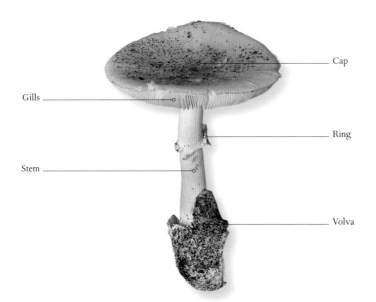

Cap

Gills

Ring

Stem

Volva

LEFT **The naming of parts** of the fruitbody, the spore-bearing organ of the Death Cap (*Amanita phalloides*).

RIGHT **Lichens are a** familiar example of a mutually beneficial, symbiotic partnership between two entirely different organisms—in this case fungi and algae.

PLANT & ANIMAL PARTNERS

Over 90 percent of the world's plant species depend on fungi for their nutrition. The two have evolved side by side and the partnership continues to this day, fungi and plants together supporting our whole global ecosystem. Other new fungal partnerships have also evolved—not only with plants, but with bacteria, algae, insects, and other animals.

HOW PLANTS GET THEIR NUTRITION

Fungi are excellent recyclers, producing enzymes that break down complex materials to release their nutrients. They were among the first colonists of dry land and interacted with early, primitive plants. The relationship may have been parasitic at first, but gradually evolved into a symbiotic one. Fungi obtain sugars from their plant partners, and plants take essential nutrients from fungi, principally nitrogen and phosphorus.

The exchange occurs through mycorrhiza ("fungus roots"). In the commonest form, endomycorrhizal fungi live inside a plant's root system. These fungi belong to the phylum Glomeromycota—an unfamiliar group to the majority of fungus enthusiasts, as most can only be seen under a microscope. Far more familiar are ectomycorrhizal associations. *Ecto* means "external," and in this association the fungi live outside the plants, forming an interface with them by wrapping their hyphae around the roots. Comparatively few plant species are involved, but these include some of our commonest trees—oak, beech, birch, willow, alder, pine, fir, spruce, hemlock, eucalyptus, and southern beech. Their fungal partners include many woodland agarics, boletes, chanterelles, and truffles.

LICHENS—TWO SPECIES IN ONE

Fungi cannot photosynthesize, but lichenized fungi have found a way round this by entering into an intimate partnership with algae or cyanobacteria (photosynthesizing bacteria). The fungi depend absolutely on their partners and never occur without them, but the algae and cyanobacteria can exist on their own—so the relationship is a bit one-sided. The algae and cyanobacteria do gain a safe home, however, and an opportunity to spread into areas they could never colonize on their own. The partnership is an extremely successful one, since lichens are extremophiles—able to grow in some of the world's most inhospitable environments.

13

FUNGUS GARDENS FOR TERMITES AND ANTS

Fungus–animal partnerships have also evolved, one of the most specialized being the termite fungi of Africa and Asia. Everyone knows that termites eat wood, but they have problems digesting it. Some species have microscopic fungi in their gut that break down cellulose, but others keep fungi in their nests that perform the same service. This partnership is so ancient that a whole genus of fungi called *Termitomyces* has evolved. The termites propagate and "garden" the fungus mycelium by bringing in fresh plant material and keeping everything at the right temperature and humidity. In Central and South America, similar fungus gardens are tended by leaf-cutting ants.

LEFT **Wood-boring ambrosia beetles**, such as *Myoplatypus flavicornis*, carry fungal species that grow in their burrows. The beetles and their larvae then graze on the fungal mycelium, rather than on the wood itself.

AMBROSIA BEETLES AND DUTCH ELM DISEASE

Bark beetles often carry fungal spores with them, sometimes in special pouches called mycangia. When burrowing into bark, the spores are released and the fungi—all of them wood-rotting species—grow in the beetle tunnels. The beetles or their larvae then graze the mycelium. This helps both fungi and beetles, but not always the trees. In the British Isles, *Scolytus* beetles spreading the exotic fungus *Ophiostoma novo-ulmi* have led to the epidemic called Dutch Elm Disease which has killed off an estimated 20 million elm trees.

NATURAL RECYCLERS

14

One of the reasons why fungi have developed a bad name for themselves—especially in the English-speaking world—is their popular association with rot and decay. Yet without decay, our whole terrestrial ecosystem would swiftly grind to a halt. It is fungi that are the great recyclers, turning dead plant matter—fallen leaves and stems, branches and trunks—into nutrient-rich humus and soil.

TURNING DEAD PLANTS INTO SOIL

Most fungi are saprotrophs—a term that means "eaters of dead matter." To rot things down and release the sugars and amino acids upon which they feed, fungi have evolved an array of useful enzymes. Some of these enzymes break down cellulose—the basic substance out of which plants are made.

The rotting process starts while leaves are still attached to the plant. Many microfungi colonize leaves, lying dormant until the leaf is ready to fall. The fungi then proliferate and start the breakdown process ahead of any competitors. When the leaf falls, there are other fungi ready and waiting. In some tropical rainforests, the leaf may not even reach the ground, since aerial webs of fungal rhizomorphs (threadlike structures) can catch a falling leaf and trap it. The aptly named Horsehair Fungus (*Marasmius crinisequi*) is one little agaric that can perform this leaf-catching trick.

ABOVE **Squirrels colonize the holes** left by rotted branches. Dead heartwood will be gradually rotted away by specialist fungi, leaving old trees hollow.

WOOD-ROTTING—A JOB FOR SPECIALISTS

All plants contain cellulose, but woody plants also contain lignin—the substance that makes wood hard. Brown rot fungi break down the cellulose and leave the brown lignin as a cake of powder. More common are the white rot species that break down both cellulose and lignin, leaving nothing much more than grayish white, stringy remains.

As with leaves, the wood-rotters get to work early. Many of them are present as small, dormant propagules in living wood, patiently waiting for their particular branch or twig to die. A change in the chemistry signals the end, and the dormant fungi get to work while the dead or dying branch is still on the tree. Most of these fungi are highly specialized, often growing on particular kinds of tree and no other.

When the branch hits the ground, however, the wood-rotting generalists battle over its remains—a struggle in which chemical weapons may be deployed to attack and defend a rich resource. Some species are quick colonizers, but they are replaced by slower, but more pugnacious, species, so that a succession of different fungi appears on a fallen branch, as it

ABOVE **Fallen branches** are decayed by a succession of different fungi that can break down both cellulose and lignin.

gradually rots away. A few highly developed specialists—mostly bracket fungi—can tackle heartwood. Found in the core of trunks and limbs, this is hard, dense, dead wood often full of tannins, oils, and other toxic chemicals. Eventually (and it may take decades), the heartwood is rotted away and the tree becomes hollow, yet still perfectly healthy—a wildlife haven in its own right.

HORNS, HOOVES, AND HAIR

Some fungi release enzymes that break down keratin, the main component of hair and feathers, hooves, horns, and skin. Most of these keratin-rotters are microscopic and some—like the Ringworm—can cause problems if they infect living skin, nails, or hair. The Horn Stalkball (*Onygena equina*) is one of the larger species, producing fruitbodies like small puffballs on old shed horns and other animal remains. Its relative, *O. corvina*, grows on old, discarded feathers.

PESTS & PARASITES

There is sometimes a fine line between a mutually beneficial relationship and a parasitic one—but a few fungi certainly cross that line and are undeniable parasites on plants, on animals, and even on other fungi. The same is true for pests. A fungus that rots down fallen trees in forests may be a useful species. But if it does the same thing to timber in the home, it is a pest.

HONEY FUNGUS—THE GARDENER'S BANE

The Honey Fungus (*Armillaria mellea*) is a wood-rotting species that has evolved a particularly efficient means of colonizing new resources, producing tough rhizomorphs (which resemble old-fashioned, black bootlaces) that can spread underground. When there is plenty of dead wood around, it is harmless. But when there is not, it will attack living trees and shrubs. In a garden, the Honey Fungus can run riot—and little can be done to stop it.

TIMBER EATERS

Household timber is generally too dry for fungi. But if the moisture content rises above 20 percent, some species can get to work. Dry Rot (*Serpula lacrymans*) is one that tolerates drier conditions than most. The waffle-like fruitbodies can also produce spores in such vast quantities that they can be a health problem in themselves. If the moisture content rises above 40 percent, then Wet Rot (*Coniophora puteana*) and other species can join in the destruction.

Creosote and other wood preservatives were invented to protect external timber from rotting, but a few fungi are creosote-tolerant. The Train Wrecker (an alternative name for *Neolentinus lepideus*) had a bad reputation for rotting old-fashioned, wooden railroad sleepers. Other fungi used to be pests of wooden telegraph poles or pit props in mines.

CATERPILLAR FUNGI

Cordyceps species attack a wide range of insects, from butterflies to beetles, wasps, and even ants. One of the best-known is the Chinese Caterpillar Fungus (*Ophiocordyceps sinensis*) which infects moth larvae. When the caterpillar goes underground to pupate, the fungus grows in the insect, eventually producing its own fruitbody above the ground. Traditional Chinese medicine regards this oddity—called "winter worm, summer grass"—as highly desirable, so that now collecting fruitbodies (with mummified caterpillar attached) is a profitable business.

ABOVE **Dried specimens of** the Chinese Caterpillar Fungus are worth their weight in gold to traditional herbalists.

FUNGI THAT HUNT WITH LASSOOS

It may seem improbable, but a few fungi are active predators, albeit on a microscopic scale. They mostly set traps for miniscule nematodes (eelworms). The species involved include the familiar Oyster Mushroom (*Pleurotus ostreatus*), which has sticky projections on its hyphae. Passing nematodes find themselves glued to the projections. The fungus assimilates the nematodes and uses them as a source of nitrogen. Some small cup fungi (*Drechslerella* species) have evolved lassoo-like traps—rings of hyphae that can swiftly constrict when triggered by a nematode passing through them.

FUNGI THAT PARASITIZE EACH OTHER

It should be no surprise to discover that some fungi parasitize their fellow fungi, often in rather peculiar ways. Among the oddest are agarics in the genus *Squamanita*. These species—all of them uncommon—parasitize the fruitbodies of other agarics, typically producing their own cap and gills on top of the host's stem.

The Lobster Fungus (*Hypomyces lactifluorum*) is another strange-looking object. It is a fungus that engulfs agarics, keeping their shape but coating them in a crust of its own miniature fruitbodies. Even stranger is the fact that these parasitized fruitbodies are considered edible and good.

ABOVE **The parasitic Lobster Fungus** covers the fruitbodies of its host fungi in a brightly colored crust.

FOOD, FOLKLORE & MEDICINE

Human beings are omnivores, and fungi have undoubtedly formed part of our diet since we first evolved. Cultural peculiarities, however, have led to some nations and communities being mycophiles—lovers of fungi—while others are mycophobic, with a deep distrust of the whole poisonous kingdom. Not surprisingly, this often colors folk beliefs and associations. The use of fungi in traditional medicine follows a similar pattern, but modern scientific medicine has been keen to explore their potential, with the result that many of today's most successful pharmaceuticals are fungus-derived.

ONE AND A HALF MILLION TONS OF MUSHROOMS

Around one and a half million tons of Cultivated Mushrooms (*Agaricus bisporus*) are produced worldwide each year. Their cultivation can be traced back to seventeenth-century France, where a substantial industry gradually developed based in cavernous, disused mines around Paris. Even today Cultivated Mushrooms in France are known as *champignons de Paris*. Modern commercial production was developed in the United States and mechanized in the Netherlands.

Perhaps surprisingly, *Agaricus bisporus* only accounts for some 40 percent of world cultivation. Other species, including the Shiitake (*Lentinula edodes*), the Oyster Mushroom (*Pleurotus ostreatus*), and the Wood Ear (*Auricularia cornea*), together make up the rest, with production and consumption predominantly in eastern Asia, though many of these species are becoming more popular in the west.

THE CALL OF THE WILD

Many edible fungi are still collected in the wild, not just by mushroom enthusiasts but on a commercial scale. The reason is that ectomycorrhizal species—those that form an intimate association with trees—cannot be cultivated away from their hosts. The Cep or Porcini (*Boletus edulis*) and the Chanterelle (*Cantharellus cibarius*) are among the most sought-after species, but in Japan a fascination with the Matsutake (*Tricholoma matsutake*)—often presented as expensive gifts—has led to a huge and lucrative import trade.

TRUFFLES—THE ULTIMATE PRIZE

Truffles (*Tuber* species) are underground fruitbodies of ectomycorrhizal fungi whose spores are spread by animals attracted by pheromones and other tempting aromas. Some of these tempt humans as well, and species such as *Tuber magnatum* have long been rare and costly items for European gourmets. In recent years, truffles have been semi-cultivated with varying success in truffières—plantations of trees inoculated with mycelium—but they still remain one of the ultimate luxury foods.

MAGIC MUSHROOMS AND WITCHES' BUTTER

In mycophilic countries, fungi often played a positive role in folk tales, some hallucinogenic species—such as the Fly Agaric (*Amanita muscaria*)—achieving an almost sacred status among shamans seeking contact with the spirit world. In mycophobic countries, they were regarded with suspicion. The Witches' Butter (*Exidia glandulosa*) was one of several fungi whose mysterious appearance could only be explained by witchcraft, while circles of the Fairy Ring Champignon (*Marasmius oreades*) marked the dangerous enclaves of the Little People.

ABOVE **Amanita muscaria**, the Fly Agaric, is everyone's idea of a traditional, fairytale toadstool, and is also a powerful hallucinogen.

THE FUNGAL PHARMACY

Fungi have long played a part in traditional medicine—especially in eastern Asia, where species such as the Lacquered Bracket (*Ganoderma lucidum*) are still highly valued today. In modern western medicine, antibiotics such as penicillin (derived from the mold *Penicillium chrysogenum*), cholesterol-lowering statins (derived from species such as *Aspergillus terreus*), and immunosuppressive cyclosporins (derived from *Tolypocladium inflatum*) are among many clinically proven pharmaceuticals with a fungal origin.

DISTRIBUTION & CONSERVATION

There are few, if any places, on planet Earth where fungi of some kind do not make themselves at home. As a group, they are ubiquitous. Even individual species tend to be widespread, at least when compared to animals and plants. Unfortunately this does not prevent some fungi from being threatened—mainly through habitat loss—making conservation a matter of increasing urgency.

ABOVE **Edible but critically endangered,** the White Ferula Oyster (*Pleurotus nebrodensis*) is known only in the wild from northern Sicily, but has now been brought into cultivation.

A WORLD OF FUNGI, FROM POLE TO POLE

No one knows how many different fungi exist, but a widely accepted estimate suggests around 1.5 million species, only a fraction of which are as yet described. These include not only the familiar larger fungi of the temperate zones, but the less well-investigated fungi of the tropics—plus countless microscopic species. We do not usually think of fungi as marine organisms, but at least 800 species are adapted to life at sea—some being found as deep as the abyssal zone, 2000–3000 fathoms (4000–6000 m) below sea level. Even Antarctica harbors more than 600 known species, including three recently discovered rotting the wood of explorer Captain Scott's expedition huts.

TEMPERATE AND TROPICAL FUNGI

Fungal species typically follow ancient distribution patterns that span the continents. In the north temperate zone, many species are found in Europe, northern Asia, and western North America. Curiously, the Great Plains often cut this distribution short, so that eastern North America has a distinctive group of fungi all its own. A pantropical distribution is equally common, though sometimes South America is left out of the circle. In the southern hemisphere, where land masses are more sparse, Australia and New Zealand have many distinctive fungi not found elsewhere.

FUNGI OF FORESTS AND WOODLANDS

When searching for fungi, most enthusiasts head for the woods. It is certainly the habitat that holds the greatest diversity of species, partly because so many fungi are leaf- and wood-rotters, partly because many of the more conspicuous fungi form associations with trees. Oddly, these ectomycorrhizal associations are less common in tropical forests where fruitbodies may sometimes be disappointingly sparse.

FUNGI OF GRASSLANDS, DUNES, AND DESERTS

Grasslands, especially when grazed, hold many interesting species, particularly in Europe. Marshes, swamps, and bogs also have distinctive fungi, some associated with wetland trees. Even the drylands—steppes, deserts, and sand dunes—have specialized species.

THREATENED HABITATS AND SPECIES

Since the presence of a fungus is mainly indicated by its fruitbodies, it is not always easy to tell whether a species is genuinely rare or whether it only produces fruitbodies rarely, and not all the larger fungi produce fruitbodies every year. With lichens (where the whole fungus is always visible), rarity is easier to assess.

At present, it seems that the most vulnerable species are those suffering habitat loss—typically through the loss of ancient forests, agricultural improvements increasing nitrogen levels, drainage of wetlands, and other wholesale changes in land use. Several countries now include larger fungi on their national "Red Lists"—lists of endangered and threatened species requiring conservation—some even giving them legal protection. Only two fungi, however, are on the global Red List of the International Union for Conservation of Nature: the White Ferula Oyster, *Pleurotus nebrodensis*, and the Boreal Felt Lichen, *Erioderma pedicellatum*, both of which are highly localized and critically endangered.

ABOVE **Destruction of habitat**, especially ancient forests and unimproved grasslands, is the main threat to fungal species worldwide.

21

COLLECTING & IDENTIFYING FUNGI

For anyone interested in identifying larger fungi there is no shortcut. You will need to examine a lot of specimens and take the time to become familiar with their typical haunts and habits, their many variations (when young or old, when wet or dry), and their distinguishing features compared to other species.

ABOVE **Spore print** (left) from the gills of *Chlorophyllum molybdites*,the False Parasol, showing its distinctive green tint.

GETTING TO KNOW YOUR LOCAL FUNGI

As with birdwatching or botanizing, gaining a familiarity with your local fungi can be a real pleasure. For larger fungi, a good local or regional field guide is essential, though for some parts of the world such guides are sadly lacking. A few species may be sufficiently distinctive to be instantly recognizable, but most require the patient use of an identification key—carefully reading descriptions, not just matching the specimen to a similar-looking photograph. Experience is essential, and joining a local fungus group or club is an excellent way of getting to see a lot of different species and share expertise.

"PERYLLOUS AND DREDFULL TO EATE"

The Grete Herball of 1526 needlessly reminded the mycophobic British that fungi are only eaten at one's peril—but this maxim remains true for anyone out mushroom-hunting for food. There are a lot of poisonous fungi out there, including some that can kill. This book is not intended as a guide to collecting fungi for food and should never be used as such. The

best advice for the would-be mushroom-hunter is to learn to identify the deadly ones. If in any doubt about your identification, never eat them.

Note that in many countries you will need the landowner's permission to collect fungi. In some areas, you may also need official permits—and many sites will be off-limits, with the right to collect edible fungi keenly protected. Collecting in nature reserves is frequently restricted, and in some countries it is against the law to collect certain rare and protected species.

FIRST STEPS IN IDENTIFYING FUNGI

With agarics, take care to collect the whole fruitbody. Never cut the stem or a deadly *Amanita* species may lose its volva and start to look like an edible mushroom. Use a flat basket or sectioned container to avoid jumbling specimens. Make notes in the field on habitat and associations. Note colors in daylight and check color changes when fruitbodies are bruised or cut. Record any smells before they disappear. A hand lens may help with tiny features. For many fungi, especially agarics, a spore print is often helpful. Take a mature cap and place it with the spore-bearing surface (the gills or pores) facing downward on a piece of glass. Cover the fruitbody with an inverted tumbler, to prevent it drying out, and leave for a few hours or overnight. The spore color should then be apparent—as long as the fungus is shedding spores (bracket fungi are often sterile).

You should now be armed with all the information you need to key a fungus out using macroscopic characters. You may not get to a species this way but you should be able to narrow your find to a genus or a group.

GUIDE TO THE FUNGI

This guide to the different kinds of fungi in this book is not a key, but may help you to identify some of the more common and widespread species— or at least discover to which group they may belong. Less than one percent of known fungal species are featured in this volume, so be aware that the particular fungus that you are looking for may not be here.

AGARICS

Fleshy fruitbodies; cap with or without stem; gills underneath cap (rarely pores) Species with gilled fruitbodies are in this section, but note that some chanterelles (pp. 476–83) have gill-like ridges or veins and some bracket fungi (pp. 364–420) have tough or woody, gill-like undersurfaces.

WHITE TO PALE-SPORED, STEMLESS OR SIDE-STEMMED
Mostly on wood

Anthracophyllum (p. 62), Campanella (p. 73), Hohenbuehelia (p. 150), Lentinellus (p. 196), Omphalotus (pp. 249, 250), Panellus (pp. 255, 256), Phyllotopsis (p. 266), Pleurotus (pp. 267–70), Rhodotus (p. 281), Schizophyllum (p. 297)

WHITE TO PALE-SPORED, CENTRAL STEM, RINGLESS, SMALL
Cap up to 2 in (50 mm) across, stem without distinct ring

Amparoina (p. 59), Asterophora (p. 65), Calocybe (pp. 69–71), Camarophyllopsis (p. 72), Crinipellis (p. 116), Cyptotrama (p. 117), Cystolepiota (p. 121), Dendrocollybia (p. 122), Favolaschia (pp. 133, 134), Filoboletus (p. 135), Gliophorus (p. 139), Heliocybe (p. 149), Humidicutis (pp. 151, 152), Hygrocybe (pp. 153–63), Laccaria (p. 180), Lactocollybia (p. 195), Lepiota (p. 200–5), Lichenomphalia (p. 216), Marasmius (pp. 224–32), Micromphale (p. 237), Mycena (pp. 238–47), Rickenella (pp. 282, 283), Roridomyces (p. 285), Tetrapyrgos (p. 307), Xeromphalina (p. 322)

WHITE TO PALE-SPORED, CENTRAL STEM, RINGLESS, LARGE
Cap typically more than 2 in (50 mm) across, stem without distinct ring

Amanita (pp. 42–58), Ampulloclitocybe (pp. 60, 61), Calocybe (pp. 69, 71), Clitocybe (pp. 79–82), Flammulina (p. 136), Gymnopus (pp. 144–46), Hygrocybe (pp. 153–63), Hygrophoropsis (p. 164), Hygrophorus (pp. 165–68), Hypsizygus (pp. 170, 171), Infundibulicybe (p. 172), Laccaria (pp. 179, 180), Lactarius (pp. 182–94), Lentinula (p. 197), Lentinus (pp. 198, 199), Lepiota (pp. 200–5), Lepista (pp. 206–8), Leucopaxillus (p. 215), Lyophyllum (pp. 218, 219), Macrocybe (p. 220), Macrocystidia (p. 221), Melanoleuca (p. 233), Phylloporus (p. 265), Pseudoclitocybe (p. 277), Russula (pp. 286–96), Squamanita (p. 298), Termitomyces (p. 306), Tricholoma (pp. 308–16), Tricholomopsis (pp. 317, 318), Xerula (p. 323)

WHITE TO PALE-SPORED, CENTRAL STEM, RINGED
Stem with distinct ring

Amanita (pp. 42–58), Armillaria (p. 63), Catathelasma (p. 75), Chlorophyllum (pp. 76, 77), Cystoderma (pp. 119–20), Floccularia (p. 137), Lepiota (pp. 200–5), Leucoagaricus (p. 211), Leucocoprinus (pp. 212–14), Limacella (p. 217), Macrolepiota (pp. 222, 223), Neolentinus (p. 248), Oudemansiella (p. 251), Tricholoma (pp. 308–16)

PINK TO REDDISH-SPORED, CENTRAL STEM

Clitopilus (p. 83), Entoloma (pp. 123–32), Lepista (pp. 206–8), Macrocystidia (p. 221), Melanophyllum (pp. 234–35), Pluteus (pp. 271–4), Rhodocollybia (p. 280), Volvariella (pp. 320, 321)

AGARICS (CONTD)

GREEN-SPORED, CENTRAL STEM

Chlorophyllum (pp. 76, 77), *Melanophyllum* (pp. 234, 235)

RUSTY TO BROWN-SPORED, STEMLESS OR SIDE-STEMMED

Mostly on wood

Crepidotus (pp. 113–15), *Tapinella* (pp. 304, 305)

RUSTY TO BROWN-SPORED, CENTRAL STEM

Agrocybe (pp. 40, 41), *Austropaxillus* (p. 66), *Bolbitius* (p. 68), *Conocybe* (pp. 84–6), *Cortinarius* (pp. 93–112), *Galerina* (p. 138), *Gymnopilus* (pp. 142, 143), *Hebeloma* (pp. 147–8), *Inocybe* (pp. 173–77), *Kuehneromyces* (p. 178), *Panaeolina* (p. 252), *Paxillus* (p. 258), *Phaeocollybia* (p. 259), *Phaeolepiota* (p. 260), *Phaeomarasmius* (p. 261), *Pholiota* (p. 262–64), *Tubaria* (p. 319)

CHOCOLATE-BROWN TO BLACK-SPORED, CENTRAL STEM

Agaricus (pp. 32–39), *Chroogomphus* (p. 78), *Coprinus* (pp. 87–92), *Cystoagaricus* (p. 118), *Gomphidius* (pp. 140, 141), *Hypholoma* (p. 169), *Lacrymaria* (p. 181), *Leratiomyces* (pp. 209, 210, 517), *Panaeolus* (pp. 253, 254), *Parasola* (p. 257), *Psathyrella* (pp. 275, 276), *Psilocybe* (pp. 278, 279), *Stropharia* (pp. 299–303)

BOLETES

Fleshy fruitbodies; cap with stem; spongelike pores underneath cap
Some bracket fungi (e.g. *Amauroderma*, p. 368, and *Boletopsis*, p. 371) also have central stems with pores below the cap. A few, mainly tropical agarics (e.g. *Favolaschia*, pp. 133, 134, *Filoboletus*, p. 135) also have pores.

Boletellus (pp. 326, 327), *Boletus* (pp. 328–42), *Chalciporus* (p. 343), *Gyroporus* (pp. 344, 345), *Heimioporus* (p. 346), *Leccinum* (pp. 347–50), *Pseudoboletus* (p. 351), *Pulveroboletus* (p. 352), *Strobilomyces* (p. 353), *Suillus* (pp. 354–58), *Tylopilus* (pp. 359–61)

BRACKET FUNGI

Hard to fleshy fruitbodies; mostly bracket or shelf-like with pores (rarely teeth) Typically on wood or at the base of trunks. Some are perennial and hard, others annual and soft. Most have caps, but some are effused and crustlike. A few have caps with central stems and may look a little like boletes (pp. 324–61).

CAP, HARD, WOODY, OR LEATHERY, NO CENTRAL STEM

Cryptoporus (p. 376), *Daedalea* (p. 377), *Daedaleopsis* (p. 378), *Datronia* (p. 379), *Echinodontium* (p. 380), *Fomes* (p. 383), *Fomitopsis* (pp. 384–85), *Ganoderma* (pp. 386–87), *Heterobasidion* (p. 392), *Hexagonia* (p. 393), *Ischnoderma* (p. 397), *Lenzites* (p. 399), *Phellinus* (p. 405), *Pseudoinonotus* (p. 414), *Pycnoporus* (p. 415), *Rigidoporus* (p. 416–17), *Trametes* (p. 419), *Trichaptum* (p. 420)

CAP HARD, WOODY, OR LEATHERY, CENTRAL STEM

Amauroderma (p. 368), *Coltricia* (p. 375), *Lignosus* (p. 400), *Microporus* (p. 402), *Polyporus* (pp. 409–11)

CAP, SOFT, FLESHY, OR PLIABLE, NO CENTRAL STEM

Abortiporus (p. 364), *Aurantiporus* (p. 369), *Bjerkandera* (p. 370), *Bondarzewia* (p. 372), *Climacodon* (p. 374), *Favolus* (p. 381), *Fistulina* (p. 382), *Gloeophyllum* (p. 388), *Grifola* (p. 389), *Hapalopilus* (p. 390), *Hydnopolyporus* (p. 394), *Inonotus* (pp. 395, 396), *Laetiporus* (p. 398), *Meripilus* (p. 401), *Phaeolus* (p. 404), *Piptoporus* (pp. 406, 407), *Plicaturopsis* (p. 408), *Polyporus* (pp. 409–11), *Postia* (pp. 412, 413)

CAP, SOFT, FLESHY, OR PLIABLE, CENTRAL STEM

Albatrellus (pp. 365–67), *Boletopsis* (p. 71), *Onnia* (p. 403), *Polyporus* (pp. 409–11)

NO CAP OR STEM, PATCH-LIKE

Ceriporia (p. 373), *Datronia* (p. 379), *Henningsomyces* (p. 391), *Inonotus* (pp. 395, 396), *Schizopora* (p. 418)

CRUST FUNGI

Variously shaped fruit-bodies; surface smooth, veined, or toothed Most form crusts on wood. Some are bracket-like, but smooth underneath (see also *Auricularia*, pp. 443–5). A few are fan- to goblet-shaped, or form rosettes. Frond-like lichens (e.g. *Parmelia*, p. 636) may look similar.

NO CAP, CRUST- OR PATCH-LIKE

Aleurodiscus (p. 421), *Coniophora* (p. 423), *Cytidia* (p. 425), *Hymenochaete* (p. 427), *Phlebia* (p. 429), *Sarcodontia* (p. 434), *Serpula* (p. 435), *Terana* (p. 440)

CAP, BRACKET- OR SHELFLIKE

Chondrostereum (p. 422), *Dictyonema* (p. 426), *Merulius* (p. 428), *Serpula* (p. 435), *Stereum* (pp. 437–39), *Thelephora* (pp. 441, 442)

CAP, FAN- OR ROSETTE-LIKE

Cymatoderma (p. 424), *Podoscypha* (pp. 430, 431), *Podoserpula* (p. 432), *Sparassis* (p. 436), *Thelephora* (p. 505)

JELLY FUNGI

Gelatinous or rubbery fruitbodies of various shapes Several cup fungi (e.g. *Ascocoryne*, p. 552, and *Bulgaria*, p. 554) are equally gelatinous. Species with branched fruitbodies resemble the club and coral fungi (pp. 484–505)

Auricularia (pp. 443–45), Calocera (pp. 446, 447), Dacrymyces (p. 448), Dacryopinax (p. 449), Exidia (pp. 450, 451), Guepinia (p. 452), Pseudohydnum (p. 453), Sebacina (p. 454), Syzygospora (p. 456), Tremella (pp. 457–60), Tremellodendron (p. 461)

TOOTH AND SPINE FUNGI

Fruitbodies with spines or teeth, instead of pores or gills Fruitbodies on the ground have stem and cap with spines underneath. Fruitbodies on wood may resemble swarms or clusters of pendant spines or are bracket-like with spines instead of pores (see also *Climacodon*, p. 374, and *Echinodontium*, p. 380). If gelatinous, see *Pseudohydnum* (p. 453)

ON GROUND

Bankera (p. 465), Hydnellum (pp. 469, 470), Hydnum (p. 471), Phellodon (p. 474), Sarcodon (p. 475)

ON WOOD OR CONES

Auriscalpium (p. 464), Deflexula (p. 466), Hericium (pp. 467, 468), Mucronella (pp. 472, 473)

CHANTERELLES

Fruitbodies often funnel- or trumpet-shaped, with smooth or veined undersurface

Cantharellus (pp. 476–79), Craterellus (pp. 480, 481), Gomphus (p. 482, 483)

CLUBS AND CORALS

Fruitbodies like clubs or elongated spindles, branched or unbranched Several jelly fungi (e.g. *Calocera*, pp. 446, 447, *Tremellodendron*, p. 461) have similarly shaped but gelatinous fruitbodies. Some unrelated flask fungi (e.g. *Cordyceps*, p. 611, *Podostroma*, p. 622) are also club- or coral-shaped.

BRANCHED

Artomyces (p. 485), Clavaria (pp. 486–90), Clavulina (p. 492, Clavulinopsis (pp. 493, 494), Lachnocladium (p. 495), Pterula (p. 498), Ramaria (pp. 499–503), Ramariopsis (p. 504), Thelephora (pp. 441, 442, 505)

UNBRANCHED

Alloclavaria (p. 484), Clavaria (pp. 486–90), Clavariadelphus (p. 491), Clavulinopsis (pp. 493, 494), Macrotyphula (p. 496), Physalacria (p. 497)

PUFFBALLS, EARTHBALLS, AND EARTHSTARS

Ball-like fruitbodies; with or without a stem or starlike base Some puffball-like species with stems may look like old but unopened agarics. Some without stems resemble truffles (pp. 603–9).

STEM

Battarrea (p. 509), Calostoma (p. 511), Chlorophyllum (p. 513), Gallacea (p. 514), Leratiomyces (p. 517), Longula (p. 518), Lycoperdon (pp. 519–21), Macowanites (p. 522), Montagnea (p. 523), Podaxis (p. 526), Tulostoma (p. 530), Weraroa (p. 531)

NO STEM, STARLIKE ARMS

Astraeus (p. 508), Geastrum (pp. 515, 516), Myriostoma (p. 524)

NO STEM, NO STARLIKE ARMS

Bovista (p. 510), Calvatia (p. 512), Pisolithus (p. 525), Rhizopogon (p. 527), Scleroderma (p. 528), Stephanospora (p. 529)

BIRD'S NEST FUNGI

Cuplike or starlike fruitbodies with "eggs" inside

Cyathus (pp. 532, 533), Nidula (p. 534), Sphaerobolus (p. 535)

STINKHORNS

Fruitbodies emerging from an "egg;" spore mass slimy, foul-smelling Remains of the egglike receptacle persist at the base of the stem. *Battarrea* (p. 509) has a similar basal "egg," but its spore mass is powdery and dry.

TUBULAR

Mutinus (pp. 542, 543), Phallus (pp. 544, 545), Staheliomyces (p. 547)

FORMING ARMS OR CAGE

Aseroe (p. 536), Clathrus (pp. 537, 538), Ileodictyon (p. 539), Lysurus (pp. 540, 541), Pseudocolus (p. 546)

CUP FUNGI

Fruitbodies disc- or cup-shaped, sometimes with a stem Fruitbodies often become distorted with age or when growing close together. Some lichens (e.g. *Teloschistes*, p. 638) and false morels (*Helvella*, pp. 595–98) also produce disc- or goblet-shaped fruitbodies, as do a few unrelated fungi (such as *Merismodes*, p. 236) and several of the crust fungi (such as *Cymatoderma*, p. 424). Drumstick-shaped fruitbodies are also found in the flask fungi (pp. 610–26) and the puffballs (pp. 508–31).

CUP-SHAPED
No stem

Aleuria (pp. 550, 551), Ascocoryne (p. 552), Bulgaria (p. 554), Caloscypha (p. 555), Disciotis (p. 562), Galiella (p. 564), Geopora (p. 565), Humaria (p. 567), Neobulgaria (p. 577), Peziza (pp. 579–83), Phillipsia (p. 584), Sarcoscypha (p. 586), Sarcosoma (p. 587), Sarcosphaera (p. 588), Tarzetta (p. 591)

GOBLET-SHAPED
Stem

Aleuria (pp. 550, 551), Caloscypha (p. 555), Chlorociboria (p. 557), Cookeina (p. 559), Dumontinia (p. 563), Lachnellula (p. 568), Lachnum (p. 569), Lanzia (p. 570), Microstoma (p. 575), Otidea (p. 578), Peziza (pp. 579–83), Tarzetta (p. 591), Urnula (p. 593)

DISC-SHAPED, WITH OR WITHOUT STEM

Ascocoryne (p. 552), Bisporella (p. 553), Bulgaria (p. 554), Catinella (p. 556), Disciotis (p. 562), Lachnellula (p. 568), Lachnum (p. 569), Neobulgaria (p. 577), Peziza (pp. 579–83), Phillipsia (p. 584), Rhizina (p. 585), Sarcoscypha (p. 586), Scutellinia (p. 589)

GOLFBALL-SHAPED
In clusters on trees of southern beech

Cyttaria (pp. 560, 561)

CLUB- OR DRUMSTICK-SHAPED
Swollen or ball-like head, long stem

Chlorovibrissea (p. 558), Leotia (pp. 571, 572), Microglossum (pp. 573, 574), Mitrula (p. 576)

MORELS

Lobed or honeycomb-like head with stem

Gyromitra (p. 594), Helvella (pp. 595–98), Mitrophora (p. 599), Morchella (pp. 600, 601), Verpa (p. 602)

27

TRUFFLES

Ball- or potato-shaped fruitbodies, wholly or partly under litter or soil False truffles, such as *Rhizopogon* (p. 527) and *Stephanospora* (p. 529) look very similar.

Elaphomyces (p. 603), Hydnotrya (p. 604), Paurocotylis (p. 605), Terfezia (p. 606), Tuber (pp. 607–9)

FLASK FUNGI

Variously shaped fruitbodies; often hard; often with a pimply surface Many of the "fruitbodies" of the flask fungi are actually sterile "stroma" in which the true fruitbodies are immersed, looking like pimples or dots under a magnifying lens. Several species look similar to the club and coral fungi (pp. 484–505).

DRUMSTICK-LIKE OR DISC-SHAPED
Ball- or disc-shaped head and stem

Claviceps (p. 610), Elaphocordyceps (pp. 613, 614), Onygena (p. 620), Poronia (p. 623)

BALL- OR CUSHION-SHAPED
Little or no stem; on wood

Daldinia (p. 612), Hypocreopsis (p. 615), Hypoxylon (p. 618), Nectria (p. 619)

CLUB- OR CORAL-SHAPED
Branched or unbranched

Cordyceps (p. 611), Ophiocordyceps (p. 621), Podostroma (p. 622), Xylaria (pp. 624–26)

PARASITIZING AGARICS
Wholly or partly covering fruitbodies in a pimply crust

Hypomyces (pp. 616, 617)

LICHENS

Shrubby, branched, hair-like, or crust-forming fungi; may be on rocks; often gray, greenish, or yellowish Lichen "fruitbodies" are actually thalli—a mixture of fungal hyphae and the cells of their associated algae or cyanobacteria. Some have small, disc-like fruitbodies arising from the thalli.

SHRUBBY OR HAIRLIKE
Finely branched or hanging in strands

Bryoria (p. 627), Cladonia (pp. 628–30), Evernia (p. 633), Letharia (p. 634), Teloschistes (p. 638), Usnea (p. 640)

LOBED OR FRONDLIKE
Flattened lobes or fronds, but not bracket-like

Collema (p. 631), Erioderma (p. 632), Lobaria (p. 635), Parmelia (p. 636), Peltigera (p. 637), Umbilicaria (p. 639), Xanthoria (p. 641)

SIZES

Note that the dimensions given for each species in the main text can only be approximations, since fruitbodies are often highly variable. The line drawings provide an alternative view, or, where appropriate, show how an immature specimen may look different from a mature one.

THE FUNGI

AGARICS

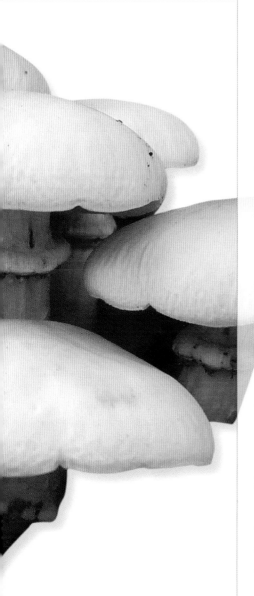

Think of the word "fungi" and it is likely that an agaric fruitbody—with its cap, gills, and stem—is the image that first comes to mind. Back in the eighteenth century, all fungi of this shape were placed in the genus *Agaricus*—hence the name "agaric." But in everyday English, they were called "mushrooms and toadstools," mushrooms being edible (very, very few) and toadstools being inedible and almost certainly poisonous (very, very many). The English used to think toads were poisonous as well, hence the association with toadstools.

Today, agarics are still referred to as mushrooms and toadstools in the British Isles, Australia, and New Zealand—but in North America, the word "mushroom" has expanded to include almost all the larger fungi. That is why, to avoid misunderstanding these globally fluid interpretations, the word "agaric" is used in this book.

Not all the fungi that produce agaric fruitbodies are closely related. Some, such as *Lentinus* species (see pages 198–99), are really just bracket fungi with gills. Others, such as *Phylloporus* species (see pages 265–96), are boletes with gills. It seems that the cap, gills, and stem shape is so successful at its job of spreading spores that it has evolved several times over.

FAMILY	Agaricaceae
DISTRIBUTION	North America, Europe, Asia, Australia, New Zealand
HABITAT	In nutrient-rich grassland and pastures, more rarely in woodland
ASSOCIATION	With grass
GROWTH FORM	On ground, singly or in troops and rings
ABUNDANCE	Common
SPORE COLOR	Chocolate-brown
EDIBILITY	Edible

HEIGHT
Up to 5 in
(120 mm)

CAP DIAMETER
Up to 6 in
(150 mm)

32

AGARICUS ARVENSIS

HORSE MUSHROOM

SCHAEFFER

The Horse Mushroom is one of the largest true mushrooms and is frequent in old pastures. When fresh, it has a sweetish smell of aniseed or almonds, and the cap and stem bruise yellow. In Britain, it was traditionally considered tougher than the smaller Field Mushroom (*Agaricus campestris*) and of uncertain edibility, hence probably its dismissive "Horse Mushroom" name (though this could also have referred to its size or to its habit of growing in horse paddocks). In fact, the species is perfectly edible. In recent years it has been commercially cultivated and marketed, usually as an expensive "exotic" mushroom.

SIMILAR SPECIES

Agaricus macrocarpus is very similar, but can be slightly larger and usually grows in woods. *Agaricus urinascens* can be even larger, and tends to develop an unpleasant ammonia smell with age. Both are edible. The poisonous *A. xanthodermus* has a narrow stem with a bulbous base that immediately becomes intense, bright yellow when cut and releases a chemical, ink-like smell.

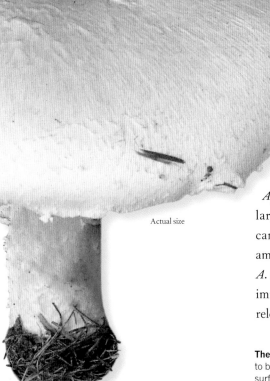

Actual size

The Horse Mushroom has a cap that expands to become domed and finally almost flat. The surface is smooth to slightly scaly, white to cream, and bruises yellow. The gills are pale grayish pink at first, turning chocolate-brown, The stem is white to cream, smooth, and with a large, pendulous ring that has a cogwheel-like marking on the underside.

FAMILY	Agaricaceae
DISTRIBUTION	North America, Europe, Asia, New Zealand
HABITAT	In grassland and roadsides, near seashore or road-salt runoff
ASSOCIATION	With grass
GROWTH FORM	On ground, singly or in troops
ABUNDANCE	Occasional
SPORE COLOR	Chocolate-brown
EDIBILITY	Edible

HEIGHT
Up to 5 in
(120 mm)

CAP DIAMETER
Up to 8 in
(200 mm)

AGARICUS BERNARDII
SALT-LOVING MUSHROOM
QUÉLET

Agaricus bernardii is a specialist, halophilic (salt-loving) species and by nature is a mushroom of seashores and salt marshes. It can still be found in such places, sometimes growing in rings, but in recent years has gradually spread inland along roads that are heavily gritted with salt in winter. The large fruitbodies often become deeply cracked and split, especially when growing in exposed places such as roadsides, and develop an unpleasant, though not inappropriate, fishy or briny smell. Despite this, the Salt-Loving Mushroom is an edible species, though not one that is greatly sought after.

SIMILAR SPECIES

Agaricus bitorquis is closely related and very similar, but usually has a double ring without a sock-like base and lacks the fishy odor of the Salt-Loving Mushroom. It seems to like compacted ground, often coming up in streets, between paving-stones, and in other urban places. It is also an edible species.

The Salt-Loving Mushroom is a squat species, with fruitbodies typically wider than tall. The caps are rounded, smooth and white at first, but often developing fissures when old, the surface cracking into sordid, often grayish scales. The gills are pink, then turn chocolate-brown. The thickish stem has an upturned ring and often a sock-like base. When cut, the flesh turns reddish brown in places (see photo below).

Actual size

FAMILY	Agaricaceae
DISTRIBUTION	North America, Europe, North Africa, Asia; probably introduced in Australia, New Zealand
HABITAT	In parks, gardens, roadsides
ASSOCIATION	In rich soil and compost, occasionally with conifers
GROWTH FORM	On ground, singly or in troops
ABUNDANCE	Common
SPORE COLOR	Chocolate-brown
EDIBILITY	Edible

HEIGHT
Up to 3 in
(80 mm)

CAP DIAMETER
Up to 5 in
(120 mm)

34

AGARICUS BISPORUS
CULTIVATED MUSHROOM
IMBACH

Agaricus bisporus was first cultivated in France in the seventeenth century. Since then, mushroom-growing has become a worldwide industry producing more than 1.5 million tons per year. In the wild, the species is usually brown and scaly. A less-common cream form was favored for cultivation until, in the 1920s, a white variant was discovered that has since dominated the market. The original brown form is now sold variously as "portabella," "crimini," or "chestnut" mushrooms, all recently invented commercial names. *Agaricus bisporus* contains protein, vitamins, and minerals, but also traces of agaratine, a known carcinogen, although the risk factor is low and on a par with that posed by peanut butter or wine.

SIMILAR SPECIES

Microscopically, *Agaricus bisporus* is an easy species to identify, since the basidia are two-spored (hence *bisporus*) instead of four-spored. It is otherwise similar to *A. subfloccosus*, which has a fibrous rather than scaly, brown cap, and *A. bitorquis*, which has a double ring. Both are edible and have flesh that turns pinkish in places when cut.

Actual size

The Cultivated Mushroom is a familiar species, but wild forms typically have brown caps, paler toward the margin, with flat feathery scales (more rarely cream and non-scaly). Gills are pinkish at first, becoming chocolate-brown. The stem is white and smooth, with a thickish but not large ring that may be weakly pendulous. The flesh turns pinkish in places when cut (see photo right).

FAMILY	Agaricaceae
DISTRIBUTION	North America, Europe, North Africa, Asia, Australia, New Zealand
HABITAT	In pastures, lawns, and short turf
ASSOCIATION	With grass, especially if manured
GROWTH FORM	On ground, in troops or rings
ABUNDANCE	Common
SPORE COLOR	Chocolate-brown
EDIBILITY	Edible

HEIGHT
Up to 3 in
(80 mm)

CAP DIAMETER
Up to 4 in
(100 mm)

AGARICUS CAMPESTRIS

FIELD MUSHROOM

LINNAEUS

35

The Field Mushroom, or Meadow Mushroom, is one of the
few species traditionally collected for food in mycophobic
countries, such as Great Britain and Ireland, where most
agarics are shunned as poisonous toadstools. Yet ironically—
despite its familiar "mushroomy" smell—it is not the easiest
edible species to identify. It typically grows in pastures,
where it can form large rings and produce abundant
fruitbodies in a good mushroom year. It can also be
found in lawns, parks, and other areas of undisturbed
short grass. The species used to be widely collected and
taken to market, but most "Field Mushrooms" offered
for sale today are expanded Cultivated Mushrooms
dishonestly renamed.

SIMILAR SPECIES

The Horse Mushroom (*Agaricus arvensis*) also grows in
pastures, but is usually much bigger and has a large, pendulous
ring. The poisonous *Entoloma sinuatum* is pink-spored, lacks
a ring, and smells mealy. The deadly *Amanita phalloides* is
white-spored, has a sack-like volva at the stem base, and gives
off a sickly sweet smell.

Actual size

The Field Mushroom has a hemispherical cap (see
photo right) that flattens as it expands. The surface is
smooth, white to grayish white, sometimes becoming
yellowish with age. The gills are pink, becoming reddish
brown and finally chocolate-brown. The stem is smooth
with a small, thin ring that often disappears. The flesh
is white, rarely changing color.

FAMILY	Agaricaceae
DISTRIBUTION	Africa, southern Asia
HABITAT	In parks, gardens, roadsides, and woodland
ASSOCIATION	In rich soil, compost, and leaf litter
GROWTH FORM	On ground
ABUNDANCE	Occasional
SPORE COLOR	Chocolate-brown
EDIBILITY	Not edible

HEIGHT
Up to 3 in
(75 mm)

CAP DIAMETER
Up to 2 in
(50 mm)

36

AGARICUS CROCOPEPLUS
GOLDEN FLEECE MUSHROOM
BERKELEY & BROOME

Berkeley and Broome, who first described this mushroom from Sri Lanka in 1871, called it "a magnificent species"—despite its rather small size. The Latin epithet *croco-peplus* means clothed in a crocus-yellow garment, which well describes its bright, but shaggy, cap. The species is widespread in southern Asia and has also been reported from Africa. Curiously, in China the name *Agaricus crocopeplus* seems to be widely applied commercially to the brown or "portabella" form of the Cultivated Mushroom (*A. bisporus*), which does not look remotely similar.

SIMILAR SPECIES

Cystoagaricus trisulphuratus is a similarly colored, tropical species, with bright yellow-orange scales. It mainly differs microscopically from the Golden Fleece Mushroom. Several tropical species of *Amanita* may also look similar, but have white gills and spores.

Actual size

The Golden Fleece Mushroom has a cap that is conical, becoming flat. The cap surface is covered in erect, fleecy scales that overhang the margin and are crocus-yellow at first, becoming tawny with age. The gills are pale pinkish brown, becoming chocolate-brown. The stem is fleecy-scaly and cap-colored, with a distinct ring.

FAMILY	Agaricaceae
DISTRIBUTION	North America, Europe, North Africa, Asia, Australia
HABITAT	In woodland
ASSOCIATION	With broadleaf trees and conifers
GROWTH FORM	On ground, in troops or rings
ABUNDANCE	Common
SPORE COLOR	Chocolate-brown
EDIBILITY	Edible

HEIGHT	Up to 6 in (150 mm)
CAP DIAMETER	Up to 6 in (150 mm)

AGARICUS SILVATICUS

BLUSHING WOOD MUSHROOM

SCHAEFFER

37

The Blushing Wood Mushroom, or Bleeding Mushroom, is one of a group of long-stalked, woodland mushrooms that turn red, often quite strikingly so, when the flesh is cut or bruised. Specimens with a particularly strong reaction used to be called *Agaricus haemorrhoidarius*. Despite the color change, it is a good, edible species, with a nutty or mushroomy smell. In promotional literature for alternative medicines, *A. silvaticus* is often confused with *A. subrufescens*. One commercial company has bizarrely claimed that the "Royal Agaricus mushroom (*Agaricus sylvaticus*)... was first discovered by a Japanese-Brazilian farmer in 1991," though the more humbly named Blushing Wood Mushroom was actually described by a German naturalist in 1762.

SIMILAR SPECIES

Agaricus langei is a very similar, reddening, woodland species best distinguished microscopically by its larger spores. *Agaricus benesii* also reddens, but has a stockier, pallid to whitish cap. The Almond Mushroom (*A. subrufescens*) may look superficially similar, but lacks the reddening reaction and smells of almond.

Actual size

The Blushing Wood Mushroom is drumstick-like when immature, but the cap expands to become weakly convex, brown to reddish brown, and covered in fine, feathery scales. The gills are pale grayish pink becoming chocolate-brown. The stem is long, smooth, and has a large, but thin, pendulous ring. The white flesh turns rapidly reddish pink to blood-red when cut (see photo right).

FAMILY	Agaricaceae
DISTRIBUTION	North America, Central and South America; probably introduced into Europe; cultivated in Asia
HABITAT	In parks, gardens, roadsides, and woodland
ASSOCIATION	In rich soil, compost, and leaf litter
GROWTH FORM	On ground, usually in clusters or troops
ABUNDANCE	Occasional
SPORE COLOR	Chocolate-brown
EDIBILITY	Edible

HEIGHT
Up to 6 in
(150 mm)

CAP DIAMETER
Up to 7 in
(180 mm)

38

AGARICUS SUBRUFESCENS
ALMOND MUSHROOM
PECK

The Almond Mushroom (so-called because of its aroma) is a native of the Americas and was once commercially cultivated in the eastern United States, until replaced by *Agaricus bisporus*. In Brazil, where it was misidentified as *A. blazei* and *A. silvaticus*, it acquired a local reputation for its supposed medicinal properties, as it was claimed to stimulate the immune system. In the 1970s, cultures were taken to Japan, where the species has subsequently been cultivated and marketed worldwide—dried and in extract form—as an alternative medicine. The Almond Mushroom has also been called *A. brasiliensis*, but this is a superfluous (and illegitimate) name.

SIMILAR SPECIES
The widespread and edible *Agaricus augustus* is similar and also has an almond smell, but all parts tend to bruise yellow on handling. The poisonous Yellow-Stainer Mushroom (*A. xanthodermus*) turns a much brighter, deeper yellow when the base of the stem is cut and lacks the reddish brown tones and sweet smell of *A. subrufescens*.

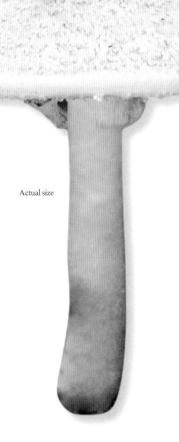

Actual size

The Almond Mushroom has a hemispherical cap that remains slightly rounded when expanded. The surface is brown to reddish brown, and densely covered with small, fibrous scales. The gills are pale pinkish brown, becoming chocolate-brown. The stem is smooth with a thin, often torn or evanescent, ring. The flesh at the base of the stem turns yellowish when cut.

FAMILY	Agaricaceae
DISTRIBUTION	North America, Europe, North Africa, Asia, Australia
HABITAT	In woodland, parks, and gardens
ASSOCIATION	With broadleaf trees and conifers
GROWTH FORM	On ground, in troops or rings
ABUNDANCE	Common
SPORE COLOR	Chocolate-brown
EDIBILITY	Poisonous

HEIGHT
Up to 6 in
(150 mm)

CAP DIAMETER
Up to 6 in
(150 mm)

AGARICUS XANTHODERMUS
YELLOW STAINER
GENEVIER

39

The Yellow Stainer, also known as the Yellow-Staining
Mushroom, belongs to a group of mushrooms that frequently
cause gastroenteritic poisoning, though some people claim to
eat them with impunity. The species is often recognizable
on sight, thanks to its white or cream color and long,
comparatively narrow stem that usually has an
abruptly bulbous base. A diagnostic feature is that
this stem base turns immediately bright yellow
when cut. The whole fruitbody also has an inky
smell, said to be stronger (and quite off-putting)
if these mushrooms are inadvertently cooked. Phenolic
metabolites (compounds related to carbolic acid) account
for both the Yellow Stainer's smell and its toxicity.

SIMILAR SPECIES
Agaricus moelleri is a closely related species, differing in having
a finely scaly, gray-brown cap. It has the same yellow-staining
reaction and is equally poisonous. The edible *A. subrufescens*
has a more reddish brown cap, a pleasant smell, and only a faint
yellowish reaction when the base of the stem is cut.

Actual size

The Yellow Stainer is a long-stemmed species with a
smooth white to cream cap, sometimes with gray or
brownish tints. The gills are pinkish gray becoming dark
chocolate-brown. The stem is long, smooth, white to
cream, with a thin pendulous ring. The base of
the stem is typically bulbous and is bright chrome
yellow when cut (see photo right).

FAMILY	Strophariaceae
DISTRIBUTION	Southern North America, Europe, North Africa, Central America, Asia
HABITAT	In woodland and hedgerows
ASSOCIATION	With broadleaf trees, particularly poplar
GROWTH FORM	On old trunks and stumps, in clusters
ABUNDANCE	Occasional
SPORE COLOR	Brown
EDIBILITY	Edible

HEIGHT
Up to 6 in
(150 mm)

CAP DIAMETER
Up to 5 in
(125 mm)

40

AGROCYBE CYLINDRACEA
POPLAR FIELDCAP
(DE CANDOLLE) MAIRE

The Poplar Fieldcap, or Black Poplar Mushroom, is commonest in warmer north temperate regions, producing clusters of fruitbodies on a range of broadleaf trees, including elm, elder, willow, and poplar. The species (often still called by its synonym *Agrocybe aegerita*) is edible and has long been semi-cultivated in Italy, where it is known as *pioppino*. The fruitbodies possess higher levels of savory, monosodium-glutamate-like components than are found in the Cep, *Boletus edulis*. The Poplar Fieldcap is now commercially grown in China, Thailand, and other countries, from where fresh and dried fruitbodies are exported, as well as being widely available for home-growing by enthusiasts.

SIMILAR SPECIES
Related *Agrocybe* species grow in troops in grass, soil, or woodchip mulch. Most other large, clustered agarics on wood are either white-spored (and often ringless), like *Hypsizygus marmoreus* and *Pleurotus* species, or rusty-spored (and often rusty-capped or scaly), like *Pholiota* species.

The Poplar Fieldcap forms fruitbodies in clusters. The caps are convex, flatter when expanded, smooth or wrinkled, brown to cinnamon-buff, becoming ivory or cream and finely cracked. The gills are buff, becoming brown. The stem is smooth, whitish, ocher to rusty toward the base, with a membranous ring. The flesh is white, brownish in the stem base.

Actual size

FAMILY	Strophariaceae
DISTRIBUTION	Western North America, Europe
HABITAT	In parks, gardens, and roadsides
ASSOCIATION	In woodchip mulch
GROWTH FORM	On ground, in clusters or troops
ABUNDANCE	Locally common
SPORE COLOR	Brown
EDIBILITY	Not edible

HEIGHT
Up to 3 in
(80 mm)

CAP DIAMETER
Up to 4 in
(100 mm)

AGROCYBE PUTAMINUM

MULCH FIELDCAP

(MAIRE) SINGER

41

Agrocybe putaminum is a fungus that is rapidly increasing its range, thanks to the modern vogue for spreading woodchips around ornamental shrubberies. The species was first described from France in 1913, from garden soil covered in plum stones. It was scarcely seen at all for the next 70 years, until in 1985 it turned up in woodchip mulch in Denmark. Since then the formerly rare *A. putaminum* has become common, spreading throughout Europe, always in mulch, and recently colonizing California. When it occurs, the Mulch Fieldcap often appears in large troops, making the most of what is clearly a rich and rewarding source of nutrients.

SIMILAR SPECIES

Two additional species of *Agrocybe* often occur in mulch. *Agrocybe rivulosa* is another recent woodchip colonist, with a wrinkled, conical cap. *Agrocybe praecox* is a more familiar, spring or early-summer species that is also common in grass. Both can be distinguished from the Mulch Fieldcap by having stems with a distinct ring.

Actual size

The Mulch Fieldcap is quite a large, fleshy agaric. The cap is hemispherical and brown when young, becoming weakly convex, smooth, matt, and pale yellow-brown. The gills are clay-brown. The stem is smooth but grooved toward the top, cap-colored, and slightly swollen toward the base, which arises from white, root-like, mycelial cords.

FAMILY	Amanitaceae
DISTRIBUTION	New Zealand
HABITAT	In woodland
ASSOCIATION	Ectomycorrhizal, with southern beech
GROWTH FORM	On ground, singly or in small troops
ABUNDANCE	Common
SPORE COLOR	White
EDIBILITY	Poisonous

HEIGHT
Up to 4 in
(100 mm)

CAP DIAMETER
Up to 4 in
(100 mm)

42

AMANITA AUSTRALIS
FAR SOUTH AMANITA
G. STEVENSON

For this species, the "Far South" means New Zealand, since *Amanita australis* is a New Zealand specialty, forming an ectomycorrhizal association with native southern beech trees. The conical or pyramid-shaped warts on the cap are the remains of the universal veil that covers the whole of the developing fruitbody. The veil breaks apart as the fruitbody expands, leaving some scaly remnants on the bulbous stem base and some on the cap. These scales or warts are easily detachable and may wash off in heavy rain, making identification more difficult.

SIMILAR SPECIES
The habitat and location should make the Far South Amanita distinctive. Its bulbous shape and colors are similar to those of the European False Death Cap (*Amanita citrina*), but the latter species has flat (not warted) veil remains on its cap. The North American *A. abrupta* does have conical warts on the cap, but both cap and warts are whitish.

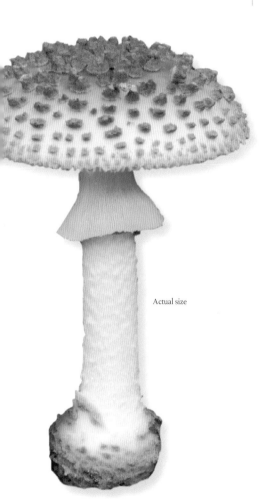

Actual size

The Far South Amanita has caps that are convex at first, becoming flat. The surface is covered in gray-brown, detachable, conical warts on a buff to ocher background. The gills are white. The white hollow stem has a membranous grooved ring, and is smooth or somewhat scurfy below. The base is abruptly bulbous, with a fringe of gray-brown veil remnants at the rim.

FAMILY	Amanitaceae
DISTRIBUTION	Southern Europe, North Africa, western Asia
HABITAT	In woodland
ASSOCIATION	Ectomycorrhizal, mainly with oak or pine
GROWTH FORM	On ground
ABUNDANCE	Occasional
SPORE COLOR	White
EDIBILITY	Edible

HEIGHT
Up to 6 in
(150 mm)

CAP DIAMETER
Up to 6 in
(150 mm)

AMANITA CAESAREA

CAESAR'S AMANITA

(SCOPOLI) PERSOON

43

The Caesar's Amanita, or Caesar's Mushroom, is a celebrated, edible species that grows in southern Europe and the Mediterranean area where it is commonly collected from the wild and sold in markets. It was said to be a favorite of the Roman emperors, who knew it as *boleti*, a name that is now used for an entirely different group of fungi. It is sometimes claimed that the emperor Claudius was killed by eating a dish of Caesar's Amanita laced, thanks to his wife Agrippina, with Death Caps (*Amanita phalloides*). This is a cautionary tale, since some *Amanita* species are genuinely lethal and *A. caesarea* has many look-alikes around the world.

SIMILAR SPECIES

Similar species occur elsewhere, most belonging in a related group known as the Slender Caesars. The American Slender Caesar (*Amanita jacksonii*) is one of several such species in the Americas. *Amanita caesareoides* from Japan and the Far East is closely related, as is *A. hemibapha* from Sri Lanka and India.

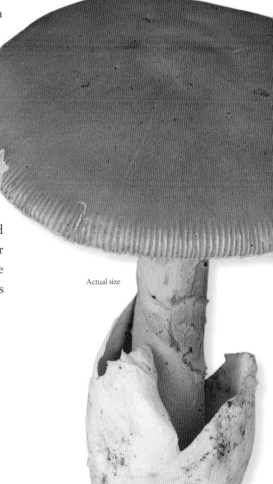

Actual size

The Caesar's Amanita has a bright orange-red cap when young, becoming paler and duller with age. The expanded cap is smooth (sometimes with patches of white veil remains), slightly sticky when damp, and striate at the margin. The gills are yellow. The stem is yellow and has a pendulous, yellow ring (see photo left). The large, sack-like volva at the stem base is white.

FAMILY	Amanitaceae
DISTRIBUTION	Western North America, Central America
HABITAT	In woodland
ASSOCIATION	Ectomycorrhizal, with firs, tan oak, and madrone
GROWTH FORM	On ground
ABUNDANCE	Locally common
SPORE COLOR	White
EDIBILITY	Edible

HEIGHT
Up to 4 in
(100 mm)

CAP DIAMETER
Up to 8 in
(200 mm)

44

AMANITA CALYPTRODERMA
PACIFIC COCCORA
G. F. ATKINSON & V. G. BALLEN

This large species is quite common along the Pacific coast of North America. One of the original scientific collectors noted that it was eaten by people of Italian descent because of its resemblance to the European *Amanita caesarea*. Fortunately for them, the Pacific Coccora happened to be an edible *Amanita* rather than a lethally poisonous one. Coccora (meaning "cocoon") is an Italian name for *A. caesarea*, which now seems to have been adopted by local American mushroom-hunters. The Pacific Coccora has also been called *A. calyptrata* and *A. lanei*, but *A. calyptroderma* is the earliest, legitimate name.

SIMILAR SPECIES
Similar but paler fruitbodies occur in western North America in the spring, but it is not yet clear whether these are also *Amanita calyptroderma* or a separate species. The true Coccora, Caesar's Amanita (*A. caesarea*), is a European species of the Mediterranean area, with bright orange caps and yellow gills.

The Pacific Coccora is completely enveloped in a thickish, white, cocoon-like veil when immature. When expanded, the remains persist as large, irregular pieces on the cap surface, which is smooth and orange-brown to golden-brown or, in the spring-fruiting form (see photo), pale yellowish. The gills are white and the stem is white to pale yellowish with a membranous ring and a large, sack-like volva at the base.

Actual size

FAMILY	Amanitaceae
DISTRIBUTION	Europe, western Asia
HABITAT	In woodland
ASSOCIATION	Ectomycorrhizal, with beech, oak, and hornbeam
GROWTH FORM	On ground
ABUNDANCE	Occasional
SPORE COLOR	White
EDIBILITY	Not edible

HEIGHT
Up to 8 in
(200 mm)

CAP DIAMETER
Up to 5 in
(120 mm)

AMANITA CECILIAE

SNAKESKIN GRISETTE

(BERKELEY & BROOME) BAS

45

The Snakeskin Grisette belongs to a group of *Amanita* species, sometimes called grisettes, that have no ring on the stem. It is a tall agaric that takes its common name from the zigzag patterning on the stem, which resembles the skin of adders. It was originally described from England in 1854 and named in honor of the Rev. M. J. Berkeley's wife Cecilia, who illustrated many of his fungal specimens. The species was formerly often called *A. inaurata* or *A. strangulata* and was thought to be widespread in America, but recent research suggests American specimens belong to one or more closely related, but as yet unnamed, species.

SIMILAR SPECIES

A similar-looking but darker species in Central and South America was formerly referred to *Amanita ceciliae*, but is now called *A. sororcula*. Related species in North America require further research. In Europe, *A. submembranacea* is similarly colored, but has a distinct, gray, sack-like volva. *Amanita beckeri* is similarly shaped, but has a brown cap and stem.

The Snakeskin Grisette is a comparatively robust, long-stemmed species. The cap is smooth, striate toward the margin, and dingy, pale to dark yellow-brown scattered with powdery, gray-brown veil remnants. The gills are white, becoming grayish. The stem is gray, with conspicuous adder-like (zigzag) markings, and gray-brown, woolly ridges and bands at the base.

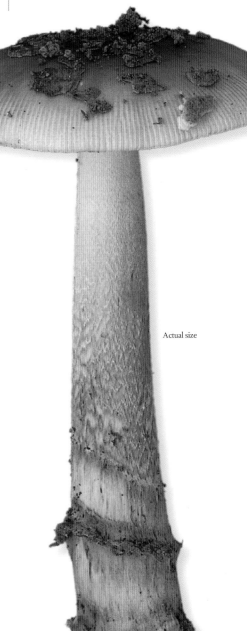

Actual size

FAMILY	Amanitaceae
DISTRIBUTION	Europe, North Africa, northern Asia
HABITAT	In woodland
ASSOCIATION	Ectomycorrhizal, with broadleaf trees and conifers
GROWTH FORM	On ground, singly or in small troops
ABUNDANCE	Common
SPORE COLOR	White
EDIBILITY	Not edible

HEIGHT
Up to 6 in
(150 mm)

CAP DIAMETER
Up to 4 in
(100 mm)

46

AMANITA CITRINA
FALSE DEATH CAP
(SCHAEFFER) PERSOON

Amanita citrina is a common species, forming associations with a wide range of trees. It is generally recognizable by its abruptly bulbous base and by its strong smell of raw potato when cut or bruised. Two varieties are often recognized, one with a white cap, the other pale yellow. The agaric known as *A. citrina* in North America often has lavender tints and may be a different species. The False Death Cap is not poisonous, but is rarely, if ever, eaten. Not only is the smell off-putting, but —as its common name suggests—mistaking it for the Death Cap could prove fatal.

SIMILAR SPECIES

The true Death Cap (*Amanita phalloides*) is usually yellowish olive, but occasionally paler or whitish, and has a sack-like volva at the base without a large bulb. It lacks the raw potato smell of the False Death Cap. *Amanita gemmata* can be similarly colored, but also lacks the smell and basal bulb. Both are poisonous.

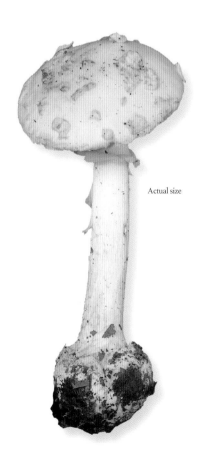

Actual size

The False Death Cap has caps that are convex at first (see photo right), becoming flatter with age. The surface is smooth, lemon-yellow (or sometimes white), and usually has some brown patches of veil adhering to it. The gills are white. The white to yellowish stem has a conspicuous ring. At the stem base is a large bulb with inconspicuous volval remains around the rim.

FAMILY	Amanitaceae
DISTRIBUTION	Europe, western Asia
HABITAT	In woodland
ASSOCIATION	Ectomycorrhizal, with conifers and broadleaf trees, particularly birch
GROWTH FORM	On ground, singly or in small troops
ABUNDANCE	Occasional
SPORE COLOR	White
EDIBILITY	Edible (when cooked)

HEIGHT
Up to 9 in
(225 mm)

CAP DIAMETER
Up to 4 in
(100 mm)

AMANITA CROCEA

ORANGE GRISETTE

(QUÉLET) SINGER

47

Amanita crocea is one of the most attractive of the grisettes, a group of *Amanita* species that lack a ring on the stem. Until recently it was thought to occur in North and Central America as well as Europe, but it seems that the American *Amanita crocea* is a closely related (but as yet unnamed) look-alike species. The Orange Grisette is said to be edible and is known to be eaten in Russia and eastern Europe, but this group of agarics is slightly suspect and can cause digestive problems—even when well-cooked.

SIMILAR SPECIES

Similar species from North and Central America have yet to be formally named. Other ringless *Amanita* species are similarly shaped, but differently colored. The European Tawny Grisette (*A. fulva*) has a warm brown cap. The orange-capped Caesar's Amanita (*A. caesarea*) has a pendulous ring.

Actual size

The Orange Grisette has caps that are conical to convex at first (see photo right), becoming umbonate. The surface is smooth, pale orange, with a striate margin. The gills are white. The ringless stem is whitish but covered in a fine, pale orange, zigzag pattern. The large, sack-like volva at the base is externally white and pale orange inside.

FAMILY	Amanitaceae
DISTRIBUTION	Eastern North America, Central America
HABITAT	In woodland
ASSOCIATION	Ectomycorrhizal, with broadleaf trees, especially oak
GROWTH FORM	On ground, singly or in small troops
ABUNDANCE	Common
SPORE COLOR	White
EDIBILITY	Poisonous

HEIGHT
Up to 8 in
(200 mm)

CAP DIAMETER
Up to 10 in
(250 mm)

48

AMANITA DAUCIPES
CARROT AMANITA
(BERKELEY & MONTAGNE) LLOYD

Many *Amanita* species develop a bulbous swelling at the base of the stem, but the Carrot Amanita outclasses them all. Its basal bulb is not just big on the surface, it roots down below the soil like a carrot. The Latin *daucipes* means "carrot-foot," and the root-like stem may even bruise orange-red when handled. Unfortunately, the Carrot Amanita is not an edible species and may well be poisonous, as are related species of *Amanita*. It also has a strong, off-putting smell, said to be sickly sweet or "like old ham."

SIMILAR SPECIES

The bulbous, rooting stem should be distinctive. *Amanita atkinsoniana* occurs in the same area and has a large, partly rooting bulb, though both bulb and cap are typically covered in rings of small, red-brown warts. The widespread Blusher (*A. rubescens*) can be similarly colored, but usually has less granular scales on the cap and lacks the carrot-like base.

Actual size

The Carrot Amanita has caps that are hemispherical, becoming convex to flat. The surface is white to pale pinkish or orange-buff, and is covered with small, granular veil remnants. The gills are white. The white stem is scaly, with a conspicuous ring. At the stem base is a large, swollen, rooting bulb that may be 6 in (150 mm) long and bruises orange to pink-red.

FAMILY	Amanitaceae
DISTRIBUTION	North America, Europe, North Africa, northern Asia; introduced in South Africa
HABITAT	In woodland
ASSOCIATION	Ectomycorrhizal, with broadleaf trees
GROWTH FORM	On ground, singly or in small troops
ABUNDANCE	Common
SPORE COLOR	White
EDIBILITY	Poisonous

HEIGHT
Up to 6 in
(150 mm)

CAP DIAMETER
Up to 6 in
(150 mm)

AMANITA EXCELSA VAR. SPISSA

GRAY-SPOTTED AMANITA

(FRIES) NEVILLE & POUMARAT

49

The Gray-Spotted Amanita is a very common species, though its precise name and status is often disputed. The variety *spissa* is said to be larger and more stocky than the slimmer and less common *Amanita excelsa* itself. It may also be the case that North American specimens represent one or more as yet unnamed, look-alike species. Its English name comes from the gray fragments of veil that remain on the cap, though they are easily removable and can sometimes be washed off by heavy rain. The species is not considered edible and is said to contain amatoxins (poisons that are also found in the Death Cap), so it is best avoided.

SIMILAR SPECIES

The less common Panthercap (*Amanita pantherina*) has a cap that is warm brown with white veil remains and a basal bulb with a distinct upper margin. The very common Blusher (*A. rubescens*) has a cap that is pinkish brown with whitish gray veil remains and flesh that turns slowly reddish pink where cut or bruised.

Actual size

The Gray-Spotted Amanita has caps that are hemispherical at first, becoming flat. The surface is smooth, gray-brown, and has irregular patches of gray veil remnants. The gills are white. The white stem has a conspicuous ring (see photo right), striate on the upper surface, below which are rings of granular veil remnants. The stem base is bulbous, without a distinct margin.

FAMILY	Amanitaceae
DISTRIBUTION	Eastern North America, Central America
HABITAT	In woodland
ASSOCIATION	Ectomycorrhizal, with conifers and broadleaf trees
GROWTH FORM	On ground, singly or in troops
ABUNDANCE	Common
SPORE COLOR	White
EDIBILITY	Probably poisonous, best avoided

HEIGHT
Up to 5 in
(125 mm)

CAP DIAMETER
Up to 4 in
(100 mm)

50

AMANITA FLAVOCONIA
YELLOW DUST AMANITA
G. F. ATKINSON

The brightly colored Yellow Dust Amanita is said to be one of the commonest *Amanita* species in eastern North America, forming mycorrhiza with a wide range of trees. Despite its attractive appearance (reminiscent of the edible Caesar's Amanita, *A. caesarea*) it is probably toxic—though no one seems to have researched this fully. So it is certainly best avoided. The warty-scurfy veil remains on the cap, which give the species its English name, are easily washed off by rain and tend to disappear quickly, leaving the cap smooth.

SIMILAR SPECIES

The rare *Amanita frostiana* occurs in the same area and looks almost identical, but has a striate margin to the cap. Yellow-orange color forms of the Fly Agaric (*A. muscaria*) are typically more robust, with more persistent warts on the cap. The edible American Slender Caesar (*A. jacksonii*) has yellow gills and a sack-like volva at the stem base.

Actual size

The Yellow Dust Amanita has caps that are conical at first, becoming flat. The surface is bright red to orange, becoming yellow-orange, covered with patches of warty, yellow veil remains at least when young. The gills are white, tinted yellow. The stem is smooth to finely scurfy, white to bright yellow, with a yellow ring and a bulbous base with yellow veil remains.

FAMILY	Amanitaceae
DISTRIBUTION	Europe, North Africa, western Asia
HABITAT	In woodland
ASSOCIATION	Ectomycorrhizal, with conifers and broadleaf trees, particularly birch
GROWTH FORM	On ground, singly or in small troops
ABUNDANCE	Common
SPORE COLOR	White
EDIBILITY	Edible when cooked

HEIGHT
Up to 6 in
(150 mm)

CAP DIAMETER
Up to 4 in
(100 mm)

AMANITA FULVA
TAWNY GRISETTE
(SCHAEFFER) FRIES

51

The Tawny Grisette is one of a group of slender *Amanita* species (sometimes assigned to their own genus, *Amanitopsis*) that have a conspicuous, sack-like volva at the base of the stem, but lack a ring. Until recently *A. fulva* was thought to be a cosmopolitan species, but it now seems that it is restricted to Europe and adjacent areas. Look-alike species occur in the Americas, Eastern Asia, and Africa. The fruitbodies of *A. fulva* are considered edible, though grisettes sometimes seem to cause unpleasant stomach upsets. They are known to contain hemolytic toxins that can cause anemia, but these should be destroyed by thorough cooking.

SIMILAR SPECIES

Most similar American species have yet to be formally named, though the dark brown *Amanita fuligineodisca* has been described from Central America and Colombia. *Amanita orientifulva* is a look-alike species from China and Japan. Many additional species are similarly shaped, but differently colored. In Europe, the Grisette (*A. vaginata*) has a gray cap, while the Orange Grisette (*A. crocea*) is self-descriptive.

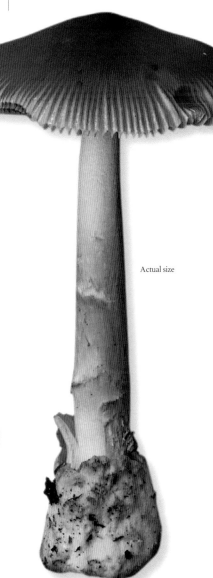

Actual size

The Tawny Grisette has caps that are conical to convex at first (see photo right), becoming umbonate. The surface is smooth, orange-brown to warm brown, with a striate margin. The gills are white. The white stem does not have a ring, but does have a large, sack-like volva at the base, which is white stained rusty brown.

FAMILY	Amanitaceae
DISTRIBUTION	Eastern North America, Central America
HABITAT	In woodland
ASSOCIATION	Ectomycorrhizal, with oak and pine
GROWTH FORM	On ground
ABUNDANCE	Occasional
SPORE COLOR	White
EDIBILITY	Edible

HEIGHT
Up to 6 in
(150 mm)

CAP DIAMETER
Up to 5 in
(120 mm)

52

AMANITA JACKSONII

AMERICAN SLENDER CAESAR

POMERLEAU

Actual size

Amanita jacksonii was originally described from Quebec and is known throughout eastern North America southward into Mexico. It was often referred to *A. hemibapha* in the past, but this is now considered to be a closely related, but distinct, species. Earlier still, it was thought to be an American form of Caesar's Mushroom (*A. caesarea*), but, as the common name suggests, *A. jacksonii* is a much more slender agaric and is also more brightly colored, especially when young. It has been called the beauty queen of *Amanita* species, not without reason. Like its European counterpart, it is considered a good edible species.

SIMILAR SPECIES

Very similar species occur elsewhere. The original *Amanita hemibapha* was described from Sri Lanka and is also known from India. *A. caesareoides* from Japan and the Far East is closely related to the American Slender Caesar and has also been called *A. hemibapha* in the past. The true Caesar's Amanita (*A. caesarea*) is a stockier Mediterranean species.

The American Slender Caesar has a brilliant red cap when young, becoming orange then yellow from the margin inward. The expanded cap is smooth, striate at the margin, and often umbonate. The gills are orange-yellow at first, becoming yellow. The stem is yellow, but covered with orange-red, adder-like patterns, and has a pendulous, orange ring. The large, sack-like volva at the stem base is white.

FAMILY	Amanitaceae
DISTRIBUTION	North America, Europe, North Africa, Central America, northern Asia; introduced in Australia, New Zealand, South Africa, and South America
HABITAT	In woodland
ASSOCIATION	Ectomycorrhizal, with broadleaf trees, particularly birch, and conifers
GROWTH FORM	On ground, singly or in troops
ABUNDANCE	Very common
SPORE COLOR	White
EDIBILITY	Poisonous (hallucinogenic)

HEIGHT
Up to 8 in
(200 mm)

CAP DIAMETER
Up to 12 in
(300 mm)

AMANITA MUSCARIA

FLY AGARIC

(LINNAEUS) LAMARCK

53

A favorite with fairy-tale illustrators, the Fly Agaric has long had a sinister reputation. It was once considered a dangerously poisonous toadstool, fit only for killing flies—hence its English and Latin names (*musca* meaning "a fly"). Although muscarine—a known fungal poison—was first isolated from its fruitbodies, it is only present in very small amounts. Its active poisons are actually muscimol and ibotenic acid, both of which are not only toxic, but hallucinogenic. The Fly Agaric was once used in shamanistic rituals in Lapland and Siberia and has fancifully been claimed as the origin of Father Christmas myths, involving flying reindeers in spirit form and figures dressed in red and white.

SIMILAR SPECIES

North and Central American collections with yellow veil remains are genetically distinct and are sometimes treated as a separate variety (*flavivolvata*). *Amanita regalis,* found in arctic and montane north temperate regions, is similar but has yellowish brown to dark brown caps. The red-capped *Amanita jacksonii* and its relatives have a large, sack-like volva at the stem base.

The Fly Agaric has caps that are convex at first, becoming flatter. The surface is smooth, scarlet (rarely orange to yellow), and is dotted with contrasting, small, white, fleecy, separable veil remnants that wash off in rain. The gills are white. The white stem has a conspicuous ring and a large, basal bulb with volval remains around the rim (see photo above).

Actual size

FAMILY	Amanitaceae
DISTRIBUTION	Eastern North America, Central America
HABITAT	In woodland
ASSOCIATION	Ectomycorrhizal, with broadleaf trees and conifers
GROWTH FORM	On ground, singly or in small troops
ABUNDANCE	Common
SPORE COLOR	White
EDIBILITY	Poisonous

HEIGHT
Up to 5 in
(125 mm)

CAP DIAMETER
Up to 4 in
(100 mm)

54

AMANITA ONUSTA
GUNPOWDER AMANITA
(HOWE) SACCARDO

The Gunpowder Amanita takes its English name from the abundant, gunpowder-gray scales or warts on the cap and on the upper part of the bulbous stem base. These are the friable remains of the universal veil that covers the developing fruitbody in its immature "button" stage. As in other *Amanita* species, they are loose and can easily be rubbed off with the finger or be washed off by heavy rain. Fruitbodies of the Gunpowder Amanita are typically smaller than average for an *Amanita* species. They are not edible and have an unpleasant smell of bleach.

SIMILAR SPECIES
Amanita miculifera is a similar east Asian species with gray warts and a rooting stem. The Carrot Amanita (*A. daucipes*) occurs in eastern North America, but is a larger species with pinkish to pale orange warts on the cap and a massively rooting stem.

The Gunpowder Amanita has caps that are convex, becoming flat. The surface is whitish to pale gray and is covered with dark gray to gray-brown, granular or conical veil remnants. The gills are white. The white stem is cottony, with an ephemeral ring and darker scales toward the bulbous, often rooting, base.

Actual size

FAMILY	Amanitaceae
DISTRIBUTION	Europe, North Africa, northern Asia; introduced in South Africa
HABITAT	In woodland, more rarely pasture
ASSOCIATION	Ectomycorrhizal, with broadleaf trees, more rarely conifers and rockrose
GROWTH FORM	On ground, singly or in small troops
ABUNDANCE	Occasional
SPORE COLOR	White
EDIBILITY	Poisonous

HEIGHT
Up to 6 in
(150 mm)

CAP DIAMETER
Up to 4 in
(100 mm)

AMANITA PANTHERINA

PANTHERCAP

KROMBHOLZ

55

The Panthercap is a rather smart-looking species with its neat brown cap and contrasting white scales. It forms associations with a wide range of trees and, more surprisingly, can also be found with the flowering plant rockrose (*Helianthemum*) in calcareous pastures. Recent research suggests that the "Panthercap" in North America belongs to one or more similar but distinct species and that collections from eastern Asia may also be distinct. Like the Fly Agaric (*Amanita muscaria*), *A. pantherina* is poisonous, containing ibotenic acid and muscimol. This makes the fungus potentially hallucinogenic, but at the risk of coma and convulsions. It is apparently seldom lethal.

SIMILAR SPECIES

The more common *Amanita excelsa* has irregular, pale gray veil remains on the cap and a base that is bulbous, but does not have a distinct margin. The equally common Blusher (*Amanita rubescens*) has a cap that is, at most, a rather watery, pinkish brown with sordid, whitish gray veil remains. It, too, has a bulb without a margin.

Actual size

The Panthercap has caps that are convex at first, becoming flatter. The surface is smooth and warm brown, and is dotted with contrasting, small, white, fleecy veil remnants. The gills are white. The stem is also white and has a conspicuous drooping ring, below which are incomplete flocculose ring zones of white veil remnants. At the stem base is a large bulb with inconspicuous volval remains around the distinct, marginate rim.

FAMILY	Amanitaceae
DISTRIBUTION	Europe, North Africa, western Asia; introduced in North America, eastern and southern Africa, South America, Australia, New Zealand
HABITAT	In woodland
ASSOCIATION	Ectomycorrhizal with broadleaf trees, more rarely conifers
GROWTH FORM	On ground, singly or in troops or rings
ABUNDANCE	Common
SPORE COLOR	White
EDIBILITY	Poisonous

HEIGHT
Up to 6 in
(150 mm)

CAP DIAMETER
Up to 5 in
(125 mm)

56

AMANITA PHALLOIDES
DEATH CAP
(FRIES) LINK

This is the archetypal poisonous toadstool, probably causing more deaths than any other species. Its shape and color should be distinctive and it also has a sickly-sweet smell, increasing with age, but is still collected by mistake for edible species. Amatoxins and phallotoxins are present, resulting in gastroenteric illness within hours and cell-damage (starting with liver failure) within days. Modern medicine, intensive care treatment, and transplant techniques have reduced fatalities in such poisoning cases to around 20 percent, but this can be no great comfort for victims. The moral is, never eat a wild fungus unless you are absolutely certain you have identified it correctly.

SIMILAR SPECIES

When button-sized, the Death Cap has been picked by mistake for ordinary mushrooms (*Agaricus* species). It has also been mistaken (particularly by Southeast Asian immigrants) for the Paddy-Straw Mushroom (*Volvariella volvacea*), which has pink (not white) spores. The yellow-olive *Tricholoma flavovirens* lacks ring or volva and has yellowish gills.

Actual size

The Death Cap has caps that are convex (see photo right) becoming flat, smooth (sometimes with patches of white veil remains), pale olive to yellowish, silvery gray, or even whitish, typically with radial streaks. The gills are white. The stem is white, often with fine zigzag markings, with a drooping, slightly grooved ring, and a large, white, sack-like volva (sometimes greenish inside) at the swollen base.

FAMILY	Amanitaceae
DISTRIBUTION	North America, Europe, Africa, Central and South America, Asia, Australia
HABITAT	In woodland
ASSOCIATION	Ectomycorrhizal with broadleaf trees and conifers
GROWTH FORM	On ground, singly or in troops
ABUNDANCE	Very common
SPORE COLOR	White
EDIBILITY	Edible when cooked

HEIGHT
Up to 4 in
(100 mm)

CAP DIAMETER
Up to 4 in
(100 mm)

AMANITA RUBESCENS

THE BLUSHER

PERSOON

57

Amanita rubescens is one of the commonest, ectomycorrhizal agarics, rather promiscuously forming associations with a wide range of different trees. It is also geographically widespread and has been accidentally introduced in some areas—including Chile and South Africa—along with plantation trees. *Rubescens* means "reddening," and fruitbodies of the Blusher slowly turn pink when bruised or cut. They are also edible, but since so many *Amanita* species are lethally poisonous, they are probably best avoided, just to be on the safe side. The fruitbodies contain a toxic (heomolytic) protein called rubescenslysin, but this does not appear to be harmful when eaten and is destroyed by cooking.

The Blusher has caps that are hemispherical, becoming flat to broadly umbonate. The surface is smooth but scattered with small patches of grayish veil remains, brown, paler toward the margin, bruising or aging pinkish. The gills are white. The stem is white at first, bruising or aging pinkish, scaly below the fragile ring, with a scurfy, bulbous base.

SIMILAR SPECIES

Recent research suggests the true *Amanita rubescens* may be restricted to Europe (though introduced elsewhere), with American and other populations possibly deserving recognition as separate species. *Amanita novinupta* is a recently recognized species from western North America with a whitish cap, blushing pink. Other *Amanita* species, such as the Panthercap (*A. pantherina*), never blush.

Actual size

FAMILY	Amanitaceae
DISTRIBUTION	North America, Europe, Central America, northern Asia
HABITAT	In woodland
ASSOCIATION	Ectomycorrhizal with broadleaf trees and conifers
GROWTH FORM	On ground, singly or in troops
ABUNDANCE	Occasional
SPORE COLOR	White
EDIBILITY	Poisonous

HEIGHT
Up to 6 in
(150 mm)

CAP DIAMETER
Up to 5 in
(125 mm)

58

AMANITA VIROSA

DESTROYING ANGEL

(FRIES) BERTILLON

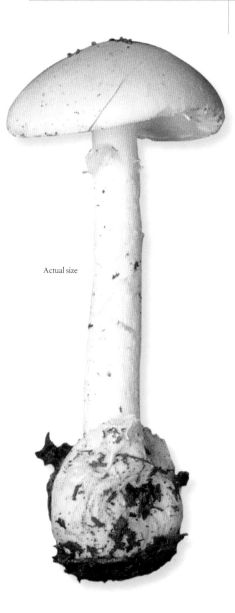

Actual size

Like the Death Cap (*Amanita phalloides*), the Destroying Angel is a classic poisonous toadstool, responsible for many fatalities throughout its range. The fruitbodies contain lethal amatoxins, causing major cell damage if eaten, starting with liver failure. The white cap, gills, and ringed stem with a volva at the bulbous base, together with the often sickly-sweet smell of the flesh, should be distinctive, but the species has sometimes been picked in its button stage by mistake for edible species. Recent molecular research indicates that the Destroying Angel comprises a complex of species around the world, but all are equally poisonous.

SIMILAR SPECIES

The true *Amanita virosa* may be restricted to Europe, with genetically distinct populations elsewhere being treated as distinct species—including *A. bisporigera* in eastern North America, *A. ocreata* in western North America, and *A. exitialis* in Asia. All appear identical or very similar in the field and are equally dangerous, if consumed.

The Destroying Angel has caps that are hemispherical, becoming flat to broadly umbonate. The surface is smooth (sometimes with patches of white veil remains), sticky when wet, and white, becoming slightly yellowish at the center. The gills are white. The stem is white, scaly below the fragile ring, with a quickly disintegrating volva at the swollen base. The flesh turns bright yellow when a drop of dilute ammonia (or other alkali) is placed on it.

FAMILY	Tricholomataceae
DISTRIBUTION	Central and South America, Eastern Asia (Japan), Pacific islands (Hawaii, New Caledonia)
HABITAT	In woodland
ASSOCIATION	With broadleaf trees
GROWTH FORM	On fallen twigs and wood , singly or in small groups
ABUNDANCE	Occasional
SPORE COLOR	White
EDIBILITY	Not edible

HEIGHT
Up to 2 in
(50 mm)

CAP DIAMETER
Up to ⅜ in
(8 mm)

AMPAROINA SPINOSISSIMA
FLAKY BONNET
(SINGER) SINGER

59

When very young, the fruitbodies of this odd little fungus look rather like tiny, spiny puffballs that are beginning to form on the surface of fallen twigs and branches. As the fruitbodies develop, however, the miniature "puffballs" develop a stem and reveal themselves as little agarics, looking rather like hairy, white *Marasmius* or *Mycena* species. In fact, *Amparoina spinosissima* has been referred to both these genera, but is so distinct that it fits neither genus well. The surface spines are very fragile, fall off easily, and are able to act as propagules—meaning they are capable of growing on to produce another fungus.

SIMILAR SPECIES
The fragile spines and mainly tropical distribution should be distinctive, but once the spines are shed, the Flaky Bonnet may looks like a white species of *Mycena*, *Hemimycena*, or *Delicatula*, many of which also grow on fallen sticks.

The Flaky Bonnet forms conical to convex caps, covered with white to pale yellowish, flaky spines or granules that fall away with age, often leaving a few at the center. The surface below the spines is smooth, very thin, striate, and white. The gills are white. The stem is finely hairy, white, often with a slightly bulbous base.

Actual size

FAMILY	Hygrophoraceae
DISTRIBUTION	Western North America
HABITAT	In woodland
ASSOCIATION	With conifers or broadleaf trees, especially alder
GROWTH FORM	On ground or very decayed wood, singly or in troops
ABUNDANCE	Common
SPORE COLOR	White
EDIBILITY	Not edible

HEIGHT
Up to 8 in
(200 mm)

CAP DIAMETER
Up to 8 in
(200 mm)

AMPULLOCLITOCYBE AVELLANEOALBA

SMOKY BROWN FUNNEL

(MURRILL) HARMAJA

60

The Smoky Brown Funnel is one of many distinctive species that grow in the forests of the Pacific northwest of North America. It is locally common in this region, often growing in troops or clusters on old, decaying logs, typically in mixed alder and conifer woodland. The species is closely related to the widely distributed Club Foot (*Ampulloclitocybe clavipes*), but can reach more than twice its size. The specific epithet *avellaneo-alba* means "hazelnut-colored and white," referring to the Smoky Brown Funnel's contrasting dark cap and white gills.

SIMILAR SPECIES

Ampulloclitocybe clavipes is a more widespread species, typically paler capped, smaller, and with a markedly swollen base. Several *Clitocybe* species, some of which are poisonous, also have decurrent gills and depressed or funnel-shaped caps.

Actual size

The Smoky Brown Funnel has a cap that is flat, becoming depressed or funnel-shaped with age, with a margin that often remains incurved. The surface is smooth to slightly scaly at the center, dark olive-brown to blackish brown. The gills are white to cream and strongly decurrent. The stem is smooth and pale cap-colored.

FAMILY	Hygrophoraceae
DISTRIBUTION	North America, Europe, Central America, northern Asia
HABITAT	In woodland
ASSOCIATION	With conifers, occasionally with broadleaf trees
GROWTH FORM	On ground, singly or in troops
ABUNDANCE	Common
SPORE COLOR	White
EDIBILITY	Poisonous (with alcohol)

HEIGHT	Up to 3 in (80 mm)
CAP DIAMETER	Up to 3½ in (90 mm)

AMPULLOCLITOCYBE CLAVIPES

CLUB FOOT

(PERSOON) REDHEAD ET AL.

61

The Club Foot is a widespread and common woodland species, normally distinct thanks to its grossly swollen stem base. It looks like a *Clitocybe* species and was formerly placed in the genus, but recent DNA research has shown it to be unrelated. Fruitbodies are widely eaten in countries as diverse as China, Mexico, and the Ukraine, but they cause a toxic reaction when consumed within several days of drinking alcohol. The symptoms, which include flushing, rapid pulse, vertigo, and even collapse, are similar to those caused by coprine in the Common Inkcap (*Coprinopsis atramentaria*).

SIMILAR SPECIES

Several *Clitocybe* species, including *C. costata*, are similar, having decurrent gills and depressed or funnel-shaped caps. Some can be seriously poisonous. The pale gray *Clitocybe nebularis* and the whitish *Infundibulicybe geotropa* often have swollen stem bases, but are normally much larger.

Actual size

The Club Foot has a cap that is umbonate at first, but becomes flat and often depressed to funnel-shaped with age. The surface is smooth and variously reddish brown to olive-brown or gray-brown. The gills are white, cream, or pale yellow and strongly decurrent. The stem is buff to gray-brown, smooth, and typically (but not always) grossly swollen and darker at the base.

FAMILY	Marasmiaceae
DISTRIBUTION	Eastern and southern Africa, southern Asia
HABITAT	In woodland
ASSOCIATION	With broadleaf trees
GROWTH FORM	On fallen twigs and branches, in troops
ABUNDANCE	Locally common
SPORE COLOR	White
EDIBILITY	Not edible

HEIGHT	Less than ⅛ in (1 mm)
CAP DIAMETER	Up to 1½ in (35 mm)

62

ANTHRACOPHYLLUM MELANOPHYLLUM
CINNABAR FAN BRACKET
(FRIES) PEGLER & T. W. K. YOUNG

Actual size

Anthracophyllum species are widespread in the tropics, subtropics, and the south temperate zone. Like *Crepidotus* species, they grow on twigs and dead stems and have a similar bracket or shell-like shape. All are tough and leathery, however, becoming hard on drying, and most have deeply colored gills (the Latin *melanophyllum* means "black-gilled"), though their spores are white. They are in the same family as *Marasmius* species, which are equally widespread in the tropics and often as brightly colored.

SIMILAR SPECIES
In Australia and New Zealand, the Orange Fan Bracket (*Anthracophyllum archeri*) is the commonest species, with orange to brown caps and gills that age from orange to brick-red. *Anthracophyllum lateritium* occurs in southeastern North America and the Caribbean and has pale to brick-red caps with darker, reddish gills.

The Cinnabar Fan Bracket forms leathery, shell-shaped fruitbodies that are laterally attached to the wood, sometimes by a rudimentary stem. The caps are furrowed or fluted, pliant at first, then rigid, pinkish red to brick-red, finally dark brown. The gills are widely spaced, bright cinnabar-red, becoming violet to purple-black with age.

FAMILY	Physalacriaceae
DISTRIBUTION	North America, Europe, northern Asia; introduced in South Africa
HABITAT	In woodland, parkland, and gardens
ASSOCIATION	With broadleaf trees
GROWTH FORM	At base of trunks, stumps, or arising from roots, in dense clusters
ABUNDANCE	Very common
SPORE COLOR	White
EDIBILITY	Edible

HEIGHT
Up to 7 in
(175 mm)

CAP DIAMETER
Up to 5 in
(125 mm)

ARMILLARIA MELLEA

HONEY FUNGUS

(VAHL) P. KUMMER

63

Despite its pleasant name, the Honey Fungus strikes terror into the hearts of gardeners, since it is an aggressive parasite of trees and shrubs that spreads quickly thanks to its long, black, underground rhizomorphs. These can often be found under the bark of fallen trees and resemble bootlaces, hence its other English name of Bootlace Fungus. A closely related species, *Armillaria ostoyae*, is particularly destructive of conifers and can spread its way through entire forests. One living in Oregon has spread over 2,000 acres (800 hectares) and is the largest known single organism on the planet. The Honey Fungus is edible, though is said to cause gastric problems for some.

SIMILAR SPECIES

The name Honey Fungus is given to a complex of related species worldwide, such as *Armillaria novae-ʒelandiae* in New Zealand. In the north temperate region, the common *A. ostoyae* produces slimmer fruitbodies with purplish tints. The equally common *A. gallica* forms small clusters, tends to have a swollen stem base, and is non-parasitic.

The Honey Fungus forms caps that are convex, becoming umbonate to slightly depressed. The cap surface is pale yellow-olive to orange-brown, darker at the center, with small, pale to dark brown scales. The gills are decurrent and cream. The stem is cream at the top, becoming dark brown at the base, with a conspicuous ring, often edged in deep yellow.

Actual size

FAMILY	Tricholomataceae
DISTRIBUTION	North America, Europe
HABITAT	In damp woodland, old lawns, and grassland
ASSOCIATION	On mosses
GROWTH FORM	On moss stems, singly or in groups
ABUNDANCE	Occasional
SPORE COLOR	White
EDIBILITY	Not edible

HEIGHT
Less than ⅛ in
(1 mm)

CAP DIAMETER
Up to ½ in
(10 mm)

64

ARRHENIA RETIRUGA
SMALL MOSS OYSTERLING
(BULLIARD) REDHEAD

The Small Moss Oysterling and similar species are quite common on damp mosses in shady areas, but because of their small size are easy to overlook. They are most frequently spotted in mossy lawns, especially when they grow in groups. All are agarics and some species look like miniature Oyster Mushrooms (*Pleurotus ostreatus*), hence their common name. *Arrhenia retiruga*, however, is an agaric that does not develop gills, but instead has a smooth or shallowly veined, spore-bearing undersurface. It is actually a parasite on mosses, releasing enzymes that break down the cell walls of the host allowing the fungal hyphae to penetrate.

SIMILAR SPECIES
Several other similarly colored *Arrhenia* species grow on mosses. They include the Moss Oysterling (*A. acerosa*), which is slightly larger and has distinct gills on the underside, *A. auriscalpium* and *A. spathulata*, both of which have distinct stems, and the very similar *A. lobata*, which can be distinguished only microscopically.

The Small Moss Oysterling forms thin fruitbodies like miniature inverted bowls, attached to moss stems at the center or side of their caps. With age, the fruitbodies may expand and become more irregular. The cap surface is smooth and gray-buff. The undersurface is smooth to shallowly veined and similarly colored or slightly paler.

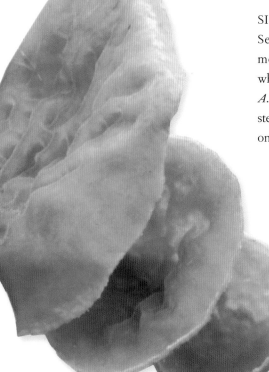

Actual size

FAMILY	Lyophyllaceae
DISTRIBUTION	North America, Europe, Central America, northern Asia
HABITAT	In woodland
ASSOCIATION	On *Russula* species, rarely *Lactarius* species
GROWTH FORM	On old fruitbodies, in clusters
ABUNDANCE	Occasional
SPORE COLOR	White
EDIBILITY	Not edible

HEIGHT
Up to 2 in
(50 mm)

CAP DIAMETER
Up to 1 in
(25 mm)

ASTEROPHORA LYCOPERDOIDES

POWDERY PIGGYBACK

(BULLIARD) DITMAR

65

Though no one could call it attractive, the Powdery Piggyback is certainly intriguing. Firstly, it is a parasite on other agarics, producing its fruitbodies in piggyback fashion on the decaying caps of its host. It has a preference for *Russula nigricans* and other *Russula* species that turn black with age, but will also occur on non-blackening species such as *R. delica* and *Lactarius vellereus*. Secondly, its caps gradually disintegrate into a brown powder, making them look like old puffballs (*lycoperdoides* means "puffball-like"). The powder is entirely composed of spiny, brown, asexual spores that are tough enough to survive all year, until a new crop of host fruitbodies appears.

SIMILAR SPECIES

In North America and Europe, *Asterophora parasitica* is found on the same hosts, but its caps never turn powdery. The Australian *A. mirabilis* is similar. Several small, pale, thin-stemmed species of *Collybia* also grow on old fruitbodies, including those of *Russula* and *Lactarius* species, but usually appear when the host has almost entirely rotted away.

The Powdery Piggyback has a hemispherical cap that is whitish and smooth at first, but the surface becomes somewhat lumpy and gradually breaks up into a fine, buff to pale brown powder. The whitish gills are often poorly formed and rather distant. The stem is smooth, whitish to pale brown.

Actual size

FAMILY	Paxillaceae
DISTRIBUTION	New Zealand
HABITAT	In woodland and parkland
ASSOCIATION	Ectomycorrhizal, with southern beeches
GROWTH FORM	On ground, singly or in scattered troops
ABUNDANCE	Common
SPORE COLOR	Brown
EDIBILITY	Poisonous

HEIGHT
Up to 4 in
(100 mm)

CAP DIAMETER
Up to 4 in
(100 mm)

66

AUSTROPAXILLUS MACNABBII

ORANGE ROLLRIM

(SINGER, J. GARCÍA & L. D. GÓMEZ) JAROSCH

The Orange Rollrim is a New Zealand specialty, one of a group of *Austropaxillus* species that occur only in the southern hemisphere. Until recently, they were thought to belong to the genus *Paxillus*, which is common in the northern parts of the globe, but DNA investigation shows they have evolved separately and form their own related, but distinct, genus. Appropriately, *Austropaxillus macnabbii* forms a mutually beneficial, ectomycorrhizal relationship with *Nothofagus* species—southern beech trees—which also occur only in the southern hemisphere. *Paxillus* species are poisonous and the Orange Rollrim may well be, too.

SIMILAR SPECIES

The Brown Rollrim (*Paxillus involutus*) is a much more widespread species, introduced in New Zealand where it grows with non-native trees. Other New Zealand species with southern beech are *Austropaxillus squarrosus*, with yellowish flesh that turns brown when cut, and *A. nothofagi*, which typically has a darker, reddish brown cap.

The Orange Rollrim forms caps that are convex at first, becoming flatter and often depressed, the margin long remaining incurved. The cap surface is whitish yellow when young, becoming yellow-orange to yellow-brown, often developing small, brown scales. The decurrent gills are cap-colored. The stem is smooth, whitish yellow, often staining yellow-brown when bruised.

Actual size

FAMILY	Bolbitiaceae
DISTRIBUTION	North America, Europe, northern Asia
HABITAT	In woodland
ASSOCIATION	With broadleaf trees
GROWTH FORM	On stumps, fallen branches, and woody fragments
ABUNDANCE	Occasional
SPORE COLOR	Rusty brown
EDIBILITY	Not edible

HEIGHT
Up to 2 in
(50 mm)

CAP DIAMETER
Up to 2 in
(50 mm)

BOLBITIUS RETICULATUS

NETTED FIELDCAP

(PERSOON) RICKEN

67

The Netted Fieldcap is probably quite common, but is easily overlooked since its fruitbodies are ephemeral and often occur singly on fallen fragments of wood half-hidden in undergrowth. As its English and Latin names indicate, *Bolbitius reticulatus* often develops a network of ridges or veins on the cap surface, though collections with an ordinary, smooth surface are equally common. The Netted Fieldcap has a remarkable resemblance to *Pluteus* species, though they are not closely related, and as a result frequently confuses collectors in the field. Its rusty brown spore print is, however, distinctive.

Actual size

SIMILAR SPECIES

The Netted Fieldcap has the habit and appearance of the Veined Shield (*Pluteus thomsonii*), but *Pluteus* species are distinguished by their pink spores that gradually color the gills. The name *Bolbitius aleuriatus* has been given to collections lacking veins on the cap surface, but is now considered a synonym.

The Netted Fieldcap forms caps that are convex becoming flat to shallowly umbonate. The cap surface is smooth or with netlike veins, sticky when damp, striate, pale to dark gray-brown with purplish or lilac tints. The gills are cream at first, becoming cinnamon to rusty brown with age (see photo right). The stem is narrow, smooth, and white.

FAMILY	Bolbitiaceae
DISTRIBUTION	North America, Europe, North Africa, Asia, Australia, New Zealand
HABITAT	In pastures and gardens
ASSOCIATION	On old manure or manured ground
GROWTH FORM	On ground, singly or in small clusters
ABUNDANCE	Common
SPORE COLOR	Pale rusty brown
EDIBILITY	Not edible

HEIGHT	CAP DIAMETER
Up to 4 in (100 mm)	Up to 1½ in (40 mm)

BOLBITIUS TITUBANS

YELLOW FIELDCAP

(BULLIARD) FRIES

68

This brightly colored little agaric, which is commonly known as the Yellow Fieldcap or the Yellow Cowpat Toadstool, looks attractive, but has a less appealing fondness for dung and manured grassland, where it can be quite common and conspicuous in damp weather. Since dung is a rich but temporary source of nutrients, coprophilous (dung-loving) fungi are usually rapid colonizers, producing ephemeral fruitbodies. *Bolbitius titubans* is just such a species, the thin and fragile fruitbodies rarely lasting for more than a day or two, just long enough to release their spores. The Yellow Fieldcap was formerly known as *B. vitellinus*, the epithet meaning "egg-yolk yellow," but the color fades even faster than the fruitbodies.

SIMILAR SPECIES

Older, faded fruitbodies can be difficult to distinguish from *Conocybe* species, such as the white-capped *C. apala*, though the Yellow Fieldcap often retains some trace of color at the cap center. Some ink caps (*Coprinopsis* species) look superficially similar but are immediately distinguished by their black gills and spores.

Actual size

The Yellow Fieldcap has a smooth but sticky, bright yellow, cone-shaped cap when young. The cap is thin, with a striate margin, and as it expands rapidly loses its color from the margin inward, becoming watery white to pale buff. The gills are pale yellowish brown, and the stem is narrow, fragile, and pale yellow in color, fading to white with age.

FAMILY	Lyophyllaceae
DISTRIBUTION	North America, Europe, northern Asia
HABITAT	In lawns and pastures, more rarely woodland
ASSOCIATION	With moss and grass
GROWTH FORM	On ground, singly or in small troops or clusters
ABUNDANCE	Common
SPORE COLOR	White
EDIBILITY	Considered edible by some

HEIGHT
Up to 2 in
(50 mm)

CAP DIAMETER
Up to 2 in
(50 mm)

CALOCYBE CARNEA

PINK DOMECAP

(BULLIARD) DONK

69

Calocybe means "beautiful mushroom" and this attractive little agaric, originally described from France, is common in lawns and short grass in Europe, though perhaps less frequent in North America. It seems to be more tolerant of fertilized grasslands than other characteristic grassland fungi such as waxcaps (*Hygrocybe* species). The Pink Domecap's color tends to fade with age, but the crowded, white to cream gills are usually distinctive. It is said to be edible, but is seldom found in quantity and is hardly worthwhile, especially since it could be confused with poisonous, grassland *Entoloma* species.

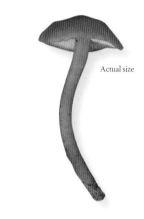

Actual size

SIMILAR SPECIES

The St .George's Mushroom (*Calocybe gambosa*) is a much larger, whitish, spring-fruiting agaric. Other related species, such as *C. ionides*, are either darker or bright yellow and are typically found in woodland. Some pinkish *Entoloma* species occur in grassland, but all have salmon-pink spores which color the gills of older specimens.

The Pink Domecap has caps that may be domed when young, but quickly become shallowly convex to flat. They are smooth, matt, and rose-pink to flesh-pink, becoming duller with buff tones when old. The gills are white to cream and very crowded. The stem is cap-colored, smooth, and usually (but not always) tapered.

FAMILY	Lyophyllaceae
DISTRIBUTION	Europe, northern Asia
HABITAT	In calcareous woodland, scrub, and grassland
ASSOCIATION	With calcareous plants
GROWTH FORM	On ground, in troops and rings
ABUNDANCE	Common
SPORE COLOR	White
EDIBILITY	Edible

HEIGHT
Up to 4 in
(100 mm)

CAP DIAMETER
Up to 6 in
(150 mm)

70

CALOCYBE GAMBOSA
ST. GEORGE'S MUSHROOM
(FRIES) DONK

The St. George's Mushroom is a spring-fruiting agaric, named after England's patron saint whose feast day is April 23rd, around the time when fruitbodies traditionally appear. It typically grows on limestone or chalk soils, and can be recognized by its color and strong mealy smell. It is a good edible species and fruitbodies are collected commercially in a range of European countries including Bulgaria, Romania, France, and Spain, from where they are widely exported. English-gathered St. George's Mushrooms were served to world leaders at a London G20 summit held in April 2010, a menu idea that has given this species an unexpectedly fashionable appeal.

SIMILAR SPECIES

Comparatively few large agarics appear in the spring, but several *Entoloma* species are of similar stature. Some, such as *Entoloma sinuatum*, are poisonous, but all can be distinguished by their salmon-pink spores. The lethal *Amanita verna* is white and spring-fruiting, but has a stem with ring and volva at the base.

Actual size

The St. George's Mushroom forms rather stout, solid-fleshed fruitbodies. The caps are domed, smooth, white to cream, sometimes with brownish tints toward the center and occasionally cracking during spells of dry weather. The gills are whitish and rather crowded. The thick stem is cap-colored and smooth, the flesh white and unchanging.

FAMILY	Lyophyllaceae
DISTRIBUTION	North America, Europe, northern Asia
HABITAT	In calcareous woodland
ASSOCIATION	With broadleaf trees and conifers
GROWTH FORM	On ground, singly or in small troops or clusters
ABUNDANCE	Occasional
SPORE COLOR	White
EDIBILITY	Edible

HEIGHT
Up to 2 in
(50 mm)

CAP DIAMETER
Up to 2 in
(50 mm)

CALOCYBE IONIDES

VIOLET DOMECAP

(BULLIARD) DONK

71

The Violet Domecap is an uncommon but widely distributed agaric, rare enough in some European countries to be placed on their national Red Lists of threatened fungal species. When found, the contrast between the violet cap and stem and the cream gills is quite striking. Fruitbodies also have a distinctly mealy smell and taste. The Violet Domecap grows in calcareous woodlands and appears to be a litter-rotting species. It was originally described and illustrated in 1792 by Jean Baptiste Bulliard, a French mycologist responsible for naming many familiar fungi, including the edible Cep (*Boletus edulis*) and the Common Inkcap (*Coprinopsis atramentaria*).

SIMILAR SPECIES

The much commoner Pink Domecap (*Calocybe carnea*) normally grows in lawns and grassland. The uncommon *C. onychina* is very similar, but the cap tends to be purple rather than violet and the gills are dull yellow. The Wood Blewit (*Lepista nuda*) has a violet cap and stem, but is usually much larger and has lilac to gray-lilac gills.

Actual size

The Violet Domecap has caps that become shallowly convex to flat. The cap surface is smooth, matt, and deep, bright violet to blackish violet, becoming duller or browner when old, the brighter colors often persisting near the margin. The gills are cream and crowded. The stem is smooth and cap-colored or a darker gray-violet.

FAMILY	Hygrophoraceae
DISTRIBUTION	North America, Europe
HABITAT	In calcareous pasture, mossy lawns, or woodland
ASSOCIATION	With moss and grass
GROWTH FORM	On ground, singly or in troops
ABUNDANCE	Occasional
SPORE COLOR	White
EDIBILITY	Not edible

HEIGHT
Up to 3 in
(75 mm)

CAP DIAMETER
Up to 1½ in
(40 mm)

CAMAROPHYLLOPSIS FOETENS
STINKING FANVAULT
(W. PHILLIPS) ARNOLDS

Actual size

The Stinking Fanvault forms caps that are convex, becoming flat or weakly depressed. The cap surface is smooth, pale gray-brown to brown. The gills are distant, decurrent, and cap-colored. The stem is smooth, tapering to the base, ocher-brown to cap-colored.

Camarophyllopsis species are small, predominantly gray-brown agarics with very arched, decurrent gills—hence the English name Fanvault. They are related to the waxcaps (*Hygrocybe* species) and occur in similar areas, typically in mossy calcareous pasture in Europe, more frequently in woodland in North America. They are all rather uncommon to rare, but quite often several species will grow together when they find a habitat they like. The Latin epithet *foetens* means "stinking," and the Stinking Fanvault is an easy species to recognize, thanks to its strong, unpleasant smell of napthalene (old-fashioned mothballs).

SIMILAR SPECIES

Other *Camarophyllopsis* species look similar, but lack the distinctive smell of the Stinking Fanvault. Most are best distinguished microscopically, though the Dotted Fanvault (*C. atropunctata*) is usually recognizable by having conspicuous black dots on its stem.

FAMILY	Marasmiaceae
DISTRIBUTION	South America
HABITAT	In woodland
ASSOCIATION	With bamboos
GROWTH FORM	On dead stems
ABUNDANCE	Occasional
SPORE COLOR	White
EDIBILITY	Not edible

HEIGHT
Less than ⅛ in (2 mm)

CAP DIAMETER
Up to 1½ in (35 mm)

CAMPANELLA AERUGINEA

TURQUOISE CAMPANELLA

SINGER

First described from Argentina, the Turquoise Campanella is widespread in South America and usually or always occurs on dead stems of bamboos. It is a relative of *Marasmius* species, but is distinct in having rather gelatinous fruitbodies with unusual, almost pore-like gills on the undersurface. If looked at closely, many agarics have veins or ridges connecting their gills, but in *Campanella* species these connecting veins have become prominent and branched, so that they appear netlike. They also like to grow on dead grass stems (including bamboos), though a few *Campanella* species are found on dead wood.

SIMILAR SPECIES

Campanella caesia is a smaller but similarly colored European species that grows on dead grass stems (and is seldom seen unless searched for). Many more *Campanella* species, some of them white, others buff or with bluish green tints, occur in the tropics and subtropics.

Actual size

The Turquoise Campanella forms thin, rather gelatinous caps that are convex at first, becoming flatter. The cap surface is smooth but ridged or fluted, translucently whitish and flushed blue-green. The gills are cap-colored, distant, and strongly interveined so that the undersurface appears almost poroid. A stem is absent, and the caps are directly attached to the surface at one side.

FAMILY	Marasmiaceae
DISTRIBUTION	Central and South America
HABITAT	In woodland
ASSOCIATION	With broadleaf trees
GROWTH FORM	On branches and sticks, in troops
ABUNDANCE	Common
SPORE COLOR	White
EDIBILITY	Not edible

HEIGHT
Up to 1 in
(25 mm)

CAP DIAMETER
Up to ¼ in
(6 mm)

74

CARIPIA MONTAGNEI
POD PARACHUTE
(BERKELEY) KUNTZE

This odd-looking little fungus resembles a strangely shaped puffball, but in fact the spores are produced on the outside, not the inside, of the podlike head. It was once treated alongside the club fungi (*Clavaria* species) and more recently thought to be related to *Podoscypha* species, but DNA research has now shown that it is actually a relative of small agarics in the genus *Marasmius*. Quite why *Caripia montagnei* has evolved its peculiar shape remains a mystery. It was named after the Caripi River on the northern borders of Brazil and is quite common in tropical and subtropical America.

SIMILAR SPECIES

The shape of *Caripia montagnei* is quite distinctive. It might be mistaken for a stalked cup-fungus, such as *Dumontinia tuberosa*, but these produce spores on their upper surfaces and are wholly unrelated. Its true relatives, such as *Marasmius rotula*, grow in a similar fashion but have ordinary, parachute-like caps with gills on the undersurface.

Actual size

The Pod Parachute forms unusual, goblet- or pod-shaped fruitbodies. The cap is smooth, whitish to cream, and flat or slightly depressed. The deeply decurrent, spore-bearing surface below is similarly colored, smooth at first, but often developing veinlike wrinkles with age. The narrow, cylindrical stem is smooth and brown to purplish brown.

FAMILY	Tricholomataceae
DISTRIBUTION	North America, continental Europe, northern Asia
HABITAT	In woodland
ASSOCIATION	Ectomycorrhizal with conifers, especially spruce
GROWTH FORM	On ground, singly or in small clusters
ABUNDANCE	Occasional
SPORE COLOR	White
EDIBILITY	Edible

HEIGHT
Up to 7 in
(180 mm)

CAP DIAMETER
Up to 12 in
(300 mm)

CATATHELASMA IMPERIALE

IMPERIAL MUSHROOM

(FRIES) SINGER

75

As befits its name, the Imperial Mushroom is a large and imposing species that typically grows with spruce in calcareous soil. It is related to *Tricholoma* species, but is distinct in having an unusual double ring, as well as gills that run down the stem. It has a noticeable smell, variously described as mealy, like cucumber, or like watermelon. The Imperial Mushroom is quite tough, but is edible and is even commercially collected for export in Romania and China. In several European countries, however, it is a rare and declining species that has been placed on national Red Lists of threatened fungal species.

SIMILAR SPECIES

In western North America there is a related species, *Catathelasma ventricosum*, which is typically rather smaller with a whitish cap. Matsutake species (*Tricholoma matsutake* and *T. magnivelare*) may look superficially similar, but do not have decurrent gills or a double ring. All are edible.

The Imperial Mushroom produces large, stout fruitbodies that are often half-buried in moss and litter. The cap is convex to flat, smooth to fibrous, sticky when young, and pale to mid-brown. The gills are strongly decurrent, whitish to cream occasionally graying with age. The thick stem tapers markedly toward the base, which may be buried. The stem is whitish above the double ring and buff below.

Actual size

FAMILY	Agaricaceae
DISTRIBUTION	North America, Africa, Central and South America, Asia, Australia
HABITAT	In grassland, parkland, and gardens
ASSOCIATION	With broadleaf trees and conifers, in rich soil or compost
GROWTH FORM	On ground, singly or in troops and rings
ABUNDANCE	Common
SPORE COLOR	Green to gray-green
EDIBILITY	Poisonous

HEIGHT
Up to 10 in
(250 mm)

CAP DIAMETER
Up to 12 in
(300 mm)

76

CHLOROPHYLLUM MOLYBDITES
FALSE PARASOL
(G. MEYER) MASSEE

The False Parasol is apparently the number-one species responsible for cases of fungal poisoning in North America, and has poisoned many other people elsewhere. It is primarily a tropical and subtropical agaric, particularly common in grassland where it can form impressive rings. It extends into temperate areas as far north as Canada, Japan, and Korea, but does not occur in Europe (except rarely in greenhouses and plant containers) or New Zealand. Its green spores are diagnostic, but do not color the gills in young fruitbodies, which are consequently mistaken for edible parasols. The toxin remains unknown, but can cause severe gastroenteritic symptoms in susceptible people.

SIMILAR SPECIES

The False Parasol is usually mistaken for the edible Parasol (*Macrolepiota procera*), which has zigzag stem markings and non-reddening flesh. It has also been mistaken for the Shaggy Parasol (*Chlorophyllum rhacodes*) and *C. brunneum*, both of which are considered edible by some, but can also be poisonous.

Actual size

The False Parasol forms caps that are almost spherical when young, becoming flat to shallowly umbonate, with a brown or pinkish brown central patch that is surrounded by small scales of similar color on a whitish background. The gills are white, becoming greenish. The stem is smooth, whitish, sometimes browning toward the base, with a large, often loose, scaly ring. The cut flesh in the stem base may turn reddish.

FAMILY	Agaricaceae
DISTRIBUTION	North America, Europe, northern Asia
HABITAT	In woodland, parkland, and gardens
ASSOCIATION	With broadleaf trees and conifers, in rich soil or compost
GROWTH FORM	On ground, singly or in groups
ABUNDANCE	Common
SPORE COLOR	White
EDIBILITY	Poisonous (to some), best avoided

HEIGHT
Up to 9 in
(225 mm)

CAP DIAMETER
Up to 9 in
(225 mm)

CHLOROPHYLLUM RHACODES

SHAGGY PARASOL

(VITTADINI) VELLINGA

77

The Shaggy Parasol (formerly known as *Macrolepiota rhacodes*) is a common north-temperate species with a preference for rich soil, often occurring in gardens, manured ground, and compost heaps. It is eaten by some people, but can cause unpleasant gastric upsets in others, so is probably best avoided. It is also very close to the decidedly poisonous False Parasol (*Chlorophyllum molybdites*), which in North America, the subtropics, and the tropics is frequently eaten by the over-confident in mistake for the Shaggy Parasol. The epithet *rhacodes* means ragged, which accurately describes the scaly cap.

SIMILAR SPECIES

The poisonous False Parasol (*Chlorophyllum molybdites*) is very similar, but develops a greenish spore print and gills when mature. *Chlorophyllum brunneum* (the Shaggy Parasol of western North America and Australia) and *C. olivieri* are also very similar, but no more toxic than *C. rhacodes*. The edible Parasol (*Macrolepiota procera*) has zigzag stem markings and is non-reddening.

The Shaggy Parasol forms caps that are almost spherical when young, becoming flat to shallowly umbonate, with a brown or red-brown central patch that is surrounded by shaggy, uplifted scales of similar color or whitish. The gills are white. The stem is smooth, whitish, browning toward the bulbous base, with a large, often loose, scaly ring. The cut flesh turns bright orange-red, fading to brownish (see photo top right).

Actual size

FAMILY	Gomphidiaceae
DISTRIBUTION	Europe, northern Asia
HABITAT	In woodland
ASSOCIATION	Probably ectomycorrhizal, with pines
GROWTH FORM	On ground, singly or in small troops
ABUNDANCE	Occasional
SPORE COLOR	Blackish gray
EDIBILITY	Edible

HEIGHT
Up to 5 in
(125 mm)

CAP DIAMETER
Up to 6 in
(150 mm)

78

CHROOGOMPHUS RUTILUS
COPPER SPIKE
(SCHAEFFER) O. K. MILLER

Chroogomphus species are quite closely related to *Gomphidius* species, but lack a ring on the stem. They are exclusively associated with pines and were presumed to be ectomycorrhizal associates, but recent research suggests they may instead be parasites—tapping into mycorrhizas formed by *Suillus* species. The Copper Spike is eaten in eastern Europe and Asia (after the slimy cap surface is removed), but does not seem to be greatly esteemed. The fruitbodies of related American species have also been used in craft-dyeing, producing a range of orange to gray-green colors.

SIMILAR SPECIES
Molecular research has shown that North American collections previously referred to as *Chroogomphus rutilus* are genetically distinct and should be called *C. ochraceus*. The North American *C. vinicolor* is also similar, but can be distinguished microscopically. The Asian *C. orientirutilus* has more reddish, less umbonate caps.

The Copper Spike has caps that are convex at first, becoming umbonate when mature, smooth, slimy when moist, and ocher-buff to wine-red or purple-brown. The gills are widely spaced and deeply decurrent, orange-gray to purple-gray. The stem is smooth, with faint zigzag markings when young, purple-brown at the top, orange below and yellow at the base.

Actual size

FAMILY	Tricholomataceae
DISTRIBUTION	North America, Europe, Central America, northern Asia, New Zealand
HABITAT	In woodland
ASSOCIATION	With broadleaf trees and conifers, in rich soil
GROWTH FORM	On ground, in troops and rings
ABUNDANCE	Common
SPORE COLOR	White
EDIBILITY	Poisonous (to some)

HEIGHT
Up to 5 in
(125 mm)

CAP DIAMETER
Up to 5 in
(125 mm)

CLITOCYBE NEBULARIS

CLOUDED FUNNEL

(BATSCH) P. KUMMER

79

The Clouded Funnel is a late-season agaric with a fondness for nitrogen-rich soil. It frequently grows in company with the Tawny Funnel (*Lepista flaccida*). The species has a distinctive smell that some find aromatic, others (particularly in North America) foul. It is possible that more than one species occurs, but research has shown that the fruitbodies contain at least 49 volatile components, giving rise to such aromas as roses, cheese, musty earth, almonds, and feces. The Clouded Funnel is sometimes eaten after parboiling, but can cause stomach problems. It contains nebularine, a cytotoxin extensively used in medical and other research.

SIMILAR SPECIES

The Trooping Funnel (*Infundibulicybe geotropa*) is of similar size and shape, but cream to pale beige. The Giant Funnel (*Leucopaxillus giganteus*) is a white species, more often found in grassland. The poisonous Livid Pinkgill (*Entoloma sinuatum*) could look similar when young, but has salmon-pink spores.

Actual size

The Clouded Funnel forms fleshy caps that are convex at first, becoming shallowly funnel-shaped when expanded. The cap surface is smooth, often with a thin, whitish bloom, pale gray to smoky, brownish gray, becoming paler toward the margin. The gills are whitish cream and weakly decurrent. The stem is cap-colored or paler, smooth, and usually swollen toward the base.

FAMILY	Tricholomataceae
DISTRIBUTION	North America, Europe, North Africa, northern Asia
HABITAT	In woodland
ASSOCIATION	With broadleaf trees
GROWTH FORM	On ground, singly or in scattered troops
ABUNDANCE	Common
SPORE COLOR	White
EDIBILITY	Edible

HEIGHT
Up to 4 in
(100 mm)

CAP DIAMETER
Up to 4 in
(100 mm)

80

CLITOCYBE ODORA
ANISEED FUNNEL
(BULLIARD) P. KUMMER

The pale jade-green colors and strong smell of aniseed are the distinctive characters of the Aniseed Funnel, a common species in woodland leaf litter. It often occurs singly, but can sometimes appear in large troops. The smell has been analyzed and comes from the volatile compound *p*-anisaldehyde, the dominant aroma produced by the fruitbodies. Not surprisingly, the species, which is edible, has occasionally been collected for its aniseed taste and may have some potential as a source of commercial flavoring products. Many other *Clitocybe* species, however, are poisonous (some even deadly) so as a group they are best avoided.

SIMILAR SPECIES

The smaller, pale brownish, striate-margined *Clitocybe fragrans* (formerly known as *C. suaveolens* or, in North America, *C. deceptiva*) is widespread, very common, and smells strongly of aniseed. The similarly pale, European *C. albofragrans* and *C. anisata*, as well as the pinkish, North American *C. oramophila*, also have the same smell.

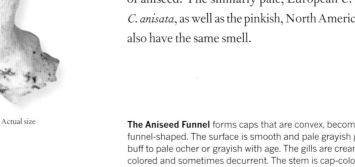

Actual size

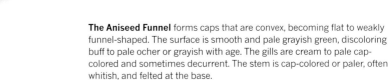

The Aniseed Funnel forms caps that are convex, becoming flat to weakly funnel-shaped. The surface is smooth and pale grayish green, discoloring buff to pale ocher or grayish with age. The gills are cream to pale cap-colored and sometimes decurrent. The stem is cap-colored or paler, often whitish, and felted at the base.

FAMILY	Tricholomataceae
DISTRIBUTION	North America, Europe, North Africa, northern Asia
HABITAT	In grassland, occasionally in scrub and woodland
ASSOCIATION	With grass or broadleaf trees
GROWTH FORM	On ground, often in troops or rings
ABUNDANCE	Common
SPORE COLOR	White
EDIBILITY	Poisonous

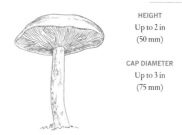

HEIGHT
Up to 2 in
(50 mm)

CAP DIAMETER
Up to 3 in
(75 mm)

CLITOCYBE RIVULOSA
FOOL'S FUNNEL
(PERSOON) P. KUMMER

81

Many *Clitocybe* species contain the poison muscarine, but some contain a higher concentration than others. The Fool's Funnel (also known as *C. dealbata*) is one of the latter, a particularly toxic species sometimes mistaken for the edible Fairy Ring Champignon (*Marasmius oreades*). Both form fairy rings and often grow together. More than 480 patients were treated for muscarine poisoning in southern France over a 25-year period up to 1998, though many of these poisonings were caused by *Inocybe* species. Fortunately all the patients recovered, but it certainly indicates the scale of fungal poisoning in many mycophilic countries.

SIMILAR SPECIES

Many small, pallid species of *Clitocybe* exist and are notoriously difficult to distinguish. The edible *Marasmius oreades* grows in similar situations to the Fool's Funnel, but is usually distinguishable by its warmer, cream to brownish colors, widely spaced, non-decurrent gills, and tough, pliable stem.

Actual size

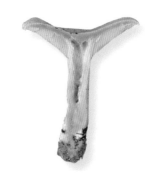

The Fool's Funnel forms caps that are convex, becoming flat to weakly funnel-shaped (see photo right). The surface is smooth and off white to grayish or pinkish buff, sometimes with watery spots when damp. The gills are cap-colored and sometimes weakly decurrent. The stem is smooth and also cap-colored.

FAMILY	Tricholomataceae
DISTRIBUTION	North America, Europe
HABITAT	In woodland
ASSOCIATION	With broadleaf trees
GROWTH FORM	On ground, singly or in scattered troops
ABUNDANCE	Occasional
SPORE COLOR	White
EDIBILITY	Not edible

HEIGHT
Up to 2 in
(50 mm)

CAP DIAMETER
Up to 1½ in
(35 mm)

82

CLITOCYBE TRULLIFORMIS
DAPPER FUNNEL
(FRIES) P. KARSTEN

This is a neat little *Clitocybe* species, with a gray cap and stem contrasting with its white to cream gills. It has a distinctly floury smell when cut. Confusion lies in its name, however, since several different *Clitocybe* species seem to have been called *C. trulliformis* at one time or another. This one is also known as *C. font-queri*, but to add to the confusion several authorities consider the latter to be a distinct species in its own right. The Latin epithet *trulliformis* means "shaped like a ladle," which hardly seems appropriate, unless the Romans used some strangely shaped ladles.

SIMILAR SPECIES
The uncommon *Clitocybe collina*, sometimes found in sand dunes, is similar but distinguished microscopically by its smaller spores. The Clouded Funnel (*C. nebularis*) also has a gray cap and stem, but is always much larger than the Dapper Funnel.

Actual size

The Dapper Funnel forms caps that are flat to depressed at the center. The surface is smooth and slightly felted, and dark to pale ash gray to brownish gray. The gills are white to cream and deeply decurrent. The stem is cap-colored, usually with some whitish mycelium at the base.

FAMILY	Entolomataceae
DISTRIBUTION	North America, Europe, North Africa, Central America, northern Asia
HABITAT	In woodland and parkland
ASSOCIATION	With broadleaf trees, especially oak, often in grass
GROWTH FORM	On ground, singly or in small groups
ABUNDANCE	Common
SPORE COLOR	Pink
EDIBILITY	Edible

HEIGHT
Up to 2 in
(50 mm)

CAP DIAMETER
Up to 3 in
(75 mm)

CLITOPILUS PRUNULUS

THE MILLER

(SCOPOLI) P. KUMMER

83

The Miller has been given its odd English name because of the
intensely mealy smell of its fruitbodies. They tend to be rather
low-growing and are often found half-hidden in grass near trees,
though they can also grow in woodland leaf litter. The Miller's
spores are pink and it belongs to the same family of fungi as
the Pinkgills (*Entoloma* species). Many of these are poisonous,
but The Miller is edible, the smell apparently disappearing on
cooking. The species was originally described in 1772 from
Slovenia by the Italian naturalist Giovanni Antonio Scopoli,
but is widespread throughout the northern hemisphere.

SIMILAR SPECIES

The less common *Clitopilus scyphoides* is a miniature version
of The Miller, best distinguished microscopically by its smaller
spores. The poisonous Fool's Funnel (*C. rivulosa*) is a whitish,
to slightly pinkish, grassland species that can look somewhat
similar, but has white (not pink) spores.

The Miller forms caps that are convex to flat, sometimes slightly depressed,
sometimes umbonate, with a lobed or wavy, inrolled margin. The surface of
the cap is suede-like, white, pale beige to gray or slightly pinkish when old.
The crowded, decurrent gills are whitish at first, becoming pale pinkish.
The stem is cap-colored and smooth.

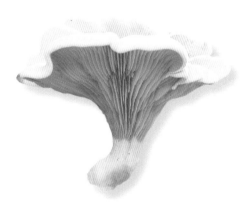

Actual size

FAMILY	Bolbitiaceae
DISTRIBUTION	Europe, North Africa
HABITAT	In pastures and lawns
ASSOCIATION	On manured or enriched grass
GROWTH FORM	On ground, singly or in scattered troops
ABUNDANCE	Locally common
SPORE COLOR	Pale rusty brown
EDIBILITY	Not edible

HEIGHT
Up to 4 in
(100 mm)

CAP DIAMETER
Up to 1 in
(25 mm)

84

CONOCYBE APALA
WHITE CONECAP
(FRIES) ARNOLDS

Actual size

The fragile White Conecap is typical of many ephemeral agarics of nutrient-rich grassland that appear in damp weather, produce their spores, and rapidly collapse. Many have black gills, such as the Pleated Inkcap (*Parasola plicatilis*), but the White Conecap is distinct in having gills that are pale rusty brown. It was formerly known as *Conocybe lactea* or *Bolbitius lacteus* and thought to be widespread in North America as well as Europe, but recent molecular research suggests that North American specimens (which often have less elongated caps) may represent a separate species called *C. albipes*.

SIMILAR SPECIES
Conocybe is a large genus, but most other species have tan to orange-brown caps. The white-capped *C. crispa*, described from North America, is two-spored and therefore easily distinguished microscopically, but may just be a variety of *C. albipes*. Other grassland agarics with white or pallid conical caps usually have white gills (*Mycena* species) or blackish gills (*Parasola* and *Panaeolus* species).

The White Conecap produces caps that are elongated or deeply conical with a smooth or finely wrinkled surface, white to cream, sometimes with ocher tints at the center. The gills are pale rusty orange. The thin, delicate stem is smooth and white, usually with a bulbous base. All parts of the fruitbody are extremely fragile.

FAMILY	Bolbitiaceae
DISTRIBUTION	North America, continental Europe, North Africa
HABITAT	In pastures and lawns
ASSOCIATION	On manured or enriched grass
GROWTH FORM	On ground, singly or in scattered troops
ABUNDANCE	Locally common
SPORE COLOR	Pale rusty brown
EDIBILITY	Not edible

HEIGHT
Up to 5 in
(125 mm)

CAP DIAMETER
Up to 1 in
(25 mm)

CONOCYBE DELIQUESCENS

BEANSPROUT FUNGUS

HAUSKNECHT & KRISAI

85

Until recently, this little species was placed in the genus *Gastrocybe* (as *G. lateritia*), since its cap never opens. DNA sequencing shows, however, that it is a *Conocybe* species, albeit a peculiar one. The Beansprout Fungus grows on lawns or in grassland in central North America and central to southern Europe, but is not always noticed since its fruitbodies are ephemeral and curiously lax. It rarely, if ever, stands upright, and its slimy caps seem close to disintegrating. Research suggests that bacteria may be the cause, possibly in some kind of mutual relationship with the fungus.

SIMILAR SPECIES

Fruitbodies of the Beansprout Fungus have a similar shape to those of the White Conecap (*Conocybe apala*), but the latter is dry and whitish throughout. Other *Conocybe* species with brown to reddish brown caps are also dry and have normal (not slimy) gills.

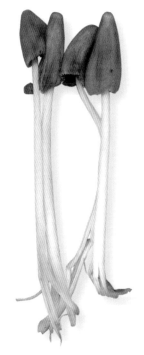

The Beansprout Fungus produces caps that are elongated or deeply conical with a wrinkled surface, very slimy, and reddish brown. The gills are cap-colored, irregular, slimy, and quickly disintegrating. The thin, lax stem is smooth and white.

Actual size

FAMILY	Bolbitiaceae
DISTRIBUTION	North America, Europe
HABITAT	In calcareous woodland, scrub, and parkland
ASSOCIATION	In leaf litter or woodchips
GROWTH FORM	On ground, singly or in scattered troops
ABUNDANCE	Occasional
SPORE COLOR	Rusty brown
EDIBILITY	Poisonous

HEIGHT
Up to 2 in
(50 mm)

CAP DIAMETER
Up to 1 in
(25 mm)

86

CONOCYBE FILARIS
FOOL'S CONECAP
(FRIES) KÜHNER

No one is likely to make a meal out of this little agaric, which is just as well. The Fool's Conecap has been shown to contain amatoxins, the same poisonous compounds that are present in the Death Cap (*Amanita phalloides*). The fruitbodies are therefore potentially lethal, though very few cases of poisoning by *Conocybe filaris* have ever been reported. The caps are hygrophanous, changing color quite markedly depending on whether it is wet or dry, but the conspicuous whitish ring is distinctive—though it is loosely attached and can easily fall off.

SIMILAR SPECIES
Conocybe species with a ring are sometimes referred to the genus *Pholiotina*. All have rusty brown spores. *Conocybe rugosa* is very similar to *C. filaris*, but has a wrinkled or furrowed cap. The poisonous *Galerina marginata* has rusty spores and a ring, but grows on wood.

Actual size

The Fool's Conecap forms caps that are convex to weakly umbonate. The surface is smooth, striate at the margin, reddish brown when damp, drying pale ocher. The gills are buff, becoming rusty brown. The stem is smooth to striate, dusted with fine flecks, ivory to silvery white at first, becoming cap-colored from the base upwards, and with a conspicuous, but loosely attached, whitish ring.

FAMILY	Psathyrellaceae
DISTRIBUTION	North America, Europe, Africa, Central and South America, Asia, Australia, New Zealand
HABITAT	In woodland
ASSOCIATION	With broadleaf trees
GROWTH FORM	On stumps and rotten (often buried) wood, in dense swarms
ABUNDANCE	Very common
SPORE COLOR	Black
EDIBILITY	Edible

HEIGHT
Up to 2 in
(50 mm)

CAP DIAMETER
Up to ½ in
(15 mm)

COPRINELLUS DISSEMINATUS

FAIRY INKCAP

(PERSOON) J. E. LANGE

87

The Fairy Inkcap is small, but makes up for its size by fruiting in vast numbers, typically on or around old stumps. Individual fruitbodies are not only small, but are also fragile, crumbling easily if picked. It is perhaps surprising, therefore, that this widespread species is collected for food by indigenous peoples in Ghana and other parts of Africa as well as in Southeast Asia. Unlike the gills of most inkcaps, those of the Fairy Inkcap do not turn to liquid when they are old. They do collapse rapidly, however, since the fruitbodies are ephemeral, seldom lasting more than a day or two.

SIMILAR SPECIES

Several small inkcaps look similar, but grow singly or in small groups. The less-common *Coprinellus hiascens* is a slightly larger look-alike that produces clusters of fruitbodies, but never large swarms. Though not so closely related, *Psathyrella pygmaea* does grow in swarms and is difficult to distinguish from the Fairy Inkcap without microscopic examination.

The Fairy Inkcap produces fruitbodies in large swarms. The caps are convex, very thin-fleshed and fragile, fluted or ridged, smooth or minutely hairy, and pale whitish to yellow-brown at first, becoming pale gray. The gills are whitish at first, becoming black. The stem is whitish to pale cap-colored and smooth.

Actual size

FAMILY	Psathyrellaceae
DISTRIBUTION	North America, Europe, northern Asia
HABITAT	In woodland, more rarely in buildings
ASSOCIATION	With broadleaf trees
GROWTH FORM	On logs and fallen branches, more rarely on structural timber, singly or in groups
ABUNDANCE	Common
SPORE COLOR	Black
EDIBILITY	Not edible

HEIGHT
Up to 6 in
(150 mm)

CAP DIAMETER
Up to 3 in
(75 mm)

88

COPRINELLUS DOMESTICUS
FIRERUG INKCAP
(BOLTON) VILGALYS ET AL

The fruitbodies of this inkcap are not in themselves remarkable, except that they appear to be growing from a rusty orange, shaggy rug. This peculiar rug is termed an ozonium, and is made up of specialized fungal mycelium. The ozonium can often be found on its own, growing on the undersides of logs and fallen branches. When conditions are right, fruitbodies arise from this shaggy mat. The Firerug Inkcap can sometimes occur in houses—hence the epithet *domesticus*—if timber or other material becomes sufficiently wet. Curiously, it has even been recorded growing on damp carpets and rugs.

SIMILAR SPECIES
Several closely related inkcaps arise from a rusty orange ozonium, including *Coprinellus radians* and *C. xanthothrix*, and they are best distinguished microscopically. If the ozonium mat is lacking (as it sometimes is), then the Firerug Inkcap is difficult to separate from other inkcaps of similar shape and size without microscopic examination.

The Firerug Inkcap produces ovoid caps at first, becoming conical and expanding. The surface is striate or shallowly fluted, ocher or buff to tan, dusted with small, whitish to brown, mealy scales at first. The gills are whitish at first, becoming black. The stem is white and smooth, often swollen at the base, usually growing from a rusty, shaggy mycelial mat.

Actual size

FAMILY	Psathyrellaceae
DISTRIBUTION	North America, Europe, Africa, Central and South America, Asia, Australia, New Zealand
HABITAT	In woodland, scrub, gardens, and roadsides
ASSOCIATION	With broadleaf trees
GROWTH FORM	On stumps and rotten (often buried) wood, in dense tufts
ABUNDANCE	Very common
SPORE COLOR	Black
EDIBILITY	Edible

HEIGHT
Up to 6 in
(150 mm)

CAP DIAMETER
Up to 1 in
(25 mm)

COPRINELLUS MICACEUS

GLISTENING INKCAP

(BULLIARD) VILGALYS, HOPPLE & JOHNSON

89

The Glistening Inkcap is a common and widespread fungus that takes its English (and Latin) names from the fine, glinting, mica-like scales on young caps. It grows in large clusters on old stumps or buried wood, often appearing in gardens, roadsides, and other disturbed ground. If the weather is damp enough, *Coprinellus micaceus* can produce crops of fruitbodies throughout the year. One researcher picked 38 lb (17 kg) of Glistening Inkcaps from a single elm stump between May and August. As it is an edible species, this may be some compensation for the scantiness of the individual fruitbodies.

Actual size

SIMILAR SPECIES

Several very similar inkcaps have been described, including the common *Coprinellus truncorum*, but they are only distinguishable microscopically and may prove to be no more than variations within *C. micaceus*. The Common Inkcap (*Coprinopsis atramentaria*) has a similar clustered habit, but is pale grayish and lacks glistening scales.

The Glistening Inkcap produces fruitbodies in dense clusters. The caps are convex, thin-fleshed, striate or shallowly fluted, dusted with small, glistening scales or granules, ocher or buff to tan. The gills are whitish at first, becoming black, and turn to liquid when old. The stem is white and smooth, becoming gray-brown toward the base.

FAMILY	Psathyrellaceae
DISTRIBUTION	North America, Europe, Africa, Central and South America, Asia, Australia, New Zealand
HABITAT	In woodland, scrub, gardens, and roadsides
ASSOCIATION	With broadleaf trees
GROWTH FORM	On stumps and rotten (often buried) wood, in dense tufts
ABUNDANCE	Very common
SPORE COLOR	Black
EDIBILITY	Poisonous

HEIGHT
Up to 6 in
(150 mm)

CAP DIAMETER
Up to 4 in
(100 mm)

90

COPRINOPSIS ATRAMENTARIA
COMMON INKCAP
(BULLIARD) REDHEAD, VILGALYS & MONCALVO

The Common Inkcap often grows in dense tufts arising from buried wood and is perhaps more common in gardens and waste ground than in its native woodlands. The epithet *atramentaria* means "inky," and Jean Baptiste Bulliard, when first describing the species in the eighteenth century, noted that ink could be made from its liquefying gills. The Common Inkcap is edible, but only by teetotallers. Fruitbodies contain a metabolite called coprine that reacts with even small amounts of alcohol (including cosmetics applied externally) to produce nausea, palpitations, and other unpleasant symptoms. This is why the inkcap has also been dubbed the Tippler's Bane.

SIMILAR SPECIES
Coprinopsis acuminata and *C. romagnesiana* are very similar, but have ocher to orange-brown caps. The less common *Coprinus alopecia* differs microscopically by its warted spores. The Glistening Inkcap (*Coprinellus micaceus*) has a similar clustered habit, but has tawny caps with glistening scales.

Actual size

The Common Inkcap produces fruitbodies in clusters. The caps are conical, thin-fleshed, rather fluted or ridged, smooth (or may have some scales at the center), and pale gray with brownish tints. The gills are whitish at first, becoming pinkish then black, turning to liquid when old. The stem is white and smooth, with a cottony, ridged veil zone above the base.

FAMILY	Psathyrellaceae
DISTRIBUTION	North America, Europe
HABITAT	In woodland, occasionally in mulch
ASSOCIATION	With broadleaf trees, especially beech
GROWTH FORM	On ground, singly or in small troops
ABUNDANCE	Occasional
SPORE COLOR	Black
EDIBILITY	Not edible

HEIGHT	Up to 12 in (300 mm)
CAP DIAMETER	Up to 3 in (75 mm)

COPRINOPSIS PICACEA

MAGPIE INKCAP

(BULLIARD) REDHEAD, VILGALYS & MONCALVO

91

The eye-catching, magpie markings of *Coprinopsis picacea* make this one of the easier inkcaps to recognize. It also has a distinctive smell of gas, dung, or mothballs, which research has shown comes from skatole, a curious organic compound used as a fixative in perfumes, but most commonly found in coal tar and feces. The Magpie Inkcap appears to be commonest in European beech woods, typically on calcareous soil, but occasionally occurs elsewhere. In recent years, it has become one of many agarics extending their natural range by colonizing the woodchips used as mulch in shrubberies and flowerbeds.

SIMILAR SPECIES

The large size, black-and-white markings, and unpleasant smell should be distinctive. A few smaller species have similar markings, including the European *Coprinopsis stangliana*, which is more gray and white and grows in calcareous grasslands, and *C. sclerotiorum*, which is rare (or overlooked) and grows on dung.

The Magpie Inkcap produces tall fruitbodies with deeply conical caps. The young cap is covered by a whitish veil that breaks up as it expands, revealing the blackish cap surface below. The gills are whitish at first, blackening with age. Cap and gills gradually deliquesce (turn liquid) from the margin inward. The long, cylindrical stem is white and finely scurfy.

Actual size

FAMILY	Agaricaceae
DISTRIBUTION	North America, Europe, North Africa, Central and South America, northern Asia, Australia, New Zealand
HABITAT	In grassland, woodland, gardens, and roadsides
ASSOCIATION	In nitrogen-rich soil or grass
GROWTH FORM	On ground, singly or in troops
ABUNDANCE	Common
SPORE COLOR	Black
EDIBILITY	Edible

HEIGHT
Up to 8 in
(200 mm)

CAP DIAMETER
Up to 3 in
(75 mm)

92

COPRINUS COMATUS
SHAGGY INKCAP
(O. F. MÜLLER) PERSOON

The Shaggy Inkcap, or Shaggy Mane, is easily identified by its scaly, cylindrical caps that have earned it the additional (if seldom used) name of Lawyer's Wig. The gills and caps turn to liquid as they age, so that old fruitbodies consist of little more than a long stalk with a few inky tatters at the top. This black inkcap liquid was sometimes used to write with before commercial inks became available. The Shaggy Inkcap is edible when young, and is now commercially cultivated in China. Recent molecular research has shown that it belongs in the family Agaricaceae, closer to ordinary shop mushrooms (*Agaricus bisporus*) than to most other inkcaps.

SIMILAR SPECIES

Coprinus sterquilinus is a widespread, smaller species that grows on dung heaps. In western North America, *C. colossus* is an uncommon, giant, woodland version of the Shaggy Inkcap, up to 20 in (500 mm) tall. The Desert Shaggy Mane (*Podaxis pistillaris*) looks similar, but the dry caps never open.

The Shaggy Inkcap forms caps that are almost cylindrical, only becoming conical in old age. The surface is densely shaggy-scaly, the top often buff to brownish, the scales similarly colored or white. The gills are white at first, becoming pink, then black. Gills and cap turn to black liquid from the base upward. The stem is smooth, white, with a loose, scaly ring.

Actual size

FAMILY	Cortinariaceae
DISTRIBUTION	North America, Europe, northern Asia, Australia
HABITAT	In woodland
ASSOCIATION	Ectomycorrhizal, with broadleaf trees
GROWTH FORM	On ground, in small troops
ABUNDANCE	Common
SPORE COLOR	Rusty brown
EDIBILITY	Edible

HEIGHT	Up to 3 in (80 mm)
CAP DIAMETER	Up to 4 in (100 mm)

CORTINARIUS ALBOVIOLACEUS

PEARLY WEBCAP

(PERSOON) FRIES

93

This attractive *Cortinarius* species belongs in the *Sericeocybe* group (*sericeus* meaning "silky") and indeed the cap surface does have a polished, silky sheen when young, with a glancing color that is somewhere between silver, gray, and pale violet. It is a fairly common species in broadleaf woodland, forming an association with beech, birch, willow, and other trees. The Pearly Webcap is unusual amongst *Cortinarius* species in being edible and is said to be consumed in Russia. Many related webcaps are lethally poisonous, however, and they are notoriously difficult to tell apart. So, as with *Amanita* species, this is a group of fungi that is best avoided.

The Pearly Webcap has dry, convex to flat caps that are smooth, silky, silvery-gray with a violet tint, later discoloring pale gray-buff. The gills are pale violet, becoming cinnamon-brown. The stem is dry, cap-colored, but deep violet at the top, smooth and silky but with fine, whitish veil remains (often in a zigzag pattern) toward the base, which is usually swollen. The flesh is pale gray-violet (see photo bottom left).

SIMILAR SPECIES

Many other webcaps are superficially similar. They include *Cortinarius traganus*, which is more strongly colored, has brownish flesh in the stem and smells of ripe pears, and *C. anomalus*, which has gray-violet colors that quickly fade and a stem wreathed with buff veil remnants. The Wood Blewit (*Lepista nuda*) has pale pinkish, not rusty brown, spores.

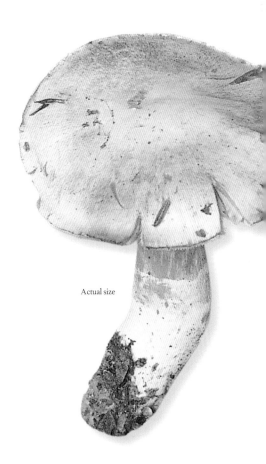

Actual size

FAMILY	Cortinariaceae
DISTRIBUTION	North America, Europe, northern Asia
HABITAT	In woodland
ASSOCIATION	Ectomycorrhizal, with birch
GROWTH FORM	On ground, singly or in scattered troops
ABUNDANCE	Common
SPORE COLOR	Rusty brown
EDIBILITY	Edible

HEIGHT
Up to 6 in
(150 mm)

CAP DIAMETER
Up to 4 in
(100 mm)

94

CORTINARIUS ARMILLATUS
RED-BANDED WEBCAP
(FRIES) FRIES

The Red-Banded Webcap, or Bracelet Cort, is a common agaric of north-temperate birch woods, usually found in sphagnum or other mosses under its partner tree. The brick-red bands or bracelets around the stem are distinctive, but similar (though often duller) bands can be found in some other species. In Russia at least, the fruitbodies are considered edible, but since *Cortinarius* species are notoriously difficult to identify with confidence and many are seriously poisonous, it would be wise not to emulate the Russians in this instance. The Red-Banded Webcap has also been used as a natural dye for wool and is said to give the yarn an attractive pink color.

SIMILAR SPECIES

In Central America, the closely related *Cortinarius quercoarmillatus* occurs with oak rather than birch. In Europe and North America, *C. haematochelis* and *C. paragaudis* can both look similar, but are generally rather more dully colored and are associated with spruce or pine.

Actual size

The Red-Banded Webcap forms caps that are hemispherical (see photo left), becoming flat or shallowly umbonate. The cap surface is smooth to finely fibrous, yellow-brown to tan, darker or reddish toward the center. The gills are grayish yellow, becoming rusty brown. The stem is pale gray-brown, with a cobwebby veil and several bands of brick-red veil remain toward the swollen base.

FAMILY	Cortinariaceae
DISTRIBUTION	Australia; introduced in New Zealand
HABITAT	In woodland
ASSOCIATION	Ectomycorrhizal, with eucalypts
GROWTH FORM	On ground, singly or in small troops
ABUNDANCE	Occasional
SPORE COLOR	Rusty brown
EDIBILITY	Probably poisonous

HEIGHT
Up to 4 in
(100 mm)

CAP DIAMETER
Up to 3 in
(75 mm)

CORTINARIUS AUSTROVENETUS

GREEN SKINHEAD

CLELAND

95

The Green Skinhead is an Australian specialty, forming a mutually beneficial association with the living roots of eucalyptus trees. It has even been featured on an Australian stamp. The species belongs in the *Dermocybe* section of *Cortinarius* and is sometimes called *Dermocybe austroveneta*. Most of the agarics in this section have orange to red caps, but the Green Skinhead is an unusual exception. Green colors are not so common in fungi and are not related to those found in plants. Isolation of the pigment in the Green Skinhead has shown it to be a previously unknown compound, now called austrovenetin after the fungus.

SIMILAR SPECIES

It has recently been suggested that a very similar, bluish green Australian species, *Cortinarius walkerae*, may be identical to *C. austrovenetus*. North-temperate *Cortinarius* species with greenish caps, such as *C. atrovirens* and *C. ionochlorus*, belong to the *Phlegmacium* section of the genus, with larger, stockier fruitbodies and bulbous stem bases.

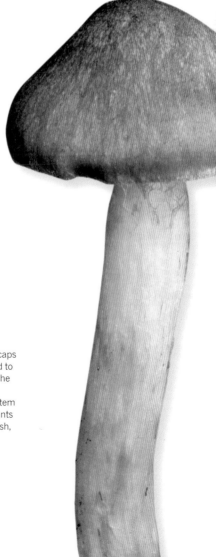

The Green Skinhead has smooth, convex caps that are slightly slimy when damp, emerald to olive-green, darkening toward the center. The gills are greenish yellow at first, becoming orange to rusty brown when mature. The stem is smooth with some cobwebby veil remnants and is cream, often tinted yellow to brownish, becoming orange to reddish at the base.

Actual size

FAMILY	Cortinariaceae
DISTRIBUTION	North America, Europe, Central America, northern Asia
HABITAT	In woodland
ASSOCIATION	Ectomycorrhizal with broadleaf trees, particularly beech and oak
GROWTH FORM	On ground, singly or in scattered troops
ABUNDANCE	Occasional
SPORE COLOR	Rusty brown
EDIBILITY	Poisonous

HEIGHT
Up to 4 in
(100 mm)

CAP DIAMETER
Up to 3 in
(75 mm)

96

CORTINARIUS BOLARIS
DAPPLED WEBCAP
(PERSOON) FRIES

The Dappled Webcap is one of the easiest *Cortinarius* species to recognize, thanks to its attractive coppery red, scaly markings. It usually forms associations with oak, beech, and possibly birch, preferring acidic woodlands. The Dappled Webcap has traditionally been placed in *Cortinarius* section *Leprocybe*, species of which typically have dry (not slimy) caps and stems, but recent DNA research has suggested it may be more closely related to species of section *Telamonia*, such as the Frosty Webcap (*C. hemitrichus*).

SIMILAR SPECIES

Cortinarius rubicundulus can be similarly colored, but lacks the distinct scales of the Dappled Webcap. It is more robust and the cap is cream at first and rather fibrous, but becomes patchily coppery red and yellowish with age. The Scaly Webcap (*C. pholideus*) has a more pointed cap, fine brown scales, and a stem wreathed in zigzag bands.

Actual size

The Dappled Webcap forms caps that are hemispherical, becoming flat. The cap surface is whitish to pale buff, covered in flat, coppery red to brick-red scales. The gills are cream to sordid yellowish, becoming rusty brown. The stem is whitish with a cobwebby veil, scaly and cap-colored below the veil. All parts bruise yellow.

FAMILY	Cortinariaceae
DISTRIBUTION	North America, Europe
HABITAT	In woodland
ASSOCIATION	Ectomycorrhizal, with conifers, particularly spruce
GROWTH FORM	On ground, singly or in scattered troops
ABUNDANCE	Occasional
SPORE COLOR	Rusty brown
EDIBILITY	Not edible

HEIGHT
Up to 5 in
(125 mm)

CAP DIAMETER
Up to 4 in
(100 mm)

CORTINARIUS CAMPHORATUS

GOATCHEESE WEBCAP

(FRIES) FRIES

97

The name *Cortinarius camphoratus* would suggest a fungus smelling strongly of camphor, yet this seems to be the one odor that no one ever reports. It certainly has a pungent smell—hence the alternative English name of Pungent Cort— but one that has been variously likened to curry powder (as in *Lactarius camphoratus*), rotting meat, old goats or goat's cheese, cold mashed potato, burnt horn, or sweaty feet. Aroma apart, it is rather an attractive agaric, though the pale lilac to violet colors quickly fade with age. It associates with conifers, particularly spruce but also with firs, and is widespread in North American and European conifer woodland.

SIMILAR SPECIES

The Gassy Webcap (*Cortinarius traganus*) is similarly colored, but young fruitbodies have pale brown rather than violet gills and its smell is often likened to overripe pears. *Cortinarius alboviolaceus* grows with broadleaf trees and lacks any distinctive smell. The Wood Blewit (*Lepista nuda*) has pale pinkish spores.

The Goatcheese Webcap forms caps that are hemispherical, becoming flat. The cap surface is smooth to finely fibrous, pale blue-violet to violet-white, becoming yellowish to buff from the center outward with age. The gills are pale blue-violet at first, becoming rusty brown. The stem is cap-colored, with a sparse, cobwebby veil, and turns yellowish buff with age.

Actual size

FAMILY	Cortinariaceae
DISTRIBUTION	North America, Europe, Central America, northern Asia
HABITAT	In woodland
ASSOCIATION	Ectomycorrhizal, with conifers, also broadleaf trees and shrubs
GROWTH FORM	On ground, singly or in scattered troops
ABUNDANCE	Locally common
SPORE COLOR	Rusty brown
EDIBILITY	Edible

HEIGHT
Up to 6 in
(150 mm)

CAP DIAMETER
Up to 5 in
(125 mm)

98

CORTINARIUS CAPERATUS
THE GYPSY
(PERSOON) FRIES

Most *Cortinarius* species have a thin, silky-fibrous veil covering the gills when young, leaving a cobwebby ring-zone (called a cortina) on the stem when the cap expands. The Gypsy, however, has a much thicker veil that leaves a distinct ring. For this reason it was long placed in the separate genus *Rozites* until recent molecular research showed that it was simply a *Cortinarius* with a thicker-than-usual veil. The Gypsy is edible and is widely collected and sometimes locally marketed in China, Mexico, Finland, eastern Europe, and Russia. An extract from the fungus has been shown to have potential antiviral properties.

SIMILAR SPECIES
The Gypsy was historically confused with *Phaeolepiota aurea*, but the latter is golden yellow and has white spores. The ringed, Himalayan *Cortinarius emodensis* has violet gills when young and is eaten in Tibet. Other ringed *Cortinarius* species occur in south temperate regions, but can be distinguished by their color.

The Gypsy forms caps that are convex to conical, becoming flat to shallowly umbonate. The cap surface is smooth to finely wrinkled, cream to ocher or light tan, sometimes pale cinnamon at the center, covered with a very thin, silvery white veil when young. The gills are whitish at first, becoming buff to brown. The stem is white, becoming cream to buff, with a distinct ring.

Actual size

FAMILY	Cortinariaceae
DISTRIBUTION	Eastern North America, Europe, northern Asia
HABITAT	In woodland
ASSOCIATION	Ectomycorrhizal, with broadleaf trees, particularly birch
GROWTH FORM	On ground, in small troops or rings
ABUNDANCE	Common
SPORE COLOR	Rusty brown
EDIBILITY	Not edible

HEIGHT
Up to 3 in
(75 mm)

CAP DIAMETER
Up to 2 in
(50 mm)

CORTINARIUS HEMITRICHUS

FROSTY WEBCAP

(PERSOON) FRIES

99

It has been said that *Cortinarius hemitrichus* follows the birch as the dolphin follows the ship, and certainly this little agaric is frequently found in acidic birch woods or even with solitary trees. It belongs in the *Telamonia* section of *Cortinarius*, a large and notoriously difficult group of species to identify successfully. The Frosty Webcap is easier than most, however, since the whitish cap scales give the fruitbodies a frosted appearance, hence the English name. Its lack of smell is also significant, since a very similar species, *C. flexipes*, smells of pelargoniums.

SIMILAR SPECIES

Many *Cortinarius* species in this group are similarly shaped and colored, but most lack the contrasting, hoary scales on the cap. The Pelargonium Webcap (*C. flexipes*) is scaly, but is typically darker, grows with conifers as well as birch, and has a distinct pelargonium ("geranium leaf") smell.

The Frosty Webcap has caps that are conical at first, becoming markedly umbonate. The cap surface is dark gray-brown when damp, pale gray-ocher when dry, and covered in fine, whitish, fibrous scales. The gills are pale gray-brown. The stem is gray-brown but covered in white, fleecy veil remnants, sometimes forming a ringlike zone.

Actual size

FAMILY	Cortinariaceae
DISTRIBUTION	North America, Central and northern South America, northern Asia
HABITAT	In woodland
ASSOCIATION	Ectomycorrhizal, with broadleaf trees, particularly oaks
GROWTH FORM	On ground, in small troops
ABUNDANCE	Occasional
SPORE COLOR	Rusty brown
EDIBILITY	Not edible

HEIGHT
Up to 3 in
(75 mm)

CAP DIAMETER
Up to 2½ in
(60 mm)

CORTINARIUS IODES
VISCID VIOLET WEBCAP
BERKELEY & M. A. CURTIS

Cortinarius species with slimy caps and stems, such as the Viscid Violet Webcap, belong in the section *Myxacium*, though recent molecular research suggests this is an artificial grouping. The slime has probably evolved to protect the developing fruitbody from desiccation and may also deter insects and other invertebrates from eating it. If fruitbodies are found in dry weather, their former sliminess may still be apparent from bits of leaves and soil adhering to the cap and stem. Alternatively, as a test, caps and stems can be kissed—the lips being particularly sensitive to stickiness—though fellow fungus forayers may consider such behavior a little odd.

SIMILAR SPECIES
Several other webcaps look similar and are equally slimy. The North American *Cortinarius iodeoides* appears more or less identical, but has a bitter taste and different microscopic characters. *Cortinarius salor* and *C. croceocaeruleus* are widespread species with slimy violet caps and stems, but neither develop the characteristic yellowish flecks of *C. iodes*.

Actual size

The Viscid Violet Webcap has caps that are convex, becoming flat to umbonate when expanded. The surface is slimy, bright violet when young, becoming paler and developing cream to yellowish flecks. The gills are violet, becoming rusty to gray-brown. The stem is slimy, pale cap-colored to whitish, and somewhat swollen at the base.

FAMILY	Cortinariaceac
DISTRIBUTION	Europe
HABITAT	In calcareous parkland and woodland
ASSOCIATION	Ectomycorrhizal, with oak, hazel, and hornbeam
GROWTH FORM	On ground, in small troops
ABUNDANCE	Rare
SPORE COLOR	Rusty brown
EDIBILITY	Not edible

HEIGHT
Up to 4 in
(100 mm)

CAP DIAMETER
Up to 5 in
(125 mm)

CORTINARIUS OLEARIOIDES

SAFFRON WEBCAP

R. HENRY

Cortinarius olearioides is a species particularly associated with oak or hazel, and it has a preference for calcareous soils. It also seems to like dry ground and may be more frequent in open parkland with scattered trees, rather than in dense, damp woodland. The fruitbodies are said to have a peculiar malt-like smell if cut. The Saffron Webcap is widespread in Europe, but is nowhere common and is rare enough in many countries to be on their national Red List of threatened fungal species.

SIMILAR SPECIES

Several other uncommon European webcaps may look similar. They include *Cortinarius alcalinophilus*, which is duller, has darker, scaly veil remains at the cap center, and prefers to grow with beech, and *C. elegantior*, which has a more tawny-brown cap and usually associates with conifers or birch.

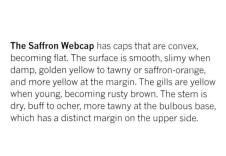

Actual size

The Saffron Webcap has caps that are convex, becoming flat. The surface is smooth, slimy when damp, golden yellow to tawny or saffron-orange, and more yellow at the margin. The gills are yellow when young, becoming rusty brown. The stem is dry, buff to ocher, more tawny at the bulbous base, which has a distinct margin on the upper side.

FAMILY	Cortinariaceae
DISTRIBUTION	North America, Europe, northern Asia
HABITAT	In woodland
ASSOCIATION	Ectomycorrhizal, with birch
GROWTH FORM	On ground, in small troops
ABUNDANCE	Occasional
SPORE COLOR	Rusty brown
EDIBILITY	Not edible

HEIGHT
Up to 6 in
(150 mm)

CAP DIAMETER
Up to 3 in
(75 mm)

102

CORTINARIUS PHOLIDEUS
SCALY WEBCAP
(FRIES) FRIES

The Scaly Webcap is a birch associate, most frequently found in mosses in peaty, acidic soils. The epithet *pholideus* means "scaly" and the small, erect scales on the cap are unusual for a *Cortinarius* species, making the Scaly Webcap look more like a *Pholiota*, at least when viewed from above. Fruitbodies are said to smell faintly of nutmeg, but are doubtfully edible and best avoided. Like most webcaps, *Cortinarius pholideus* is restricted to temperate regions. Webcaps become rarer in the subtropics and are almost absent from the tropics, so it seems as if the whole genus may have evolved in cool climates.

SIMILAR SPECIES
The combination of dry, scaly cap and dry, girdled stem distinguishes the Scaly Webcap. The Girdled Webcap (*Cortinarius trivialis*) looks superficially similar, but has a smooth, slimy cap and equally slimy stem. In North America, *C. squamulosus* has a dry, scaly, brown cap, but lacks girdles on its grossly bulbous stem.

Actual size

The Scaly Webcap has caps that are convex (see photo top left) to conical, becoming umbonate. The surface is dry, dull brownish yellow, covered in fine, erect, dark brown scales. The gills are pale brown, tinted blue-violet when young, becoming rusty brown. The stem is dry, brownish white, sometimes tinted violet at the top when young, with irregular girdles of dark brown scales.

FAMILY	Cortinariaceae
DISTRIBUTION	Europe, northern Asia
HABITAT	In calcareous woodland
ASSOCIATION	Ectomycorrhizal, with broadleaf trees, especially beech
GROWTH FORM	On ground, in troops or rings
ABUNDANCE	Occasional
SPORE COLOR	Rusty brown
EDIBILITY	Edible

HEIGHT
Up to 10 in
(250 mm)

CAP DIAMETER
Up to 10 in
(250 mm)

CORTINARIUS PRAESTANS

GOLIATH WEBCAP

(CORDIER) GILLET

103

As the name suggests, the Goliath Webcap produces big fruitbodies—among the largest of all the webcaps—that can be an impressive sight when they form a ring. Unfortunately, it is a rare species over much of its range, restricted to chalk and limestone woodlands, though it is said to be not uncommon in some areas. Unusually for a webcap, it is edible, but is too rare to be collected for food and is protected by law in some European countries. The Goliath Webcap has a very sticky cap but a dry stem, and belongs in the *Phlegmacium* section of *Cortinarius*.

SIMILAR SPECIES

The related *Cortinarius cumatilis* can look similar, but grows with conifers and is typically half the size with a more bluish violet cap. Many other species in section *Phlegmacium* (with sticky caps and dry stems) have brownish caps and violet veil remains, but few of them are remotely the size of the Goliath Webcap.

The Goliath Webcap has caps that are hemispherical, becoming flat. The surface is smooth, becoming radially wrinkled, sticky when damp, purplish brown becoming red-brown, with whitish veil remains when young. The gills are pale gray-violet, becoming brown. The stem is smooth, white, with violet veil remains when young, typically swollen toward the base.

Actual size

FAMILY	Cortinariaceae
DISTRIBUTION	North America, Europe, northern Asia
HABITAT	In woodland
ASSOCIATION	Ectomycorrhizal, with conifers
GROWTH FORM	On ground, in small troops
ABUNDANCE	Occasional
SPORE COLOR	Rusty brown
EDIBILITY	Poisonous

HEIGHT
Up to 4 in
(100 mm)

CAP DIAMETER
Up to 3 in
(75 mm)

CORTINARIUS RUBELLUS
DEADLY WEBCAP
COOKE

104

Cortinarius rubellus, also known as *C. speciossimus* or *C. orellanoides*, is an extremely toxic fungus, responsible for several recent near-fatal poisonings in Scotland and in Scandinavia. Along with the related Fool's Webcap (*C. orellanus*), the Deadly Webcap contains a compound called orellanine that can lead to kidney failure if eaten—often after a delay of several days or even weeks. The species occurs with pine, spruce, and other conifers and is widespread in Europe, but less well-known in North America and Asia (where similar toxic *Cortinarius* species may also be present).

SIMILAR SPECIES

In the Scottish poisoning cases, the Deadly Webcap was mistaken for the edible Chanterelle (*Cantharellus cibarius*). The latter species has thick, decurrent, gill-like ridges on the undersurface of its cap and produces a white (not rusty brown) spore print.

Actual size

The Deadly Webcap has caps that are conical to convex, becoming umbonate when expanded. The surface is smooth to silky fibrous, tawny to reddish orange. The gills are ocher when young, becoming rusty brown (see photo right). The stem is dry, cap-colored or paler, with yellowish zigzag patterns of veil remains.

FAMILY	Cortinariaceae
DISTRIBUTION	North America, Europe, northern Asia
HABITAT	In woodland
ASSOCIATION	Ectomycorrhizal, with conifers and broadleaf trees
GROWTH FORM	On ground, in small troops
ABUNDANCE	Common
SPORE COLOR	Rusty brown
EDIBILITY	Probably poisonous

HEIGHT
Up to 4 in
(100 mm)

CAP DIAMETER
Up to 2 in
(50 mm)

CORTINARIUS SANGUINEUS

BLOODRED WEBCAP

(WULFEN) GRAY

The epithet *sanguineus* means "of blood," and the dark crimson colors of the Bloodred Webcap are a distinctive feature of this small, but striking, agaric. It belongs in the *Dermocybe* section of *Cortinarius,* and the color comes mainly from the pigments emodin and dermocybin which have been isolated from fruitbodies. These compounds are the reason why this species has long been a favorite with natural dyers. Emodin (commoner in young fruitbodies) produces a range of yellow to orange colors, while dermocybin (commoner in older fruitbodies) produces vibrant reds, pinks, and purples.

SIMILAR SPECIES

Other *Cortinarius* species in section *Dermocybe* are of similar shape and size, but none have the uniform, dark crimson colors of *C. sanguineus*. *Cortinarius cinnabarinus* is a larger species with broadleaf trees that can be entirely red when young, but ages more reddish brown on the cap.

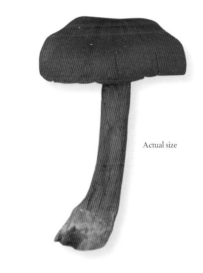

Actual size

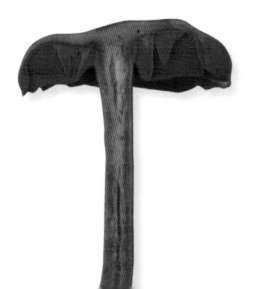

The Bloodred Webcap has caps that are at first hemispherical, becoming flat to shallowly umbonate. The surface is finely silky-fibrous and deep carmine, becoming duller with age. The gills are cap-colored (see photo left). The stem too is pale cap-colored, with cobwebby, ocher to reddish veil remains when young.

FAMILY	Cortinariaceae
DISTRIBUTION	North America, Europe
HABITAT	In woodland
ASSOCIATION	Ectomycorrhizal, with conifers and birch
GROWTH FORM	On ground, in small troops
ABUNDANCE	Common
SPORE COLOR	Rusty brown
EDIBILITY	Probably poisonous

HEIGHT
Up to 4 in
(100 mm)

CAP DIAMETER
Up to 2 in
(50 mm)

CORTINARIUS SEMISANGUINEUS
SURPRISE WEBCAP
(FRIES) GILLET

Actual size

From above, fruitbodies of *Cortinarius semisanguineus* look like many other small brownish agarics. The surprise is when you turn a cap over and see the dark red gills. The Latin name rather gives the game away, since the species is half-like its close relative the Bloodred Webcap (*C. sanguineus*), which is red on the cap as well as the stem. Both are sometimes placed in the genus *Dermocybe*. Like its relative, the Surprise Webcap is a sought-after species by fungal dyers, producing a range of colors from reds and pinks to purple.

SIMILAR SPECIES
Though entirely red when young, *Cortinarius cinnabarinus* usually develops a more brownish cap with age, but retains a reddish stem. Other brown-capped *Cortinarius* species in section *Dermocybe* may look similar from above, but have gills that are yellow to orange or rusty tan.

The Surprise Webcap has caps that are hemispherical at first, becoming flat to shallowly umbonate. The surface is finely silky-fibrous and yellow-brown to olive-brown. The gills are blood-red (see photo left), becoming rusty with age. The stem is ocher to yellow-brown, with cobwebby veil remains when young.

FAMILY	Cortinariaceae
DISTRIBUTION	North America, Europe
HABITAT	In woodland
ASSOCIATION	Ectomycorrhizal, with broadleaf trees, especially beech
GROWTH FORM	On ground, in groups or rings
ABUNDANCE	Occasional
SPORE COLOR	Rusty brown
EDIBILITY	Not edible

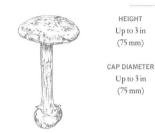

HEIGHT
Up to 3 in
(75 mm)

CAP DIAMETER
Up to 3 in
(75 mm)

CORTINARIUS SODAGNITUS

BITTER BIGFOOT WEBCAP

ROB. HENRY

107

The Bitter Bigfoot Webcap belongs in *Cortinarius* section *Phlegmacium*, a group of large and rather squat agarics with slimy caps. The swollen "bigfoot" base, often with a distinct rim or margin at the top, is typical of many *Phlegmacium* species. All are generally uncommon or rare, but in certain woodlands— particularly old beechwoods on calcareous soil—several different species can be found growing together. A particular feature of *Cortinarius sodagnitus* and related species is that the caps turn bright pink-red when a drop of dilute ammonia (or other alkali) is placed on them. Investigation has shown that this is due to novel compounds—dubbed "sodagnitins"— produced by the fungus.

Actual size

SIMILAR SPECIES

The Mealy Bigfoot Webcap (*Cortinarius caerulescens*) and *C. terpsichores* are both of similar shape and color, though often somewhat larger. They are best distinguished microscopically. The North American *C. velicopius* is of similar shape, but a deep, dark violet. Older fruitbodies with faded colors may not be identifiable to species.

The Bitter Bigfoot Webcap produces convex caps that are slimy, smooth, and deep violet when young, discoloring to ocher in parts when old. The gills are grayish with a violet edge when young (see photo right), becoming gray-brown to rusty brown. The stem is white to violet with a cobwebby violet veil and a large bulb at the base with a distinct margin.

FAMILY	Cortinariaceae
DISTRIBUTION	North America, Europe, northern Asia
HABITAT	In woodland
ASSOCIATION	Ectomycorrhizal, with conifers
GROWTH FORM	On ground, in small troops
ABUNDANCE	Occasional
SPORE COLOR	Rusty brown
EDIBILITY	Not edible

HEIGHT
Up to 5 in
(125 mm)

CAP DIAMETER
Up to 5 in
(125 mm)

108

CORTINARIUS TRAGANUS
GASSY WEBCAP
(FRIES) FRIES

The Gassy Webcap has caps that are hemi-spherical at first, becoming flat. The surface is smooth and silky, violet becoming paler with yellowish tints. The gills are pale to yellow-brown, becoming rusty. The stem is smooth, with a cobwebby girdle, pale cap-colored at the top, becoming yellowish brown toward the swollen base. The flesh is tan to brownish in the stem (see photo bottom right).

This is a handsome *Cortinarius* species, but since the epithet *traganus* relates to goats, the smell is considerably less attractive. Curiously, many people claim it has an odor of overripe pears and it may be that two or more closely related species have been bundled together under the same name. The Gassy Webcap is locally common under conifers, particularly in the remaining old-growth forests of northern North America, and can be found under both spruce and pine. Its edibility is unknown but suspect. It may well prove to be poisonous, like so many other *Cortinarius* species.

SIMILAR SPECIES

Many other webcaps look similar. *Cortinarius camphoratus* has violet gills when young and is said to stink of rotten flesh, goats, or burnt horn. *Cortinarius alboviolaceus* is silvery violet, grows with broadleaf trees, and lacks any distinctive smell. The Wood Blewit (*Lepista nuda*) has pale pinkish, not rusty brown, spores.

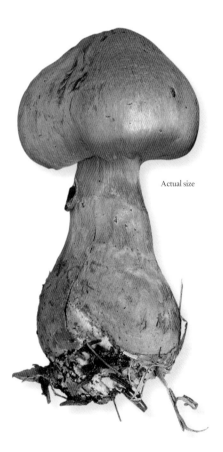

Actual size

FAMILY	Cortinariaceae
DISTRIBUTION	North America, Europe, Asia
HABITAT	In woodland
ASSOCIATION	Ectomycorrhizal, with birch
GROWTH FORM	On ground, in groups or rings
ABUNDANCE	Common
SPORE COLOR	Rusty brown
EDIBILITY	Edible

HEIGHT
Up to 6 in
(150 mm)

CAP DIAMETER
Up to 5 in
(120 mm)

CORTINARIUS TRIUMPHANS
BIRCH WEBCAP
FRIES

109

This is a common species that seems to occur exclusively with birch trees. It belongs in *Cortinarius* section *Phlegmacium*, so has the hallmark slimy cap and dry stem associated with the group. The sight of these large, brightly colored agarics must have impressed Swedish mycologist Elias Fries, since he gave them the epithet *triumphans* (the triumphant *Cortinarius*) when he first described the species in 1838. The Birch Webcap is edible and is consumed in Sweden, but difficulties in making confident identifications in *Cortinarius*—a genus with well over 500 species—make it best avoided. Some of its relatives are very poisonous.

Actual size

SIMILAR SPECIES
Cortinarius saginus is a very similar species, but has a browner cap and grows with conifers. *Cortinarius cliduchus* (and *C. olidus*, if distinct) has stem scales that are more yellow and grows with beech. The Girdled Webcap (*C. trivialis*) has a slimy stem with more conspicuous bands of veil remnants.

The Birch Webcap produces convex caps that are slimy, smooth but sometimes fibrous at the margin, and bright ocher to yellow-brown. The gills (see photo right) are grayish white with a bluish tint, becoming gray-brown to rusty brown. The stem is white but covered in ocher-brown, scaly veil remnants forming incomplete bands, and is typically swollen just above the base.

FAMILY	Cortinariaceae
DISTRIBUTION	Western North America, Europe, northern Asia
HABITAT	In woodland
ASSOCIATION	Ectomycorrhizal, with broadleaf trees, particularly willow, aspen, and oak
GROWTH FORM	On ground, in small troops
ABUNDANCE	Common
SPORE COLOR	Rusty brown
EDIBILITY	Not edible

HEIGHT
Up to 5 in
(125 mm)

CAP DIAMETER
Up to 4 in
(100 mm)

110

CORTINARIUS TRIVIALIS
GIRDLED WEBCAP
J. E. LANGE

The Girdled Webcap is a characteristic species of damp or boggy woodlands where it can often be quite common (the epithet *trivialis* means "commonplace"). Its English name comes from the thick, scaly bands that girdle the stem and which help to make it one of the more easily recognizable *Cortinarius* species. Although inedible to humans, it is apparently beloved of red squirrels. A report from Finland found that these fungi, together with boletes and *Russula* species, form about a quarter of the squirrel's winter diet. They collect the fruitbodies when fresh and store them in trees where they dry out, ready for consumption through the winter months.

SIMILAR SPECIES
Cortinarius collinitus (originally described from an oak wood) is probably an earlier name for the Girdled Webcap. The name has, however, been used for a similar conifer species that has pale violet, rather than white, bands on the stem. Other brown species with slimy caps and stems lack such conspicuous bands.

Actual size

The Girdled Webcap has caps that are convex (see photo right), becoming flat to umbonate. The surface is slimy, yellow to reddish brown with olive tones. The gills are pale clay tinged with violet at the edge, quickly becoming rusty brown. The stem is slimy, white at the top, tan-brown toward the base, with a series of thick, irregular girdles of white and brownish, glutinous veil remnants.

FAMILY	Cortinariaceae
DISTRIBUTION	North America, Europe, northern Asia
HABITAT	In wet woodland
ASSOCIATION	Ectomycorrhizal, with willow
GROWTH FORM	On ground, in small troops
ABUNDANCE	Locally common
SPORE COLOR	Rusty brown
EDIBILITY	Probably poisonous, best avoided

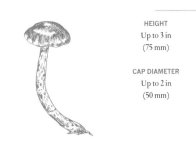

HEIGHT
Up to 3 in
(75 mm)

CAP DIAMETER
Up to 2 in
(50 mm)

CORTINARIUS ULIGINOSUS

MARSH WEBCAP

BERKELEY

Many fungi have evolved a tolerance, or even a preference, for growing in marshes, bogs, and swamps. The Marsh Webcap is just such a fungus (the epithet *uliginosus* means "of marshes") and forms an association with willows. It has the typical shape and yellow-red-rusty colors of species in the *Dermocybe* section of *Cortinarius*. Like others in this section, the fruitbodies contain chemicals which, when mixed with an alkali, produce a range of red tones and were traditionally used as natural dyes. The color of the young gills is important for separating *Dermocybe* species, so older specimens found on their own may not be identifiable.

SIMILAR SPECIES

Other *Cortinarius* species in section *Dermocybe* look similar, but the bright colors and the habitat of the Marsh Webcap should be distinct. *Cortinarius croceoconus* has duller colors and grows with conifers. The common *C. croceus* grows with a wide range of trees, but has a duller, yellow-brown to reddish brown cap.

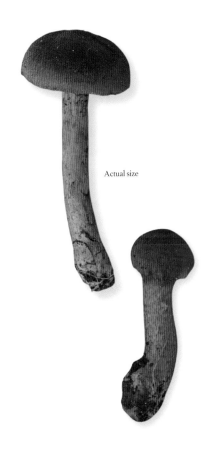

Actual size

The Marsh Webcap has caps that are almost conical at first (see photo right), becoming umbonate when expanded. The surface is finely silky-fibrous and bright brick-red, but duller with age. The gills are bright lemon-yellow at first, becoming rusty brown. The stem is ocher with bands of red veil remains, becoming darker toward the base. The flesh is pale yellow.

FAMILY	Cortinariaceae
DISTRIBUTION	North America, Europe, Central America, northern Asia, Australia, New Zealand
HABITAT	In woodland
ASSOCIATION	Ectomycorrhizal, with broadleaf trees and conifers
GROWTH FORM	On ground, in troops
ABUNDANCE	Occasional
SPORE COLOR	Rusty brown
EDIBILITY	Edible

HEIGHT Up to 5 in (125 mm)	
CAP DIAMETER Up to 6 in (150 mm)	

112

CORTINARIUS VIOLACEUS
VIOLET WEBCAP
(LINNAEUS) GRAY

The Violet Webcap is a large, distinctively colored agaric and one of the simpler *Cortinarius* species to recognize in the field. Its somber violet caps are, however, surprisingly easy to overlook especially when growing in undergrowth. It is a widespread species but not a common one, though when found it often occurs in troops. It sometimes has a faint aroma of cedarwood when fresh. Unlike most webcaps, *C. violaceus* is edible (if sometimes bitter) but is not widely collected for this purpose. Since many webcaps are dangerously poisonous, all are best avoided. The species is also used in dyeing.

SIMILAR SPECIES

Collections growing with conifers have sometimes been considered a separate species, *Cortinarius hercynicus*, differing microscopically in spore shape. The Violet Webcap is otherwise distinct thanks to its dark colors, large size, and finely scaly cap surface. The Wood Blewit (*Lepista nuda*) is paler, smooth-capped, and has pale pink spores.

Actual size

The Violet Webcap has caps that are hemispherical, becoming flat to broadly umbonate. The cap surface is dry, finely velvety to scaly, dark violet becoming violet-gray when old. The gills are cap-colored becoming violet-brown. The stem is pale cap-colored, often with concolorous adder-like markings when young, swollen toward the base.

FAMILY	Inocybaceae
DISTRIBUTION	North America, Europe, Central America
HABITAT	In woodland
ASSOCIATION	With broadleaf trees
GROWTH FORM	On dead branches and stumps
ABUNDANCE	Occasional
SPORE COLOR	Brown
EDIBILITY	Not edible

HEIGHT
Less than ⅛ in (2 mm)

CAP DIAMETER
Up to 1 in (25 mm)

CREPIDOTUS CINNABARINUS

CINNABAR OYSTERLING

PECK

113

Though by no means large, the fruitbodies of this little *Crepidotus* species are quite spectacularly colored a deep, rich red—a surprisingly bright color for an agaric in this otherwise rather somber genus. The Cinnabar Oysterling was first described from North America, where it is widespread but uncommon. It has since been found in scattered sites in Europe, including the British Isles, where it is not only uncommon, but distinctly rare. Like other species in the genus, *Crepidotus cinnabarinus* produces a brown spore print if left for a few hours on a glass slide or piece of white paper.

SIMILAR SPECIES

Most other *Crepidotus* species have whitish to pale brown fruitbodies. A very similar red species, *C. rubrovinosus*, is, however, known from Central America and a paler, rose-pink species, *C. roseoornatus*, is known from a few locations in continental Europe. Both are best distinguished microscopically.

Actual size

The Cinnabar Oysterling forms wide, shell-shaped, rather soft fruitbodies laterally attached to wood. The caps are weakly convex, hairy at first, becoming smoother, and bright cinnabar-red. The gills are cap-colored at first, becoming brown with age as the spores mature.

FAMILY	Inocybaceae
DISTRIBUTION	North America, continental Europe, Central and South America
HABITAT	In woodland
ASSOCIATION	With broadleaf trees, more rarely conifers
GROWTH FORM	On dead branches
ABUNDANCE	Common
SPORE COLOR	Brown
EDIBILITY	Not edible

HEIGHT
Less than ⅛ in
(3 mm)

CAP DIAMETER
Up to 1 ½ in
(35 mm)

114

CREPIDOTUS CROCOPHYLLUS
SAFFRON OYSTERLING
(BERKELEY) SACCARDO

Most *Crepidotus* species are white-capped, brown-gilled, small, and dull, but the Saffron Oysterling is a large and distinctive species, with gills that are brightly colored in shades of saffron yellow to orange. The cap surface can be variable, especially in the color and extent of the fibrils or scales, and this may have led early mycologists to describe the Saffron Oysterling under several different names. Unusually, recent research—which often reveals several "hidden" species masquerading under one name—has shown that all these names, both American and European, refer to a single, widespread species.

SIMILAR SPECIES
The Peeling Oysterling (*Crepidotus mollis*) is similarly shaped and sometimes scaly, but has duller colors, with gills that are whitish to buff becoming brown. The Olive Oysterling (*Panellus serotinus*) and the Oyster Rollrim (*Tapinella panuoides*) both have pinkish orange gills, but are larger with darker olive-tinted or brown caps.

Actual size

The Saffron Oysterling forms wide, shell-shaped, rather soft fruitbodies, laterally attached to wood. The caps are weakly convex, with a smooth, cream to ocher-brown surface covered in reddish brown fibrils or fine scales. The gills are yellow to orange, becoming brown with age as the spores mature.

FAMILY	Inocybaceae
DISTRIBUTION	North America, Europe, North Africa, Central America, northern Asia
HABITAT	In woodland
ASSOCIATION	With broadleaf trees
GROWTH FORM	On dead trunks, stumps, and logs, often in tiers
ABUNDANCE	Common
SPORE COLOR	Brown
EDIBILITY	Not edible

HEIGHT	Less than ⅛ in (3 mm)
CAP DIAMETER	Up to 3 in (75 mm)

CREPIDOTUS MOLLIS

PEELING OYSTERLING

(SCHAEFFER) STAUDE

115

In damp weather, it is possible to peel off the transparent, rubbery-gelatinous cap cuticle of this otherwise rather non-descript species, hence the name Peeling Oysterling. Its alternative name—Soft Slipper—is more or less a translation of *Crepidotus mollis*, referring to the soft and flabby fruitbodies. The extent to which the cap has reddish brown fibers or scales is highly variable. As a result, some authorities have recognized a second, smaller species, *C. calolepis*, as being consistently scaly, whereas the true *C. mollis* has a smooth, or only slightly scaly, cap.

SIMILAR SPECIES

The Saffron Oysterling (*Crepidotus crocophyllus*) is similarly shaped and fibrous-scaly, but is more brightly colored, with yellow to orange gills. Most other *Crepidotus* species—very common on twigs and dead plant stems—are much smaller, having smooth, whitish caps less than 1 in (25 mm) in diameter and pale brown gills.

The Peeling Oysterling forms wide, shell-shaped, soft or flabby fruitbodies (almost gelatinous when wet), laterally attached to wood. The caps are weakly convex, with a smooth, whitish to buff or pale brown surface sometimes covered in fine, reddish brown fibers or scales. The gills are whitish, becoming pale pinkish brown with age.

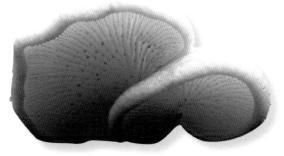

Actual size

FAMILY	Marasmiaceae
DISTRIBUTION	North America
HABITAT	In woodland
ASSOCIATION	With broadleaf trees
GROWTH FORM	On dead twigs and branches, in scattered groups
ABUNDANCE	Common
SPORE COLOR	White
EDIBILITY	Not edible

HEIGHT
Up to 2 in
(50 mm)

CAP DIAMETER
Up to 1½ in
(35 mm)

116

CRINIPELLIS ZONATA
ZONED HAIRY PARACHUTE
(PECK) SACCARDO

Crinipellis means "hairy skinned," and species in the genus, all of them rather small, are distinguished by having the cap surface covered in long hairs. They are otherwise similar to *Marasmius* species, often growing in groups and swarms on small twigs and stems. The Zoned Hairy Parachute is a North American species, with its long but matted hairs forming zones on the cap. It is entirely harmless, but in South America a deceptively attractive, pink-capped relative called *Crinipellis perniciosa* is a serious pest of cocoa trees, causing witches' broom disease.

SIMILAR SPECIES

Two related North American species, *Crinipellis campanella* and *C. piceae*, produce fruitbodies on conifer wood. Both have rather smaller caps with the hairs not distinctly zoned. In Europe, *C. scabella* is a similar species, but typically occurs on dead grass stems rather than on wood.

Actual size

The Zoned Hairy Parachute forms convex caps (see photo right), flattening but often centrally depressed when expanded. The cap surface is densely covered in zones of tawny to reddish brown hairs on a cream to buff background. The gills are white. The stem is finely hairy and cap-colored.

FAMILY	Physalacriaceae
DISTRIBUTION	North America, Africa, Central and South America, Asia, Australia, New Zealand
HABITAT	In woodland
ASSOCIATION	With broadleaf trees
GROWTH FORM	On dead branches
ABUNDANCE	Occasional
SPORE COLOR	White
EDIBILITY	Not edible

HEIGHT
Up to 2 in
(50 mm)

CAP DIAMETER
Up to 1 in
(25 mm)

CYPTOTRAMA ASPRATA

GOLDEN SCRUFFY

(BERKELEY) REDHEAD & GINNS

117

This colorful agaric is widespread on rotten wood in the tropics, but can sometimes be found in temperate woodlands (though not in Europe). The conspicuous scales are formed by several smaller spines bending together and adhering at the tip, a feature also seen in some puffballs. *Cyptotrama asprata*, however, is more closely related to the Velvet Shank (*Flammulina velutipes*) than to puffballs, according to recent molecular research. Previously it had been the cause of much mystification and argument among the experts, who had variously placed it in no less than ten different genera: *Lentinus, Lepiota, Collybia, Pleurotus, Tricholoma, Marasmius, Armillaria, Xerula, Tricholomopsis,* and *Gymnopus.*

Actual size

SIMILAR SPECIES

Young, brightly colored fruitbodies of the temperate *Pholiota flammans* can look very similar, while *P. squarrosa* and *Phaeomarasmius erinaceus* are equally scaly, but rather duller and more rusty brown. All, however, have brown spores (not white) that gradually color the gills.

The Golden Scruffy has caps that are convex at first and entirely covered with yellow to orange conical scales that (under a magnifying lens) are made up of spines that meet at their tips. These scales gradually fall away with age. The gills are white to cream and somewhat decurrent. The stem is the same color as the cap or paler, and is covered in similar scales.

FAMILY	Agaricaceae
DISTRIBUTION	Africa, southern Asia
HABITAT	In parks, gardens, roadsides, and woodland
ASSOCIATION	In rich soil, compost, and leaf litter
GROWTH FORM	On ground
ABUNDANCE	Common
SPORE COLOR	Chocolate-brown
EDIBILITY	Not edible

HEIGHT
Up to 3 in
(75 mm)

CAP DIAMETER
Up to 2 in
(50 mm)

118

CYSTOAGARICUS TRISULPHURATUS

SCALY TANGERINE MUSHROOM

(BERKELEY) SINGER

This splendid-looking species was first described by the noted British mycologist, the Reverend Miles Joseph Berkeley, based on a collection made by his daughter in Zanzibar. It is now known to be widespread throughout tropical Africa, as well as India and South-Eastern Asia. The Scaly Tangerine Mushroom's unusual, angular spores led it to be placed in the small genus *Cystoagaricus*, but recent DNA research suggests it is a true mushroom (*Agaricus* species) and its scientific name may well change back to Berkeley's original *Agaricus trisulphuratus*.

SIMILAR SPECIES

The Golden Fleece Mushroom (*Agaricus crocopeplus*) is very similar and also occurs in tropical Africa and Asia. Its shaggy scales are more bright yellow than orange, but it mainly differs microscopically from the Scaly Tangerine Mushroom. Several tropical *Amanita* species are also scaly and brightly colored, but have white gills and spores.

The Scaly Tangerine Mushroom has a cap that is hemispherical at first, becoming convex to flat. The cap surface is covered in fleecy scales that overhang the margin and are bright yellow-orange to orange. The gills are whitish at first, becoming chocolate-brown. The stem is fleecy-scaly and cap-colored, with a distinct ring.

Actual size

FAMILY	Agaricaceae
DISTRIBUTION	North America, Europe, northern Asia, New Zealand
HABITAT	In mossy grassland and woodland
ASSOCIATION	With broadleaf trees, conifers, and moss
GROWTH FORM	On ground, singly or in groups
ABUNDANCE	Common
SPORE COLOR	White
EDIBILITY	Not edible

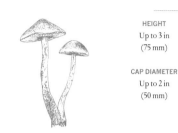

HEIGHT
Up to 3 in
(75 mm)

CAP DIAMETER
Up to 2 in
(50 mm)

CYSTODERMA AMIANTHINUM

EARTHY POWDERCAP

(SCOPOLI) FAYOD

119

Cystoderma amianthinum is by far the commonest of the powdercap species, frequently found in mossy pastures and lawns as well as in woodlands. The epithet *amianthinum* means "unspotted," which is hardly helpful, but the bright ocher colors and shaggy stem should be distinctive; it has an alternative English name of Saffron Powdercap. It often has an earthy smell, but not so noticeably as that of the Pearly Powdercap (*C. carcharias*). Very rarely, fruitbodies are parasitized by another agaric, luridly called the Powdercap Strangler (*Squamanita paradoxa*). The parasite replaces the cap and upper stem of its host with its own violet cap and stem, but leaves the ocher lower stem intact.

Actual size

SIMILAR SPECIES

Other *Cystoderma* and *Cystodermella* species are generally less common and restricted to woodlands. *Cystoderma jasonis* is very similar, but with a somewhat browner cap. It is best distinguished microscopically by its longer spores. *Cystodermella cinnabarina* and *C. granulosa* have reddish brown or brick-colored caps.

The Earthy Powdercap forms caps that are convex, becoming flat to shallowly umbonate, with a finely granular surface when young, later smooth or radially wrinkled, bright ocher to ocher-tan, with white veil remnants hanging from the margin. The gills are white to cream. The stem is smooth above the evanescent ring, but cap-colored and granular-scaly below.

FAMILY	Agaricaceae
DISTRIBUTION	North America, Europe, northern Asia
HABITAT	In woodland
ASSOCIATION	With conifers
GROWTH FORM	On ground, singly or in small groups
ABUNDANCE	Occasional
SPORE COLOR	White
EDIBILITY	Not edible

HEIGHT
Up to 3 in
(75 mm)

CAP DIAMETER
Up to 2½ in
(60 mm)

120

CYSTODERMA CARCHARIAS

PEARLY POWDERCAP

(PERSOON) FAYOD

The Pearly Powdercap should be distinctive thanks to its pale, granular cap and stem and its persistent ring. But additionally it has an unpleasant smell, variously described as moldy, musty, earthy, or even gas-like. This has been analyzed and found to be the organic compound geosmin (or "earth-smell"), one of the main components in the smell of rain on soil after a long hot spell. It is not such a common species as *Cystoderma amianthinum*, preferring to grow in conifer litter rather than mossy grass. The epithet *carcharias* means "sharp-pointed," presumably with reference to the granular scales.

SIMILAR SPECIES

The strong smell and pale pinkish tints should distinguish the Pearly Powdercap from other *Cystoderma* and *Cystodermella* species, most of which are darker brick-red or have yellowish tints. Several species of *Cystolepiota* have pinkish, granular to powdery scales on the cap and stem, but they lack the prominent ring of *Cystoderma carcharias*.

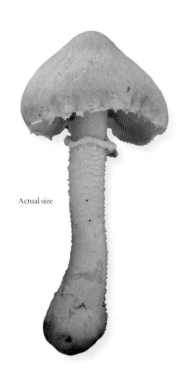

Actual size

The Pearly Powdercap has pale grayish white caps, usually with a pinkish flush. The caps are convex, becoming umbonate, and have a finely granular surface, with whitish veil remnants hanging from the margin. The gills are white to cream. The stem is smooth and white above the persistent, upward-pointing ring, but cap-colored and granular below.

FAMILY	Agaricaceae
DISTRIBUTION	North America, Europe, southwestern Asia
HABITAT	In calcareous woodland
ASSOCIATION	With broadleaf trees
GROWTH FORM	On ground, singly or in groups
ABUNDANCE	Occasional
SPORE COLOR	White
EDIBILITY	Not edible

HEIGHT
Up to 3 in
(75 mm)

CAP DIAMETER
Up to 1 in
(25 mm)

CYSTOLEPIOTA BUCKNALLII

LILAC DAPPERLING

(BERKELEY & BROOME) SINGER & CLÉMENÇON

121

Like their close relatives in *Lepiota*, *Cystolepiota* species are predominantly species of chalk and limestone woodlands. The Lilac Dapperling is one of the most distinctive and easily recognized species, not only because of its color but also because of its surprising smell. The fungus has been shown to produce the odoriferous compound indole, which smells strongly of coal gas—the same smell and the same compound that characterizes the Sulfur Knight (*Tricholoma sulphureum*). The fungus was first collected around 1881 by local mycologist Cedric Bucknall in the limestone woodlands near Bristol, England, and named in his honor.

SIMILAR SPECIES

The powdery veil remnants, color, cream gills, and coal-gas smell are diagnostic. Other *Cystolepiota* species with powdery veil remnants are white to pinkish, but never violet. The unrelated *Inocybe geophylla* var. *lilacina* is of similar size and color, but is not powdery and has clay-brown gills.

Actual size

The Lilac Dapperling forms fruitbodies that when young are entirely covered in granular or floccular, violet veil remnants that are gradually shed with age. The caps are hemispherical, barely expanding, and with age become cream with violet tints. The gills are cream. The stem is cream at the very top, but dark violet below.

FAMILY	Tricholomataceae
DISTRIBUTION	Western North America, Europe
HABITAT	In woodland
ASSOCIATION	With species of *Lactarius* and *Russula*
GROWTH FORM	On decayed remains of fruitbodies
ABUNDANCE	Occasional
SPORE COLOR	White
EDIBILITY	Not edible

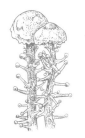

HEIGHT
Up to 3 in
(75 mm)

CAP DIAMETER
Up to ½ in
(10 mm)

122

DENDROCOLLYBIA RACEMOSA

BRANCHED SHANKLET

(PERSOON) R. H. PETERSEN & REDHEAD

The Branched Shanklet is small, but quite extraordinary. Its stem bears a series of side branches, each ending in a small knob containing asexual spores—an alternative method of propagation and a feature unique to this species. A further oddity is that the Branched Shanklet grows in the rotten remains of other agarics, specifically brittlegills (*Russula* species) and milkcaps (*Lactarius* species), though these are usually so decayed as to be unrecognizable. Fruitbodies arise from sclerotia, small, hard kernels of fungal tissue that can persist in the soil until the host's fruitbodies eventually reappear.

SIMILAR SPECIES

No other agaric has the characteristic side branches of *Dendrocollybia racemosa*. However, several *Collybia* species, including the Lentil Shanklet (*C. tuberosa*), are of similar shape and size. They also arise from sclerotia (though these are typically paler, ocher to red-brown) among the remains of *Lactarius* and *Russula* fruitbodies.

The Branched Shanklet forms caps that are convex, becoming flat to weakly umbonate. The cap surface is smooth to finely wrinkled, pale gray to gray-brown. The gills are cap-colored. The stem is narrow, cap-colored, and smooth, but with numerous short side-branches that terminate in tiny, spherical knobs. The stem arises from a hard, black, spherical sclerotium.

Actual size

FAMILY	Entolomataceae
DISTRIBUTION	Europe, northern Asia
HABITAT	In pastures and scrub
ASSOCIATION	With moss and grass
GROWTH FORM	On ground, singly or in small groups
ABUNDANCE	Locally common
SPORE COLOR	Salmon-pink
EDIBILITY	Probably poisonous, best avoided

HEIGHT
Up to 2 in
(50 mm)

CAP DIAMETER
Up to 1½ in
(35 mm)

ENTOLOMA CHALYBEUM VAR. *LAZULINUM*

INDIGO PINKGILL

(FRIES) NORDELOOS

123

The Indigo Pinkgill is a typical species of *Entoloma* subgenus of *Leptonia*, nearly all of which (in Europe at least) are found in old, mossy pastures and lawns. Their fruitbodies are comparatively small and delicate, rather like *Mycena* species, so they are usually quite easy to recognize as a group—though not so easy to identify to species. Quite a few of them have dark bluish caps, similar to those of the Indigo Pinkgill. This particular variety takes its Latin name, *lazulinum*, from the rare, dark blue gemstone, lapis lazuli.

SIMILAR SPECIES

Normal *Entoloma chalybeum* differs from the variety mainly in having a non-striate, rather scalier cap, and the two were formerly thought to be separate species. *Entoloma corvinum* also has a non-striate cap but is distinguished by having white, rather than bluish, gills when young. The Blue-Edged Pinkgill (*E. serrulatum*) is similarly colored, but its gills have a distinct blue edge.

The Indigo Pinkgill forms conical to hemispherical caps, becoming convex to flat. The cap surface is smooth to finely scaly at the center, striate when damp (non-striate in ordinary *E. chalybeum*), indigo-blue to blackish blue, becoming duller with age. The gills are bluish when young, becoming grayish pink. The stem is smooth, pale cap-colored, with a white, downy base.

Actual size

FAMILY	Entolomataceae
DISTRIBUTION	New Zealand
HABITAT	In woodland
ASSOCIATION	With broadleaf trees and conifers
GROWTH FORM	On ground, singly or in groups
ABUNDANCE	Occasional
SPORE COLOR	Salmon-pink
EDIBILITY	Not edible

HEIGHT
Up to 3 in
(75 mm)

CAP DIAMETER
Up to 1 in
(25 mm)

124

ENTOLOMA GLAUCOROSEUM
JADE PINKGILL
E. HORAK

The Jade Pinkgill is a recently described species, so far only known from New Zealand where it has been found in mixed, native forests. As with other green fungi, the color has nothing to do with chlorophyll—the green of plant leaves—but comes from a variety of pigments peculiar to fungi. Whether these colors have any function, or whether they are just by-products of natural compounds present in the fruitbodies, is unclear—but they certainly produce some attractive, and unusual-looking, species.

SIMILAR SPECIES
The Green Stem Pinkgill (*Entoloma rodwayi*) is a brighter green species, known from Australia. The rather smelly Mousepee Pinkgill (*E. incanum*) is a north-temperate species with an olive cap and bright green stem. The Verdigris Waxcap (*Gliophorus viridis*) is another green New Zealand agaric, but has white gills and spores.

Actual size

The Jade Pinkgill forms caps that are convex, becoming flat or centrally depressed. The cap surface is smooth to finely scaly, striate, and gray-green to jade-green, darker at the center. The gills are pale pinkish, becoming salmon-pink. The stem is smooth, cap-colored at the top, becoming yellowish green toward the base.

FAMILY	Entolomataceae
DISTRIBUTION	North America, Europe, northern Asia
HABITAT	In calcareous pastures and scrub, rarely woodland
ASSOCIATION	With moss and grass
GROWTH FORM	On ground, singly or in small groups
ABUNDANCE	Locally common
SPORE COLOR	Salmon-pink
EDIBILITY	Probably poisonous

HEIGHT
Up to 4 in
(100 mm)
CAP DIAMETER
Up to 2 in
(50 mm)

ENTOLOMA INCANUM

MOUSEPEE PINKGILL

(FRIES) HESLER

125

This little agaric may look attractive, but the English name highlights its unfortunate smell. Indeed, it was originally called *Agaricus murinus* ("the mouse agaric") by the author and illustrator James Sowerby. The current epithet *incanum* means hoary, presumably with reference to the downy, white stem base. *Entoloma incanum* is a species of mossy, calcareous pastures and can be locally common in such sites. Though the caps may be inconspicuous, especially when older, the green stems and turquoise bruising reaction are distinctive. The Mousepee Pinkgill is unlikely to be eaten, but like most *Entoloma* species may well be poisonous.

Actual size

SIMILAR SPECIES

Older specimens lose their colors (but not their smell), though the top of the stem normally remains green, distinguishing the Mousepee Pinkgill from similar, small, brownish *Entoloma* species in grassland. The Parrot Waxcap (*Hygrocybe psittacina*) is a common, green, grassland species, but is extremely slimy and has white (not pink) spores.

The Mousepee Pinkgill forms hemispherical caps, becoming convex to flat with a depressed center (see photo right). The cap surface is smooth to finely scaly at the center, striate when damp, olive to olive-brown, drying paler. The gills are green-tinted, becoming salmon-pink. The stem is smooth, yellow-green to olive, bruising bright blue-green, with a white, downy base.

FAMILY	Entolomataceae
DISTRIBUTION	Eastern North America, Central and South America, Eastern Asia
HABITAT	In damp woodland
ASSOCIATION	With broadleaf trees and conifers
GROWTH FORM	On ground, singly or in small groups
ABUNDANCE	Common
SPORE COLOR	Salmon-pink
EDIBILITY	Probably poisonous

HEIGHT
Up to 4 in
(100 mm)

CAP DIAMETER
Up to 2 in
(50 mm)

126

ENTOLOMA MURRAYI
UNICORN PINKGILL
(BERKELEY & M. A. CURTIS) SACCARDO

The Unicorn Pinkgill was originally collected in New England by Dennis Murray (hence the Latin epithet). It was formally described in 1859 by the Reverends Berkeley and Curtis, who thought it an "extremely pretty species," which indeed it is. The unusual elongated point at the top of the cap has presumably given it the common name Unicorn or Yellow Unicorn. Murray collected the species "in wet grounds," and it seems to have a preference for wet woodland areas, where it may be locally common. The closely related Salmon Pinkgill (*Entoloma quadratum*) is poisonous and it seems probable that the Unicorn Pinkgill is equally so.

SIMILAR SPECIES
Older specimens may resemble faded *Entoloma quadratum*, which is similarly shaped but orange-pink. Both species can become dull buff with age. *Entoloma luteum* is yellowish but drabber, with a less distinctly pointed cap. Yellow, sharply conical waxcaps (*Hygrocybe* species) have white (not pink) spores.

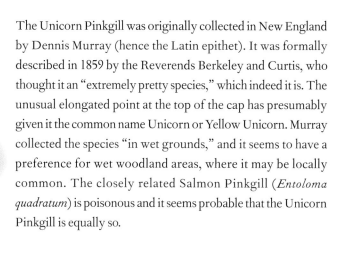

The Unicorn Pinkgill forms a conical cap, typically with a pointed protrusion at the center. The cap surface is smooth and bright yellow when young, fading to pale buff when old. The gills are pale yellow at first, becoming salmon-pink. The thin stem is cap-colored and smooth.

Actual size

FAMILY	Entolomataceae
DISTRIBUTION	Eastern North America, Africa (Madagascar), Central America, Eastern Asia
HABITAT	In woodland
ASSOCIATION	With broadleaf trees and conifers
GROWTH FORM	On ground, singly or in small groups
ABUNDANCE	Common
SPORE COLOR	Salmon-pink
EDIBILITY	Poisonous

HEIGHT
Up to 4 in
(100 mm)

CAP DIAMETER
Up to 2 in
(50 mm)

ENTOLOMA QUADRATUM
SALMON PINKGILL
(BERKELEY & M. A. CURTIS) E. HORAK

127

A number of pink-spored *Entoloma* species have caps that frequently develop a point at the top, like a pixie's bonnet in a fairy book. The Salmon Pinkgill is the most strikingly colored of these species and is quite common and widespread in eastern North America and Eastern Asia. The name *E. quadratum* refers to its distinctive spores, which appear four-sided (cube-like) under a microscope, but it is often still called *E. salmoneum*, a later synonym. It seems too small and delicate to be eaten, which is just as well. Research has shown it to be one of the most poisonous of the pinkgills.

SIMILAR SPECIES

The shape and color of young specimens are distinctive, but older, faded specimens may resemble *Entoloma murrayi*, which is similarly shaped but yellow, or *E. luteum*, which is drabber with a less distinctly pointed cap. Brightly colored, sharply conical waxcaps (*Hygrocybe* species) have white (not pink) spores.

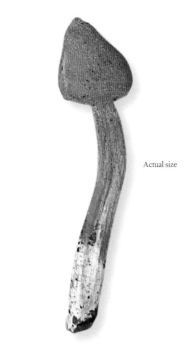

Actual size

The Salmon Pinkgill forms a conical cap, typically with a pointed protrusion at the center. The cap surface is smooth and bright salmon to orange when young, fading to sordid yellowish buff when old. The gills are salmon-pink, even when old. The thin stem is cap-colored, sometimes developing a greenish tint, and smooth.

FAMILY	Entolomataceae
DISTRIBUTION	North America, Europe, northern Asia
HABITAT	In woodland
ASSOCIATION	With broadleaf trees
GROWTH FORM	On ground, singly or in troops
ABUNDANCE	Common
SPORE COLOR	Salmon-pink
EDIBILITY	Poisonous

HEIGHT
Up to 6 in
(150 mm)

CAP DIAMETER
Up to 5 in
(120 mm)

128

ENTOLOMA RHODOPOLIUM
WOOD PINKGILL
(FRIES) P. KUMMER

The Wood Pinkgill seems to be a common agaric in broadleaf woodlands, but is part of a complex of poorly understood forms and species, all of which require further research. It was originally named by Swedish mycologist Elias Fries, but it is not clear whether European collections belong to one species or several. North American collections may turn out to be closely related, but distinct. One form, previously known as *Entoloma nidorosum*, has quite a strong nitrous (bleachlike) smell, wheareas other collections have at most a faint mealy odor. Most are known to be poisonous and all are best avoided.

SIMILAR SPECIES

Many different forms, varieties, and related species have been described that are not well characterized or are difficult to distinguish. The Livid Pinkgill (*Entoloma sinuatum*) is also similar, but is typically larger, fleshier, and paler and has a cap that is never striate.

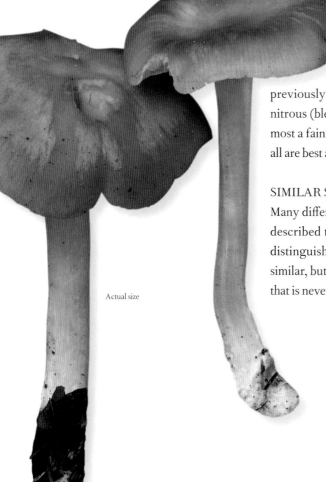

Actual size

The Wood Pinkgill is a large species with a convex to flat cap that sometimes becomes weakly depressed or weakly umbonate. The cap is smooth, striate at the margin when damp, and yellowish brown to pale grayish brown. The gills are white at first, then dingy pink. The stem is white, sometimes tinted grayish brown, smooth but finely fibrous, with a silky sheen.

FAMILY	Entolomataceae
DISTRIBUTION	North America, Europe
HABITAT	In calcareous woodland and grassland
ASSOCIATION	With broadleaf trees and mossy grass
GROWTH FORM	On ground, singly or in groups
ABUNDANCE	Occasional to rare
SPORE COLOR	Salmon-pink
EDIBILITY	Not edible

HEIGHT
Up to 3 in
(75 mm)

CAP DIAMETER
Up to 1½ in
(35 mm)

ENTOLOMA ROSEUM
ROSY PINKGILL
(LONGYEAR) HESLER

129

The Rosy Pinkgill belongs in the *Leptonia* group of *Entoloma* species and, as such, is typical of mossy pastures in Europe, but is more frequently found in woodland elsewhere. It has a preference for calcareous soils and is sometimes found in coastal dune vegetation. The species was originally described from North America, but is uncommon to rare there and is equally so in Europe. Indeed, the Rosy Pinkgill has been placed on the national Red Lists of threatened fungal species in several countries, including Denmark and the Netherlands.

SIMILAR SPECIES

Similar pink-capped species include *Entoloma catalaunicum*, which usually has bluish tints, especially in the stem, and *E. callirhodon*, which has lilac tints. Neither is common and both have a colored gill edge. The Pink Domecap (*Calocybe carnea*) is common, grows in similar situations, and has a pinkish cap—but white gills and spores.

The Rosy Pinkgill forms caps that are convex, sometimes becoming slightly depressed at the center. The surface of the cap is finely fibrous-scaly, rose-pink with a darker, often red-brown center. The gills are white to pink at first (see photo top right), becoming salmon-pink. The stem is smooth, cap-colored, but with white mycelium toward the base.

Actual size

FAMILY	Entolomataceae
DISTRIBUTION	North America, Europe, northern Asia
HABITAT	In woodland
ASSOCIATION	With broadleaf trees, often on clay or basic soil
GROWTH FORM	On ground, singly or in small groups
ABUNDANCE	Common
SPORE COLOR	Pink
EDIBILITY	Poisonous

HEIGHT
Up to 6 in
(150 mm)

CAP DIAMETER
Up to 8 in
(200 mm)

130

ENTOLOMA SINUATUM
LIVID PINKGILL
(BULLIARD) P. KUMMER

The Livid Pinkgill (once also known as *Entoloma lividum* or *E. eulividum*) is one of the largest north-temperate *Entoloma* species, typically found in broadleaf woodland, particularly on clay soils. It has a sweet to mealy smell and has long been noted as a poisonous species, the symptoms being mainly gastroenteritic. A nineteenth-century English author found himself "continually and fearfully purged" after eating "a very small piece for luncheon." Its large size and pink gills may attract collectors looking for Field Mushrooms (*Agaricus campestris*) or the St. George's Mushrooms (*Calocybe gambosa*).

SIMILAR SPECIES

The Wood Pinkgill (*Entoloma rhodopolium*) is similar, but is usually smaller and has a darker cap with a striate margin. It sometimes has a nitrous smell and is equally poisonous, as are most other pinkgills. The edible Miller (*Clitopilus prunulus*) also smells mealy but has a white, felted cap and is normally much smaller, with more crowded gills.

Actual size

The Livid Pinkgill forms fleshy caps that are convex, becoming flat to shallowly umbonate. The cap surface is smooth, pale grayish ocher to yellow-brown or gray-brown. The gills are white to yellowish when young (see photo right), becoming salmon-pink with age. The stem is smooth and whitish to pale cap-colored.

FAMILY	Entolomataceae
DISTRIBUTION	North America, northern Asia
HABITAT	In woodland
ASSOCIATION	With broadleaf trees and conifers
GROWTH FORM	On ground, singly or in groups
ABUNDANCE	Occasional
SPORE COLOR	Salmon-pink
EDIBILITY	Not edible

HEIGHT
Up to 3 in
(75 mm)

CAP DIAMETER
Up to 2 in
(50 mm)

ENTOLOMA VIOLACEUM
VIOLET PINKGILL
MURRILL

131

This is one of a group of *Entoloma* species with fibrous-scaly caps, sometimes referred to the genus *Trichopilus* (meaning "hairy cap"). They occur in woodland, but are often more frequent in pastures in Europe, where they grow alongside waxcaps (*Hygrocybe* species). Most are grayish to brown-capped, but the Violet Pinkgill—of North America and northern Asia—can be strikingly colored in various shades of purple, violet, or violet-black. Its edibility is unknown, but since many *Entoloma* species are poisonous, it is best left well alone.

SIMILAR SPECIES

The Lilac Pinkgill (*Entoloma porphyrophaeum*) is a widespread, north-temperate species—locally common in grassland in Europe—that is typically larger and has a grayish cap with no more than a hint of pale violet in the gray. The North American *Leptonia violacea* is a thin-stemmed species with a shape more like that of *E. quadratum*.

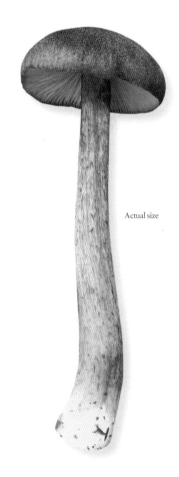

Actual size

The Violet Pinkgill forms caps that are convex, becoming weakly umbonate. The cap surface is finely fibrous-scaly, purple to violet or dull violet-brown. The gills are white at first, becoming salmon-pink. The stem is fibrous-scaly and pale cap-colored, but white toward the base.

FAMILY	Entolomataceae
DISTRIBUTION	Africa (Madagascar), Central and South America, Eastern Asia, Australia, New Zealand
HABITAT	In woodland
ASSOCIATION	With broadleaf trees
GROWTH FORM	On ground, singly or in groups
ABUNDANCE	Locally common
SPORE COLOR	Salmon-pink
EDIBILITY	Not edible

HEIGHT
Up to 4 in
(100 mm)

CAP DIAMETER
Up to 2 in
(50 mm)

132

ENTOLOMA VIRESCENS
SKYBLUE PINKGILL
(BERKELEY & M. A. CURTIS) E. HORAK EX COURTECUISSE

Actual size

Bright blue colors are rare in fungi, but this spectacular agaric is an eye-catching exception. *Entoloma virescens* was originally described from Japan, but several similar fungi were subsequently described from Madagascar, Singapore, and New Zealand. Current opinion suggests they are all the same species, but more research is needed. In New Zealand (where it has also been called *E. hochstetteri*), the Skyblue Pinkgill has almost become a national fungus. Not only has it been depicted on postage stamps, but it even features on the New Zealand $50 banknote—a unique accolade for a magnificent species.

SIMILAR SPECIES

The striking color should be unmistakable in fresh, young fruitbodies, but older specimens may turn dull greenish. In north temperate areas, the Violet-Blue Pinkgill (*Entoloma euchroum*) grows on rotten wood, has a flatter cap, and is a different shade of blue. Many other less vivid, steely-blue or gray-blue pinkgill species occur.

The Skyblue Pinkgill forms caps that are conical, sometimes with a central point, smooth, often splitting with age, bright blue fading to greenish or partly ocher in color. The gills are pale blue at first, becoming salmon to brownish pink. The stem is pale cap-colored. All parts stain green when bruised or cut.

FAMILY	Mycenaceae
DISTRIBUTION	Africa (Madagascar), South-Eastern Asia; introduced into Europe (Italy), East Africa, Australia, New Zealand
HABITAT	In woodland
ASSOCIATION	With broadleaf trees, more rarely conifers, ferns, and herbaceous plants
GROWTH FORM	On dead branches, twigs, and stems, in clusters or troops
ABUNDANCE	Locally common
SPORE COLOR	White
EDIBILITY	Not edible

HEIGHT
Up to 2 in
(50 mm)

CAP DIAMETER
Up to 1 in
(25 mm)

FAVOLASCHIA CALOCERA

ORANGE PORE FUNGUS

R. HEIM

133

Favolaschia calocera was an attractive but little-known species described from Madagascar in 1945, until it was found growing in New Zealand in the 1960s. Since then it has appeared in several quite separate places, from Italy to Australia, and shows all the signs of an invasive fungus extending its range. It is believed to be native to Madagascar and South-Eastern Asia, but accidentally introduced elsewhere. Recent Italian collections have been found growing on conifer wood, old fern stems, and other herbaceous debris, which indicates that it is a species that is highly adaptable and may well spread further.

Actual size

SIMILAR SPECIES

When first found in New Zealand, *Favolaschia calocera* was mistaken for *F. thwaitesii*, a common, tropical species first described from Sri Lanka and known from Asia and Africa. Though equally brightly colored, *F. thwaitesii* is generally much smaller and has little or no stem. It also differs microscopically.

The Orange Pore Fungus produces convex or shell-like caps, laterally attached to wood, usually by a distinct stem. The cap surface is smooth or covered with raised bumps (mirroring the undersurface) and bright orange (see photo above). The pores are orange, shallow, and irregularly polygonal. The stem is cylindrical, smooth, and orange to yellow-orange.

FAMILY	Mycenaceae
DISTRIBUTION	South-Eastern Asia, New Zealand
HABITAT	In woodland
ASSOCIATION	With broadleaf trees
GROWTH FORM	On dead trunks, stumps, and logs, in small clusters
ABUNDANCE	Common
SPORE COLOR	White
EDIBILITY	Not edible

HEIGHT
Less than ⅛ in
(1 mm)

CAP DIAMETER
Up to 3 in
(75 mm)

134

FAVOLASCHIA PUSTULOSA
WHITE PORE FUNGUS
(JUNGHUHN) KUNTZE

This rather attractive, almost translucent fungus was first described from Java by the German mycologist Friedrich Junghuhn in 1838. It has subsequently been found elsewhere in South-Eastern Asia, New Zealand, and many of the Pacific islands. Although their spore-producing surface is poroid, *Favolaschia* species are actually related to gilled agarics in the genus *Mycena,* which often have a similar, semitranslucent texture. The White Pore Fungus is one of the largest species in the group and is particularly common in New Zealand, where it frequently grows on wood of the endemic tawa tree.

SIMILAR SPECIES
Favolaschia species are quite frequent in the tropics, though most produce much smaller fruitbodies. Two such species, *F. cyatheae* and *F. austrocyatheae,* are white and also occur in New Zealand, but are restricted to old tree-fern fronds. A similar Asian species, *F. peziziformis,* occurs on old palm fronds, as does the tropical American *F. varariotecta.*

The White Pore Fungus produces rubbery, convex or shell-like caps. The surface is translucent white, and smooth or covered with raised bumps (mirroring the undersurface). The pores are white, shallow, and irregularly polygonal. Fruitbodies are laterally attached to wood, sometimes by a very short white stem.

Actual size

FAMILY	Mycenaceae
DISTRIBUTION	Southern and eastern Asia, Australia
HABITAT	In wet woodland and rainforest
ASSOCIATION	With broadleaf trees
GROWTH FORM	On trunks, stumps, and logs, in clusters
ABUNDANCE	Common
SPORE COLOR	White
EDIBILITY	Not edible

HEIGHT
Up to 3 in
(75 mm)

CAP DIAMETER
Up to 1½ in
(40 mm)

FILOBOLETUS MANIPULARIS

LUMINOUS PORE-BONNET

(BERKELEY) SINGER

135

The Luminous Pore-Bonnet looks very much like a *Mycena* species from a distance, but closer examination shows the undersurface is made up of pores—as in a bolete—rather than gills. Appearances are not deceptive, however, since *Filoboletus manipularis* is indeed a close relative of *Mycena* species, belonging in the same family. It was originally described from Sri Lanka and is a species of rainforests and wet woodlands in Asia, Australia, and the Pacific islands. When night falls, the bioluminescent fruitbodies glow in the dark—like the much larger Moonlight Mushroom (*Omphalotus japonicus*).

SIMILAR SPECIES

A related species with very small pores, *Filoboletus gracilis*, grows in the American tropics. *Favolaschia* species, such as the White Pore Fungus (*F. pustulosa*), also have pores instead of gills, but most produce fruitbodies that are laterally attached (like small brackets) and often lack a stem.

Actual size

The Luminous Pore-Bonnet forms caps that are conical to convex, becoming flatter and often umbonate. The cap surface is smooth but thin, appearing dimpled from the pores below, white to cream with brownish tints toward the center. The pores are round and whitish. The brittle stem is smooth and whitish, brownish and hairy toward the base.

FAMILY	Physalacriaceae
DISTRIBUTION	North America, Europe, northern Asia
HABITAT	In woodland
ASSOCIATION	With broadleaf trees, particularly elm
GROWTH FORM	On dead trunks and stumps, in dense clusters
ABUNDANCE	Common
SPORE COLOR	White
EDIBILITY	Edible , best avoided uncooked

HEIGHT
Up to 4 in
(100 mm)

CAP DIAMETER
Up to 3 in
(75 mm)

136

FLAMMULINA VELUTIPES
VELVET SHANK
(CURTIS) SINGER

Flammulina velutipes is unusual in being frost-tolerant and in North America is sometimes called the Winter Mushroom. Research has shown that the fungus not only produces glycerol and other cryoprotectants (antifreeze compounds) when temperatures drop, but that low temperatures actually trigger fruiting. The Velvet Shank is also a popular edible species, long cultivated in Japan, where it is called Enoki. Cultivated fruitbodies, grown in darkness in a high concentration of carbon dioxide, are pallid, long-stemmed, and have tiny caps. They are marketed as Golden Needles. The Velvet Shank contains a cardiotoxin called flammutoxin. It is destroyed by heat, but regular consumption of the raw fungus is perhaps best avoided.

SIMILAR SPECIES

Recent research has revealed the existence of a number of closely related species. They include *Flammulina populicola* on aspen in western North America, *F. elastica* mainly on willows in Europe, and *F. ononis* on roots of restharrow (*Ononis* species), also in Europe. All are best distinguished microscopically.

Actual size

The Velvet Shank has caps that are convex at first, becoming flat. The surface is smooth, slimy in wet weather, pale to deep orange-brown, with a paler, striate margin. The gills are whitish to pale yellowish or pale buff. The stem is densely but finely velvety, often rather flattened; it is yellowish at first, becoming orange-brown then blackish-brown from the base upward.

FAMILY	Agaricaceae
DISTRIBUTION	North America, continental Europe, Central America, northern Asia
HABITAT	In dry grassland (woodland in America)
ASSOCIATION	With aspen, more rarely conifers (in America)
GROWTH FORM	On ground, singly or in troops
ABUNDANCE	Occasional
SPORE COLOR	White
EDIBILITY	Edible

HEIGHT
Up to 4 in
(100 mm)

CAP DIAMETER
Up to 4 in
(100 mm)

FLOCCULARIA LUTEOVIRENS

YELLOW BRACELET

(ALBERTINI & SCHWEINITZ) POUZAR

Floccularia luteovirens was originally described from Germany and is a rare but distinctive species in central Europe—so rare that it is legally protected in some countries. It grows in dry grassland and steppes, becoming less rare eastward. On the Tibetan plateau it is known as Sercha and is a common edible species, sold in markets. In western North America, however, it is normally found with aspens (occasionally conifers). Such a different habitat suggests that two species are involved and, indeed, the American agaric has been considered a distinct variety (var. *americana*) of *F. luteovirens*. Clearly more research is required.

SIMILAR SPECIES

A related species, *Floccularia albolanaripes*, occurs in western North America, but has a browner, less scaly cap. It is also edible. *Cyptotrama asprata* is yellow and scaly, but is much smaller and grows on wood. *Cystoagaricus trisulphuratus* has chocolate-brown gills when mature.

Actual size

The Yellow Bracelet forms convex caps, flatter when expanded, that are scaly and bright lemon yellow to ocher when fresh, the scales often fringing the margins. The gills are white to pale yellow. The stem is thick and often bulbous at the base; it is smooth and white above the small double ring, often covered with lemon-yellow scales below.

FAMILY	Strophariaceae
DISTRIBUTION	North America, Europe, northern Asia
HABITAT	In woodland
ASSOCIATION	With conifers, occasionally broadleaf trees
GROWTH FORM	On stumps, dead trunks, and sawdust or mulch, in clusters
ABUNDANCE	Common
SPORE COLOR	Brown
EDIBILITY	Poisonous

HEIGHT
Up to 3 in
(75 mm)

CAP DIAMETER
Up to 1½ in
(40 mm)

138

GALERINA MARGINATA
FUNERAL BELL
(BATSCH) KÜHNER

Actual size

Galerina is a large genus of small, brown agarics, many of which grow in sphagnum and other mosses. They look pretty much the same in the field and can only be distinguished microscopically. *Galerina marginata*, however, is comparatively large and grows in clusters on wood, making identification less difficult. The flesh when crushed smells mealy. As the English names— Funeral Bell and Deadly Galerina— make clear, this is a lethally poisonous fungus, containing proportionately more amatoxin than the Death Cap (*Amanita phalloides*). It is easily mistaken for the edible *Kuehneromyces mutabilis* and less easily mistaken for hallucinogenic *Psilocybe* species—though such mistakes have apparently occurred.

SIMILAR SPECIES
Based on DNA evidence, the North American *Galerina autumnalis* and *G. venenata* are now considered to be synonymous with *G. marginata*. The similar-looking Sheathed Woodtuft (*Kuehneromyces mutabilis*) is an edible species, the stem of which is distinctly scaly below the ring. It lacks the mealy smell of *Galerina marginata*.

The Funeral Bell forms densely clustered fruitbodies with convex to flat caps. The cap surface is smooth, slightly slimy when fresh, ocher-tawny to pale brown, becoming paler or buff when drying. The gills are ocher or pale brown to tawny. The stem is smooth, whitish to buff, with an evanescent ring, becoming brownish toward the base with age.

FAMILY	Hygrophoraceae
DISTRIBUTION	Australia, New Zealand
HABITAT	In woodland
ASSOCIATION	With broadleaf trees and conifers
GROWTH FORM	In litter and moss, singly or in small groups
ABUNDANCE	Occasional
SPORE COLOR	White
EDIBILITY	Not edible

HEIGHT
Up to 2 in
(50 mm)

CAP DIAMETER
Up to 1½ in
(35 mm)

GLIOPHORUS VIRIDIS
VERDIGRIS WAXCAP
(G. STEVENSON) E. HORAK

139

It is not surprising that the Verdigris Waxcap was initially confused with the north-temperate Parrot Waxcap (*Hygrocybe psittacina*) and consequently went unrecognized until the 1960s. Both species are predominantly green and slimy, but this small, Australasian waxcap is a rather cooler shade of jade or malachite-green and has additional distinct features. It may belong in the genus *Hygrocybe* with most of the other waxcaps. Indeed, it is generally given the name *H. stevensoniae* in Australia, after mycologist Greta Stevenson who originally described it from New Zealand.

SIMILAR SPECIES
A very similar green species, *Gliophorus graminicolor*, also occurs in Australia and New Zealand and is best distinguished microscopically, though some reports suggest it has an unpleasant smell. The Parrot Waxcap (*Hygrocybe psittacina*) occurs in the north temperate zone and is more grass-green, typically becoming yellow in places.

Actual size

The Verdigris Waxcap forms caps that are convex, becoming flat. The surface is smooth, very slimy, striate at the margin, green to jade-green, fading with age. The gills are weakly decurrent and whitish to pale cap-colored. The stem is smooth, very slimy, and cap-colored but yellowish toward the base.

FAMILY	Gomphidiaceae
DISTRIBUTION	North America, Europe, Central America
HABITAT	In woodland
ASSOCIATION	Probably ectomycorrhizal, with conifers, particularly spruce and Douglas fir
GROWTH FORM	On ground
ABUNDANCE	Occasional
SPORE COLOR	Blackish gray
EDIBILITY	Edible, once cap covering removed

HEIGHT
Up to 4 in
(100 mm)

CAP DIAMETER
Up to 5 in
(125 mm)

GOMPHIDIUS GLUTINOSUS
SLIMY SPIKE
(SCHAEFFER) FRIES

140

Gomphidius species are quite closely related to boletes in the genus *Suillus*, but have gills rather than pores. Like *Suillus*, they are exclusively associated with conifers and were presumed to be ectomycorrhizal associates. However, recent research on a related species, *G. roseus*, has suggested they may be parasites—though this may not be true for all *Gomphidius* species. The Slimy Spike, also known as the Slimecap, is normally found with spruce and fir, but is sometimes reported with pine and other conifers. The fruitbodies are said to be edible, once the slimy covering of the cap is peeled off.

SIMILAR SPECIES
Several similarly colored species occur in North America. *Gomphidius oregonensis* is a western species forming clustered fruitbodies, while *G. largus*, as the name suggests, is an exceptionally large species. Both are best distinguished microscopically. The slimy-capped bolete *Suillus luteus* can look similar in the field, but is immediately distinguished by having pores not gills.

The Slimy Spike has caps that are convex, becoming weakly funnel-shaped when mature, smooth but slimy, and grayish purple to gray-brown. The gills are widely spaced and deeply decurrent, white at first, becoming gray and darkening with age. The slimy stem has a gelatinous, dark ring zone below the gills; it is white to grayish, bright yellow toward the base.

Actual size

FAMILY	Gomphidiaceae
DISTRIBUTION	Europe, northern Asia
HABITAT	In woodland
ASSOCIATION	Parasitic on ectomycorrhizas, with conifers, particularly pine
GROWTH FORM	On ground
ABUNDANCE	Occasional
SPORE COLOR	Blackish gray
EDIBILITY	Edible

HEIGHT
Up to 2½ in
(60 mm)

CAP DIAMETER
Up to 2½ in
(60 mm)

GOMPHIDIUS ROSEUS
ROSY SPIKE
(FRIES) FRIES

141

Gomphidius roseus is an attractively colored European and northern Asian species with a look-alike counterpart in North America called *G. subroseus*. It has long been noticed that fruitbodies always seem to occur near pines, intermixed with the bolete *Suillus bovinus*. Now research has indicated that the Rosy Spike may not form ectomycorrhizas itself, but parasitizes the ectomycorrhizas formed between the bolete and the pine tree. It basically taps into the two-way nutrient exchange and helps itself for free. The American *G. subroseus* may do the same thing, since it is typically found with *Suillus lakei* near Douglas fir.

SIMILAR SPECIES
Pale fruitbodies may resemble equally pale fruitbodies of the normally more purplish Slimy Spike (*Gomphidius glutinosus*), but the latter has a distinctive yellow stem base. In the field, the caps of the Rosy Spike often look like those of *Russula* species, but (when inspected more closely) the gills and stems are completely different.

Actual size

The Rosy Spike has caps that are convex at first, becoming flat or weakly depressed when mature, smooth but slimy, and pale pink to deep coral-pink, sometimes with grayish tints. The gills are widely spaced and deeply decurrent, white at first (see photo right), becoming gray. The slimy stem has a gelatinous ring at the base of the gills and is white, sometimes with pinkish tints.

FAMILY	Strophariaceae
DISTRIBUTION	Europe, southern Asia, Australia
HABITAT	In woodland and parkland
ASSOCIATION	With palms, broadleaf trees, and conifers
GROWTH FORM	On stumps, fallen wood, woodchips, and sawdust
ABUNDANCE	Occasional
SPORE COLOR	Rusty brown
EDIBILITY	Probably poisonous , best avoided

HEIGHT
Up to 4 in
(100 mm)

CAP DIAMETER
Up to 3 in
(75 mm)

142

GYMNOPILUS DILEPIS
MAGENTA RUSTGILL
(BERKELEY & BROOME) SINGER

Gymnopilus dilepis was first described from Sri Lanka and was subsequently found in India and Southeast Asia, growing on coconut stumps or in oil palm plantations. It was something of a surprise, therefore, when this colorful agaric appeared in woodchips in England, where it has since been found in several different places. Clearly, like the Redlead Roundhead (*Leratiomyces ceres*), the Magenta Rustgill is an exotic woodchip colonizer—but a tropical one, possibly taking advantage of the raised temperatures created in wood and sawdust piles as they turn to compost.

SIMILAR SPECIES

Gymnopilus purpuratus is a look-alike species that has also appeared as an exotic in Europe, possibly originating in South America. It is best distinguished microscopically. The common, north-temperate Plums and Custard (*Tricholomopsis rutilans*) looks similar from above, but has yellow gills (with white spores) and lacks a ring on the stem.

Actual size

The Magenta Rustgill forms caps that are convex, becoming flat or shallowly umbonate. The cap surface is scaly, red-purple to magenta, fading to grayish and finally rusty ocher. The gills are pale yellowish (see photo right), becoming rusty. The stem is pale cap-colored, finely fibrous, with a ragged ring.

FAMILY	Strophariaceae
DISTRIBUTION	North America, Europe, North Africa, South America, Asia, Australia, New Zealand
HABITAT	In woodland
ASSOCIATION	With broadleaf trees, more rarely with conifers
GROWTH FORM	On trunks and stumps, or arising from buried wood, singly or clustered
ABUNDANCE	Common
SPORE COLOR	Rusty brown
EDIBILITY	Poisonous

HEIGHT
Up to 8 in
(200 mm)

CAP DIAMETER
Up to 8 in
(200 mm)

GYMNOPILUS JUNONIUS

SPECTACULAR RUSTGILL

(FRIES) P. D. ORTON

143

The Spectacular Rustgill can be as showy and impressive as its English name suggests, forming brightly colored clusters on stumps and dead trees. It is often still called *Gymnopilus spectabilis*, but the epithet actually belongs to *Phaeolepiota aurea*. The Spectacular Rustgill has an intensely bitter taste and is reputed to be hallucinogenic, at least in Japan and eastern North America where it is sometimes called the Laughing Gym. Since research has revealed no hallucinogenic compounds in European fruitbodies, it is possible that more than one species is involved. The Spectacular Rustgill has also been used as a natural dye, giving yellow and gold colors.

SIMILAR SPECIES

In western North America, *Gymnopilus ventricosus* is said to be a similar, but distinct, conifer species distinguishable microscopically by its smaller spores. Many other *Gymnopilus* species have the same rusty orange colors, but are much smaller. The Golden Bootleg (*Phaeolepiota aurea*) can look very similar, but is smooth-capped and does not grow on wood.

The Spectacular Rustgill forms large, fleshy caps that are convex, becoming flat or shallowly umbonate. The cap surface is finely scaly-fibrous, bright ocher or rusty orange, the scales similarly colored or slightly darker. The gills are pale yellowish, becoming rusty. The stem is cap-colored or paler, smooth to fibrous, with a distinct ring, and is usually swollen toward the base.

Actual size

FAMILY	Marasmiaceae
DISTRIBUTION	North America, Europe, North Africa, Central America, northern Asia
HABITAT	In woodland and scrub
ASSOCIATION	With broadleaf trees, particularly oak
GROWTH FORM	On ground, singly or in troops
ABUNDANCE	Very common
SPORE COLOR	White
EDIBILITY	Probably edible

HEIGHT
Up to 3 in
(80 mm)

CAP DIAMETER
Up to 2½ in
(60 mm)

144

GYMNOPUS DRYOPHILUS
RUSSET TOUGHSHANK
(BULLIARD) MURRILL

This is one of the most familiar and ubiquitous fungi in north temperate woodlands, sometimes dismissed by fungus forayers as a "weed" species simply because it is so common. *Dryophilus* means "lover of oakwoods," and the species is particularly common in grass or leaf litter under oaks, though it will also occur with other trees, as well as in hedgerows and scrub. It is said to be edible, but small, tough, and hardly worthwhile. Very occasionally, the Russet Toughshank is parasitized by another fungus, *Syzygospora tumefaciens*, that produces remarkable, gelatinous galls on the cap.

SIMILAR SPECIES

Several closely related species are similar. *Gymnopus aquosus* is a spring- and summer-fruiting species, distinguished by its pale, uniformly colored cap and slightly bulbous stem base with pinkish rhizomorphs. *Gymnopus ocior* in Europe and *G. earleae* in North America also fruit early, but have deeply colored, reddish brown caps and pale yellow (or orange-yellow) gills.

The Russet Toughshank forms caps that are convex at first and flat when expanded. The cap surface is smooth, somewhat greasy when damp, pale russet-orange at first, becoming cream or ocher, more deeply colored (pale russet or dull orange) toward the center. The gills are whitish. The stem is narrow, smooth, quite tough, and cap-colored.

Actual size

FAMILY	Marasmiaceae
DISTRIBUTION	Europe, North Africa, northern Asia
HABITAT	In woodland
ASSOCIATION	With oak, rarely other broadleaf trees
GROWTH FORM	At base of stumps or living trees
ABUNDANCE	Common
SPORE COLOR	White
EDIBILITY	Not edible

HEIGHT
Up to 6 in
(150 mm)

CAP DIAMETER
Up to 4 in
(100 mm)

GYMNOPUS FUSIPES

SPINDLE TOUGHSHANK

(BULLIARD) GRAY

145

Forming clusters of fruitbodies at the base of trunks and stumps, the Spindle Toughshank (formerly called *Collybia fusipes*) is a common associate of oaks, especially of old trees in parkland. It is often conspicuous in dry weather, when there are few other agarics to be seen. The long, half-buried stems arise from black, underground sclerotia (the fungal equivalent of plant tubers). These sclerotia are formed amongst the roots of living trees, on which the Spindle Toughshank is parasitic, causing a root rot. Studies have shown that this rarely kills trees, but does diminish their growth, causing commercial losses in forestry crops.

SIMILAR SPECIES

The long, root-like stems and clustered growth at the base of oak trees should be diagnostic. *Gymnopus acervatus* also forms clusters and may be similarly colored, but the fruitbodies are smaller and usually occur in association with conifers. Some *Mycena* species grow in clusters with oaks, but have small caps and narrow stems.

Actual size

The Spindle Toughshank forms cartilaginous fruitbodies in dense clusters. The caps are convex to shallowly umbonate, smooth, dark red-brown when damp, drying pale pinkish buff, often becoming flecked with dark spots. The gills are pale cap-colored. The stem is often compressed or twisted, swollen but then tapering and root-like; it is pale cap-colored but brownish black toward the base.

FAMILY	Marasmiaceae
DISTRIBUTION	Western North America, Europe, North Africa, northern Asia
HABITAT	In woodland
ASSOCIATION	With broadleaf trees
GROWTH FORM	On ground in leaf litter, in clusters or small troops
ABUNDANCE	Common
SPORE COLOR	White
EDIBILITY	Not edible

HEIGHT
Up to 3 in
(80 mm)

CAP DIAMETER
Up to 2½ in
(60 mm)

146

GYMNOPUS PERONATUS
WOOD WOOLLYFOOT
(BOLTON) GRAY

The Wood Woollyfoot is a common, woodland, leaf-litter species, at least in Europe. In North America it appears to be restricted to the northwest. It is easily recognizable by its buff to brownish gills (though the spores are white) and the hairy or woolly base to the stem. The epithet *peronatus* means "wearing boots of untanned leather," which Yorkshire mycologist James Bolton, who first described the species in 1788, must have thought appropriate to its shaggy look. The Wood Woollyfoot is not edible, being both tough and acrid or peppery. This taste may help to distinguish it from some similar, related species.

SIMILAR SPECIES

In eastern North America, *Gymnopus subnudus* has often been mistaken for the Wood Woollyfoot, but can be distinguished by its bitter (but not acrid) taste and its lack of yellowish tones in the cap. *Gymnopus biformis* is also similar, but has paler, narrower gills and a mild taste.

The Wood Woollyfoot produces caps that are smooth, matt to finely fibrillose, and pale yellow-brown to pale gray-brown. The gills are widely spaced and buff to pale brownish (see photo left). The stems are narrow, tough, and pale cap-colored (sordid whitish in dry weather), with a slightly swollen, often curved and rooting base covered in whitish, fluffy-woolly mycelium.

Actual size

FAMILY	Strophariaceae
DISTRIBUTION	North America, Europe, northern Asia; introduced in Australia, New Zealand, South America
HABITAT	In woodland
ASSOCIATION	Ectomycorrhizal, with broadleaf trees and conifers
GROWTH FORM	On ground, often in troops or circles
ABUNDANCE	Common
SPORE COLOR	Pale clay-brown
EDIBILITY	Poisonous

HEIGHT
Up to 5 in
(125 mm)

CAP DIAMETER
Up to 4 in
(100 mm)

HEBELOMA CRUSTULINIFORME

POISON PIE

(BULLIARD) QUÉLET

147

Despite its name, the Poison Pie is by no means the most poisonous of agarics, but if eaten it will certainly produce an unpleasant bout of gastroenteritis. *Crustuliniforme* means "shaped like a little pie." This pie, however, contains a triterpene toxin called hebelomic acid, though it is not clear if this is actually the cause of poisoning. Other *Hebeloma* species have a similar chemistry and, for culinary purposes, all should be avoided. *Hebeloma crustuliniforme* is ectomycorrhizal with a wide range of trees, and in parts of Europe it has been cultured and used to help establish pine and other seedlings in reclaimed land.

SIMILAR SPECIES

Species in the genus *Hebeloma* are difficult to distinguish, even when examined microscopically. Field characteristics of *H. crustuliniforme* include the droplets on the gills and the granules or flecks on the stem. The flesh is bitter and smells of radishes. The common *H. sacchariolens* and related species have a strong, unpleasantly sweet smell.

Actual size

The Poison Pie has convex caps becoming flatter (see photo right) and sometimes umbonate. The surface is smooth, slightly slimy, cream to pale buff. The gills are white, then clay-buff, with small droplets on the edges in damp weather. The stem is whitish, widening toward the base, and dotted with small, whitish flecks or granules, especially near the top.

FAMILY	Strophariaceae
DISTRIBUTION	North America, Europe, northern Asia
HABITAT	In woodland
ASSOCIATION	Ectomycorrhizal, with broadleaf trees, in old latrines of moles, mice, and shrews
GROWTH FORM	On ground, singly or in small groups
ABUNDANCE	Occasional
SPORE COLOR	Pale clay-brown
EDIBILITY	Poisonous

HEIGHT
Up to 5 in
(125 mm)

CAP DIAMETER
Up to 4 in
(100 mm)

148

HEBELOMA RADICOSUM
ROOTING POISON PIE
(BULLIARD) RICKEN

Although ectomycorrhizal, *Hebeloma radicosum* is also an ammonia-loving agaric with a peculiar specialization. It grows in and takes its nutrients from old, underground, mole latrines, and less commonly from those of mice and shrews. The long, rooting stem can be traced down into the earth to the tunnels and chambers below, which is where the fruitbody develops. Several other ammonia-loving *Hebeloma* species are stimulated to produce fruitbodies by the decomposition of buried cadavers, making them of potential interest in forensic taphonomy (the study of graves). *Hebeloma syrjense* has even been called the Corpse Finder, though mostly it marks the graves of birds and small mammals.

SIMILAR SPECIES

As well as its rooting stem, *Hebeloma radicosum* is distinguished by its ring and smell of marzipan. *Hebeloma radicosoides* is a similar, ringed and rooting Japanese species that grows on urea-enriched soil. The Gypsy (*Cortinarius caperatus*) is ringed and may look similar, but has more deeply colored gills and lacks a rooting stem.

The Rooting Poison Pie has convex caps becoming flatter with age. The surface is smooth, somewhat slimy, cream to pale buff, often with gray-brown scales. The gills are clay-buff. The stem is whitish with a distinct ring, generally smooth above the ring and with fleecy scales below. The stem continues below ground, becoming smooth, and taproot-like.

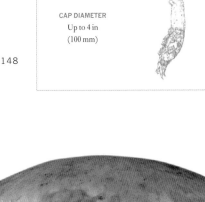

Actual size

FAMILY	Polyporaceae
DISTRIBUTION	North America, South America. Possibly introduced in southern Europe (Italy) and South Africa
HABITAT	In woodland
ASSOCIATION	With broadleaf trees
GROWTH FORM	On stumps, logs, and dead branches
ABUNDANCE	Occasional
SPORE COLOR	White
EDIBILITY	Not edible

HEIGHT
Up to 1½ in (40 mm)
CAP DIAMETER
Up to 2 in (50 mm)

HELIOCYBE SULCATA

SUNRAY SAWGILL

(BERKELEY) REDHEAD & GINNS

149

The Sunray Sawgill is closely related to species of *Lentinus* and has the same sawlike, serrated edge to the gills. It is also related to bracket fungi such as the Dryad's Saddle (*Polyporus squamosus*), and has a tough, leathery texture. This helps it survive on exposed dead wood—its favorite habitat. The ridges and furrows on the cap are sometimes so strongly marked that they take on the appearance of a sunburst—hence its English name. The species mainly occurs in America, the old Italian and South African collections possibly being introductions.

SIMILAR SPECIES

The small but tough fruitbodies with their deeply furrowed, scaly caps should be distinctive. Many *Lentinus* species are equally leathery and of similar size, but they typically develop funnel-shaped caps, whereas those of the Sunray Sawgill remain more-or-less convex to flat.

Actual size

The Sunray Sawgill forms caps that are convex to flat or umbonate. The cap surface is scaly and deeply furrowed toward the margin, the scales tawny to reddish brown on a buff background. The gills have notched or serrated edges and are white to pale yellowish. The stem is whitish, with small, brown scales in the lower part.

FAMILY	Pleurotaceae
DISTRIBUTION	Eastern North America, Europe, northern Asia
HABITAT	In woodland
ASSOCIATION	With broadleaf trees
GROWTH FORM	On dead branches
ABUNDANCE	Occasional
SPORE COLOR	White
EDIBILITY	Not edible

HEIGHT
Up to ¼ in
(5 mm)

CAP DIAMETER
Up to 2½ in
(60 mm)

150

HOHENBUEHELIA MASTRUCATA
WOOLLY OYSTER
(FRIES) SINGER

The Woolly Oyster is a widespread species, found on dead branches of various broadleaf trees, including beech, hazel, birch, and maple. It is generally uncommon and is on the national Red Lists of threatened fungal species in several European countries. Like *Pleurotus* species, the mycelium of *Hohenbuehelia mastrucata* increases its nutrient intake by catching microscopic nematode worms on sticky traps. *Mastrucata* means "wearing a sheepskin," which is an apt description of this woolly species. The genus was named after the Austrian mycologist and poet Ludwig Samuel Joseph David Alexander Freiherr von Hohenbühel Heufler zu Rasen und Perdonneg, but thankfully only in part.

SIMILAR SPECIES
Hohenbuehelia atrocaerulea is similar, but has a darker, gray to blackish or bluish brown cap. The woolly-capped *Schizophyllum commune* is leathery tough and has unusual split gills on the undersurface. Most other similarly shaped species, including the edible oyster caps (*Pleurotus* species), have smooth caps.

The Woolly Oyster forms bracket-like, fan-shaped fruitbodies laterally attached to wood. The caps are weakly convex to flat, dingy white to pale grayish brown, and densely covered in whitish, erect, fleecy scales. The gills are white to pale yellowish. The stem is absent or reduced to a whitish point.

Actual size

FAMILY	Hygrophoraceae
DISTRIBUTION	Southeast Asia (Borneo), Australia, New Zealand
HABITAT	In woodland
ASSOCIATION	With broadleaf trees, often in moss
GROWTH FORM	On ground, singly or in small groups
ABUNDANCE	Occasional
SPORE COLOR	White
EDIBILITY	Not edible

HEIGHT	Up to 3 in (75 mm)
CAP DIAMETER	Up to 3 in (75 mm)

HUMIDICUTIS LEWELLINIAE

MAUVE SPLITTING-WAXCAP

(KALCHBRENNER) A. M. YOUNG

151

This attractive agaric is an Australasian specialty, occurring in damp woodland and forests, but has also been recorded from Mount Kinabalu in Borneo and may be more widespread. It is referred to *Humidicutis*, a small genus that contains a group of waxcaps microscopically distinct from the true waxcaps (*Hygrocybe* species), though still part of the same family. Most *Humidicutis* species have rather brittle, conical caps that split apart as they expand. The Mauve Splitting-Waxcap was first collected in Victoria by a Miss Lewellin in 1880 and sent to the Hungarian mycologist Károly Kalchbrenner, who named the new species in her honor.

SIMILAR SPECIES

Two other brightly colored, violet or lilac waxcaps are known in Australia, *Hygrocybe cheelii* and *H. reesiae*. Both can be distinguished by their strongly decurrent gills. The widespread Parrot Waxcap (*H. psittacina*) has pink to violet color forms, but is always intensely slimy in damp weather.

Actual size

The Mauve Splitting-Waxcap forms caps that are conical, becoming flat to umbonate and typically splitting when expanded. The surface is smooth to finely fibrous, pale to deep lilac or violet, sometimes grayish at the center. The gills are pale cap-colored. The stem is smooth and cap-colored at first, becoming watery yellowish from the base upward when old.

FAMILY	Hygrophoraceae
DISTRIBUTION	North America, Central America
HABITAT	In woodland
ASSOCIATION	With broadleaf trees and conifers
GROWTH FORM	On ground or on very rotten fallen wood, singly or in small groups
ABUNDANCE	Common
SPORE COLOR	White
EDIBILITY	Edible

HEIGHT
Up to 4 in
(100 mm)

CAP DIAMETER
Up to 2 in
(50 mm)

152

HUMIDICUTIS MARGINATA

ORANGE-GILLED WAXCAP

(PECK) SINGER

As the English name suggests, the distinctive feature of this little waxcap are the bright orange gills that retain their color even when the cap—which is hygrophanous (changing color when moist)—becomes pale, through dryness or with age. The species was formerly placed in the genus *Hygrocybe* along with other waxcaps, but actually belongs in *Humidicutis*, most of whose members are from Australia, New Zealand, and the Pacific islands. The Orange-Gilled Waxcap is the only member of the genus known from the north temperate zone. Fruitbodies are edible, but insubstantial and apparently tasteless.

SIMILAR SPECIES

One form of the species has gills that are more yellow than orange, while another has caps with olive-brown tints at the center. Several *Hygrocybe* species may have yellow-orange gills, such as the Blackening Waxcap (*H. conica*) and the Fibrous Waxcap (*H. intermedia*), but differ in other characters.

Actual size

The Orange-Gilled Waxcap forms caps that are conical to convex, becoming umbonate. The surface is smooth, yellow-orange to orange when damp, drying pale yellow to whitish. The gills are deep yellow-orange to orange (see photo right). The fragile stem is smooth and yellow to pale cap-colored.

FAMILY	Hygrophoraceae
DISTRIBUTION	Eastern North America, Caribbean islands, northern Asia
HABITAT	In woodland or mossy grass
ASSOCIATION	With broadleaf trees and conifers
GROWTH FORM	On ground, clustered or in troops
ABUNDANCE	Occasional
SPORE COLOR	White
EDIBILITY	Unknown, best avoided

HEIGHT
Up to 2 in
(50 mm)

CAP DIAMETER
Up to 2½ in
(60 mm)

HYGROCYBE CAESPITOSA

CLUSTERED WAXCAP

MURRILL

153

The American mycologist William Murrill originally found this little waxcap growing in clusters amongst moss in a pasture near Bronx Park in the city of New York. The epithet *caespitosa* means "clustered," but fruitbodies do not always grow this way and are often found singly or in troops. As with most waxcaps in North America, *Hygrocybe caespitosa* is more frequently found in woodland than in grassland—despite Murrill's original collection. The Clustered Waxcap has no distinctive smell and its edibility is unknown, though it is said to have a taste reminiscent of raw potato.

SIMILAR SPECIES

Hygrocybe caespitosa looks a little like a small Meadow Waxcap (*Hygrocybe pratensis*), but the cap of the Clustered Waxcap is usually more yellowish or honey-colored and the scales (absent in the Meadow Waxcap) are distinctive.

Actual size

The Clustered Waxcap forms caps that are hemispherical, becoming flat to slightly depressed. The cap surface is finely scaly, the scales olive-brown to blackish brown on a whitish to yellow or ocher-buff background. The gills are thick, slightly decurrent, and whitish to pale yellow. The stem is smooth and whitish to pale yellow.

FAMILY	Hygrophoraceae
DISTRIBUTION	North America, Europe, northern Asia
HABITAT	In pasture and mossy lawns, also in woodland
ASSOCIATION	With moss and grass
GROWTH FORM	On ground, singly or in troops
ABUNDANCE	Occasional
SPORE COLOR	White
EDIBILITY	Not edible

HEIGHT
Up to 5 in
(125 mm)

CAP DIAMETER
Up to 3 in
(75 mm)

154

HYGROCYBE CALYPTRIFORMIS
PINK WAXCAP
(BERKELEY) FAYOD

The Pink Waxcap is a charismatic and easily recognized agaric that has become a flagship species for fungal conservation in Britain and Europe, its image appearing on posters, leaflets, and postage stamps. It is generally considered a rare species of old, unimproved grassland, but in the British Isles it has a stronghold, being relatively common in old unfertilized lawns and even graveyards. In much of Europe, however, it is still rare, since its grassland habitats are declining. As with most waxcaps, *Hygrocybe calyptriformis* is more normally found in woodland in North America.

SIMILAR SPECIES

Other waxcaps of similar shape, such as *Hygrocybe conica*, are differently colored, often yellow to orange-red. Pink forms of the Lilac Bonnet (*Mycena pura*) can look very similar, but their caps are never conical or pointed and they more typically grow in leaf litter.

Actual size

The Pink Waxcap forms pointed, conical caps that often split at the margin as they expand. The cap surface is smooth, slightly greasy, pink to lilac-pink, fading with age. The gills are white to pale cap-colored. The fragile stem is smooth and white, but sometimes flushed pale pink especially at the top.

FAMILY	Hygrophoraceae
DISTRIBUTION	North America, Europe, Africa, Central and South America, Antarctica (islands), Asia, Australia, New Zealand
HABITAT	In pasture, mossy lawns, or woodland
ASSOCIATION	With moss and grass
GROWTH FORM	On ground, singly or in troops
ABUNDANCE	Common
SPORE COLOR	White
EDIBILITY	Not edible

HEIGHT
Up to 4 in
(100 mm)

CAP DIAMETER
Up to 3 in
(75 mm)

HYGROCYBE CONICA

BLACKENING WAXCAP

(SCHAEFFER) P. KUMMER

155

This is not only the commonest waxcap, it is also by far the most widespread, reported from the tropics to the poles. It may well represent a complex of species worldwide. As the name suggests, the Blackening Waxcap is immediately recognizable by turning black where bruised and with age. Its alternative name of the Witch's Hat refers to the characteristically pointed cap. Old, entirely black fruitbodies can often be found dotted amongst their younger, brighter companions. Though *Hygrocybe conica* prefers unimproved grasslands, it is more tolerant of degraded conditions than other waxcaps and will grow on roadside verges or even playing fields. In some areas, including North America, it seems to prefer woodlands.

SIMILAR SPECIES

Several forms have sometimes been recognized as separate species, including *H. conicoides*, a microscopically distinct waxcap of coastal dunes; *H. olivaceonigra*, a greenish form; *H. pseudoconica*, a larger form, previously misnamed *H. nigrescens*; *H. singeri*, that has a sticky stem; and *H. conicopalustris*, a small marshland form.

The Blackening Waxcap forms pointed, conical caps that often split as they expand. The cap surface is smooth, greasy, yellow to orange or scarlet, sometimes with olive tones. The gills are thick, whitish to yellow or yellow-orange. The stem is smooth, whitish to yellow or yellow-orange. All parts bruise and age black (see photo above).

Actual size

FAMILY	Hygrophoraceae
DISTRIBUTION	Europe
HABITAT	In calcareous to neutral pasture and mossy lawns
ASSOCIATION	With moss and grass
GROWTH FORM	On ground, singly or in troops
ABUNDANCE	Occasional
SPORE COLOR	White
EDIBILITY	Not edible

HEIGHT
Up to 4 in
(100 mm)

CAP DIAMETER
Up to 3 in
(75 mm)

156

HYGROCYBE INTERMEDIA
FIBROUS WAXCAP
(PASSMORE) FAYOD

The fibrous cap and streaky-fibrous stem are distinctive features of this comparatively large and brightly colored waxcap. Despite its size and color, *Hygrocybe intermedia* can be an easy species to overlook since it typically produces fruitbodies in midsummer, several months before most other waxcaps appear. The Fibrous Waxcap appears to be restricted to Europe and is locally common in the British Isles, but is considered rare in many other countries, where old, unimproved pastures are a disappearing habitat. As a result it features on several national Red Lists of threatened fungal species.

SIMILAR SPECIES
Hygrocybe intermedia often turns gray when bruised, particularly near the stem base. It can then be mistaken for the widespread Blackening Waxcap (*H. conica*) which, however, has a smooth (not fibrous) cap and stem, is rarely so consistently orange, and gradually turns black throughout.

Actual size

The Fibrous Waxcap forms caps that are conical, becoming umbonate to flat and often splitting. The cap surface is finely fibrous, dry, bright orange to orange-red. The gills are yellow, flushed orange. The stem is finely fibrous and cap-colored, becoming yellow to whitish at the base. The stem base often bruises grayish.

FAMILY	Hygrophoraceae
DISTRIBUTION	North America, Europe
HABITAT	In mossy heathland and marshes
ASSOCIATION	With moss and grass
GROWTH FORM	On ground, singly or in troops
ABUNDANCE	Locally common
SPORE COLOR	White
EDIBILITY	Not edible

HEIGHT
Up to 2 in
(50 mm)

CAP DIAMETER
Up to 1½ in
(35 mm)

HYGROCYBE LILACINA

LILAC WAXCAP

(P. KARSTEN) M. M. MOSER

157

This is one of several waxcap species that are arctic-alpine specialists, at home in Greenland, Alaska, Labrador, northern Scandinavia, and the Cairngorms of Scotland, as well as the Alps. The Lilac Waxcap typically grows in marshy areas of dwarf-scrub heath, under tussocks of grass, and in snowbeds, sheltering its fruitbodies amongst the moss to protect them from wind and cold. Like the Parrot Waxcap (*Hygrocybe psittacina*), the colors of *Hygrocybe lilacina* are highly variable and, though lilac to violet are typical of the species, individual fruitbodies may be more yellow to orange-brown.

SIMILAR SPECIES

Hygrocybe citrinopallida is a similar arctic-alpine species, but prefers drier sites and has fruitbodies that are always yellow to yellow-white. In more temperate areas, the woodland *Hygrocybe viola* has violet to purple tints, but it is a rare species, very small, and without any yellow tints.

Actual size

The Lilac Waxcap has caps that are convex, becoming flat or depressed at the center. The surface is smooth, striate when damp, yellow to orange-brown at first developing lilac to gray-violet tints. The gills are weakly decurrent and cap-colored. The stem is smooth, lilac to yellow or brownish.

FAMILY	Hygrophoraceae
DISTRIBUTION	North America
HABITAT	In boggy areas or wet, mossy woodland
ASSOCIATION	With broadleaf trees
GROWTH FORM	On ground, singly or in troops
ABUNDANCE	Occasional
SPORE COLOR	White
EDIBILITY	Not edible

HEIGHT
Up to 3 in
(75 mm)

CAP DIAMETER
Up to 1½ in
(40 mm)

158

HYGROCYBE NITIDA
SHINING WAXCAP
(BERKELEY & M. A. CURTIS) MURRILL

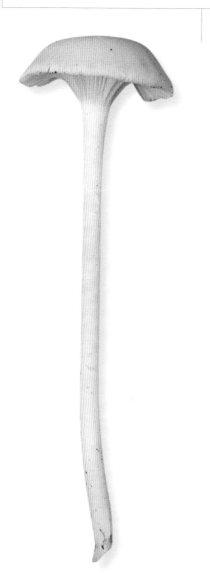

Some waxcap species have particular habitat preferences and for *Hygrocybe nitida* the preference is for bogs, swamps, and marshy ground where it often grows amongst mosses. The epithet *nitida* means "shining," and when fresh and damp it is a brightly colored little species with a glistening cap and stem. The color fades with age, but usually persists in the gills and stem base. The species was one of many new American fungi discovered by the Rev. Moses Ashley Curtis and sent to his English collaborator and fellow divine, the Rev. Miles Joseph Berkeley, for identification and description.

SIMILAR SPECIES

A very similar species, *Hygrocybe vitellina*, occurs in Europe and also likes marshy ground. Most other yellow waxcaps are either not slimy or have caps that are not centrally depressed. The Glutinous Waxcap (*H. glutinipes*) is slimy and sometimes yellow (more frequently orange), but its gills are not decurrent.

The Shining Waxcap forms caps that are convex, becoming centrally depressed. The cap surface is smooth, striate and slimy when damp, pale to chrome-yellow, fading to pale yellow or whitish. The gills are decurrent and pale to chrome-yellow (see photo left). The fragile stem is smooth, slimy, and cap-colored.

Actual size

FAMILY	Hygrophoraceae
DISTRIBUTION	North America, Europe, northern Asia
HABITAT	In pasture and mossy lawns, also in woodland
ASSOCIATION	With moss and grass
GROWTH FORM	On ground, singly or in troops
ABUNDANCE	Occasional
SPORE COLOR	White
EDIBILITY	Not edible

HEIGHT
Up to 5 in
(125 mm)

CAP DIAMETER
Up to 4 in
(100 mm)

HYGROCYBE OVINA
BLUSHING WAXCAP
(BULLIARD) KÜHNER

159

Most waxcaps are brightly colored, but the Blushing Waxcap is a somber exception—though it does blush pinkish red when cut or bruised. The epithet *ovinus* means "pertaining to sheep," though quite why the original author found the fungus sheeplike is unclear, unless he was reminded of their excrement. Like most waxcaps in Europe, it is certainly most frequent in sheep pastures—cattle often being too heavy-footed for fungal fruitbodies to thrive. The Blushing Waxcap is one of the rarer European species and is on the national Red Lists of threatened fungal species in several countries.

SIMILAR SPECIES
Hygrocybe subovina is a look-alike species from southeastern North America with a peculiar smell of burnt sugar, whereas the Blushing Waxcap smells nondescript or slightly nitrous when old. The Mealy Meadowcap (*Porpoloma metapodium*) is an uncommon, European fungus that also bruises pinkish red. It can be distinguished in the field by its strong mealy smell.

Actual size

The Blushing Waxcap forms hemispherical caps, becoming irregularly convex to flat. The cap surface is smooth, sometimes cracking into scales when old, and is dark gray when young, becoming black-brown. The gills are widely spaced and pale cap-colored. The stem is smooth, often compressed or furrowed, and cap-colored. All parts turn pinkish red when cut or bruised.

FAMILY	Hygrophoraceae
DISTRIBUTION	North America, Europe, North Africa, Central and South America, northern Asia, Australia, New Zealand
HABITAT	In pasture, mossy lawns, more rarely woodland
ASSOCIATION	With moss and grass
GROWTH FORM	On ground, singly or in troops
ABUNDANCE	Locally common
SPORE COLOR	White
EDIBILITY	Edible

HEIGHT
Up to 4 in
(100 mm)

CAP DIAMETER
Up to 4 in
(100 mm)

160

HYGROCYBE PRATENSIS
MEADOW WAXCAP
(PERSOON) MURRILL

The Meadow Waxcap is one of the larger waxcap species, widespread and locally common in unimproved pastures and mossy grassland. It belongs in a group of waxcaps with decurrent gills that are sometimes placed in the genus *Camarophyllus*. The epithet *pratensis* means "of meadows," but despite its name it can occasionally be found in woodland (particularly in North America), where it can easily be confused with the Oak Woodwax (*Hygrophorus nemoreus*), which looks similar but is an ectomycorrhizal tree associate. Unusually among the waxcaps, *Hygrocybe pratensis* is generally considered a good, edible species.

SIMILAR SPECIES
Hygrocybe pratensis var. *pallida* is identical, but entirely whitish to cream. The Snowy Waxcap (*Hygrocybe virginea*) is also white, but has a less fleshy cap that is striate when damp. *Hygrophorus nemoreus* is a woodland species, similar to the Meadow Waxcap, but often larger, with a slightly scaly cap and minutely warted upper stem.

Actual size

The Meadow Waxcap forms caps that are hemispherical, becoming flat to slightly depressed. The cap surface is smooth, dry, pale orange-buff to flesh-brown. The gills are thick, decurrent, and pale cap-colored. The stem is smooth and whitish to pale cap-colored.

FAMILY	Hygrophoraceae
DISTRIBUTION	North America, Europe, North Africa, Central and South America, northern Asia
HABITAT	In pasture, mossy lawns, or woodland
ASSOCIATION	With moss and grass
GROWTH FORM	On ground, singly or in troops
ABUNDANCE	Common
SPORE COLOR	White
EDIBILITY	Considered edible by some

HEIGHT
Up to 3 in
(75 mm)

CAP DIAMETER
Up to 1½ in
(40 mm)

HYGROCYBE PSITTACINA

PARROT WAXCAP

(SCHAEFFER) P. KUMMER

161

The Parrot Waxcap is one of the commoner waxcap species, quite often found in older lawns and parkland. Its name is taken from its striking colors, usually starting deep grass-green and later developing shades of yellow and orange—sometimes even pink, lilac, or blue. The green fades in sunlight, but is almost always retained at the top of the stem. In all but the driest weather, fruitbodies are extremely slimy and slippery, so, although said to be edible, they can hardly be pleasant to eat. They were once reported to contain psilocybin, a hallucinogenic compound, but later research has found no evidence for this.

Actual size

SIMILAR SPECIES

Hygrocybe perplexa is sometimes considered a distinct species or variety, having a dark brick-red cap. The Heath Waxcap (*Hygrocybe laeta*) is similarly slimy, with a dull orange to flesh-colored cap, decurrent flesh-colored gills, gray-green tints at the stem top, and a preference for acidic heaths and moorland.

The Parrot Waxcap forms caps that are convex, becoming flat or umbonate. The cap surface is smooth, slimy when damp, typically deep green when young, fading to yellow, less commonly violet, blue-violet, or pink, fading to pinkish. The gills are cap-colored. The stem is smooth, slimy, and cap-colored.

FAMILY	Hygrophoraceae
DISTRIBUTION	North America, Europe, northern Asia
HABITAT	In pasture and mossy lawns, also reported from woodland
ASSOCIATION	With moss and grass
GROWTH FORM	On ground, singly or in troops
ABUNDANCE	Occasional
SPORE COLOR	White
EDIBILITY	Edible

HEIGHT
Up to 6 in
(150 mm)

CAP DIAMETER
Up to 6 in
(150 mm)

162

HYGROCYBE PUNICEA
CRIMSON WAXCAP
(FRIES) P. KUMMER

This handsome species is probably the largest of the waxcaps and makes a splendid sight when growing in huge troops, as it sometimes does in favored sites. In Europe at least, it is considered a good indicator for old, waxcap-rich grasslands and is only found in company with eight or more other waxcap species. As such, it is considered a rare and threatened species in several countries. In North America, *Hygrocybe punicea* is typically reported from woodlands—but many such reports and photos refer to a large, scarlet agaric that does not resemble the European Crimson Waxcap and merits further research.

SIMILAR SPECIES
The commoner Scarlet Waxcap (*Hygrocybe coccinea*) is typically smaller, bright scarlet (not dark blood-red), and has a smooth (not fibrous) stem. The uncommon Splendid Waxcap (*H. splendidissima*) is also bright scarlet but larger, has a dry (not waxy or sticky) cap, a smooth stem, and a distinctive, honey-like smell when drying.

Actual size

The Crimson Waxcap forms caps that are convex to conical, becoming umbonate to flat and often splitting. The surface is smooth, waxy, sticky when damp, dark to blood-red with a thin, yellow margin, the surface often becoming semi-opaque and grayish, the colors fading to ocher-buff. The gills are cap-colored with a yellow edge. The stem is finely fibrous, and dry, streaky orange-red to yellow, whitish at the base.

FAMILY	Hygrophoraceae
DISTRIBUTION	Europe, North Africa; introduced in New Zealand
HABITAT	In calcareous pasture and mossy lawns
ASSOCIATION	With moss and grass
GROWTH FORM	On ground, singly or in troops
ABUNDANCE	Locally common
SPORE COLOR	White
EDIBILITY	Not edible

HEIGHT
Up to 2 in
(50 mm)

CAP DIAMETER
Up to 2 in
(50 mm)

HYGROCYBE RUSSOCORIACEA

CEDARWOOD WAXCAP

(BERKELEY & J. K. MILLER) P. D. ORTON & WATLING

163

This little waxcap may not stand out amongst its brightly colored relatives, but it does have a distinct scent, said to be of Russian leather—hence the epithet *russocoriacea*. Classic (and expensive) Russian leather was cured and treated with a variety of additives, including birch and seal oil. However, it was the sandalwood, added mainly as a dyestuff, that gave the leather its distinctive smell. It is this which is the characteristic aroma of *Hygrocybe russocoriacea*, despite its English name. It is one of the waxcaps that prefer old, unimproved chalk or limestone grasslands where it may be locally common.

SIMILAR SPECIES

The Cedarwood Waxcap is easily mistaken for small specimens of the common Snowy Waxcap (*Hygrocybe virginea*), which is similarly colored (though usually whiter), lacks any aroma, and is typically larger. White woodwaxes (*Hygrophorus* species) occur in woodlands, usually have slimy caps, and smell goaty or unpleasant if they smell at all.

Actual size

The Cedarwood Waxcap has caps that are hemispherical, becoming convex to flat and depressed at the center. The surface is smooth, striate when damp, ivory-white often with pale ocher tints toward the center (see photo above right). The gills are weakly decurrent and cap-colored. The stem is smooth, cap-colored, tapering toward the base.

FAMILY	Hygrophoropsidaceae
DISTRIBUTION	North America, Europe, Central and South America, northern Asia, Australia, New Zealand
HABITAT	In woodland, occasionally in scrub and woodchip mulch
ASSOCIATION	With conifers, less commonly with broadleaf trees
GROWTH FORM	On ground, often in troops
ABUNDANCE	Common
SPORE COLOR	White
EDIBILITY	Not edible

HEIGHT
Up to 2 in
(50 mm)

CAP DIAMETER
Up to 3 in
(75 mm)

164

HYGROPHOROPSIS AURANTIACA
FALSE CHANTERELLE
(WULFEN) MAIRE

Actual size

Hygrophoropsis aurantiaca is such an attractive and colorful agaric when fresh, that it seems a shame it should only be known for not being a Chanterelle. It is a widespread wood-rotting species producing a brown rot, mainly of conifer-wood debris in litter. It can sometimes fruit in large swarms and is one of many species that have recently colonized woodchip mulch, so that it can now be found in roadside and city-center shrubberies as well as its native woodland. It is eaten, at least by indigenous peoples, in China, Mexico, and possibly elsewhere, but is not considered worthwhile and is said to cause stomach problems for some.

SIMILAR SPECIES

The real Chanterelle (*Cantharellus cibarius*) is never deep orange and has thick, gill-like veins rather than the true gills of the False Chanterelle. *Hygrophoropsis morganii* is a smaller and uncommon, pinkish species with a sweetish smell. Poisonous *Omphalotus* species are large and clustered, typically growing at the base of broadleaf trees.

The False Chanterelle forms caps that are convex to flat, becoming funnel-shaped. The surface is downy to felty, yellow-orange to ocher-buff, sometimes with brownish tints, paler to whitish ocher when dry or old. The gills are decurrent, deep orange to orange-red, thin and pliable, often forked and discoloring with age. The stem is smooth, hollow and cap-colored, browning from the base upward when old.

FAMILY	Hygrophoraceae
DISTRIBUTION	North America, Europe, North Africa, northern Asia
HABITAT	In woodland
ASSOCIATION	Ectomycorrhizal, with beech
GROWTH FORM	On ground, in troops
ABUNDANCE	Locally common
SPORE COLOR	White
EDIBILITY	Not edible

HEIGHT
Up to 4 in
(100 mm)

CAP DIAMETER
Up to 3 in
(75 mm)

HYGROPHORUS EBURNEUS
IVORY WOODWAX
(BULLIARD) FRIES

165

Hygrophorus eburneus is one of several species of woodwax that are whitish to cream, very slimy, and have an odd, unpleasant smell that has been likened to that of goats—or more specifically the larvae of goat moths. Like all *Hygrophorus* species, the Ivory Woodwax is mycorrhizal and is typically found with beech trees. The name seems to have been used more widely for collections found with other trees, so that it is not clear whether all interpretations of the Ivory Woodwax refer to the same species.

SIMILAR SPECIES
Hygrophorus cossus is a similar species associated with oak. It tends to be larger with a cap that discolors grayish. Its birch counterpart is *H. hedrychii* with caps that eventually discolor pink. *Hygrophorus discoxanthus* is another beech species, but discolors yellow to rusty-brown. All have a similar goaty smell.

Actual size

The Ivory Woodwax has caps that are convex, variously becoming flat to slightly depressed or umbonate. The surface is smooth, very slimy when moist, white becoming ivory to cream at the center. The gills are weakly decurrent, white to cream (see photo left) or slightly pinkish. The stem is slimy and cap-colored.

FAMILY	Hygrophoraceae
DISTRIBUTION	North America, Europe, northern Asia
HABITAT	In woodland
ASSOCIATION	Ectomycorrhizal, with pine
GROWTH FORM	On ground, in needle litter
ABUNDANCE	Common
SPORE COLOR	White
EDIBILITY	Edible

HEIGHT
Up to 6 in
(150 mm)

CAP DIAMETER
Up to 3 in
(75 mm)

166

HYGROPHORUS HYPOTHEJUS
HERALD OF WINTER
(FRIES) FRIES

As the English name indicates, this is a late-season agaric typically occurring in pine woods at the onset of winter. It will sometimes even fruit after the first frosts. In damp weather, fruitbodies are exceedingly slimy, especially on the stem, and are also rather variable in color with one form (var. *aureus*) developing caps that are yellow to orange. In its normal form, the contrast between the dark gray-brown caps and yellow gills is striking. The Herald of Winter is edible but apparently tasteless and is generally not considered worthwhile.

SIMILAR SPECIES
Other woodwax species with olive-brown to gray-brown caps—such as the North American *Hygrophorus fuligineus*—have white gills and lack the yellow-orange colors of the Herald of Winter. Orange-capped color forms may be mistaken for the orange- to red-capped Splendid Woodwax (*H. speciosus*), but the latter grows with larch.

Actual size

The Herald of Winter has caps that are convex (see photo right), becoming flat to depressed. The surface is smooth, slimy when moist, olive-brown to gray-brown (more rarely yellow to orange), but paler toward the margin. The gills are widely spaced, decurrent, pale yellow to yellow-orange. The stem is white to pale yellow, slimy, with a ring zone, often stained yellow-orange.

FAMILY	Hygrophoraceae
DISTRIBUTION	North America, Europe, Central America, northern Asia
HABITAT	In calcareous woodland
ASSOCIATION	Ectomycorrhizal, with broadleaf trees, especially oak
GROWTH FORM	On ground, singly or in troops or rings
ABUNDANCE	Locally common
SPORE COLOR	White
EDIBILITY	Edible

HEIGHT	Up to 5 in (125 mm)
CAP DIAMETER	Up to 6 in (150 mm)

HYGROPHORUS RUSSULA

PINKMOTTLE WOODWAX

(SCHAEFFER) KAUFFMAN

167

When first seen in the field, the Pinkmottle Woodwax has the
size, shape, and appearance of a *Russula* species, hence its Latin
epithet and alternative common name of False Russula. The
pink to deep red mottling is distinctive, however, as is the solid
feel of the fruitbodies (*Russula* fruitbodies are generally rather
brittle). *Hygrophorus russula* is said to be common and widely
eaten in countries as diverse as Guatemala, Russia, and Bhutan.
In most of Europe, however, it is a declining species, on the
national Red Lists of threatened fungi in many countries and
considered extinct in Great Britain and the Netherlands.

SIMILAR SPECIES
The Blotched Woodwax (*Hygrophorus erubescens*) is a similar
species, sometimes bruising yellow, associated with spruce.
Hygrophorus purpurascens has traces of a cobwebby veil and is
associated with spruce and pines. True *Russula* species are more
brittle, never have decurrent gills, and (though often similarly
colored) are rarely mottled.

The Pinkmottle Woodwax has caps that are convex, becoming flat. The
surface is smooth to slightly scaly, sometimes slimy when moist, white
to pale pink at first, developing dark pink to wine-red spots, eventually
becoming dark wine-red. The gills are sometimes weakly decurrent, white
then mottled pink to wine-red. The stem is smooth and cap-colored.

Actual size

FAMILY	Hygrophoraceae
DISTRIBUTION	North America, continental Europe, northern Asia
HABITAT	In woodland
ASSOCIATION	Ectomycorrhizal, with larch
GROWTH FORM	On ground, in needle litter
ABUNDANCE	Locally common
SPORE COLOR	White
EDIBILITY	Said to be edible

HEIGHT
Up to 4 in
(100 mm)

CAP DIAMETER
Up to 3 in
(75 mm)

168

HYGROPHORUS SPECIOSUS

SPLENDID WOODWAX

PECK

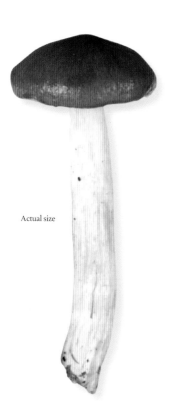

Actual size

The brilliant colors of the Splendid Woodwax are more reminiscent of those seen in waxcaps (*Hygrocybe* species) than the normally less eye-catching woodwaxes. *Hygrophorus speciosus*, however, is an ectomycorrhizal species, forming an association with larches. It was one of more than 2,500 new species of fungi originally described by Charles Horton Peck, New York State Botanist from 1867 to 1915. It is not, however, restricted to North America, being found with native larch in central Europe and elsewhere. The Splendid Woodwax is said to be edible but is not commonly collected for food, although it has been used in Scandinavia as a natural dye.

SIMILAR SPECIES

Few other woodwax fungi are so brightly colored. *Hygrophorus pyrophilus*, known from California, has darker red caps and yellow to orange gills. The normally brown-capped Herald of Winter (*H. hypothejus*) occasionally produces a color form (var. *aureus*) with a yellow to orange cap, but this is typically a pine associate.

The Splendid Woodwax has caps that are convex, becoming flat. The surface is smooth, slimy when moist, bright orange to orange-red, paler toward the margin and fading with age. The gills are weakly decurrent, white to pale yellow (see photo right). The stem is white, slimy, sometimes with a ring zone, often stained yellow-orange near the base.

FAMILY	Strophariaceae
DISTRIBUTION	North America, Europe, Central America, North Africa, northern Asia, Australia, New Zealand
HABITAT	In woodland
ASSOCIATION	With broadleaf trees, less commonly with conifers
GROWTH FORM	On stumps and logs, clustered
ABUNDANCE	Very common
SPORE COLOR	Purple-brown
EDIBILITY	Poisonous

HEIGHT
Up to 4 in
(100 mm)

CAP DIAMETER
Up to 3 in
(75 mm)

HYPHOLOMA FASCICULARE

SULFUR TUFT

(HUDSON) P. KUMMER

169

The Sulfur Tuft is probably the commonest temperate-woodland agaric, often growing in huge clusters on stumps and fallen logs. The innately yellow gills and purple-brown spores combine to give an odd, greenish gray, glancing effect to the gills that is diagnostic once seen. The species has been tested as a biocontrol agent for the tree-destroying Honey Fungus (*Armillaria* species), since it will rapidly colonize cut stumps and actively exclude competitors, preventing the Honey Fungus from gaining a foothold. Sulfur Tuft contains triterpenoid toxins known as fasciculols that have led to many cases of fungal poisoning—despite the intensely bitter taste of the fruitbodies.

SIMILAR SPECIES

Two related species are similar, but only locally common. The Brick Tuft (*Hypholoma lateritium*) can be distinguished by its larger, brick-red caps. The Conifer Tuft (*H. capnoides*) is a much duller species, restricted to conifer woods, with gray to gray-brown gills. All three species can sometimes appear on the ground, growing from buried wood.

The Sulfur Tuft produces fruitbodies in dense clusters. The caps are convex, becoming flatter with age. The surface is pale sulfur-yellow, becoming orange-tan toward the center, smooth but with marginal veil fragments. The gills are yellow at first, becoming greenish gray to purplish black. The stem is yellow with a cobwebby veil zone, becoming orange-tan and scaly below.

Actual size

FAMILY	Lyophyllaceae
DISTRIBUTION	North America, northern Asia (possibly also Europe)
HABITAT	In woodland
ASSOCIATION	With broadleaf trees
GROWTH FORM	On trunks, clustered
ABUNDANCE	Occasional
SPORE COLOR	White
EDIBILITY	Edible

| HEIGHT | Up to 8 in (200 mm) |
| CAP DIAMETER | Up to 3 in (75 mm) |

170

HYPSIZYGUS MARMOREUS

BEECH MUSHROOM

(PECK) H. E. BIGELOW

The Beech Mushroom is a commercial name for an agaric cultivated since the 1970s in Japan, where it is known as *Buna-shimeji*. It is now widely grown and marketed elsewhere as it has a rich flavor and long shelf-life. White-capped and brown-capped strains are cultivated, both developing an attractive mottled or marbled pattern on the cap surface. The species, first described from the United States and traditionally eaten by indigenous peoples, may be the same as *Hypsizygus tessulatus*, previously described from France. Further research is required to see whether the European, Asian, and American forms are distinct or all the same.

SIMILAR SPECIES

The Elm Leech (*Hypsizygus ulmarius*) is similar, but tends to produces large, solitary, white caps with a surface that is sometimes cracked, but not marbled. The related *Lyophyllum decastes* produces large clusters of brown-capped fruitbodies, but they, too, are not marbled and typically grow among roots or at the base of trees, not from trunks.

Actual size

The Beech Mushroom produces fruitbodies in dense clusters. The caps are convex at first becoming somewhat flatter with age. The surface is smooth, but develops a mottled or marbled appearance, and is either white or buff-brown. The gills are white at first, becoming buff or slightly pinkish. The stem is central, but typically curved, smooth, and white.

FAMILY	Lyophyllaceae
DISTRIBUTION	North America, Europe, northern Asia
HABITAT	In woodland
ASSOCIATION	With broadleaf trees, particularly elm, poplar, and (in America) box elder
GROWTH FORM	On trunks, often singly
ABUNDANCE	Occasional
SPORE COLOR	White
EDIBILITY	Edible

HEIGHT
Up to 4 in
(100 mm)

CAP DIAMETER
Up to 7 in
(175 mm)

HYPSIZYGUS ULMARIUS

ELM LEECH
(BULLIARD) REDHEAD

171

The oddly named Elm Leech—also known as the Elm Oyster—is a large and conspicuous fungus, rare to uncommon in Europe, but locally common in North America on box elder. It tends to grow singly or in small groups on living trunks, often from wounds or knotholes. Like its close relative the Beech Mushroom (*Hypsizygus marmoreus*), the Elm Leech has been sold as an edible fungus (under the name "elm oyster"), but mainly in the form of spawn for home-grown cultivation. The rather daunting generic name *Hypsi-zygus* means "high-attached," referring to the tendency of these fungi to produce fruitbodies high up on tree trunks.

The Elm Leech has caps that are convex at first, becoming flatter with age. The surface is smooth, cracking when old, white becoming sordid yellowish. The gills are white at first, becoming cream to pale ocher. The stem is central, but typically curved, smooth, and white, becoming sordid yellowish.

SIMILAR SPECIES

Hypsizygus marmoreus is very similar to the Elm Leech, but produces clustered caps with a surface that often becomes finely marbled. Some cultivated strains are also brown, rather than white. The long-stemmed oyster cap *Pleurotus dryinus* is large and white, but has deeply decurrent gills and veil remnants on the cap edge and stem.

Actual size

FAMILY	Tricholomataceae
DISTRIBUTION	North America, Europe, northern Asia
HABITAT	In woodland
ASSOCIATION	With broadleaf trees
GROWTH FORM	On ground, in troops or rings
ABUNDANCE	Locally common
SPORE COLOR	Cream
EDIBILITY	Edible

HEIGHT
Up to 6 in
(150 mm)

CAP DIAMETER
Up to 7 in
(175 mm)

172

INFUNDIBULICYBE GEOTROPA
TROOPING FUNNEL
(BULLIARD) HARMAJA

The Trooping Funnel (also known as *Clitocybe geotropa*) is widely considered a good edible species, despite the flesh sometimes developing a slightly rancid smell, and experiments in commercial cultivation have been made in China. Care needs to be taken, however, since there are many other fungi with pale, funnel-shaped fruitbodies that are poisonous. The Trooping Funnel typically grows in troops and rings, some of which can be of impressive size. One of the largest such rings was reported from France in the 1950s. It was more than a third of a mile (600 m) in diameter and was estimated to be approximately 700 years old.

SIMILAR SPECIES

Clitocybe gigas and *C. maxima* (as interpreted in North America) are very similar, but can be distinguished microscopically by their differently shaped spores. The Giant Funnel (*Leucopaxillus giganteus*) is also similar, but is larger, whiter, and typically grows in grassland. The Cloudy Funnel (*Clitocybe nebularis*) produces smoky, whitish gray fruitbodies.

Actual size

The Trooping Funnel has fleshy caps that become slightly depressed to deeply funnel-shaped, often with an umbo. The cap surface is smooth, sordid cream to flesh-colored or pale beige. The gills are whitish to pale flesh-colored. The stem is whitish to cap-colored, often downy, and slightly wider toward the base.

FAMILY	Inocybaceae
DISTRIBUTION	Europe, western Asia
HABITAT	In woodland
ASSOCIATION	Ectomycorrhizal, with broadleaf trees and conifers
GROWTH FORM	On ground, singly or in troops
ABUNDANCE	Occasional
SPORE COLOR	Brown
EDIBILITY	Poisonous

HEIGHT
Up to 4 in
(100 mm)

CAP DIAMETER
Up to 3 in
(75 mm)

INOCYBE BONGARDII

FRUITY FIBERCAP

(WEINMANN) QUÉLET

173

This is one of several *Inocybe* species with an unusual and distinctive smell. As the English name indicates, the aroma is fruity and is usually likened to pears. Unfortunately, this is not an indication of edibility since, like most other fibercaps, *Inocybe bongardii* contains the toxin muscarine and is distinctly poisonous. The species was named after August Gustav Heinrich von Bongard, a German botanist who worked mainly in what was then the Russian colony of Alaska. The Fruity Fibercap, however, seems to be restricted to Europe and adjacent parts of western Asia.

SIMILAR SPECIES

In Europe and North America, the Pear Fibercap (*Inocybe fraudans*) has a similar aroma but an ocher-brown cap. It was formerly known as *I. pyriodora* (meaning "smelling of pears"). Another pear-scented species is the Greenflush Fibercap (*Inocybe corydalina*), but its fruitbodies develop greenish turquoise tints with age.

Actual size

The Fruity Fibercap has caps that are conical (see photo top left), becoming convex to umbonate. The surface is scaly, the scales dull pinkish to cinnamon or beige on a paler background. The gills are pale grayish brown. The stem is smooth and whitish to cap-colored, developing pink to pink-brown stains.

FAMILY	Inocybaceae
DISTRIBUTION	North America
HABITAT	In woodland
ASSOCIATION	Ectomycorrhizal, with broadleaf trees and conifers
GROWTH FORM	On ground, singly or in troops
ABUNDANCE	Common
SPORE COLOR	Brown
EDIBILITY	Poisonous

HEIGHT
Up to 4 in
(100 mm)

CAP DIAMETER
Up to 2 in
(50 mm)

174

INOCYBE CAESARIATA
CAESAR'S FIBERCAP
(FRIES) P. KARSTEN

Actual size

This is a common North American, scaly-hairy species of *Inocybe*, but its name is a bit of a puzzle. The Caesar's Fibercap was originally described from Sweden by the great mycologist Elias Fries, but the description is inadequate by modern standards and it is not certain which fungus Fries had in mind. In Europe, *Inocybe caesariata* has been interpreted as a species growing with pines in sand dunes, and has been renamed *I. heimii*. In North America, however, *I. caesariata* has been interpreted as a species growing with broadleaf trees in woodland. It sounds as though two similar but different fungi are involved—so further research is required.

SIMILAR SPECIES
Inocybe terrigena is similar, but is larger, has a fragile ring or ring-zone on the stem, and grows with conifers. The Greenfoot Fibercap (*Inocybe calamistrata*) also has a scaly cap and stem, but is darker brown with bluish green tints toward the stem base.

The Caesar's Fibercap has caps that are convex, becoming flatter. The surface is fibrous to scurfy-scaly, the scales ocher to tawny on a paler ocher background. The gills are pale ocher becoming ocher-brown. The stem is sparsely but distinctly scaly and cap-colored or paler.

FAMILY	Inocybaceae
DISTRIBUTION	North America, Europe, North Africa, Central America, northern Asia
HABITAT	In woodland
ASSOCIATION	Ectomycorrhizal, with broadleaf trees and conifers
GROWTH FORM	On ground, often in small troops
ABUNDANCE	Occasional
SPORE COLOR	Brown
EDIBILITY	Poisonous

HEIGHT
Up to 4 in
(100 mm)
CAP DIAMETER
Up to 2 in
(50 mm)

INOCYBE CALAMISTRATA

GREENFOOT FIBERCAP

(FRIES) GILLET

175

Fibercaps are common, mainly temperate, ectomycorrhizal fungi with perhaps as many as 350 species so far described. All have brown spores and most are poisonous, some dangerously so. They are not easy to distinguish to species, even when examined microscopically, but the Greenfoot Fibercap is an exception, thanks to its scaly fruitbody and to the unusual, blue-green stem base. The color has suggested the presence of the hallucinogenic compound psilocybin, but this is unproven. The species more probably contains the toxic compound muscarine, in common with other fibercaps. Its Latin epithet *calamistrata* means "curled with a curling iron," which is a reference to the upturned scales.

SIMILAR SPECIES

Inocybe hystrix is also covered in brown scales on cap and stem, but has paler, contrasting gills and lacks the green-blue stem base of *I. calamistrata*. In western North America *I. hirsuta* var. *maxima* sometimes has a bluish stem base, but is distinguished by its reddish brown scales.

The Greenfoot Fibercap has caps that are convex to shallowly conical, dark brown, and densely covered with erect, often curled scales. The gills are cap-colored. The stem is scaly and dark brown, but blue-green toward the base. The scales may partly wear away in older specimens. The flesh is whitish and reddens slightly when bruised or cut.

Actual size

FAMILY	Inocybaceae
DISTRIBUTION	Europe, western and northern Asia
HABITAT	In calcareous woodland
ASSOCIATION	Ectomycorrhizal, with broadleaf trees, especially beech
GROWTH FORM	On ground, often in large troops
ABUNDANCE	Occasional
SPORE COLOR	Brown
EDIBILITY	Poisonous

HEIGHT
Up to 4 in
(100 mm)

CAP DIAMETER
Up to 4 in
(100 mm)

176

INOCYBE ERUBESCENS
DEADLY FIBERCAP
A. BLYTT

Actual size

This is a comparatively large species, fruiting in early summer in chalk or limestone woodland, often in extensive troops. The reddening fruitbodies, often smelling of overripe fruit, are unusual and distinctive, so it is surprising to find that many poisonings—including a mass poisoning in Germany—have been recorded as a result of eating this species. Some poisonings have proved fatal. Like most fibercaps, *Inocybe erubescens* contains muscarine, a toxin that can induce profuse sweating, salivation, nausea, vomiting, and diarrhoea within minutes of ingestion. Treatment with atropine (itself a toxin) is normally successful and most patients recover quite quickly.

SIMILAR SPECIES

Some true mushrooms (*Agaricus* species) have whitish caps, brownish gills, and turn reddish when cut, but all have rings on the stem, convex to flat caps, and chocolate-brown spores that color the mature gills. Young Chanterelles (*Cantharellus cibarius*) may also resemble young *Inocybe erubescens*, but they have thickish, wrinkle-like veins not gills.

The Deadly Fibercap has caps that are conical, becoming umbonate when expanded, smooth or finely fibrous, often splitting, whitish at first then buff with reddish streaks, sometimes entirely reddish. The gills are pallid, then grayish brown. The stem is smooth and cap-colored, developing reddish streaks or stains. The base is often slightly bulbous and the cut flesh reddens.

FAMILY	Inocybaceae
DISTRIBUTION	North America, Europe, North Africa, Central America, northern Asia
HABITAT	In woodland
ASSOCIATION	Ectomycorrhizal, with broadleaf trees and conifers
GROWTH FORM	On ground, often in small troops
ABUNDANCE	Common
SPORE COLOR	Brown
EDIBILITY	Poisonous

HEIGHT
Up to 2 in
(50 mm)

CAP DIAMETER
Up to 1 in
(25 mm)

INOCYBE GEOPHYLLA VAR. LILACINA

LILAC FIBERCAP

(PECK) GILLET

177

The Lilac Fibercap is a common and widespread agaric capable of forming associations with a range of different trees. It has long been considered a color variant of the even commoner White Fibercap (*Inocybe geophylla*), which appears identical apart from the color. Recent molecular research has, however, suggested that the Lilac Fibercap may not only be an independent species, but that several similar species may be involved in a worldwide *geophylla* complex. If this proves to be true, then the "real" Lilac Fibercap belongs to eastern North America, where it was first described by New York mycologist Charles Horton Peck.

SIMILAR SPECIES

In western Australia, a similar-looking species previously thought to be the Lilac Fibercap has recently been described as *Inocybe violaceocaulis*. Other look-alike species have been described from Southeast Asia, but have rarely been collected. Similarly shaped, violet to pinkish *Hygrocybe* and *Mycena* species are never brown-gilled and have white spores.

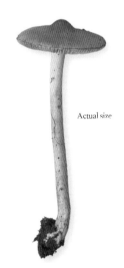

Actual size

The Lilac Fibercap has caps that are conical at first (see photo right), expanding with age and usually umbonate, smooth or finely fibrous, pale lilac or pinkish violet, becoming ocher or tan at the center. The gills are pale lilac at first, becoming grayish brown. The stem is smooth and cap-colored, often whitish toward the base, which is sometimes slightly bulbous. The flesh is whitish to lilac.

FAMILY	Strophariaceae
DISTRIBUTION	North America, Europe, Africa, northern Asia, Australia, New Zealand
HABITAT	In woodland
ASSOCIATION	With broadleaf trees, rarely conifers
GROWTH FORM	On stumps and dead trunks, in large clusters
ABUNDANCE	Common
SPORE COLOR	Brown
EDIBILITY	Edible

HEIGHT
Up to 4 in
(100 mm)

CAP DIAMETER
Up to 3 in
(75 mm)

178

KUEHNEROMYCES MUTABILIS
SHEATHED WOODTUFT
(SCHAEFFER) SINGER & A. H. SMITH

The Sheathed Woodtuft is a common species, typically growing in large clusters on stumps and dead trunks. It looks a little like a miniature *Pholiota* species and, indeed, has sometimes been called *Pholiota mutabilis*. The fruitbodies are edible and in recent years have been commercially cultivated in China, from where they are now exported worldwide. They are not recommended for collecting in the wild, however, since the Sheathed Woodtuft is notoriously difficult to distinguish from the seriously poisonous Funeral Bell, which is equally common and also grows in tufts on wood.

SIMILAR SPECIES
The very similar Funeral Bell (*Galerina marginata*) is a dangerously poisonous species; it is smooth to fibrous (rather than scaly) below the ring and has a mealy smell. *Kuehneromyces lignicola* is also smooth below the ring, but is not known to be poisonous. The rarely recorded *K. leucolepidotus* has whitish scales on the stem.

Actual size

The Sheathed Woodtuft forms densely clustered fruitbodies with convex to weakly umbonate caps. The cap surface is smooth, slightly slimy when damp, dark yellow-brown to tan, becoming ocher from the center when drying. Gills are pale cap-colored to rusty brown. The stem is smooth and cream above the distinct ring, scaly below the ring, and dark reddish brown toward the base.

FAMILY	Hydnangiaceae
DISTRIBUTION	Eastern North America, Europe, Africa, Central and South America, Asia, Australia, New Zealand
HABITAT	In woodland
ASSOCIATION	Ectomycorrhizal, with broadleaf trees, more rarely with conifers
GROWTH FORM	On ground, often in large troops
ABUNDANCE	Very common
SPORE COLOR	White
EDIBILITY	Edible

HEIGHT
Up to 3 in
(75 mm)

CAP DIAMETER
Up to 2 in
(50 mm)

LACCARIA AMETHYSTINA

AMETHYST DECEIVER

COOKE

179

This is a very common species, with what appears to be an almost worldwide distribution. It is capable of forming ectomycorrhizal associations with a wide range of plants and seems to be a rapid colonizer of plantations and other new sites. Recent research in Japan indicates that the Amethyst Deceiver is very much an ammonia-loving fungus, preferring "enriched" soils, rather like some *Hebeloma* species. It can also grow on contaminated soils, though it often picks up the contaminants—especially arsenic. This may be rather alarming for an edible species, but the levels are harmless (unless the fungus is growing on grossly polluted sites).

SIMILAR SPECIES

In western North America, *Laccaria amethysteo-occidentalis* is a very similar conifer species, only distinguishable microscopically. In Central America, *L. gomezii* is also similar but has crowded gills. The widespread *L. bicolor* is violet at the base of the stem, but otherwise pinkish brown. Small violet to purple *Cortinarius* species have brown spores.

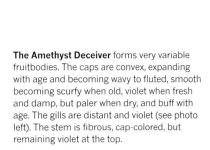

Actual size

The Amethyst Deceiver forms very variable fruitbodies. The caps are convex, expanding with age and becoming wavy to fluted, smooth becoming scurfy when old, violet when fresh and damp, but paler when dry, and buff with age. The gills are distant and violet (see photo left). The stem is fibrous, cap-colored, but remaining violet at the top.

FAMILY	Hydnangiaceae
DISTRIBUTION	North America, Europe, Africa, Central and South America, Asia, Australia, New Zealand
HABITAT	In woodland
ASSOCIATION	Ectomycorrhizal, with broadleaf trees, more rarely conifers
GROWTH FORM	On ground, often in large troops
ABUNDANCE	Very common
SPORE COLOR	White
EDIBILITY	Edible

HEIGHT
Up to 3 in
(75 mm)

CAP DIAMETER
Up to 2 in
(50 mm)

180

LACCARIA LACCATA
THE DECEIVER
(SCOPOLI) COOKE

Laccaria laccata (here including var. *pallidifolia*) is an extremely common and widespread species. It has been given its odd English name because of its exceptional ability to deceive fungus forayers. It does this by changing its appearance quite markedly in dry, damp, and wet weather. The cap, like that of many other agarics, is hygrophanous, meaning that it is opaque when dry but becomes semitranslucent when wet. A dry Deceiver cap may be buff to ocher and rather scurfy, but rain can turn it pinkish brown, smooth, and striate at the margin. Only when the wide, flesh-colored gills are seen is the deception unmasked.

SIMILAR SPECIES

Many very similar species of *Laccaria* are known worldwide, most only distinguishable microscopically. They include *L. fraterna*, a eucalyptus associate that has spread around the globe with its partner trees, and *L. maritima*, a species that is mainly found in coastal dunes.

The Deceiver has caps that are convex, expanding with age, becoming wavy to fluted at the margin. They are smooth becoming scurfy when old, pinkish brown to orange-brown with a striate margin when damp, and paler, sordid ocher, or buff when dry. The gills are distant and pinkish to flesh-colored (see photo left). The stem is fibrous and cap-colored.

Actual size

FAMILY	Psathyrellaceae
DISTRIBUTION	North America, Europe, Central America, northern Asia, New Zealand
HABITAT	In disturbed ground in woodland, parks, gardens
ASSOCIATION	With trees, grass, or on bare ground
GROWTH FORM	On ground, singly or in groups
ABUNDANCE	Common
SPORE COLOR	Black
EDIBILITY	Possibly poisonous , best avoided

HEIGHT
Up to 6 in
(150 mm)

CAP DIAMETER
Up to 6 in
(150 mm)

LACRYMARIA LACRYMABUNDA

WEEPING WIDOW

(BULLIARD) PATOUILLARD

181

Unlike most agarics, *Lacrymaria lacrymabunda* has a preference for disturbed and compacted ground and can appear in large numbers in such areas. It often occurs in company with the Orange Peel Fungus (*Aleuria aurantia*) and the bracket fungus *Abortiporus biennis*. The latter grows on buried wood, so possibly *L. lacrymabunda* utilizes the same resource. Its curious English name comes from the spore-blackened veil fragments hanging from the cap margin and the water droplets that weep from the gills. The Weeping Widow is sometimes listed as edible, but has also been recorded as causing gastric poisoning, so is probably best avoided.

SIMILAR SPECIES

Other *Lacrymaria* species are much less common. The North American *L. rigidipes* is similar but smaller, while the European *L. glareosa* is smaller with a less fibrous cap. *Lacrymaria pyrotricha* has an orange or tawny cap. Some *Psathyrella* species may look similar, but most are smaller and less fibrous, without the weeping gills.

The Weeping Widow has convex caps that may become weakly umbonate. The surface is finely fibrous, dingy buff to tan, becoming browner with age, with fibrous veil remnants hanging from the margin, often blackish from spores. The gills are blackish with a whitish margin (see photo right), often dripping in damp weather. The stem is finely fibrous, pale cap-colored, with a cobwebby ring zone.

Actual size

FAMILY	Russulaceae
DISTRIBUTION	North America, Europe, North Africa, northern Asia
HABITAT	In woodland
ASSOCIATION	Ectomycorrhizal, with broadleaf trees and conifers
GROWTH FORM	On ground, often in small troops
ABUNDANCE	Common
SPORE COLOR	Pale ocher
EDIBILITY	Edible

HEIGHT
Up to 3 in
(75 mm)

CAP DIAMETER
Up to 2 in
(50 mm)

182

LACTARIUS CAMPHORATUS

CURRY MILKCAP

(BULLIARD) FRIES

Actual size

This small, reddish brown milkcap achieves distinction not for its looks, but for its smell. As the English name suggests, it has an aroma of curry powder, or more specifically of cumin or fenugreek seeds. The smell is more pronounced in fruitbodies that are partly dried. Investigation of the European *Lactarius helvus*, which has a similar smell, suggests that the compound responsible may be sotolon, an ingredient used by the food industry to flavor curry powder and synthetic maple syrup. The Curry Milkcap is eaten in China, and has been commercially collected in Scotland as an unusual gourmet food item.

SIMILAR SPECIES

In western North America, the Candy Cap (*Lactarius fragilis* var. *rubidus*) is similar, but has reddish caps and a sweet smell, suggestive of both fenugreek and maple syrup. The eastern *L. fragilis* is similar, but has more rusty orange caps. Both are edible. The European *L. helvus* is a large, pale, conifer and birch associate and is curry-scented but poisonous, at least when raw.

The Curry Milkcap has caps that are convex, becoming weakly funnel-shaped with age and often umbonate (see photo left). The surface is smooth, dry, and dark brick to reddish brown, paling toward the margin. The gills are pale cinnamon-buff, becoming orange-brown. The stem is smooth, cap-colored, or darker purple-brown. The flesh is pinkish buff, exuding a watery, white latex.

FAMILY	Russulaceae
DISTRIBUTION	Europe, northern Asia; introduced in Australia
HABITAT	In woodland
ASSOCIATION	Ectomycorrhizal, with pines
GROWTH FORM	On ground
ABUNDANCE	Common
SPORE COLOR	Cream to pinkish buff
EDIBILITY	Edible

HEIGHT
Up to 3 in
(75 mm)

CAP DIAMETER
Up to 5 in
(125 mm)

LACTARIUS DELICIOSUS

SAFFRON MILKCAP

(LINNAEUS) GRAY

183

As the Latin epithet suggests, the Saffron Milkcap is a much-appreciated edible species and a particular feature of Catalan cuisine, where these agarics are known as *rovellons*. The species is extensively collected for commercial marketing and export. Once eaten, it has the alarming quality of temporarily turning urine red. It grows with pines on neutral and calcareous soils and is locally common. Molecular research has shown that *Lactarius deliciosus* is a Eurasian fungus, but one or more related (and equally edible) species occur in North America where they have also been called *Lactarius deliciosus*. Currently these American species lack a scientific name.

SIMILAR SPECIES

Similar Eurasian pine species are *Lactarius sanguifluus* and *L. vinosus*, both of which exude red or wine-red latex, the greenish-capped *L. semisanguifluus* with orange latex that turns red, and the dull-colored *L. quieticolor*, which lacks conspicuous stem spots. All of these are edible, although *L. sanguifluus* contains toxic sesquiterpines.

The Saffron Milkcap has caps that are convex, becoming weakly funnel-shaped, smooth, slightly slimy when moist, and salmon with concentric orange spots, bruising grayish green. The decurrent gills are cap-colored. The hollow stem (see photo right) is pale cap-colored, often with orange blotches. The orange flesh exudes a sparse, bright orange latex, slowly turning grayish green.

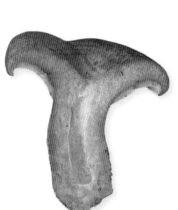

Actual size

FAMILY	Russulaceae
DISTRIBUTION	Europe
HABITAT	In calcareous woodland
ASSOCIATION	Ectomycorrhizal, with spruce
GROWTH FORM	On ground
ABUNDANCE	Common
SPORE COLOR	Cream to pinkish buff
EDIBILITY	Edible

HEIGHT
Up to 3 in
(75 mm)

CAP DIAMETER
Up to 5 in
(125 mm)

184

LACTARIUS DETERRIMUS
FALSE SAFFRON MILKCAP
GRÖGER

This common European species is the spruce counterpart of the true Saffron Milkcap (*Lactarius deliciosus*) which grows with pines. It is usually recognizable by its habitat, by the brighter colors of its cap, and by its tendency to turn green where bruised or damaged, when frosted, or simply with age. The False Saffron Milkcap is one of the few spruce specialists that grows happily in plantations as well as native spruce forest. It seems rather unfair to call it "false," since it is also edible and widely collected, though perhaps not considered as choice as the real thing.

SIMILAR SPECIES
The Saffron Milkcap (*Lactarius deliciosus*) is similar, but has a duller cap and occurs with pines, not spruce. *Lactarius salmonicolor* is a European species occurring with firs and has a bright salmon to orange cap, typically without greenish tints.

Actual size

The False Saffron Milkcap has caps that are convex, becoming depressed to funnel-shaped. The surface is smooth, slightly slimy when moist, and salmon to orange, discoloring jade-green to grayish green (see photo right). The gills are decurrent and cap-colored. The stem is pale cap-colored, turning grayish green. The flesh is mainly orange, exuding a bright orange latex that slowly reddens.

FAMILY	Russulaceae
DISTRIBUTION	Europe, northern Asia
HABITAT	In woodland
ASSOCIATION	Ectomycorrhizal, with broadleaf trees and conifers
GROWTH FORM	On ground, often in small troops
ABUNDANCE	Locally common
SPORE COLOR	Pale pinkish buff
EDIBILITY	Not edible

HEIGHT
Up to 4 in
(100 mm)

CAP DIAMETER
Up to 5 in
(125 mm)

LACTARIUS FULIGINOSUS

SOOTY MILKCAP

(FRIES) FRIES

185

The Latin *fuliginosus* means "sooty," and both the cap and
stem of the Sooty Milkcap have a smoky-brown appearance.
It is one of a group of related species that, when cut, exude
a slightly acrid, whitish latex that slowly turns pink if left to
dry on the flesh and gills. Research has shown that this latex
contains compounds called chromenes that are toxic to insects,
possibly deterring them from feeding on the fruitbodies. It is
even speculated that the color change from white to pink (the
result of oxidization) may be an insect-warning sign.

SIMILAR SPECIES

Several other species, including the North
American *Lactarius fumosus*, are very
similar to the Sooty Milkcap and are
best distinguished microscopically.
The Velvet Milkcap (*L. lignyotus*) also
exudes a latex that turns pink, but is a
strict spruce associate, with a much darker
cap and stem.

The Sooty Milkcap has caps that are convex at first (see photo
top right), becoming flat or depressed. The surface is smooth,
dry, and pale gray-brown. The gills are pale ocher to buff,
becoming dull pinkish when old. The stem is pale cap-
colored, but whitish at the top. The flesh is white, exuding
a white latex that turns pink.

Actual size

FAMILY	Russulaceae
DISTRIBUTION	North America, Central America, South America (Colombia)
HABITAT	In woodland
ASSOCIATION	Ectomycorrhizal, with pine or oak
GROWTH FORM	On ground
ABUNDANCE	Occasional
SPORE COLOR	White
EDIBILITY	Edible

HEIGHT
Up to 4 in
(100 mm)

CAP DIAMETER
Up to 6 in
(150 mm)

186

LACTARIUS INDIGO
INDIGO MILKCAP
(SCHWEINITZ) FRIES

Very few agarics have the deep blue colors of the handsome Indigo Milkcap. It even has bright blue flesh when cut and exudes an equally blue latex. The color comes from an azulene pigment produced by the fungus. Since the species is edible and even sold in markets in Mexico, this makes *Lactarius indigo* one of the few naturally occurring blue foods. The species belongs in the *Deliciosi* section of the milkcaps, but is unusual within the group for associating with oaks and possibly other broadleaf trees, as well as conifers. *Lactarius deliciosus* and its relatives are mostly strict conifer associates.

The Indigo Milkcap has caps that are convex, becoming weakly funnel-shaped, smooth, slightly slimy when moist, and concentrically zoned in shades of silvery gray and blue. The decurrent gills are blue to bluish gray. The stem is cap-colored, often with darker blotches. The flesh is deep blue, exuding a blue latex.

SIMILAR SPECIES

Asian reports of the Indigo Milkcap refer to the similar-looking *Lactarius subindigo*, which recent molecular research confirms as distinct. In Europe, a color form of *L. quieticolor* (once considered a separate species, *L. hemicyaneus*) sometimes has bluish tones in the cap and flesh, but is unlikely to be confused with the true *L. indigo*.

Actual size

FAMILY	Russulaceae
DISTRIBUTION	Eastern North America, continental Europe, northern Asia
HABITAT	In woodland
ASSOCIATION	Ectomycorrhizal, with spruce
GROWTH FORM	On ground, often in small troops
ABUNDANCE	Locally common
SPORE COLOR	Cream
EDIBILITY	Edible

HEIGHT
Up to 4 in
(100 mm)

CAP DIAMETER
Up to 4 in
(100 mm)

LACTARIUS LIGNYOTUS
VELVET MILKCAP
FRIES

187

The striking contrast between the white gills and the dark velvet cap and stem make *Lactarius lignyotus* one of the most handsome of the milkcaps. It was originally described from Sweden and occurs in native spruce forests in Europe and northern Asia. In North America, however, it has been recorded with other conifers and it is quite possible that molecular research may reveal that these American milkcaps are distinct. The Velvet Milkcap is mild-tasting (not bitter or acrid) and is consumed in eastern Europe, but is not generally valued as an edible fungus. The epithet *lignyotus* means "smoky."

SIMILAR SPECIES

Several other species, including the Sooty Milkcap (*Lactarius fuliginosus*), have latex that turns pink, but caps and stems that are a paler gray-brown and grow with broadleaf trees. In western North America, *L. fallax* is similar to the Velvet Milkcap, but is said to have more crowded gills and is associated with firs.

Actual size

The Velvet Milkcap has caps that are convex, becoming weakly funnel-shaped with a central pimple, smooth, velvety, and dark sepia, often with a crinkled margin. The gills are white to cream (see photo right), sometimes with a gray-brown edge, becoming dull pinkish when old, and bruising blackish. The stem is cap-colored, smooth to velvety. The flesh is white, exuding a white latex that turns pink.

FAMILY	Russulaceae
DISTRIBUTION	Eastern North America, Europe, Africa, Asia
HABITAT	In woodland
ASSOCIATION	Ectomycorrhizal, with broadleaf trees
GROWTH FORM	On ground, often in small troops
ABUNDANCE	Common
SPORE COLOR	White
EDIBILITY	Poisonous (edible after processing)

HEIGHT
Up to 5 in
(125 mm)

CAP DIAMETER
Up to 6 in
(150 mm)

188

LACTARIUS PIPERATUS

PEPPERY MILKCAP

(LINNAEUS) PERSOON

As both its Latin and English names suggest, the Peppery Milkcap has an acrid taste. It is nonetheless widely eaten, but may cause problems if consumed raw. In eastern Europe, it is one of several species that are traditionally parboiled (with a change of water) and then salted or pickled for later use. Fruitbodies smell of honey or apples when drying. *Lactarius piperatus* is also said to be eaten in the tropics, including sub-Saharan Africa and Thailand, but these reports may refer to look-alike species. The fungus contains terpenoid compounds called lactapiperanols, which have been tested for potential medicinal properties.

SIMILAR SPECIES

Several very similar species exist. *Lactarius glaucescens* can be distinguished by the slow greening of the latex, while the North American *L. neuhoffii* has yellowing latex. The Eurasian *L. vellereus* has a velvety cap and mild latex (though the flesh is acrid), while the North American *L. subvellereus* is similar, but with acrid latex.

Actual size

The Peppery Milkcap has caps that are convex, becoming weakly funnel-shaped. The surface is matt to slightly shiny, whitish to cream. The decurrent gills are very crowded, cream, sometimes tinted orange (see photo left). The stem is smooth, and cap-colored, browning with age from the often tapered base. The flesh is very firm, and white, exuding a white latex.

FAMILY	Russulaceae
DISTRIBUTION	North America, Europe, northern Asia; introduced in New Zealand
HABITAT	In woodland, parks, and gardens
ASSOCIATION	Ectomycorrhizal, with birch
GROWTH FORM	On ground, often in troops and rings
ABUNDANCE	Common
SPORE COLOR	Cream
EDIBILITY	Poisonous (edible after processing)

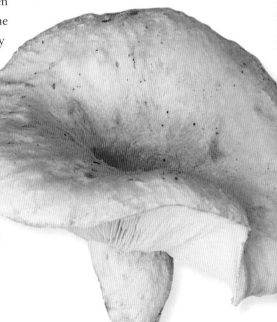

HEIGHT
Up to 3 in
(75 mm)

CAP DIAMETER
Up to 4 in
(100 mm)

LACTARIUS PUBESCENS

BEARDED MILKCAP

(FRIES) FRIES

189

The Bearded Milkcap is a common species, often occurring in large numbers with birches in parks, gardens, and roadside plantings. Research has shown that it will readily colonize the roots of birch seedlings if it is already present in a nearby, older tree. Like the Woolly Milkcap, the Bearded Milkcap has an acrid taste and can cause gastroenteritic poisoning if eaten raw or simply cooked. Despite this, it is still consumed by some people in Russia and other parts of eastern Europe, but only after removing most of the toxins by parboiling the fungus twice and salting it down.

SIMILAR SPECIES

Three other birch milkcaps may look similar. The Woolly Milkcap (*Lactarius torminosus*) is distinguished by its pink to salmon colors. The Yellow Bearded Milkcap (*L. repraesentaneus*) has latex that turns violet. The European *L. scoticus* is a smaller, more slender species, having a fringed rather than woolly margin to the cap.

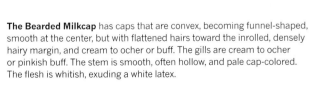

The Bearded Milkcap has caps that are convex, becoming funnel-shaped, smooth at the center, but with flattened hairs toward the inrolled, densely hairy margin, and cream to ocher or buff. The gills are cream to ocher or pinkish buff. The stem is smooth, often hollow, and pale cap-colored. The flesh is whitish, exuding a white latex.

Actual size

FAMILY	Russulaceae
DISTRIBUTION	North America, Europe, North Africa, western and northern Asia
HABITAT	In woodland
ASSOCIATION	Ectomycorrhizal, with hazel
GROWTH FORM	On ground, often in small troops
ABUNDANCE	Common
SPORE COLOR	Pale buff
EDIBILITY	Possibly poisonous (edible after processing)

HEIGHT
Up to 3 in
(75 mm)

CAP DIAMETER
Up to 4 in
(100 mm)

190

LACTARIUS PYROGALUS
FIERY MILKCAP
(BULLIARD) FRIES

This unassuming hazel associate bears the epithet *pyrogalus*, which means "fire-milk." The chili-like hotness of the latex certainly lives up to its name and is a diagnostic characteristic of the species. Despite this fiery taste, *Lactarius pyrogalus* is eaten in Russia (probably after processing) and even sold in markets in Turkey, although elsewhere it is regarded as inedible or possibly poisonous. The species was originally described from France and is common wherever its ectomycorrhizal partner grows. Its apparently exclusive partnership with hazel is unusual, since most other fungi that associate with hazel are generalists and are also found with beech and other trees.

SIMILAR SPECIES

The uncommon *Lactarius circellatus* is a similar, acrid species with paler, less distant gills associated with hornbeam. The very common *L. blennius* and *L. fluens* are similarly colored and have moderately acrid latex that turns greenish gray, but both have whitish to cream gills and are strict beech associates.

The Fiery Milkcap has caps that are convex, becoming flatter with age, smooth, and gray-buff to gray-brown, often concentrically zoned. The gills are rather distant, weakly decurrent, and pale orange-cream to orange-buff (see photo top left). The stem is cream to pale cap-colored. The flesh is white to buff, exuding a white latex that dries greenish gray.

Actual size

FAMILY	Russulaceae
DISTRIBUTION	Europe, northern Asia
HABITAT	In woodland
ASSOCIATION	Ectomycorrhizal, with oak
GROWTH FORM	On ground, often in small troops
ABUNDANCE	Very common
SPORE COLOR	White to pale yellowish
EDIBILITY	Not edible

HEIGHT
Up to 3 in
(75 mm)

CAP DIAMETER
Up to 3 in
(75 mm)

LACTARIUS QUIETUS
OAKBUG MILKCAP
(FRIES) FRIES

191

Lactarius quietus is a very common species in Europe, almost ubiquitous with oaks. Although its colors are not distinctive, its peculiar and unpleasant smell is diagnostic. It is said to resemble the smell emitted by bed bugs or by pentatomid bugs (commonly known as stink bugs) and is best likened to rancid vegetable oil. *Lactarius subumbonatus*, a brown-capped, orange-gilled species also found with oaks, has the same smell but even stronger and was once known as *L. cimicarius* (*cimicarius* meaning "of bed bugs"). The Oakbug Milkcap is sometimes said to be edible, though the taste is usually described as unpleasant or slightly acrid.

SIMILAR SPECIES

A North American species, *Lactarius quietus* var. *incanus*, is larger, darker, and lacks a distinctive smell. In southern Europe, *L. decipiens* is similarly colored but is also larger and smells of pelargoniums. The very common Mild Milkcap (*L. subdulcis*) is more orange-brown, associates with beech, and lacks any distinctive smell.

The Oakbug Milkcap has caps that are convex (see photo immediate right), somewhat flatter when mature, smooth, dry, and pinkish buff to pale cinnamon or brick, often with concentric rings of darker spots. The gills are pale cap-colored, the stem somewhat darker. The flesh is cream to pinkish buff, exuding a white latex, sometimes with a yellowish tint.

Actual size

FAMILY	Russulaceae
DISTRIBUTION	North America, continental Europe, northern Asia
HABITAT	In calcareous woodland
ASSOCIATION	Ectomycorrhizal, with spruce
GROWTH FORM	On ground, often in small troops
ABUNDANCE	Common
SPORE COLOR	Pale cream
EDIBILITY	Poisonous (edible after processing)

HEIGHT
Up to 4 in
(100 mm)

CAP DIAMETER
Up to 8 in
(200 mm)

192

LACTARIUS SCROBICULATUS
SPOTTED MILKCAP
(SCOPOLI) FRIES

The Spotted Milkcap is one of several *Lactarius* species that have a woolly cap, at least toward the margin. It takes its English and Latin names from the sunken spots or blotches on the stem— a feature that is termed "scrobiculate." Like the commoner *Lactarius torminosus*, the latex of *L. scrobiculatus* is acrid and eating fruitbodies may cause stomach upsets. The Spotted Milkcap is nonetheless consumed in eastern Europe after boiling and salting or pickling. Two varieties (var. *canadensis* and var. *montanus*) are recognized in North America, and they differ slightly from the European type.

SIMILAR SPECIES

In continental Europe, several similar, but paler, species also occur with spruce, including *Lactarius leonis*, *L. auriolla*, and *L. tuomikoskii*. In North America, *L. smithii* (formerly called *L. scrobiculatus* var. *pubescens*) occurs with pines. It has a less blotchy stem and a cap that is only woolly at the margin.

The Spotted Milkcap has caps that are convex becoming depressed, smooth at the center, but increasingly hairy toward the margin, cream-ocher to ocher-orange with slightly darker, concentric zones. The gills are cream. The stem is cream to pale cap-colored, smooth but with darker, slightly sunken spots. The flesh is white, exuding a white latex that turns sulfur-yellow.

Actual size

FAMILY	Russulaceae
DISTRIBUTION	North America, Europe, North Africa, northern Asia
HABITAT	In woodland
ASSOCIATION	Ectomycorrhizal, with birch
GROWTH FORM	On ground, often in small troops
ABUNDANCE	Common
SPORE COLOR	Cream
EDIBILITY	Poisonous (edible after processing)

HEIGHT
Up to 3 in
(75 mm)

CAP DIAMETER
Up to 5 in
(125 mm)

LACTARIUS TORMINOSUS

WOOLLY MILKCAP

(SCHAEFFER) GRAY

This is the commonest of several milkcaps that have a conspicuously hairy or woolly margin. The epithet *torminosus* means "griping" and the Woolly Milkcap is an acridly poisonous species, producing severe stomach upsets if consumed. Surprisingly, therefore, it is not only consumed, but even relished, in Finland, Russia, and other parts of eastern Europe. Typically, the fungus is parboiled twice (with a change of cooking water) to remove most of the toxins and then salted down for winter use, when its peppery taste is valued. In the past, it was said to have been roasted and added to coffee in Norway, though it is not clear why.

SIMILAR SPECIES

The Bearded Milkcap (*Lactarius pubescens*) also has a woolly-hairy margin and is equally common with birch, but is distinguished by its paler, often cream to ocher or yellow-pink colors. *Lactarius mairei* is similarly colored, but a rarer species that grows with oaks on calcareous soil.

Actual size

The Woolly Milkcap has caps that are convex, becoming funnel-shaped, smooth at the center, but with flattened hairs toward the inrolled, densely hairy margin, pale pink to salmon with slightly darker concentric zones. The gills are white to pale pinkish buff. The stem is whitish to pale cap-colored, smooth but with pinkish spots. The flesh is white, exuding a white latex.

FAMILY	Russulaceae
DISTRIBUTION	North America, Europe, northern Asia
HABITAT	In woodland
ASSOCIATION	Ectomycorrhizal, with broadleaf trees and conifers
GROWTH FORM	On ground, often in small troops
ABUNDANCE	Locally common
SPORE COLOR	White
EDIBILITY	Edible

HEIGHT
Up to 4 in
(100 mm)

CAP DIAMETER
Up to 7 in
(175 mm)

194

LACTARIUS VOLEMUS
FISHY MILKCAP
(FRIES) FRIES

The Fishy Milkcap is known for being very variable in appearance, so it is no great surprise to discover that recent molecular research suggests that the name has been applied to a complex of closely related species. All these species (which are not yet fully characterized) have unusually copious latex and share the same peculiar, fishy smell. Despite this aroma, the Fishy Milkcap is considered edible and is widely collected for local markets in Asia, even commercially exported from China. The abundant latex contains polyisoprene, which has been investigated in Japan as a non-allergenic alternative to natural rubber.

SIMILAR SPECIES
The American and Asian *Lactarius hygrophoroides* is of similar size and color, but has very distant gills, non-browning latex, and no fishy smell. *Lactarius corrugis* and the European *L. rugatus* are also similar, but both have distinctly wrinkled caps and lack the Fishy Milkcap's diagnostic smell.

Actual size

The Fishy Milkcap has caps that are convex, somewhat flatter when mature, smooth, dry, and pale orange to deeper orange-brown or brick. The gills are cream to buff, brown-spotted where latex has dried. The stem is cap-colored or paler, bruising darker brick. The flesh is cream, exuding an abundant white latex that gradually turns brown.

FAMILY	Marasmiaceae
DISTRIBUTION	Central and South America
HABITAT	In woodland
ASSOCIATION	With broadleaf trees
GROWTH FORM	On fallen wood and litter, singly or in troops
ABUNDANCE	Occasional
SPORE COLOR	White
EDIBILITY	Unknown, best avoided

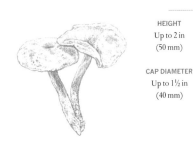

HEIGHT
Up to 2 in
(50 mm)

CAP DIAMETER
Up to 1½ in
(40 mm)

LACTOCOLLYBIA AURANTIACA

ORANGE MILKSHANK

SINGER

195

Lactocollybia species are mainly found in the tropics and subtropics, growing in small troops on dead wood and litter. They are related to temperate *Gymnopus* species, which were formerly placed in the genus *Collybia*. The prefix *lacto* means "milk," and the fruitbodies contain a latex like that of *Lactarius* species, but not so copious or visible. Most *Lactocollybia* species are white or dull-colored, but the Orange Milkshank is quite eye-catching. A related species (*L. aequatorialis*) is eaten by native peoples in the Amazon rainforest, but the edibility of *L. aurantiaca* is unknown.

SIMILAR SPECIES

Lactocollybia modesta is a related South American species with a yellow cap. Also in South and Central America is an unusual, and distantly related yellow-orange species called *Hymenogloea papyracea*. Its undersurface lacks gills and is smooth to weakly veined. The stem, however, is brown.

Actual size

The Orange Milkshank forms caps that are convex at first, becoming depressed to shallowly funnel-shaped. The cap surface is velvety to finely scurfy, yellow-orange to orange. The gills are slightly decurrent, whitish to yellowish. The stem is velvety-scurfy and cap-colored.

FAMILY	Auriscalpiaceae
DISTRIBUTION	North America, Europe, Central America, northern Asia
HABITAT	In woodland
ASSOCIATION	With broadleaf trees, especially birch
GROWTH FORM	On stumps, logs, and dead branches, in dense clusters
ABUNDANCE	Occasional
SPORE COLOR	White
EDIBILITY	Not edible

HEIGHT
Up to 3 in
(75 mm)

CAP DIAMETER
Up to 3 in
(75 mm)

196

LENTINELLUS COCHLEATUS
ANISEED COCKLESHELL
(PERSOON) P. KARSTEN

One of the distinguishing features of the Aniseed Cockleshell are the sawlike gill edges, a character shared by several other *Lentinus* and *Lentinellus* species. A more specific character is the strong aniseed smell of the fruitbodies, said by some to have additional spicy components. Research in France has shown that the fungus produces two volatile anise compounds plus two cinnamon compounds, suggesting that the Aniseed Cockleshell has commercial potential in the production of aromatic oils and flavorings. Curiously, the species belongs in the Auriscalpiaceae, making it more closely related to some of the coral and tooth fungi than to most other agarics.

SIMILAR SPECIES

The related *Lentinellus vulpinus* produces larger fruitbodies with a woolly cap surface and without the aniseed smell. Fruitbodies of *L. flabelliformis* and *L. ursinus* also lack the smell and have little or no stems. Oyster caps (*Pleurotus* species) lack the smell and the notched gill edges.

Actual size

The Aniseed Cockleshell produces fruitbodies in dense clusters, with stems often fused at the base. The deeply funnel-shaped caps are open down one side, smooth, tan to pinkish brown. The decurrent, whitish to pale cap-colored gills have serrated edges. The stem is often ridged, compressed, or twisted, pale cap-colored, becoming dark brown from the base upward.

FAMILY	Marasmiaceae
DISTRIBUTION	East Asia, Australia, New Zealand
HABITAT	In woodland
ASSOCIATION	With broadleaf trees, particularly Japanese Chinquapin (or "shii")
GROWTH FORM	On logs and dead branches
ABUNDANCE	Occasional
SPORE COLOR	White
EDIBILITY	Edible

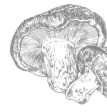

HEIGHT
Up to 3 in
(75 mm)

CAP DIAMETER
Up to 6 in
(150 mm)

LENTINULA EDODES

SHIITAKE

(BERKELEY) PEGLER

The Shiitake is a well-known edible species that has been semi-cultivated on logs in China since at least the tenth century. In recent years, sawdust-based cultivation methods have resulted in the fungus being grown commercially on a vast scale, not only in China, but around the world. With over 1.5 million tons produced each year, the Shiitake is second only to the Cultivated Mushroom (*Agaricus bisporus*) in popularity and has now become a familiar sight on supermarket shelves. A polysaccharide compound called lentinan has been isolated from fruitbodies, which initial research suggests may have some potential as an antitumor agent.

The Shiitake forms hemispherical caps, flattening when expanded, smooth at first but breaking into scales with age, buff to dark purplish gray or brown, with a paler margin that is flecked with white, cobwebby veil remnants when young. The gills are whitish to cream. The stem is pale cap-colored or pinkish buff, fibrous, sometimes with a ring zone, and small, pale to brownish scales below.

SIMILAR SPECIES

Molecular research has identified five distinct groups of the Shiitake, but it is not clear if they should be regarded as distinct species. New Zealand collections have been referred to *Lentinula novae-ʒelandiae*, those from Australia and New Guinea to *L. lateritia*, but both are interfertile with *L. edodes* from China and Japan.

Actual size

FAMILY	Polyporaceae
DISTRIBUTION	Southern North America, Central and South America
HABITAT	In woodland
ASSOCIATION	With broadleaf trees
GROWTH FORM	On stumps, logs, and dead branches
ABUNDANCE	Common
SPORE COLOR	White
EDIBILITY	Edible

HEIGHT
Up to 3 in
(75 mm)

CAP DIAMETER
Up to 2½ in
(60 mm)

LENTINUS CRINITUS
FRINGED SAWGILL
(LINNAEUS) FRIES

198

Actual size

Lentinus crinitus is a species of the American tropics and subtropics, where it is quite common on logs and fallen branches. The fruitbodies are thin-capped but leathery—being more closely related to bracket-like *Polyporus* species than to most other agarics. Despite its toughness, the Fringed Sawgill is collected and eaten by indigenous people in parts of South America. The species has also been evaluated for possible use as a bioremediation agent, since the enzymes it produces to rot down wood are equally capable of breaking down chemical dyes and other pollutants.

SIMILAR SPECIES

The tropical American *Lentinus swartzii* is similar, but with a rather larger, more distinctly scaly cap. Another tropical American species, *L. bertieri*, has a cap that is densely hairy all over. The equally hirsute *L. villosus* is its African counterpart.

The Fringed Sawgill forms leathery caps that are deeply funnel-shaped, smooth becoming stiffly hairy toward the margin, yellowish brown to dark reddish, purplish, or grayish brown. The gills are decurrent with notched or serrated edges and pale ocher. The stem is finely scurfy, pale cap-colored, sometimes with small, blackish brown scales in the lower part.

FAMILY	Polyporaceae
DISTRIBUTION	North America, Europe, Africa, western Asia
HABITAT	In woodland
ASSOCIATION	With broadleaf trees, especially willow and poplar
GROWTH FORM	On stumps, logs, and dead branches, in clusters
ABUNDANCE	Occasional
SPORE COLOR	White
EDIBILITY	Edible

HEIGHT
Up to 4 in
(100 mm)

CAP DIAMETER
Up to 4 in
(100 mm)

LENTINUS TIGRINUS
TIGER SAWGILL
(BULLIARD) FRIES

199

The Tiger Sawgill appears misnamed since no part of the fruitbody is striped. But apparently the epithet *tigrinus* refers to the "American tiger" or jaguar, which is spotted and flecked like the fruitbodies of this attractive, clustered agaric. In parts of North America, fruitbodies are sometimes found with caps that fail to open fully, the gills obscured by a veil-like covering. Such fruitbodies were once thought to belong to a separate, almost puffball-like, species called *Lentodium squamulosum*, but research has shown that they are occasionally produced by the normal Tiger Sawgill as a result of a small genetic variation.

SIMILAR SPECIES
The tropical and subtropical *Lentinus squarrosulus*, cultivated for food in Southeast Asia, looks superficially similar, but the cap and stem scales are white at first and the gills do not have sawlike edges. The less common *Lentinus concinnus*, known from southern Asia and Madagascar, does have serrated gills, but produces smaller fruitbodies with reddish brown scales.

The Tiger Sawgill produces rather leathery fruitbodies in clusters, with stems occasionally fused at the base. The caps are convex at first, becoming deeply funnel-shaped, whitish to cream but with blackish brown scales. The gills are decurrent with serrated edges, whitish to pale yellowish. The stem is yellowish with small, blackish brown scales in the lower part.

Actual size

FAMILY	Agaricaceae
DISTRIBUTION	North America, Europe, Africa, Central America, Asia, New Zealand
HABITAT	In woodland, parks, and gardens
ASSOCIATION	With broadleaf trees on rich, calcareous soil
GROWTH FORM	On ground, singly or in small groups
ABUNDANCE	Common
SPORE COLOR	White
EDIBILITY	Probably poisonous, best avoided

HEIGHT
Up to 5 in
(125 mm)

CAP DIAMETER
Up to 6 in
(150 mm)

200

LEPIOTA ASPERA
FRECKLED DAPPERLING
(PERSOON) QUÉLET

Actual size

The Freckled Dapperling is one of the largest *Lepiota* species, frequently appearing in rich soil and often found in parks and gardens. It has recently become quite common in woodchips used as a mulch in shrubberies and flower beds. Like the Stinking Dapperling (*Lepiota cristata*), it has a strong, rubbery smell when cut or bruised. Despite its offputting aroma, the species is said to be eaten in various parts of the world, including China, Madagascar, and Mexico. It would, however, be foolhardy to sample it since accounts of its edibility may be based on misidentifications, and several similar species are seriously poisonous.

SIMILAR SPECIES

Many similar species occur, including a complex difficult to separate from *Lepiota aspera*. Some may be poisonous. *Lepiota hystrix* and *L. calcicola* also have conical warts, a ring, and a rubbery smell. Their gill edges are often dark, but otherwise they are best distinguished microscopically. Several other warted *Lepiota* species are also very similar, but are generally smaller or lack a membranous ring.

The Freckled Dapperling has convex caps that become flat or umbonate, brownish at the center, paler or cream toward the margin, and densely covered in brown scales or warts that are conical and deciduous at the center. The gills are white to cream. The stem is cream, brownish toward the swollen base; it has a membranous, pendulous ring with scaly underside.

FAMILY	Agaricaceae
DISTRIBUTION	Europe, northern Asia
HABITAT	In woodland, parks, and gardens
ASSOCIATION	With broadleaf trees on rich soil
GROWTH FORM	On ground, singly or in small groups
ABUNDANCE	Occasional
SPORE COLOR	White
EDIBILITY	Poisonous

HEIGHT
Up to 3 in
(75 mm)

CAP DIAMETER
Up to 2 in
(50 mm)

LEPIOTA BRUNNEOINCARNATA
DEADLY DAPPERLING
CHODAT & C. MARTIN

201

The Deadly Dapperling is one of several extremely poisonous
species of *Lepiota*, most of which cause problems when
consumed in mistake for edible Parasols (*Macrolepiota procera*).
Like many *Lepiota* species, *L. brunneoincarnata* prefers a
mild climate. It is not uncommon through much of the north
temperate zone, but becomes more frequent southward,
particularly in the Mediterranean area, which is where most
recent hospitalizations and deaths have occurred. The poisons
responsible are amatoxins, similar to those found in the Death
Cap (*Amanita phalloides*). These cause liver failure and may also
affect the kidneys and other organs.

SIMILAR SPECIES
Many similar-looking *Lepiota* species occur. The Fatal
Dapperling (*L. subincarnata*), for example, is typically pinkish
and less stocky, but is best distinguished microscopically. The
equally dangerous *L. helveola* usually has a membranous
ring. Edible *Macrolepiota* species are much larger and have a
conspicuous, movable ring.

Actual size

The Deadly Dapperling has convex caps that become flat or umbonate. The
cap center is blackish brown to dark red-brown, splitting toward the margin
into concentric rings of scales on a whitish to pinkish buff background. The
gills are white to cream. The stem is similarly colored, with incomplete rings
of small, cap-colored scales below the ring zone.

FAMILY	Agaricaceae
DISTRIBUTION	North America, Europe, northern Asia, New Zealand
HABITAT	In woodland, parks, and gardens
ASSOCIATION	With broadleaf trees and conifers
GROWTH FORM	On ground, singly or in small groups
ABUNDANCE	Common
SPORE COLOR	White
EDIBILITY	Probably poisonous, best avoided

HEIGHT
Up to 3 in
(75 mm)

CAP DIAMETER
Up to 3 in
(75 mm)

202

LEPIOTA CRISTATA
STINKING DAPPERLING
(BOLTON) P. KUMMER

Lepiota cristata is perhaps the commonest temperate *Lepiota* species, being more tolerant of non-calcareous soils than most of its relatives. It needs fairly rich soil, but can turn up in many kinds of woodland, along roadsides, and in gardens. It has not been given an attractive English name, but it does indeed have a strong, unpleasant, rubbery smell. The same smell occurs in a few look-alike species and also in the Freckled Dapperling (*Lepiota aspera*), so is not in itself diagnostic. Like all *Lepiota* species, the Stinking Dapperling is probably poisonous, but is not known to be dangerously so.

SIMILAR SPECIES

Many similar, but less common, species are known. *Lepiota apatelia*, *L. cristatoides*, and the Californian *L. castaneidisca* are almost identical in the field and can only be distinguished microscopically. Other *Lepiota* species of similar size may have more scaly or ringless stems, differently colored caps, or lack the rubbery smell. All should be avoided for culinary purposes.

Actual size

The Stinking Dapperling has caps that become flat or weakly umbonate when expanded. The cap center is orange-brown to reddish brown, splitting toward the margin into sparse scales on a whitish background (see photo right). The gills are white to cream. The stem is similarly colored, though sometimes pinkish at the base, with a membranous, loosely attached ring.

FAMILY	Agaricaceae
DISTRIBUTION	North America, Europe, northern Asia
HABITAT	In calcareous woodland
ASSOCIATION	With conifers, more rarely broadleaf trees
GROWTH FORM	On ground, singly or in small groups
ABUNDANCE	Common
SPORE COLOR	White
EDIBILITY	Poisonous

HEIGHT
Up to 3 in
(75 mm)

CAP DIAMETER
Up to 1½ in
(40 mm)

LEPIOTA FELINA

CAT DAPPERLING

(PERSOON) P. KARSTEN

203

The Cat Dapperling is typically found in calcareous conifer woods and is distinctly poisonous. It is not clear why it reminded the great Dutch mycologist Christiaan Persoon of a cat, but it was he who gave it the name *felina,* which means "catlike." In fact, the Cat Dapperling looks similar to many other *Lepiota* species, except for the very dark, almost black, colors of its scaly cap and ring. Perhaps it was the smell that Persoon found catlike, but it is more usually thought of as rubbery—like that of the Stinking Dapperling (*Lepiota cristata*), though not quite so strong.

SIMILAR SPECIES

Many other *Lepiota* species have scaly markings similar to those of the Cat Dapperling, but typically their scales are paler or pinkish to reddish brown rather than dark brown to black. The Skullcap Dapperling (*Leucocoprinus brebissonii*) is similarly colored, but thin-fleshed and more delicate, with a white ring.

Actual size

The Cat Dapperling has convex caps that become flat or weakly umbonate. The cap center is dark sepia to black-brown, splitting toward the margin into concentric scales on a cream background. The gills are cream. The stem is cream, sometimes flushed brown or pinkish, with a small, flattened, often incomplete, cap-colored ring below which are sparse, cap-colored scales.

FAMILY	Agaricaceae
DISTRIBUTION	Western North America
HABITAT	In woodland, parks, and gardens
ASSOCIATION	With broadleaf trees on rich soil
GROWTH FORM	On ground, singly or in small groups
ABUNDANCE	Common
SPORE COLOR	White
EDIBILITY	Not edible

HEIGHT
Up to 6 in
(150 mm)

CAP DIAMETER
Up to 3 in
(75 mm)

204

LEPIOTA FLAMMEATINCTA

FLAMING PARASOL

KAUFFMAN

The sleevelike ring on the stalk indicates that the Flaming Parasol is not a true *Lepiota* species, but belongs in the genus *Leucoagaricus*, though for some reason it has not yet been placed there. Like many *Leucoagaricus* species, it has a remarkable staining reaction—the cap and stem (but not the gills) turning bright scarlet where bruised, scratched, or cut. Most members of this group of species grow in rich soils in warm locations and are quite often found in gardens or alongside compost heaps, as well as in nutrient-rich woodlands.

SIMILAR SPECIES

Leucoagaricus erythrophaeus is a very similar species also found in western North America. It can be distinguished in the field by having gills that bruise scarlet (unlike those of the Flaming Parasol). *Leucoagaricus brunnescens* is its eastern North American counterpart. Several red- or scarlet-staining species, such as *L. badhamii*, are also known in Europe.

Actual size

The Flaming Parasol has convex caps that become flat or weakly umbonate. The cap center is red-brown to dark purple brown, splitting toward the margin into fine scales on a whitish background. The gills are white. The stem is whitish above the membranous ring (see photo left), with fine, cap-colored scales below. The cap and stem bruise bright vermilion to scarlet.

FAMILY	Agaricaceae
DISTRIBUTION	North America, Europe, northern Asia, New Zealand
HABITAT	In woodland, parks, and gardens
ASSOCIATION	With broadleaf trees on rich soil
GROWTH FORM	On ground, singly or in small groups
ABUNDANCE	Common
SPORE COLOR	White
EDIBILITY	Poisonous

HEIGHT
Up to 2 in
(50 mm)

CAP DIAMETER
Up to 2 in
(50 mm)

LEPIOTA SUBINCARNATA

FATAL DAPPERLING

J. E. LANGE

205

Lepiota subincarnata (formerly also known as *L. josserandii*) is a comparatively common species that has been responsible for many poisonings and several deaths in North America and Europe, hence its English names of the Fatal Dapperling and Deadly Parasol. It is variable in shape and color and difficult to distinguish from related agarics without using a microscope, but no similar-looking *Lepiota* species should be eaten since most are potentially lethal. Like the Death Cap (*Amanita phalloides*), the Fatal Dapperling contains amatoxins in sufficiently high quantities to cause liver failure. Even with advanced medical care and the availability of liver transplants, fatalities still occur in 10–15 percent of serious amatoxin poisonings.

SIMILAR SPECIES

Many similar-looking *Lepiota* species occur. The equally toxic Deadly Dapperling (*L. brunneoincarnata*) is usually stockier and rarely quite as pink, but is best distinguished microscopically. *Lepiota helveola* is similar and also dangerous, but usually has a membranous ring. Edible *Macrolepiota* species are much larger and have a conspicuous, movable ring.

Actual size

The Fatal Dapperling has convex caps that become weakly umbonate or flat. The cap center is pinkish red to red-brown, splitting toward the margin into concentric rings of scales on a cream background. The gills are white to cream. The stem is whitish to pinkish, with a poorly defined ring or ring zone, below which are incomplete bands of small, cap-colored scales.

FAMILY	Tricholomataceae
DISTRIBUTION	North America, Europe, northern Asia
HABITAT	In woodland
ASSOCIATION	With broadleaf trees and conifers, in rich soil
GROWTH FORM	On ground, in troops or rings
ABUNDANCE	Very common
SPORE COLOR	Cream
EDIBILITY	Edible, though best avoided

HEIGHT
Up to 3 in
(75 mm)

CAP DIAMETER
Up to 4 in
(100 mm)

206

LEPISTA FLACCIDA
TAWNY FUNNEL
(SOWERBY) PATOUILLARD

The Tawny Funnel is a very common, late-season agaric, often found growing with the Clouded Funnel (*Clitocybe nebularis*). Both fungi are nitrophiles, liking rich soil, and have probably become commoner over the last century near farms and towns, thanks to increasing use of fertilizers. *Lepista flaccida* is variable in color and has also been called *Clitocybe* (or *Lepista*) *inversa* and *C. gilva*. Although edible, it is not highly regarded and can easily be confused with poisonous species. Fruitbodies are also known to accumulate arsenic and cadmium from the soil. An isolate called clitocine has been investigated for antitumor activity.

SIMILAR SPECIES
Similar funnel-shaped, tawny, tan, or reddish brown agarics are found in the genus *Clitocybe*. The Ribbed Funnel (*C. costata*) and *C. gibba* are smaller and paler, usually pinkish buff to pinkish tan. *Clitocybe sinopica* is deeper colored, but typically grows on old fire sites and has whitish, root-like cords at the base of the stem.

Actual size

The Tawny Funnel has fleshy caps that become flat or slightly depressed to deeply funnel-shaped with an inrolled margin. The surface of the cap is smooth, ocher-tan to orange-tan or reddish brown, sometimes flecked with darker spots when old. The crowded gills are deeply decurrent, whitish at first, becoming pale ocher to orange. The stem is whitish to cap-colored.

FAMILY	Tricholomataceae
DISTRIBUTION	North America, Europe, North Africa, Central America, northern Asia, Australia, New Zealand
HABITAT	In woodland, pastures, and scrub
ASSOCIATION	With trees or grass, in rich soil
GROWTH FORM	On ground, in troops or rings
ABUNDANCE	Very common
SPORE COLOR	Pale pinkish cream
EDIBILITY	Edible (if cooked)

HEIGHT
Up to 5 in
(125 mm)

CAP DIAMETER
Up to 4 in
(100 mm)

LEPISTA NUDA

WOOD BLEWIT

(BULLIARD) COOKE

207

The Wood Blewit is common in nitrogen-rich soil, not only in woodlands but also in pastures and lawns. Fruitbodies are very variable, ranging in color from an attractive bright violet to dull brownish gray. This may be explained by recent research that shows that *Lepista nuda* is not a single entity, but a complex of as yet unnamed species. All are edible, however, though they may cause gastroenteritic problems for some, particularly if undercooked. In recent years, Wood Blewits have even been brought into cultivation in Europe, where they are frequently marketed as *pieds bleus*.

SIMILAR SPECIES

Lepista sordida is a smaller, thinner species with duller colors, often growing in manured or composted places. It is almost impossible to distinguish from small fruitbodies of the Wood Blewit, which become equally dull when old. Violet *Cortinarius* species are distinguishable by having cobwebby veil remnants and rusty brown spores and gills.

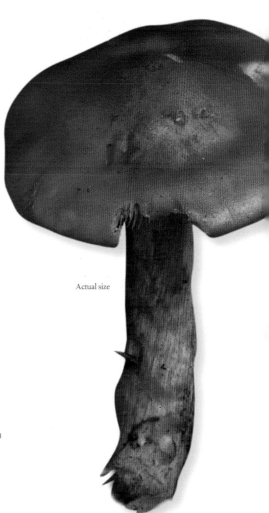

Actual size

The Wood Blewit forms caps that are convex at first (see photo left), becoming flat, slightly depressed, or shallowly umbonate when expanded. The cap surface is smooth, bright to dull violet when damp, often with gray or brown tints, paler when dry with ocher-buff tints. The gills are pale violet to dull violet-gray. The stem is smooth to finely fibrous and cap-colored.

FAMILY	Tricholomataceae
DISTRIBUTION	North America, Europe, North Africa, northern Asia
HABITAT	In pastures and scrub
ASSOCIATION	In grass
GROWTH FORM	On ground, in troops or rings
ABUNDANCE	Occasional
SPORE COLOR	Pale pinkish cream
EDIBILITY	Edible (if cooked)

HEIGHT
Up to 4 in
(100 mm)

CAP DIAMETER
Up to 5 in
(125 mm)

208

LEPISTA PERSONATA
FIELD BLEWIT
(FRIES) COOKE

Blewits are one of the very few larger fungi to have a genuine English name, rather than one that has been invented by naturalists. This is probably because they were once widely eaten in the English Midlands, particularly in Nottinghamshire, and sold in local markets. They were even sold in the London markets before cultivated mushrooms became commonplace. Nowadays, blewits are once again available— but this time for the gourmet market and at a substantially higher price. The Field Blewit (also known as *Lepista saeva*) is less common than the Wood Blewit (*L. nuda*), but is equally edible, when well-cooked. It has an alternative common name of Blue Leg, a reference to its violet stem.

SIMILAR SPECIES

The Field Blewit is distinguished by its contrasting cream to yellowish brown cap and violet stem. It is often confused with the Wood Blewit (*Lepista nuda*) which, despite its English name, frequently grows in grassland. The grassland *L. panaeolus* has a gray-brown, often spotted, cap, but lacks the violet stem.

Actual size

The Field Blewit forms fleshy caps that are convex at first, flat or slightly depressed when expanded. The cap surface is smooth, cream to ocher-brown or pale beige. The gills are whitish to pale pinkish, slightly brownish when old. The stem is smooth to finely fibrous, bright violet, becoming reddish brown with age from the base upward.

FAMILY	Strophariaceae
DISTRIBUTION	Australia; introduced in western North America, Europe, southern Africa, New Zealand
HABITAT	In woodland, parkland, and gardens
ASSOCIATION	On rich soil and woodchip mulch
GROWTH FORM	On ground, usually in large, often clustered troops
ABUNDANCE	Common
SPORE COLOR	Purple-brown
EDIBILITY	Not edible

HEIGHT
Up to 3 in
(75 mm)
CAP DIAMETER
Up to 3 in
(75 mm)

LERATIOMYCES CERES

REDLEAD ROUNDHEAD

(COOKE & MASSEE) SPOONER & BRIDGE

209

The Redlead Roundhead has long been a mystery. It was first noticed in sawdust and woodchips in England in the 1950s, when it was referred to as *Stropharia aurantiaca*, a little-known orange-capped form of a normally brown fungus. It subsequently appeared in the Netherlands, then elsewhere in Europe, then in California, and so on around the globe, following the increased use of woodchips as a flowerbed mulch. Everyone considered it an alien species—but from where? Eventually it was traced to Australia, where it had been described as *Agaricus ceres* back in the 1880s. Now renamed *Leratiomyces ceres*, the mystery of the origin of the Redlead Roundhead may finally have been solved.

Actual size

SIMILAR SPECIES

Until recently the Redlead Roundhead was misidentified as *Stropharia aurantiaca*. The true *S. aurantiaca* (now named *Leratiomyces squamosus* var. *thraustus*) is an uncommon, orange-capped form of a brown-capped, European agaric, distinguished from *L. ceres* microscopically and by being slender and long-stemmed.

The Redlead Roundhead has convex caps at first, becoming shallowly umbonate. The caps are smooth (with whitish veil remnants around the margins when young), sticky when damp, and deep orange to orange-red. The gills are pale grayish to purplish brown. The stem is whitish, sometimes staining orange or rusty, with a fleeting ring zone and scattered scales toward the base.

FAMILY	Strophariaceae
DISTRIBUTION	North America, Europe
HABITAT	In woodland
ASSOCIATION	With broadleaf trees
GROWTH FORM	On buried wood or woody remains, singly or in troops
ABUNDANCE	Occasional
SPORE COLOR	Purple-brown
EDIBILITY	Not edible

HEIGHT
Up to 7 in
(175 mm)

CAP DIAMETER
Up to 2 in
(50 mm)

210

LERATIOMYCES SQUAMOSUS VAR. *THRAUSTUS*
SLENDER ROUNDHEAD
(KALCHBRENNER) BRIDGE & SPOONER

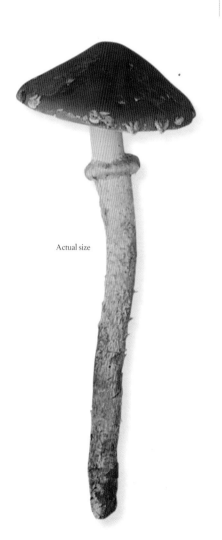

Actual size

With its long, slender stem and orange cap, the Slender Roundhead is an attractive and distinctive agaric, but is nowhere common. It occurs occasionally in woodland leaf litter, where it decomposes small fragments of buried wood. Until recently, there was much debate about which genus the Slender Roundhead belonged to and it has been variously placed in *Hypholoma*, *Psilocybe*, and *Stropharia*. Investigation of its DNA, however, has revealed that none of these placements is correct. It actually belongs in *Leratiomyces*—a genus of mainly Australasian fungi.

SIMILAR SPECIES

The Slender Roundhead was formerly much confused with the Redlead Roundhead (*Leratiomyces ceres*), but the latter species—common in woodchip mulch—has less slender, more compact fruitbodies with an orange-red cap. The ordinary form of *L. squamosus* is distinguished by its cream to brownish cap.

The Slender Roundhead has convex caps, becoming flatter. The caps are smooth (with whitish veil remnants around the margin when young), sticky when damp, and yellow-orange to red-brown (in the variety *thraustus*). The gills are pale grayish to gray-brown. The stem is whitish at its upper end, orange-brown below, with a distinct ring and abundant whitish scales toward the base.

FAMILY	Agaricaceae
DISTRIBUTION	North America, southern Europe, Africa, Central and South America, eastern Asia, Australia
HABITAT	In calcareous woodland, parkland, and gardens
ASSOCIATION	With broadleaf trees
GROWTH FORM	On ground, singly or in small groups
ABUNDANCE	Locally common
SPORE COLOR	White
EDIBILITY	Not edible

HEIGHT
Up to 6 in (150 mm)

CAP DIAMETER
Up to 4 in (100 mm)

LEUCOAGARICUS RUBROTINCTUS

RUBY DAPPERLING

(PECK) SINGER

211

Leucoagaricus species are related to *Lepiota* species, but tend to be larger and more slender with a distinct (not partial) ring on the stem. The Ruby Dapperling, which is also known as the Red-eyed Parasol, is one of the most widespread and easily recognized species, thanks to its attractive colors. It is, however, rather rare in some places—including Europe, where it is restricted to the Mediterranean area—but more common in others, particularly in North America, from where it was originally described. It is quite possible that *Leucoagaricus rubrotinctus* represents a group of closely related species worldwide.

SIMILAR SPECIES

Several *Leucoagaricus* species—such as the European *L. wychanskyi*—have caps that are rosy pink and may look like pale specimens of the Ruby Dapperling. Other *Leucoagaricus* species, such as *L. badhamii* and *Lepiota flammeatincta*, have reddish brown to purple-brown caps that turn immediately scarlet when scratched or bruised.

The Ruby Dapperling has convex caps that become flat or weakly umbonate when expanded. The cap center is pinkish red to orange-red or red-brown, typically splitting or cracking toward the margin and breaking up into scales on a whitish background. The gills are white. The stem is whitish with a white, membranous ring.

Actual size

FAMILY	Agaricaceae
DISTRIBUTION	Southern North America, southern Europe, Africa, Central and South America, southern Asia; introduced elsewhere with houseplants
HABITAT	In woodland (also in flowerpots and greenhouses)
ASSOCIATION	With broadleaf trees, on rich soil
GROWTH FORM	On ground, in small groups
ABUNDANCE	Common
SPORE COLOR	White
EDIBILITY	Probably poisonous, best avoided

HEIGHT
Up to 3 in
(75 mm)

CAP DIAMETER
Up to 2 in
(50 mm)

212

LEUCOCOPRINUS BIRNBAUMII
PLANTPOT DAPPERLING
(CORDA) SINGER

This fragile, but colorful, tropical agaric has found itself a peculiar niche, growing with houseplants in flowerpots around the world. It has presumably spread with commercial potting compost, but why this particular species should be such a successful and ubiquitous colonist is unclear. In its natural state, the Plantpot Dapperling grows in tropical and subtropical forests, extending northward into southern North America and Europe. It was originally described from a greenhouse in Prague, where it was found by Herr Garten-Inspektor Birnbaum. Some reports list it as causing gastrointestinal poisoning if eaten.

SIMILAR SPECIES
Leucocoprinus straminellus and *L. flavescens* are paler species, best distinguished microscopically. Both have occasionally been found in greenhouses. In its natural habitat, *L. birnbaumii* could be confused with the widespread *L. fragilissimus*, which has white gills. *Leucocoprinus sulphurellus*, described from the West Indies, bruises a remarkable blue-green.

Actual size

The Plantpot Dapperling has thin, convex to conical caps that become flat or weakly umbonate. The cap is bright canary yellow when young, fading and becoming brownish with age, covered in loose, granular scales. The gills are pale yellow. The stem is swollen toward the base, similarly colored, with scattered, granular scales and a small, easily shed ring.

FAMILY	Agaricaceae
DISTRIBUTION	North America, Europe, Africa, Central America, Asia, New Zealand
HABITAT	In woodland
ASSOCIATION	With broadleaf trees on rich soil
GROWTH FORM	On ground, singly or in small groups
ABUNDANCE	Occasional
SPORE COLOR	White
EDIBILITY	Not edible

HEIGHT	Up to 3 in (75 mm)
CAP DIAMETER	Up to 3 in (75 mm)

LEUCOCOPRINUS BREBISSONII

SKULLCAP DAPPERLING

(GODEY) LOQUIN

213

Leucocoprinus species are delicate, thin-capped relatives of *Leucoagaricus* and *Lepiota* species. They look a little like white-spored inkcaps (*leuco* means "white"), but unlike most inkcaps their gills never turn to liquid. None is known to be seriously toxic, though some may be mildly poisonous. Most *Leucocoprinus* species are tropical, but the Skullcap Dapperling is an exception, often occurring in rich soil in temperate woodlands. It has been suggested that increased use of nitrate fertilizers may have made this species more common in recent years, though a recent analysis of Dutch data does not support this.

Actual size

SIMILAR SPECIES

Leucocoprinus venezuelanus is a widespread and very similar tropical species, best distinguished microscopically by its smaller spores. Several temperate *Lepiota* species, such as *L. felina*, have a dark central spot, but all are thicker-fleshed with rings that are rarely fully-formed or complete, if present at all.

The Skullcap Dapperling has convex to conical caps at first, becoming flat. The caps have a dark gray-brown to black central spot, surrounded by fine dark scales on a white background. The gills are white, yellowing slightly with age. The stem is white, swollen, and sometimes pinkish toward the base, with scattered, granular scales and a small, easily shed ring.

FAMILY	Agaricaceae
DISTRIBUTION	Southern North America, southern Europe, Africa, Central and South America, southern and eastern Asia, Australia, New Zealand
HABITAT	In woodland
ASSOCIATION	With broadleaf trees
GROWTH FORM	On ground, in small groups
ABUNDANCE	Common
SPORE COLOR	White
EDIBILITY	Not edible

HEIGHT
Up to 4 in
(100 mm)

CAP DIAMETER
Up to 2 in
(50 mm)

214

LEUCOCOPRINUS FRAGILISSIMUS
FRAGILE DAPPERLING
(RAVENEL) PATOUILLARD

The epithet *fragilissimus* means "extremely fragile," and this is one of the most ephemeral of agarics, with a cap that is often as thin and translucent as fine tissue paper. In tropical heat and humidity, fruitbodies that expand in the night may be half-shriveled up by daybreak, making it difficult to find a perfect specimen. The Fragile Dapperling is a common and widespread species, originally described from the southeastern United States but found throughout the tropics and subtropics, as far north as Japan and as far south as New Zealand.

SIMILAR SPECIES

The common Plantpot Dapperling (*Leucocoprinus birnbaumii*) is a similar tropical and subtropical species, but is less transparently fragile and is entirely yellow (including the gills). *Leucocoprinus straminellus* and *L. flavescens* are two paler yellow, tropical species, but are also more robust than the Fragile Dapperling.

Actual size

The Fragile Dapperling has very thin, convex to conical caps, flat when expanded. The cap is pale yellow when young, then whitish, but remaining yellow to yellow-brown at the center, covered in loose, granular scales. The gills are white to yellowish white. The stem is whitish to yellowish white, with scattered, granular scales and a small, easily shed ring.

FAMILY	Tricholomataceae
DISTRIBUTION	North America, Europe, Central America, northern Asia, New Zealand
HABITAT	In pasture and woodland clearings
ASSOCIATION	With grass
GROWTH FORM	On ground, in rings
ABUNDANCE	Occasional
SPORE COLOR	White
EDIBILITY	Edible

HEIGHT
Up to 6 in
(150 mm)
CAP DIAMETER
Up to 16 in
(400 mm)

LEUCOPAXILLUS GIGANTEUS

GIANT FUNNEL

(SOWERBY) SINGER

215

The Giant Funnel certainly produces massive fruitbodies, though they are not always as funnel-shaped as the English name suggests. They are particularly impressive when growing in large rings in grassland, which is a typical growth pattern for the species. Very old rings may be broken up into partial arcs, so that it looks as if the fruitbodies are following a long, curving line. The Giant Funnel is an edible species with an aromatic or radishlike smell. It has been used to produce an antibiotic called clitocybin (the species was formerly called *Clitocybe gigantea*). A further metabolite, called clitocine, has been shown to have antitumor properties.

SIMILAR SPECIES

Leucopaxillus candidus is sometimes considered a separate, upland species, but is hardly distinct. The Trooping Funnel (*Infundibulicybe geotropa*) is similar, but is a woodland species, with a longer stem and a cap that becomes beige to buff. *Lactarius piperatus* and the shorter-stemmed *L. vellereus* are also similar, but exude a white latex.

Actual size

The Giant Funnel forms fleshy caps that are convex at first, becoming shallowly funnel-shaped when expanded. The cap surface is smooth, dry, almost velvety, and ivory-white, developing yellow-brown stains when old with an inrolled margin. The crowded gills are cap-colored and decurrent. The stem is short, cap-colored, and smooth.

FAMILY	Hygrophoraceae
DISTRIBUTION	North America, Europe, South America, arctic Asia, New Zealand
HABITAT	In moorland and mountains
ASSOCIATION	Lichenized, with algae
GROWTH FORM	On ground, in soil and peat
ABUNDANCE	Occasional
SPORE COLOR	White
EDIBILITY	Not edible

HEIGHT Up to 1 in (25 mm)	
CAP DIAMETER Up to 1 in (25 mm)	

216

LICHENOMPHALIA ALPINA
ALPINE NAVEL
(BRITZELMAYR) REDHEAD ET AL

Actual size

Most lichens, such as *Xanthoria elegans*, belong in the Ascomycota and produce fruitbodies that are cup- or disc-shaped, often much smaller and less visible than their encrusting or foliose thalli. The Alpine Navel, however, is a lichen that belongs in the Basidiomycota and produces agaric fruitbodies that are much larger than their rather inconspicuous thalli (which consist of small, grayish green scales found around the base of the fruitbody). As the name *Lichenomphalia alpina* indicates, this brightly colored, little agaric is found mainly in arctic and alpine areas, growing among mosses and other lichens.

SIMILAR SPECIES
The commoner and more widespread Heath Navel (*Lichenomphalia umbellifera*) is similarly shaped, but is pale brown. Waxcaps (*Hygrocybe* species) belong in the same family and several are bright yellow. *Hygrocybe vitellina* is yellow and has decurrent gills, but its gills are never as sparse and distant as those of the Alpine Navel.

The Alpine Navel forms caps that are convex, becoming flat. The cap surface is smooth, with a wavy or scalloped margin, bright yellow to pale yellow (see photo left). The gills are decurrent, few and distant, and pale yellow. The stem is smooth and pale cap-colored.

FAMILY	Amanitaceae
DISTRIBUTION	North America, Europe, Asia
HABITAT	In calcareous woodland
ASSOCIATION	With broadleaf trees and conifers
GROWTH FORM	On ground, singly or in small groups
ABUNDANCE	Occasional
SPORE COLOR	White
EDIBILITY	Not edible

HEIGHT
Up to 6 in
(150 mm)

CAP DIAMETER
Up to 6 in
(150 mm)

LIMACELLA GUTTATA

WEEPING SLIMECAP

(PERSOON) KONRAD & MAUBLANC

217

Limacella species are less well-known relatives of *Amanita* species and may look similar, but lack a volva at the base of the stem. They also have slimy caps, the slime being remnants of a sticky veil. The Latin *Limacella* means "a little slug," which hardly seems fair since these agarics are far larger (and more attractive) than the average slug. They have a strong preference for calcareous and limestone woodlands, where they often occur in company with *Lepiota* species. The Weeping Slimecap has a slightly mealy smell and is sometimes said to be edible, though similar-looking *Amanita* species may be lethally poisonous.

SIMILAR SPECIES

In North America, *Limacella solidipes* is a similar species that is white when young, but may age pinkish buff. The widespread and normally whitish *L. illinita* may sometimes produce similarly colored fruitbodies, but it has a slimy stem without a conspicuous ring. Ringed, white-gilled *Amanita* and *Leucoagaricus* species do not normally have slimy caps.

Actual size

The Weeping Slimecap has convex caps at first (see photo left), becoming shallowly umbonate when expanded. The caps are smooth, slimy when damp, often splitting, and cream to pale tan or pinkish tan. The gills are white. The stem is dry, whitish to cream with a slightly bulbous base and a membranous, pendulous ring that often becomes gray-spotted.

FAMILY	Lyophyllaceae
DISTRIBUTION	North America, Europe, northern Asia
HABITAT	In woodland and parkland
ASSOCIATION	With broadleaf trees and conifers, often in grass
GROWTH FORM	On ground, in dense clusters
ABUNDANCE	Common
SPORE COLOR	White
EDIBILITY	Best avoided

HEIGHT
Up to 4 in
(100 mm)

CAP DIAMETER
Up to 4 in
(100 mm)

218

LYOPHYLLUM CONNATUM
WHITE DOMECAP
(SCHUMACHER) SINGER

Like the Clustered Domecap (*Lyophyllum decastes*), the White Domecap forms dense mounds of fruitbodies in grass or litter near trees, and was once thought to be no more than an unpigmented form of the same fungus. Molecular investigation has shown, however, that it is distinct species in its own right. The White Domecap is usually considered to be edible and has even been cultivated experimentally in China. However, research has revealed that fruitbodies contain compounds that might be mutagenic, so it is perhaps best avoided or only sampled with caution.

SIMILAR SPECIES

The entirely white, ringless, and scaleless fruitbodies growing in large clusters on the ground should be distinctive—but small clusters or clusters of immature fruitbodies could easily be mistaken for a number of other white-capped species (including members of *Clitocybe*), some of which may be poisonous.

Actual size

The White Domecap forms caps that are convex at first, flattening when expanded. The cap surface is smooth, sometimes with a silky sheen, often wavy at the margin, and entirely white. The gills are white. The stem is smooth, tapering toward the base, and is also white, though all parts of the fruitbody may discolor yellowish with age.

FAMILY	Lyophyllaceae
DISTRIBUTION	North America, Europe, Central America, northern Asia
HABITAT	In woodland and parkland
ASSOCIATION	With broadleaf trees and conifers, often in grass
GROWTH FORM	On ground, in dense clusters
ABUNDANCE	Common
SPORE COLOR	White
EDIBILITY	Edible

HEIGHT
Up to 5 in
(125 mm)

CAP DIAMETER
Up to 6 in
(150 mm)

LYOPHYLLUM DECASTES

CLUSTERED DOMECAP

(FRIES) SINGER

219

The Clustered Domecap typically forms dense mounds of fruitbodies in grass or litter near trees, possibly growing from dead roots or buried wood. It has long been considered a very variable fungus and recent molecular research has shown that it is a complex of at least five species, only one of which, the east Asian *Lyophyllum shimeji*, has yet been formally named. *Lyophyllum decastes* (including *L. shimeji*) is cultivated for food in China and Japan and is now exported worldwide. The fungus is also widely collected and eaten elsewhere, and in North America has picked up the unappealing name Fried Chicken Mushroom, apparently on the basis of its texture.

The Clustered Domecap forms caps that are convex at first, flattening when expanded. The cap surface is smooth with a silky sheen, gray to pale gray-brown with a peelable cuticle. The gills are whitish to cream, becoming slightly brownish when old. The stem is smooth with a silky sheen, white to slightly brownish, and the flesh is fairly tough and elastic.

SIMILAR SPECIES

If they are distinct species (rather than just color forms), then *Lyophyllum fumosum* differs in its darker cap and grayish gills, while *L. loricatum* has brown, slightly sticky caps. Molecular research has shown the entirely white *L. connatum* to be clearly distinct. Many other agarics (some of them poisonous) grow in similar dense clusters.

Actual size

FAMILY	Tricholomataceae
DISTRIBUTION	North America (Florida), Central and South America
HABITAT	In woodland, scrub, and grassland
ASSOCIATION	With grass and scrub
GROWTH FORM	On ground, singly or in troops
ABUNDANCE	Locally common
SPORE COLOR	White
EDIBILITY	Edible (when cooked)

HEIGHT
Up to 28 in
(700 mm)

CAP DIAMETER
Up to 40 in
(1000 mm)

220

MACROCYBE TITANS
AMERICAN TITAN
(H. E. BIGELOW & KIMBROUGH) PEGLER ET AL

This is a big fungus. The American Titan routinely produces fruitbodies that are 20 in (500 mm) across and occasionally gives rise to extraordinary specimens that are double the size. It is certainly the largest agaric in the Americas and is only rivaled elsewhere by the African *Termitomyces titanicus*. The species appears in both woodland and grasslands, sometimes in lawns or roadsides, and in Central America has been recorded arising from a nest of wood-cutting ants. It may just like disturbed ground. It is said to be edible, at least when cooked, but can develop an unpleasant smell.

The American Titan forms caps that are convex, becoming flat to weakly depressed. The cap surface is smooth, yellowish buff, becoming whiter. The gills are white to pale buff. The thick stem is smooth at first and cap-colored, breaking up into small, sometimes darker scales.

SIMILAR SPECIES
The American Titan was originally described in the genus *Tricholoma* and smaller specimens could be mistaken for a large, pale *Tricholoma* species. In South America, the related *Macrocybe praegrandis* has similar fruitbodies up to 20 in (500 mm) across, but with smooth and distinctly bulbous stems.

¼ actual size

FAMILY	Marasmiaceae
DISTRIBUTION	North America, Europe, northern Asia
HABITAT	In woodland, also in woodchip mulch
ASSOCIATION	With broadleaf trees and conifers
GROWTH FORM	On ground, singly or in scattered troops
ABUNDANCE	Locally common
SPORE COLOR	Whitish to pinkish brown
EDIBILITY	Not edible

HEIGHT	Up to 3 in (75 mm)
CAP DIAMETER	Up to 2 in (50 mm)

MACROCYSTIDIA CUCUMIS

CUCUMBER CAP

(PERSOON) JOSSERAND

221

This is a dapper-looking species when fresh, easy to recognize by its rather smart, almost black cap edged with cream. Unfortunately it smells—supposedly of cucumbers, but actually of old herrings. It is common in Europe, less so in North America, but is spreading rapidly thanks to the increased use of woodchip mulch, which the Cucumber Cap relishes. Although it belongs in the mainly white-spored Marasmiaceae, its spores are often pinkish or even deep pinkish brown. A novel compound called cucumin has been isolated from the Cucumber Cap and it has potential antibacterial properties.

SIMILAR SPECIES

The dark, cream-edged caps and strong smell should be distinctive. *Marasmius alliaceus* has a reddish brown cap, blackish stem, and smells of garlic. Similar larger *Marasmius* species having dark reddish to purplish brown stems, lack any notable smell, and often have paler caps.

Actual size

The Cucumber Cap forms caps that are conical, becoming flatter. The cap surface is smooth, dark purplish or blackish brown when damp, drying paler, with a contrasting cream margin. The gills are cream to yellowish, becoming pink. The stem is finely velvety; it is cream at the top, becoming yellowish to reddish brown below and black-brown at the base.

FAMILY	Agaricaceae
DISTRIBUTION	Europe
HABITAT	In grassy woodlands, parkland, pastures, and dune grassland
ASSOCIATION	With broadleaf trees and grass
GROWTH FORM	On ground, singly or in small troops
ABUNDANCE	Locally common
SPORE COLOR	White
EDIBILITY	Edible

HEIGHT
Up to 8 in
(200 mm)

CAP DIAMETER
Up to 5 in
(125 mm)

222

MACROLEPIOTA MASTOIDEA

SLENDER PARASOL

(FRIES) SINGER

This is a slimmer species than the Parasol (*Macrolepiota procera*) and usually has a prominent, nipplelike umbo at the center (*mastoidea* means "breastlike"). It seems to tolerate less rich soil than other *Macrolepiota* and *Chlorophyllum* species and has a preference for pastures and coastal grassland, where it can be found in company with waxcaps (*Hygrocybe* species) and may be locally common. Until recently it was split into several species, including *M. gracilenta*, *M. rickenii*, and *M. konradii*, but molecular research has shown that these are just variants of the same fungus.

SIMILAR SPECIES

The Slender Parasol is rather variable in color, but the comparatively slender shape and strongly umbonate cap are distinctive. *Macrolepiota clelandii* is a similar Australian species, whilst *M. neomastoidea* is a similar (but poisonous) species of eastern Asia. The Parasol (*M. procera*) is larger and has stem scales that form zigzag markings.

Actual size

The Slender Parasol forms caps that are hemispherical, becoming strongly umbonate when expanded. The cap surface is pale pinkish to grayish brown at the center, breaking up toward the margin into small scales on a cream background. The gills are white to cream. The stem is similarly colored and sprinkled with small, pale scales, with a conspicuous ring, and a swollen to bulbous base.

FAMILY	Agaricaceae
DISTRIBUTION	North America, Europe, Africa, Central and South America, western and northern Asia, New Zealand
HABITAT	In rich soil in grassy woodlands, parkland, roadsides, and dunes
ASSOCIATION	With broadleaf trees and grass
GROWTH FORM	On ground, singly or in troops and rings
ABUNDANCE	Common
SPORE COLOR	White
EDIBILITY	Best avoided

HEIGHT
Up to 16 in
(400 mm)

CAP DIAMETER
Up to 12 in
(300 mm)

MACROLEPIOTA PROCERA

PARASOL

(SCOPOLI) SINGER

223

The Latin *procera* means "tall," and the Parasol is certainly a large and impressive agaric, capable of producing caps the size of dinner-plates. The Parasol was originally described from Italy by the naturalist Giovanni Scopoli and appears to be widespread, though recent molecular research suggests that some "Parasols" (particularly in the Americas) may be separate species. All are edible, but care needs to be taken to distinguish them from the poisonous False Parasol (*Chlorophyllum molybdites*) and especially from lethally toxic *Lepiota* species which may be similarly patterned, though much smaller.

SIMILAR SPECIES

The zigzag pattern of stem scales is a distinctive character of the Parasol and its close relatives (such as the Australian *Macrolepiota clelandii*), differentiating it from the poisonous False Parasol (*Chlorophyllum molybdites*), which additionally has green spores, and the Shaggy Parasol (*C. rhacodes*), which has reddening flesh.

Actual size

The Parasol forms drumstick-like fruitbodies when young (see photo left). The expanded caps are flat but umbonate, dark brown at the center, breaking up toward the margin into paler scales on a cream background. The gills are white to cream. The stem is white to cream, with bands of brownish scales in zigzag patterns, with a conspicuous, movable ring, and a swollen to bulbous base.

FAMILY	Marasmiaceae
DISTRIBUTION	Europe
HABITAT	In woodland
ASSOCIATION	With beech
GROWTH FORM	On fallen wood and leaf litter
ABUNDANCE	Locally common
SPORE COLOR	White
EDIBILITY	Edible

HEIGHT
Up to 8 in
(200 mm)

CAP DIAMETER
Up to 2½ in
(60 mm)

224

MARASMIUS ALLIACEUS

GARLIC PARACHUTE

(JACQUIN) FRIES

As both its English and Latin names indicate, this species smells strongly of garlic or onions and has some of their distinctive taste. It is considered edible and is one of the many agaric species collected for food in eastern Europe, but is very thin-fleshed. The aroma comes from the decomposition of a novel compound called γ-Glutamyl-marasmin. The same compound has also been found in *Marasmius scorodonius* and *M. querceus*, two related species with the same smell. Fruitbodies have also produced antibiotics called alliacols, which have now been synthesized and may have some potential medical applications.

SIMILAR SPECIES

The related North American *Marasmius copelandii* has a similar smell. The American and European *M. scorodonius* also has a garlic smell, but can be distinguished by its polished, orange-yellow stem that becomes dark red-brown toward the base. The uncommon European *M. querceus* (also called *M. prasiosmus*) has a velvety, reddish stem and grows in oak litter.

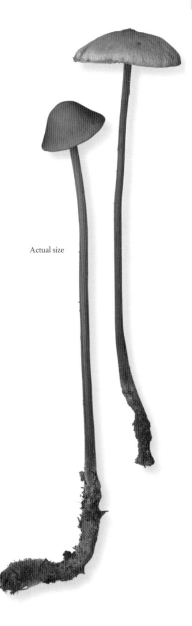

Actual size

The Garlic Parachute forms convex caps, flattening when expanded. The cap surface is smooth, yellow-brown to dark red-brown, slightly striate at the margin when damp. The gills are whitish with pinkish to grayish tints. The long stem is finely velvety, often flattened, dark gray-brown to black.

FAMILY	Marasmiaceae
DISTRIBUTION	North America, Europe, northern Asia
HABITAT	In woodland
ASSOCIATION	With conifers, also with broadleaf trees and heather
GROWTH FORM	In leaf litter and on heather stems, in swarms
ABUNDANCE	Common
SPORE COLOR	White
EDIBILITY	Not edible

HEIGHT
Up to 2 in
(50 mm)

CAP DIAMETER
Up to ½ in
(15 mm)

MARASMIUS ANDROSACEUS

HORSEHAIR PARACHUTE

(LINNAEUS) FRIES

225

Many small *Marasmius* species produce fine, hairlike rhizomorphs—root-like bundles of hyphae protected by a polished coating—that help the fungus spread rapidly through leaf litter or over living stems and branches, without drying out. Most of these little agarics are tropical, but the Horsehair Parachute is a common, north-temperate species. The wiry stems are similar to the rhizomorphs and sometimes have hairs branching off them, especially at the base. Curiously, a survey in eastern North America found that 85 percent of bird's nests in upland spruce forest were lined with Horsehair Parachute rhizomorphs.

SIMILAR SPECIES

The similar Horsehair Fungus (*Marasmius crinisequi*) is a common tropical species that produces abundant, aerial rhizomorphs. In North America and northern Asia, *M. pallidocephalus* is a similar conifer species, but it has yellow-brown caps with dark brown stems and rhizomorphs. The widespread *M. quercophilus* is a brown-stemmed species on broadleaf litter, especially oak.

Actual size

The Horsehair Parachute forms convex caps, flattening but often centrally depressed when expanded. The cap surface is smooth but corrugated, buff to pinkish brown, paler or cream toward the margin. The gills are distant, colored as the cap margin. The long, thin, wiry stem is shiny and dark red-brown to black.

FAMILY	Marasmiaceae
DISTRIBUTION	Sub-Saharan Africa, Central and South America, southern and Eastern Asia, Australia
HABITAT	In woodland
ASSOCIATION	With broadleaf trees
GROWTH FORM	On dead and living branches and leaves
ABUNDANCE	Common
SPORE COLOR	White
EDIBILITY	Not edible

HEIGHT
Up to ¼ in
(5 mm)

CAP DIAMETER
Up to ¼ in
(5 mm)

226

MARASMIUS CRINISEQUI

HORSEHAIR FUNGUS

F. MUELLER EX KALCHBRENNER

The Horsehair Fungus has tiny fruitbodies, but produces abundant, hairlike rhizomorphs—black strands of hyphae—that grow over living stems and branches, like a half-unraveled net. In tropical rainforests, these rhizomorphs allow the fungus to spread through the canopy, attaching itself to new food resources and even trapping and securing dead leaves before they fall to the forest floor. The fruitbodies typically arise from the rhizomorphs on side-strands (which form their stems), so can sometimes be found hanging in mid-air between two rhizomorph-festooned trees. The Latin epithet *crinis-equi* means "horsehair."

SIMILAR SPECIES

Several similar, rhizomorph-producing species occur in the tropics, some in the genus *Marasmius*, others in the genus *Crinipellis*. The Horsehair Parachute (*M. androsaceus*) is a north-temperate species that also has horsehairlike stems and rhizomorphs, but more typically grows on the ground through fallen leaf and needle litter.

 Actual size

The Horsehair Fungus forms convex caps with a central depression, often with a small umbo. The cap surface is smooth but corrugated, cream to pale orange-buff, often browner at the center. The gills are distant, white to buff. The long, thin, wiry stem is white at the top, black below, arising from similar black rhizomorphs.

FAMILY	Marasmiaceae
DISTRIBUTION	Southern North America, Africa, Central and South America, southern Asia, Australia
HABITAT	In woodland
ASSOCIATION	With broadleaf trees
GROWTH FORM	In leaf litter, on fallen leaves
ABUNDANCE	Common
SPORE COLOR	White
EDIBILITY	Not edible

HEIGHT
Up to 2 in
(50 mm)

CAP DIAMETER
Up to ½ in
(15 mm)

MARASMIUS HAEMATOCEPHALUS

MAUVE PARACHUTE

(MONTAGNE) FRIES

227

First described from Brazil, the Mauve Parachute is a widely distributed tropical and subtropical species, frequently appearing in swarms on fallen leaf litter. The epithet *haematocephalus* means "blood-red cap," but the Mauve Parachute is more typically pinkish red to purple, and has an alternative English name of the Pink Bonnet. Brightly colored *Marasmius* species such as this are among the commonest agarics in rainforests, with scores of different species—yellow, orange, red, and purple—often growing together on dead leaves and fallen twigs. The tropics are so rich in these fungi that many new species undoubtedly remain to be discovered and described.

SIMILAR SPECIES

Marasmius haematocephalus may be a complex of closely related species worldwide. Two very similar species, *M. aratus* and *Marasmius distantifolius*, have been described from southeastern Asia (Malaysia and Singapore) and are best distinguished microscopically. *M. pulcherripes* is a pinkish species found in north-temperate woodland, often with conifers.

Actual size

The Mauve Parachute forms small, thin caps that remain convex. The cap surface is smooth but ridged or fluted, pinkish red, mauve, or reddish purple. The gills are distant and white to pinkish, or pale cap-colored. The long, thin stem is smooth, dark red-brown to brown.

FAMILY	Marasmiaceae
DISTRIBUTION	Europe
HABITAT	In woodland
ASSOCIATION	With holly
GROWTH FORM	In leaf litter, on fallen leaves
ABUNDANCE	Locally common
SPORE COLOR	White
EDIBILITY	Not edible

HEIGHT
Up to 2 in
(50 mm)

CAP DIAMETER
Less than ¼ in
(5 mm)

228

MARASMIUS HUDSONII
HOLLY PARACHUTE
(PERSOON) FRIES

Several small *Marasmius* species have evolved specialist niches, only growing on their specific host plants. *Marasmius buxi*, for example, grows only on fallen leaves of box, while the commoner *M. epiphylloides* grows on ivy leaves. The Holly Parachute is similarly specialized and is only found on fallen leaves of holly. It also has an additional preference for mild, damp climates and is consequently rarer eastward in Europe. The extraordinarily long cap hairs are a unique feature of this diminutive species, making it easy to recognize with a hand lens or a keen pair of eyes.

SIMILAR SPECIES

The occurrence on old fallen holly leaves and the long hairs on the cap make the Holly Parachute unique and unmistakable. Other small *Marasmius* species may be similarly colored, but grow on sticks, stems, or leaves of other plants and have smooth or pleated caps.

Actual size

The Holly Parachute forms small caps that remain convex. The cap surface is smooth, white becoming cream to pale reddish brown, sparsely covered with fine, erect, red-brown hairs or bristles less than ⅛ in (1 mm) long. The gills are distant and cap-colored. The long, thin stem is smooth and white at the top, becoming bristly and dark red-brown toward the base.

FAMILY	Marasmiaceae
DISTRIBUTION	North America, Europe, North Africa, Central and South America, northern Asia, Australia, New Zealand
HABITAT	In pastures, lawns, and grassland
ASSOCIATION	With grass
GROWTH FORM	In grass, in rings
ABUNDANCE	Common
SPORE COLOR	White
EDIBILITY	Edible

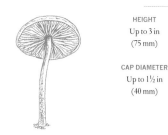

HEIGHT	Up to 3 in (75 mm)
CAP DIAMETER	Up to 1½ in (40 mm)

MARASMIUS OREADES

FAIRY RING CHAMPIGNON

(BOLTON) FRIES

229

The Fairy Ring Champignon is a common species in grassland, producing rather rubbery fruitbodies with the unusual ability to shrivel up in dry weather and then revive to produce more spores after rainfall. Most other agaric fruitbodies simply decay if dried and remoistened. This is perhaps one reason why the Fairy Ring Champignon seems so common, since its long-lasting fruitbodies keep springing back to life from early summer onward. Despite its small size, it is a good edible species and is even commercially collected and exported from countries as various as France, Bulgaria, and China.

SIMILAR SPECIES

Marasmius oreades is not the only agaric to form rings in grassland. Poisonous species also produce them, such as the Fool's Funnel (*Clitocybe rivulosa*), which can be distinguished by its whitish to pinkish buff cap and less distant gills, and *Lepiota oreadiformis*, which looks very similar from above, but has a ring or veil remnants on the stem.

Actual size

The Fairy Ring Champignon forms convex caps that become flat and often weakly umbonate. The cap surface is smooth, cream to pale yellow-brown or pinkish brown, darker at the center, pale when dry. The gills are distant and pale cap-colored (see photo right). The tough stem is smooth and cap-colored.

FAMILY	Marasmiaceae
DISTRIBUTION	Eastern North America, Central America, eastern Asia
HABITAT	In woodland
ASSOCIATION	With conifers and broadleaf trees
GROWTH FORM	In leaf litter, often in troops
ABUNDANCE	Occasional
SPORE COLOR	White
EDIBILITY	Not edible

HEIGHT
Up to 2 in
(50 mm)

CAP DIAMETER
Up to ½ in
(15 mm)

230

MARASMIUS PULCHERRIPES
ROSY PARACHUTE
PECK

Actual size

The Rosy Parachute forms small, thin, convex caps, often with a central pimple. The cap surface is smooth but ridged or fluted, pinkish red to wine-red, yellowish pink, or grayish pink. The gills are distant and whitish. The long, thin stem is smooth, polished, reddish pink at first, becoming dark brown from the base upward.

The Rosy Parachute is an attractive little agaric first described from the northeastern United States, but subsequently recorded southward into Mexico. It is also known from Japan and eastern Asia, though it is possible that these rather separate Asian collections represent an unnamed, look-alike species. The Rosy Parachute is a litter-rotter, growing in fallen leaves or conifer needles. As in many *Marasmius* species, the fruitbodies can persist during periods of dry weather and then revive, unharmed, when the rains return. This enables the fungus to release its spores rapidly whenever conditions are damp and ideal for germination.

SIMILAR SPECIES

The Mauve Parachute (*Marasmius haematocephalus*) is a similar, reddish purple species with a tropical and subtropical distribution. In North America and Asia, the Orange Pinwheel (*M. siccus*) and *M. fulvoferrugineus* are both similarly shaped, but when fresh have pale and deep orange caps respectively.

FAMILY	Marasmiaceae
DISTRIBUTION	North America, Europe, northern Asia
HABITAT	In woodland, hedgerows, and scrub
ASSOCIATION	With broadleaf trees
GROWTH FORM	On sticks, dead twigs, and woody detritus, in small clusters or troops
ABUNDANCE	Very common
SPORE COLOR	White
EDIBILITY	Not edible

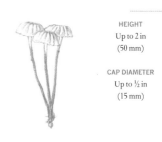

HEIGHT	Up to 2 in (50 mm)
CAP DIAMETER	Up to ½ in (15 mm)

MARASMIUS ROTULA

COLLARED PARACHUTE

(SCOPOLI) FRIES

231

This little agaric has caps that look like tiny, pleated parachutes, typical of many of these small *Marasmius* species. It is exceptionally common, often covering twigs, sticks, and small bits of wood with dense clusters of fruitbodies. These are often the first agarics to be seen after rainfall, since the fruitbodies revive quickly after drying out. The gills are not directly attached to the top of the stem, but to a small, whitish collar around it—hence the common name Collared Parachute. Its alternative name of the Pinwheel comes from its resemblance to the pleated paper toy.

SIMILAR SPECIES

Several other small *Marasmius* species have gills attached to a collar. In eastern North America, *M.capillaris* is similar but grows on fallen leaves. Also growing on leaves but more widespread, *M. bulliardii* has cream to pale brown caps. *Marasmius limosus* grows in marshes on the dead stems of reeds and rushes.

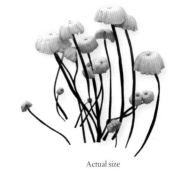

Actual size

The Collared Parachute forms hemispherical caps, flattened or depressed at the center, often with a central pimple. The cap surface is ridged or fluted, white to cream, developing gray to brownish tints. The gills are distant, whitish, and attached to a collar around the top of the stem. The thin, wiry stem is smooth, polished, dark purplish to brownish black.

FAMILY	Marasmiaceae
DISTRIBUTION	West Africa
HABITAT	In woodland
ASSOCIATION	With broadleaf trees
GROWTH FORM	In leaf litter, often in troops
ABUNDANCE	Occasional
SPORE COLOR	White
EDIBILITY	Not edible

HEIGHT
Up to 7 in
(175 mm)

CAP DIAMETER
Up to 4 in
(100 mm)

232

MARASMIUS ZENKERI
ZENKER'S STRIPED PARACHUTE
HENNINGS

Zenker's Striped Parachute is one of the larger *Marasmius* species and its umbrella-like caps make a splendid sight trooping through the leaf litter in tropical African rainforests. Constant rain sometimes allows the cobwebby, whitish mycelium (from which the fruitbodies arise) to cover and bind the surface of the leaf litter, instead of hiding underneath—as is typical of leaf-rotting fungi in temperate forests. The species was originally discovered by botanist Georg August Zenker in the former German colony of Cameroon, but has since been found in forests throughout western Africa.

SIMILAR SPECIES

Though the banded cap of Zenker's Striped Parachute may appear distinctive, there are several other tropical species with similar caps. *Marasmius bekolacongoli*, also from West Africa, has a purplish and pale green-yellow striped cap, with pale green-yellow gills. The tropical Asian *M. purpureostriatus* is purple-striped, but is much smaller than *M. zenkeri*.

Actual size

Zenker's Striped Parachute forms convex caps, becoming flat to umbonate. The cap surface is smooth but ridged or fluted; the ridges are dull purple to purple-gray, with paler furrows in between. The gills are distant and pale violet. The long stem is smooth, polished, and yellowish brown to dark reddish brown in color.

FAMILY	Tricholomataceae
DISTRIBUTION	North America, Europe, North Africa, Central America
HABITAT	In woodland, scrub, and grassland
ASSOCIATION	With broadleaf trees and conifers
GROWTH FORM	On ground, singly or in troops
ABUNDANCE	Common
SPORE COLOR	Cream
EDIBILITY	Edible

HEIGHT
Up to 5 in
(125 mm)

CAP DIAMETER
Up to 5 in
(125 mm)

MELANOLEUCA COGNATA

SPRING CAVALIER

(FRIES) KONRAD & MAUBLANC

233

Agarics in the genus *Melanoleuca* superficially resemble *Tricholoma* species, but are typically gray-brown with whitish gills and often occur in grassland as well as woods. They are difficult to identify to species, but *Melanoleuca cognata* is an exception, thanks to its ocher to orange tints (especially noticeable in the gills), its comparatively large size, and its sweetish, sometimes unpleasant smell. It also frequently produces fruitbodies in the spring, as well as later in the year. It is said to be edible, but no one seems to recommend it.

SIMILAR SPECIES

Most other *Melanoleuca* species have whitish or dull gray-brown caps and whitish gills. The salmon-buff gills of the Spring Cavalier may suggest an *Entoloma* species, such as the equally sweet-smelling, but poisonous, Livid Pinkgill (*E. sinuatum*). *Entoloma* species, however, have salmon-pink (not white or cream) spores.

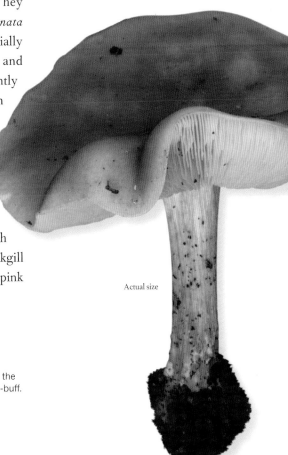

Actual size

The Spring Cavalier forms convex caps, becoming flat or depressed at the center and umbonate. The cap surface is smooth, ocher-buff to orange-buff. The gills are salmon-buff to pale yellow-orange. The stem is similarly colored, finely fibrous, typically with a somewhat bulbous base.

FAMILY	Agaricaceae
DISTRIBUTION	Europe, northern Asia
HABITAT	In calcareous woodland and scrub
ASSOCIATION	With broadleaf trees
GROWTH FORM	On ground, singly or in small groups
ABUNDANCE	Occasional
SPORE COLOR	Bluish green
EDIBILITY	Not edible

HEIGHT
Up to 2 in
(50 mm)

CAP DIAMETER
Up to 1 in
(25 mm)

234

MELANOPHYLLUM EYREI
GREENSPORED DAPPERLING
(MASSEE) SINGER

When first seen, *Melanophyllum eyrei* looks like any other little, dull brown agaric and is easily passed by in the search for something more interesting. If collected, however, the extraordinary, dark green gills are revealed—a unique feature of species in this genus. *Melanophyllum*, meaning "dark-gilled," is closely related to the white-spored genus *Lepiota* and species of both have been given the English name "dapperlings." All of them typically prefer rich, calcareous soils in mild climates. The Greenspored Dapperling was named after the Rev. William Eyre, who first found it in Hampshire, England.

SIMILAR SPECIES

Similar green-spored *Melanophyllum* species have been found in West Africa (Burkina Faso) and Central America (Belize), but have not yet been described. The related False Parasol (*Chlorophyllum molybdites*) has green to green-gray spores which eventually color the gills, but is a much larger fungus with a scaly cap and prominent ring.

Actual size

The Greenspored Dapperling forms convex caps, becoming flat or shallowly umbonate. The cap surface is finely granular when young, becoming smooth, cream to buff or yellow-brown, darker at the center, with veil remains at the margin. The gills are gray-green to blue-green. The stem is finely granular to smooth, cap-colored to pale pinkish brown at the base.

FAMILY	Agaricaceae
DISTRIBUTION	North America, Europe, northern Asia, Australia, New Zealand
HABITAT	In calcareous woodland, parkland, and gardens
ASSOCIATION	With broadleaf trees
GROWTH FORM	On ground, clustered or in small groups
ABUNDANCE	Occasional
SPORE COLOR	Green (becoming dark red)
EDIBILITY	Not edible

HEIGHT
Up to 2 in
(50 mm)

CAP DIAMETER
Up to 1½ in
(35 mm)

MELANOPHYLLUM HAEMATOSPERMUM

REDSPORED DAPPERLING

(BULLIARD) KREISEL

235

This little agaric has been given rather misleading English and Latin names, since its spores are actually green when fresh, though they turn dark red and eventually black as they dry. Its gills, however, are red from the start and are a unique feature of the species. The powdery scales on the cap and stem are loose and easily washed off by rain. A former name, *Melanophyllum echinatum*, refers to their granular appearance (*echinatum* meaning "spiny"). The Redspored Dapperling has a liking for rich soil and is frequently found in gardens and even old compost heaps. It is a widespread species, though nowhere very common.

SIMILAR SPECIES

The Redspored Dapperling belongs in the same family as ordinary mushrooms (*Agaricus* species) and related, but smaller, *Micropsalliota* species. Some tropical species have caps and stems covered with powdery granules, and a few may have reddish gills when partly mature, but all have spores that are chocolate-brown, never green to red.

Actual size

The Redspored Dapperling forms convex caps, becoming flat or shallowly umbonate. The cap surface is covered in powdery, loose granules when young, dark gray-brown to brown, paler toward the margin, which has whitish veil remains. The gills are pinkish red, becoming darker red. The stem is reddish or purplish brown, and is initially covered in powdery brown granules.

FAMILY	Niaceae
DISTRIBUTION	North America, Europe, northern Asia
HABITAT	In woodland
ASSOCIATION	With broadleaf trees, especially alder
GROWTH FORM	On dead branches and twigs
ABUNDANCE	Common
SPORE COLOR	Brown
EDIBILITY	Not edible

HEIGHT
Less than ⅛ in
(1 mm)

CAP DIAMETER
Less than ⅛ in
(1 mm)

236

MERISMODES FASCICULATA
CROWDED CUPLET
(SCHWEINITZ) EARLE

Although its fruitbodies look just like small cup fungi, such as the Snowy Disco (*Lachnum virgineum*), the Crowded Cuplet is actually related to the agarics. It belongs to a group of species called "cyphelloid fungi" (*cyphella* meaning "ear-cup"), most of which are inconspicuous and not easy to recognize without a microscope. The Crowded Cuplet, however, is one that can be identified in the field, thanks to its habit of growing in dense clusters, usually on dead, but still attached, branches and twigs.

SIMILAR SPECIES
Merismodes anomala is a closely related species with similar but more saucer-shaped fruitbodies that grow in dense swarms rather than in clusters. Many of the true cup fungi, such as the Snowy Disco (*Lachnum virgineum*), also have fruitbodies of similar shape and color, but they are rarely if ever so densely clustered as the Crowded Cuplet.

Actual size

The Crowded Cuplet forms fruitbodies in dense, crowded clusters. Each fruitbody is deeply cup-shaped to goblet-shaped, sometimes with a short stalk; the outer surface and margin are covered in brown hairs, the inner surface is smooth, and cream to buff or pale brown.

FAMILY	Marasmiaceae
DISTRIBUTION	North America, Europe, northern Asia
HABITAT	In woodland
ASSOCIATION	With broadleaf trees
GROWTH FORM	On dead branches and sticks, in small troops
ABUNDANCE	Common
SPORE COLOR	White
EDIBILITY	Not edible

HEIGHT
Up to 1 in
(25 mm)

CAP DIAMETER
Up to 1 in
(25 mm)

MICROMPHALE FOETIDUM
FETID PARACHUTE
(SOWERBY) SINGER

237

Species of *Micromphale* have an unfortunate, but well-earned reputation for smelling bad, the fruitbodies giving off a fetid stench of rotting cabbages. They are quite closely related to the Garlic Parachute (*Marasmius alliaceus*) and its allies, most of which are similarly strong-smelling but with garlicky or oniony odors. Their closest relatives, however, belong in *Gymnopus* and the Fetid Parachute—also known as the Stinking Pinwheel— is sometimes placed in this genus. It is a fairly common species, typically growing on sticks or small branches in leaf litter.

SIMILAR SPECIES
The Cabbage Parachute (*Micromphale brassicolens*) is a similar species with a similar smell. It tends to grow on leaves in litter, but is best distinguished microscopically by its smaller spores. A species with much smaller fruitbodies, *M. perforans*, grows on fallen conifer needles. It too smells bad.

Actual size

The Fetid Parachute forms convex caps, becoming depressed at the center. The surface of the cap is smooth, yellow-brown to reddish brown, striate, darker in the stripes and at the center. The gills are often slightly decurrent, pale pinkish brown. The tough stem is cap-colored when young, rapidly becoming dark purplish brown from the tapered base upward.

FAMILY	Mycenaceae
DISTRIBUTION	North America, Europe, Central America, northern Asia
HABITAT	In woodland
ASSOCIATION	With broadleaf trees and conifers
GROWTH FORM	On fallen twigs and wood , singly or in small groups
ABUNDANCE	Occasional
SPORE COLOR	White
EDIBILITY	Not edible

HEIGHT
Up to 2 in
(50 mm)

CAP DIAMETER
Up to 1 in
(25 mm)

238

MYCENA ADONIS
SCARLET BONNET
(BULLIARD) GRAY

This is an attractive little species, but one that is easily overlooked since it frequently grows in small numbers, half-hidden in litter or undergrowth. The English name Scarlet Bonnet is a little misleading, since fruitbodies are typically bright coral or deep pink, and it has an alternative English name of Coral-pink Bonnet. Color forms that are particularly red have sometimes been placed in a separate variety (*Mycena adonis* var. *coccinea*). The epithet *adonis* presumably refers to the blood shed by the mythical youth Adonis when he was killed by a boar while hunting, drops of which turned into red flowers—or, in this version of the myth, into small, pink fungi.

SIMILAR SPECIES
The Pink Bonnet (*Mycena rosella*) has a deeper pink edge to its gills and grows in troops in conifer-needle litter. *Mycena pterigena* is also pink with a deeper pink gill edge, but grows on fern debris. The Flame Bonnet (*M. strobilinoides*) can be scarlet when young, but has deeper orange-scarlet gill edges.

The Scarlet Bonnet forms conical caps at first, becoming convex to flat and sometimes umbonate. The cap surface is smooth, striate at the margin, scarlet to coral when young, becoming salmon to pale pink with age. The gills are whitish to pale pink. The fragile stem is smooth and white to pale cap-colored.

Actual size

FAMILY	Mycenaceae
DISTRIBUTION	Western North America, northern Asia
HABITAT	In woodland
ASSOCIATION	With conifers
GROWTH FORM	On fallen needles, in troops
ABUNDANCE	Common
SPORE COLOR	White
EDIBILITY	Not edible

HEIGHT
Up to 2 in
(50 mm)
CAP DIAMETER
Up to 1 in
(25 mm)

MYCENA AURANTIIDISCA

TANGERINE BONNET

MURRILL

239

The bright orange colors make this little *Mycena* a distinctive species—at least when found in its typical habitat, growing in troops under conifers. It appears to be commonest in the forests of northwestern America, but is known further south to California and has also been recorded from Japan. It is one of many *Mycena* species that specialize in decomposing fallen needles, turning them into humus. The fungal mycelium spreads under the surface and can sometimes be seen as a white, cobwebby mass if the litter layer is lifted up or disturbed.

SIMILAR SPECIES

The widespread Orange Bonnet (*Mycena acicula*) is similar, but typically smaller and is usually found growing in ones and twos on tiny fragments of litter in broadleaf woodland. The Flame Bonnet (*M. strobilinoides*) is found in conifer litter, but is orange throughout—including the stem and gills.

Actual size

The Tangerine Bonnet forms conical caps, becoming convex to umbonate. The cap surface is smooth, striate at the margin, bright orange at the center, but fading to yellow or whitish toward the margin. The gills are white to slightly yellowish. The slender stem is smooth and white, yellowish toward the base.

FAMILY	Mycenaceae
DISTRIBUTION	Europe, northern Asia
HABITAT	In woodland
ASSOCIATION	With beech trees
GROWTH FORM	In leaf litter, usually in small troops
ABUNDANCE	Locally common
SPORE COLOR	White
EDIBILITY	Not edible

HEIGHT
Up to 5 in
(125 mm)

CAP DIAMETER
Up to 1 in
(25 mm)

240

MYCENA CROCATA
SAFFRONDROP BONNET
(SCHRADER) P. KUMMER

Actual size

Mycena crocata specializes in rotting down fallen beech leaves and seems to be restricted to beech woods, particularly in calcareous woodlands where the trees are native, rather than planted. It often grows in company with the Garlic Parachute (*Marasmius alliaceus*), which is another beech specialist with similar requirements. The epithet *crocata* means "saffron-colored;" if cut or bruised, the fruitbodies of the Saffrondrop Bonnet release an orange-red or deep saffron latex, which is a distinctive feature of the species. This latex sometimes stains the cap and gills with orange streaks.

SIMILAR SPECIES

The Burgundydrop Bonnet (*Mycena haematopus*) grows clustered on wood and exudes a dark red latex. *Mycena sanguinolenta* also bleeds red, but grows in troops on conifer needles and leaf litter. Other orange-stemmed species, such as *M. strobilinoides*, have orange gills or do not exude a latex.

The Saffrondrop Bonnet forms conical caps, becoming convex to umbonate. The cap surface is smooth, pale orange-brown at the center, becoming gray to whitish toward the margin (see photo right). The gills are white. The stem is smooth, pale yellow at the top, becoming orange to orange-red toward the base. All parts exude an orange-red latex when cut.

FAMILY	Mycenaceae
DISTRIBUTION	North America, Europe, northern Asia, New Zealand
HABITAT	In woodland
ASSOCIATION	With broadleaf trees and conifers
GROWTH FORM	On dead wood, leaf litter, usually in small groups
ABUNDANCE	Common
SPORE COLOR	White
EDIBILITY	Not edible

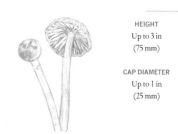

HEIGHT
Up to 3 in
(75 mm)

CAP DIAMETER
Up to 1 in
(25 mm)

MYCENA EPIPTERYGIA

YELLOWLEG BONNET

(SCOPOLI) GRAY

241

Mycena epipterygia can usually be recognized by its sliminess in damp weather—the cap, the gill edges, and the stem all being covered in a sticky, translucent layer that can often be peeled off like a gelatinous skin. The stem is always pale yellow (hence the English name) but the cap color is very variable. Several different forms and varieties have been described, but further molecular research is needed to sort them out. The off-putting epithet *epi-pterygia* means "upon a small wing," though it is less than clear to what this might refer.

SIMILAR SPECIES

Mycena vulgaris is a similarly slimy species growing in conifer litter, but its fruitbodies are gray-brown without any yellow tints. *Mycena renati*, though not slimy, has pinkish to reddish brown caps and yellow stems. It typically grows in clusters on broadleaf wood.

Actual size

The Yellowleg Bonnet forms conical caps, becoming convex to flat. The cap surface is smooth, slimy when damp, striate at the margin, pale pinkish gray to pale brown or pale olive-brown. The gills are whitish to pale pinkish with a slimy, gelatinous edge. The fragile stem is smooth, slimy when damp, and pale yellow.

FAMILY	Mycenaceae
DISTRIBUTION	North America, Europe, northern Asia
HABITAT	In woodland
ASSOCIATION	With broadleaf trees, especially beech
GROWTH FORM	On trunks, stumps, and logs, in clusters
ABUNDANCE	Common
SPORE COLOR	White
EDIBILITY	Not edible

HEIGHT
Up to 3 in
(75 mm)

CAP DIAMETER
Up to 1½ in
(40 mm)

242

MYCENA HAEMATOPUS
BURGUNDYDROP BONNET
(PERSOON) P. KUMMER

Many rather similar-looking *Mycena* species grow in clusters on wood, but *Mycena haematopus* is one of the easiest ones to identify, since its fruitbodies ooze a blood-red latex when cut. The epithet *haematopus* means "bloody foot," the reaction being most evident when the stem is damaged. This copious flow of liquid may help deter slugs and other invertebrates from grazing on the fruitbodies. The Burgundydrop Bonnet, also known as The Bleeder, is best treated as inedible, although a few texts cite it as edible. The startling, blood-red color of the latex has been investigated and comes from novel alkaloid pigments called haematopodins, isolated from the fungus.

SIMILAR SPECIES
An equally common bleeding species, *Mycena sanguinolenta*, produces smaller, non-clustered fruitbodies that appear in troops and swarms on needle and leaf litter. The less widespread Saffrondrop Bonnet (*M. crocata*) grows in beech litter and exudes a deep orange latex when cut.

The Burgundydrop Bonnet forms hemispherical caps, with a surface that is smooth, half-striate, flesh-pink to reddish brown, darker in the center, and often cream at the margin. The gills are cream to pinkish, often with a dark edge. The fragile stem is slightly powdery when young, becoming smooth and cap-colored. All parts exude a dark red latex when cut.

Actual size

FAMILY	Mycenaceae
DISTRIBUTION	Southern South America, Australia, New Zealand
HABITAT	In woodland
ASSOCIATION	With broadleaf trees
GROWTH FORM	On trunks, stumps, and logs, in troops or clusters
ABUNDANCE	Common
SPORE COLOR	White
EDIBILITY	Not edible

HEIGHT
Up to 1 in
(25 mm)

CAP DIAMETER
Up to 1 in
(25 mm)

MYCENA INTERRUPTA
PIXIE'S PARASOL
(BERKELEY) SACCARDO

243

The Pixie's Parasol is the Australian name for this attractive and unusual blue species, often found in troops or clusters on the sides of rotten logs and fallen trunks. Like many smaller *Mycena* species, the fruitbodies arise from a pad of fungal mycelium, which remains as a disc or ring at the base of the stem. *Mycena interrupta* typically grows in southern beech forests and occurs in Chile as well as Australia, New Zealand, and New Caledonia. This reflects a Gondwanan distribution pattern, a relic of the time when South America, Antarctica, and Australasia were joined together in the supercontinent of Gondwana.

SIMILAR SPECIES
The bright blue colors and clustered growth on wood should be distinctive, most other *Mycena* species being at most bluish gray or (in the north-temperate *M. amicta*) partly bluish when young. In Brazil, Central America, and the Caribbean, *Clitocybula azurea* produces remarkably similar fruitbodies, also growing in troops on rotten wood.

Actual size

The Pixie's Parasol forms hemispherical caps, becoming slightly depressed at the center. The cap surface is smooth, slimy, striate, bright blue when young, but darker at the center, paler or duller with age. The gills are white with blue edges. The fragile stem is whitish, smooth, dry, and attached to the wood by a blue-edged basal disc.

FAMILY	Mycenaceae
DISTRIBUTION	North America, Australia, New Zealand
HABITAT	In woodland
ASSOCIATION	With broadleaf trees, especially beech
GROWTH FORM	On trunks, stumps, and logs, in clusters
ABUNDANCE	Common
SPORE COLOR	White
EDIBILITY	Not edible

HEIGHT
Up to 3 in
(75 mm)

CAP DIAMETER
Up to 1½ in
(40 mm)

244

MYCENA LEAIANA
LEA'S ORANGE BONNET
(BERKELEY) SACCARDO

Often found in large clusters, fruitbodies of *Mycena leaiana* are easy to distinguish because of their bright orange colors and the darker edges to their gills. The fungus contains an orange-yellow pigment called leaianafulvene, which has been shown to have antibiotic properties. It was originally collected from Cincinnati in the United States by Thomas Gibson Lea and was named in his honor by the English mycologist, the Rev. M. J. Berkeley, who received Lea's collections for identification. The Lea's Orange Bonnet has the alternative common name of the Golden Fairy Helmet. It (or something very like it) has also been recorded from Australia and New Zealand, sometimes as the separate variety, *M. leaiana* var. *australis*.

SIMILAR SPECIES

The North American Flame Bonnet (*Mycena strobilinoides*) is also bright orange with deeply colored gill edges, but occurs in troops in conifer needles, rather than clustered on broadleaf wood. *Mycena aurantiomarginata* is a more widespread species with orange gill edges but a dingier, olive-brown cap. It also occurs in troops, in conifer and broadleaf litter.

Actual size

The Lea's Orange Bonnet forms convex caps, becoming flatter. The cap surface is smooth, slimy, striate at the margin, bright orange when young, becoming paler and duller with age. The gills are pale salmon to yellow-orange, and with deeply colored, orange-red edges. The stem is smooth to hairy at the base, sticky when damp, and yellow-orange to cap-colored.

FAMILY	Mycenaceae
DISTRIBUTION	North America, Europe, North Africa, Central America, northern Asia
HABITAT	In woodland
ASSOCIATION	With broadleaf trees and conifers
GROWTH FORM	On ground and in leaf litter, singly or in troops
ABUNDANCE	Very common
SPORE COLOR	White
EDIBILITY	Probably poisonous, best avoided

HEIGHT
Up to 3 in
(75 mm)

CAP DIAMETER
Up to 2 in
(50 mm)

MYCENA PURA

LILAC BONNET

(PERSOON) P. KUMMER

245

Mycena pura might be better called the Occasionally Lilac Bonnet, since it seems to occur in an extraordinary range of colors—from pink to dull yellow. The commonest are lilac, purple, or rose, but no less than 11 different color forms have been recognized. Microscopically these forms look much the same and all have an aroma of radish, but it seems likely that *M. pura* will turn out to be a complex of species once DNA samples are compared. At least some of the fungi called "Lilac Bonnet" contain the toxin muscarine, so, although *M. pura* is considered edible in some countries, it is best avoided.

SIMILAR SPECIES

In north temperate areas, *Mycena pelianthina*, growing in beech and other leaf litter, looks and smells similar, but has a dark purplish brown edge to its gills. In Australia, *M. vinacea* is a similar-looking, dull reddish-lilac species. The Wood Blewit (*Lepista nuda*) can be similarly colored, but is a substantially larger agaric.

Actual size

The Lilac Bonnet forms convex caps, becoming flat to weakly umbonate or depressed. The cap surface is smooth, striate, hygrophanous (changing color with humidity), pink to rose, purple to purple-brown, lilac, violet-gray, rarely dull ocher to bluish or whitish. The gills are whitish to pale pink or lilac. The stem is smooth, hairy at the base, whitish to cap-colored.

FAMILY	Mycenaceae
DISTRIBUTION	North America, continental Europe
HABITAT	In woodland
ASSOCIATION	With conifers
GROWTH FORM	On ground and needle litter, singly or in troops
ABUNDANCE	Common
SPORE COLOR	White
EDIBILITY	Not edible

HEIGHT
Up to 2 in
(50 mm)

CAP DIAMETER
Up to 1 in
(25 mm)

246

MYCENA STROBILINOIDES
FLAME BONNET
PECK

Actual size

Though individual fruitbodies are small, the bright scarlet and orange colors make the Flame Bonnet an eye-catching little agaric when growing in large troops among conifer needles. It was originally described from Mount Olympus, Washington, and is a locally common species in parts of North America, but has only rarely been reported from montane areas of central Europe. The epithet s*trobilinoides* usually means "like a conifer cone," which may seem puzzling, but in this case it actually means "like *Agaricus strobilinus,*" an old name for the Scarlet Bonnet (*Mycena adonis*).

SIMILAR SPECIES

In North America and (rarely) Europe, *Mycena oregonensis* is a similar species on conifer needles, but often has a pointed umbo at the cap center, and is typically more yellow-orange. In North America, Australia, and New Zealand, Lea's Orange Bonnet (*Mycena leaiana*) looks similar, but grows in clusters on wood.

The Flame Bonnet forms convex caps, becoming flatter. The cap surface is smooth, striate at the margin, scarlet when young, becoming orange and yellower with age. The gills are pale yellow to yellow-orange with scarlet to orange-red edges. The stem is smooth to hairy at the base and cap-colored.

FAMILY	Mycenaceae
DISTRIBUTION	Australia, New Zealand
HABITAT	In woodland
ASSOCIATION	With broadleaf trees
GROWTH FORM	On fallen twigs and leaf litter
ABUNDANCE	Common
SPORE COLOR	White
EDIBILITY	Not edible

HEIGHT
Up to 1 in
(25 mm)

CAP DIAMETER
Up to ½ in
(10 mm)

MYCENA VISCIDOCRUENTA

RUBY BONNET

CLELAND

247

Small but brilliantly colored, this little agaric is quite common in damp gullies and rainforests in Australia and New Zealand. The sliminess of the cap and stem is an unusual feature for a *Mycena* species, so it is perhaps not surprising that recent DNA research indicates that the Ruby Bonnet is so distinct that it should be placed in its own genus, *Cruentomycena*, along with a similar species from Eastern Asia. Oddly, its DNA suggests that it is related to the Bitter Oysterling (*Panellus stipticus*), which would hardly be guessed from its appearance.

SIMILAR SPECIES

Other brightly colored *Mycena* species, such as the Scarlet Bonnet (*M. adonis*), do not have the slimy cap and stem of the Ruby Bonnet. The latter's sliminess is, in fact, more suggestive of waxcaps (*Hygrocybe* species), but these are typically found in moss in old pastures or woodlands, never associated with sticks and leaf litter.

Actual size

The Ruby Bonnet forms caps that are hemispherical at first, becoming convex to flat or slightly depressed. The cap surface is smooth, slimy when damp, striate at the margin, bright red when fresh. The gills are pale cap-colored. The stem is smooth, slimy when damp, and cap-colored.

FAMILY	Polyporaceae
DISTRIBUTION	North America, Europe, North Africa, Central America, northern Asia, Australia, New Zealand
HABITAT	In woodland and on cut timber
ASSOCIATION	With conifers
GROWTH FORM	On dead trunks, roots, and timber, singly or in small clusters
ABUNDANCE	Occasional
SPORE COLOR	White
EDIBILITY	Edible

HEIGHT
Up to 5 in
(125 mm)

CAP DIAMETER
Up to 12 in
(300 mm)

248

NEOLENTINUS LEPIDEUS
SCALY SAWGILL
(FRIES) REDHEAD & GINNS

The Scaly Sawgill causes a brown rot of conifer wood and has an unusually high tolerance for creosote, once widely used as a wood preservative. In the past it earned a bad reputation by causing extensive damage to timber used for pit props, telegraph poles, and railroad sleepers—hence its rather fanciful alternative name of Train Wrecker. The fruitbodies need light to form properly and if grown in darkness (for example, on mine timbers) develop into strange, elongated, stagshorn shapes. The Scaly Sawgill is an edible species and is said to be consumed in China, but the mature fruitbodies become quite tough and leathery.

SIMILAR SPECIES

In western North America, *Neolentinus ponderosus* is a similar but larger species found mainly on ponderosa pine, lacking a ring or large scales on the stem. Other *Neolentinus* and *Lentinus* species with serrated or sawlike gill edges typically lack a veil, grow on broadleaf wood, or have smaller or less scaly fruitbodies.

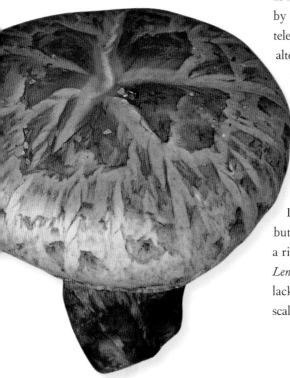

Actual size

The Scaly Sawgill forms convex caps, becoming flat or weakly funnel-shaped. The cap surface is smooth at first, breaking up into pale ocher to brown scales. The gills are somewhat decurrent, whitish, with a sawlike edge. The stem is cap-colored and scaly, blackish brown toward the base, with an evanescent whitish ring or ring remains.

FAMILY	Marasmiaceae
DISTRIBUTION	Eastern North America, Europe
HABITAT	In woodland and parkland
ASSOCIATION	With broadleaf trees, particularly oak
GROWTH FORM	At base of trunks, stumps, or arising from roots, in clusters
ABUNDANCE	Locally common
SPORE COLOR	White
EDIBILITY	Poisonous

HEIGHT
Up to 8 in
(200 mm)

CAP DIAMETER
Up to 8 in
(200 mm)

OMPHALOTUS ILLUDENS

JACK O'LANTERN

(SCHWEINITZ) BRESINSKY & BESL

249

Fruitbodies of *Omphalotus illudens*, especially the gills, are sometimes bioluminescent and glow in the dark, hence the name Jack O'Lantern. The species is poisonous, causing gastric upsets, and has quite frequently been collected and eaten in error for the edible Chanterelle (*Cantharellus cibarius*), though the two fungi hardly look alike. The fungal toxins are thought to be novel "illudin" compounds, several of which have been extracted from fruitbodies. The compounds are cytotoxic (toxic to cells) and one of them, illudin S or lampterol (in a modified form called irofulven), has undergone extensive clinical trials as a potential anticancer agent.

SIMILAR SPECIES

Several other *Omphalotus* species are equally poisonous. They include the Olive-Tree Jack O'Lantern (*O. olearius*), common on olive trees in southern Europe, and the olive-tinted Western Jack O'Lantern (*O. olivascens*) which occurs in western North America. The edible Chanterelle (*Cantharellus cibarius*) is smaller, not clustered, and has thick veins rather than gills.

The Jack O'Lantern forms clusters of fruitbodies. The caps are convex, becoming flat to shallowly funnel-shaped with an inrolled margin that often splits. The surface of the cap is smooth and bright orange to orange-tan. The gills are decurrent, widely spaced, and cap-colored. The stem is sometimes off-center, smooth but fibrous, pale cap-colored, and tapering toward the base.

Actual size

FAMILY	Marasmiaceae
DISTRIBUTION	Northeastern Asia
HABITAT	In woodland
ASSOCIATION	With broadleaf trees, particularly beech and maple
GROWTH FORM	On trunks, singly or in tiers
ABUNDANCE	Common
SPORE COLOR	White
EDIBILITY	Poisonous

HEIGHT
Up to 1 in
(25 mm)

CAP DIAMETER
Up to 12 in
(300 mm)

250

OMPHALOTUS JAPONICUS
MOONLIGHT MUSHROOM
(KAWAMURA) KIRCHMAIR & O. K. MILLER

The Moonlight Mushroom forms fruitbodies laterally attached to wood. The caps are convex, becoming flat. The cap surface is smooth to fibrous-scaly, yellowish at first, becoming cinnamon to purple-brown. The gills are decurrent and whitish. The stem is short, but with a distinct ring.

Until recently, the Moonlight Mushroom was placed in its own genus and called *Lampteromyces japonicus*. Molecular research has, however, shown that it is an *Omphalotus* species and indeed it has much in common with the Jack O'Lantern (*O. illudens*). Both fungi are poisonous, the Moon Mushroom sometimes being eaten in mistake for Oyster Mushrooms (*Pleurotus ostreatus*) or Shiitake (*Lentinula edodes*); both are bioluminescent, the glowing gills of the Moonlight Mushroom giving it its common name; and both contain the cytotoxin illudin S or lampterol, a potentially useful antitumor agent.

SIMILAR SPECIES

The poisonous Moonlight Mushroom has been confused with the edible *Lentinula edodes*. The latter species, though similarly colored, is not bracket-shaped, but has a hemispherical cap and central stem. The equally edible *Pleurotus ostreatus* is bracket-shaped, but usually has no stem and never has a ring.

Actual size

FAMILY	Physalacriaceae
DISTRIBUTION	Europe, northern Asia
HABITAT	In woodland
ASSOCIATION	On broadleaf trees, particularly beech
GROWTH FORM	On living and fallen trunks, in clusters
ABUNDANCE	Common
SPORE COLOR	White
EDIBILITY	Edible

HEIGHT
Up to 3 in
(75 mm)

CAP DIAMETER
Up to 4 in
(100 mm)

OUDEMANSIELLA MUCIDA

PORCELAIN FUNGUS

(SCHRADER) HÖHNEL

251

Oudemansiella mucida fruitbodies typically grow in clusters high up on dead branches of old beeches, rarely on sycamore and other broadleaf trees. Light shining through their thin-fleshed, ivory-white caps gives them the name Porcelain Fungus, though when seen close up their Latin epithet *mucida*, meaning "slimy," is more appropriate. The genus is named after the nineteenth-century Dutch mycologist, Corneille Oudemans. *Oudemansiella mucida* has been found to contain an antibiotic called mucidin that has been widely researched and clinically used to treat human fungal infections. Despite the slimy surface (which can be peeled off), the fruitbodies are edible and consumed in China and Russia.

SIMILAR SPECIES

The related *Oudemansiella canarii* grows in southern North America (Florida), as well as Central and South America, but has pinkish-orange tints and lacks a conspicuous ring. *Oudemansiella platensis*, known from Central and South America, is similar but grayer and also lacks a ring. Additional species occur in Africa and southern Asia.

Actual size

The Porcelain Fungus forms thin-fleshed, convex caps that become flatter when expanded. The surface is smooth or slightly wrinkled, very slimy, and tinted olive-gray when young, becoming ivory white with a pale ocher-brown center. The gills are white and rather distant. The stem is white, thickening and flecked olive-gray toward the base, with a conspicuous ring, which is white above and gray below.

FAMILY	Psathyrellaceae
DISTRIBUTION	North America, Europe, Africa, Central and South America, Asia, Australia, New Zealand
HABITAT	In pastures, parks, lawns, and other grassland
ASSOCIATION	With grass on rich soil
GROWTH FORM	In grass, singly or in scattered troops
ABUNDANCE	Very common
SPORE COLOR	Dark brown
EDIBILITY	Not edible

HEIGHT
Up to 3 in
(75 mm)

CAP DIAMETER
Up to 1 in
(25 mm)

252

PANAEOLINA FOENISECII
BROWN MOTTLEGILL
(PERSOON) MAIRE

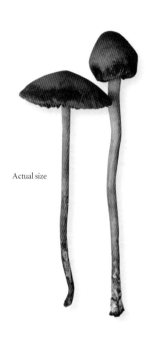

Actual size

Few people would claim that the Brown Mottlegill—also known as the Haymaker—is a particularly exciting species, but it is by far the commonest little agaric to occur in garden lawns. Its caps are strongly hygrophanous, changing color as they dry out. The dark brown spores ripen unevenly on the gills, giving them a mottled appearance. Because it is so common on lawns, the Brown Mottlegill is often picked and consumed by toddlers and consequently accounts for many anxious hospital enquiries. However, despite a few reports (possibly based on misidentifications), it is not known to be toxic, nor, as is sometimes claimed, is it hallucinogenic.

SIMILAR SPECIES
Many small, dull-colored agarics grow in grass. *Panaeolus* species are very similar in shape and color, but have black (rather than brown) mottled gills. Inkcaps (*Parasola* species) have black, non-mottled gills. *Galerina* and *Conocybe* species in grass and moss may also look similar, but have rusty brown gills and spores.

The Brown Mottlegill forms convex caps that are smooth, dull yellow-brown to purplish brown when damp, drying pale ocher-brown to buff. The gills are dark brown and mottled (see photo left), with a whitish edge. The fragile stem is buff, becoming darker brown from the base upward.

FAMILY	Psathyrellaceae
DISTRIBUTION	North America, Europe, North Africa, Central and South America, northern Asia, Australia, New Zealand
HABITAT	In pastures
ASSOCIATION	With herbivore dung
GROWTH FORM	On dung or manured grass, singly or in small groups
ABUNDANCE	Common
SPORE COLOR	Black
EDIBILITY	Not edible

HEIGHT
Up to 4 in
(100 mm)

CAP DIAMETER
Up to 1½ in
(40 mm)

PANAEOLUS PAPILIONACEUS

PETTICOAT MOTTLEGILL

(BULLIARD) QUÉLET

253

The Petticoat Mottlegill sounds charming, but like most *Panaeolus* species it is a dung-lover, occurring directly on old herbivore dung or on manured ground. It takes its English name from the whitish veil remnants which hang, petticoatlike, from the margin of the cap. It is also known as the Bell-shaped Panaeolus; in fact, this little agaric has garnered no less than 12 English names, since until recently it was separated into several species, based mainly on the very variable cap features. The Bell Mottlegill (*Panaeolus campanulatus*), the Wrinkled Panaeolus (*P. retirugis*), and the Gray Mottlegill (*P. sphinctrinus*) are all now considered synonyms.

SIMILAR SPECIES

The Egghead Mottlegill (*Panaeolus semiovatus*) is much larger and has a ringed stem. The Brown Mottlegill (*Panaeolina foenisecii*) is of similar size, but has brown gills and lacks the white veil remains at the cap margin. Other small *Panaeolus* species have mottled black gills, but also lack the marginal veil remains.

Actual size

The Petticoat Mottlegill forms hemispherical caps that may be smooth (see photo left) or wrinkled, and vary in color from ivory to cream, buff, grayish, tan, or reddish brown. Whitish veil remains hang from the margin when fresh. The gills are mottled black. The stem is smooth, cap-colored, but often covered in fine whitish particles when fresh.

FAMILY	Psathyrellaceae
DISTRIBUTION	North America, Europe, North Africa, Central America, northern Asia, New Zealand
HABITAT	In pastures
ASSOCIATION	With herbivore dung
GROWTH FORM	On dung, singly or in small groups
ABUNDANCE	Common
SPORE COLOR	Black
EDIBILITY	Not edible

HEIGHT Up to 7 in (175 mm)	
CAP DIAMETER Up to 3 in (75 mm)	

254

PANAEOLUS SEMIOVATUS

EGGHEAD MOTTLEGILL

(SOWERBY) S. LUNDELL & NANNFELDT

Panaeolus semiovatus is one of the easier mottlegills to recognize, thanks to its slimy cap and the ring on the stem (often collapsing, but still visible as a blackish zone). It is a coprophilous (dung-loving) species, appearing on horse, cow, and other dung in pastures. Fruitbodies of the Egghead Mottlegill, also known as the Dung Roundhead, can be quite small but are often surprisingly large, bearing in mind that dung fungi have to produce their fruitbodies rapidly, before their resource disappears. Spores from the fruitbodies fall onto grass, are eaten by herbivores, pass through the gut, and are deposited along with the dung, ensuring that the cycle continues.

SIMILAR SPECIES

Other *Panaeolus* species are generally smaller and lack a ring on the stem. In southern North America and subtropical regions, the Gold Cap (*Psilocybe cubensis*) is a similarly large, ringed species on dung, but has a less slimy, cream to yellow-brown cap, and non-mottled gills.

Actual size

The Egghead Mottlegill forms convex caps that are smooth or wrinkled, slimy when damp, and ivory to cream or buff. The gills are dark gray, becoming mottled black (see photo right). The stem is smooth, somewhat bulbous at the base, whitish to cap-colored, with a ring or ring zone (often blackened by spores).

FAMILY	Mycenaceae
DISTRIBUTION	North America, Europe, northern Asia
HABITAT	In woodland
ASSOCIATION	With broadleaf trees
GROWTH FORM	On dead trunks, stumps, and branches, singly or clustered
ABUNDANCE	Common
SPORE COLOR	Pale yellowish
EDIBILITY	Edible

PANELLUS SEROTINUS

OLIVE OYSTERLING

(PERSOON) KÜHNER

HEIGHT
Up to ½ in
(10 mm)

CAP DIAMETER
Up to 4 in
(100 mm)

255

The epithet *serotinus* means "late" and fruitbodies of the Olive Oysterling typically appear late in the season, often after the first frosts; it is also known as the Late Oyster for this reason. It is considered an edible species, at least in China and Japan (where it is known as *mukitake*), and cultivation trials have been undertaken. However, it is generally considered inferior to the easily cultivated Oyster Mushrooms (*Pleurotus* species), partly because the cap has a gelatinous skin that makes it slimy in damp weather. Recent research suggests *Panellus serotinus* fruitbodies contain compounds of potential use in alleviating some types of liver disease.

SIMILAR SPECIES

The slimy cap with its olive or greenish tints should distinguish the Olive Oysterling from other *Panellus* species and from the true Oyster Mushrooms (*Pleurotus* species). The Peeling Oysterling (*Crepidotus mollis*) and Saffron Oysterling (*C. crocophyllus*) are somewhat similar, but lack olive tints and have brown spores.

Actual size

The Olive Oysterling forms wide, shell-shaped, soft fruitbodies laterally attached to wood. The caps are weakly convex, smooth, slimy when damp, ocher-olive to dark olive-brown, often with green and orange tints. The gills are ocher to buff or pale orange-buff. The stem, when present, is short, often very wide, and ocher to orange-buff.

FAMILY	Mycenaceae
DISTRIBUTION	North America, Europe, North Africa, Central America, western and northern Asia, Australia, New Zealand
HABITAT	In woodland
ASSOCIATION	With broadleaf trees, rarely conifers
GROWTH FORM	On dead trunks, stumps, and branches, in tiers or clusters
ABUNDANCE	Common
SPORE COLOR	Whitish
EDIBILITY	Not edible

HEIGHT
Up to ½ in
(10 mm)

CAP DIAMETER
Up to 1 in
(25 mm)

256

PANELLUS STIPTICUS
BITTER OYSTERLING
(BULLIARD) P. KARSTEN

Actual size

When the undersurface is examined, the Bitter Oysterling is easily recognized by its pale, wedge-like stem and brown gills. As its English name suggests, it is not an edible species, though the Latin epithet acknowledges its former medical use as a styptic to staunch the flow of blood. Curiously, some populations of the fungus from eastern North America are bioluminescent, with both the mycelium and the fruitbodies (mainly the gills) glowing in the dark. A metabolite called panal has been isolated from the fungus, which may be responsible for this phenomenon.

SIMILAR SPECIES

The much less common *Panellus ringens* is similar, but has purplish tints to the cap and lacks the wedge-like stem of *P. stipticus*. *Crepidotus* species may be similarly shaped, but are brown-spored and also lack the distinctive stem. The Splitgill (*Schizophyllum commune*) has a hairy, grayish cap and pinkish brown, split gills.

The Bitter Oysterling forms wide, shell-shaped fruitbodies attached to wood by a short, lateral stem. The caps are weakly convex, finely velvety, ocher-buff to pinkish brown or yellow-brown. The gills are cap-colored (see photo above). The stem is short, finely hairy, very wide at the top, and cream to pale buff.

FAMILY	Psathyrellaceae
DISTRIBUTION	North America, Europe, North Africa, Central and South America, Asia, Australia, New Zealand
HABITAT	In pastures, parks, lawns, and other grassland
ASSOCIATION	With grass on rich soil
GROWTH FORM	In grass, singly or in scattered troops
ABUNDANCE	Common
SPORE COLOR	Black
EDIBILITY	Not edible

HEIGHT
Up to 3 in
(75 mm)
CAP DIAMETER
Up to 1 in
(25 mm)

PARASOLA PLICATILIS

PLEATED INKCAP

(CURTIS) REDHEAD ET AL

This delicate little agaric, ribbed like a Japanese paper parasol, is common in lawns and short grass in wet weather. The fruitbodies are as fragile and ephemeral as they look, seldom lasting more than a few hours before collapsing. The Pleated Inkcap—also known as the Japanese Umbrella—appears to be widespread, recorded in grasslands around the world, but it is possible that some of these records refer to similar-looking inkcap species. Until recently the Pleated Inkcap was called *Coprinus plicatilis*, but molecular research has shown that it belongs, with a number of allied species, in its own separate genus.

SIMILAR SPECIES

Many small inkcaps, particularly the common *Parasola leiocephala*, look almost identical to the Pleated Inkcap and are frequently confused with it. Some grow in soil or leaf litter, rather than grass, but they are best distinguished microscopically. *Leucocoprinus* species can also look similar, but have white gills and ringed stems.

Actual size

The Pleated Inkcap forms delicate caps that are almost cylindrical at first, but flat or with a slightly depressed center when expanded. The surface is smooth, becoming ridged or pleated, buff to tawny-brown (remaining so at center), becoming grayish white. The gills are black. The fragile stem is smooth, white at first, becoming pale gray to buff.

FAMILY	Paxillaceae
DISTRIBUTION	North America, Europe, North Africa, northern Asia; introduced in southern South America, Australia, New Zealand
HABITAT	In woodland and parkland
ASSOCIATION	Ectomycorrhizal, with conifers and broadleaf trees, particularly birch
GROWTH FORM	On ground, singly or in scattered troops
ABUNDANCE	Very common
SPORE COLOR	Brown
EDIBILITY	Poisonous

HEIGHT
Up to 4 in
(100 mm)

CAP DIAMETER
Up to 5 in
(125 mm)

258

PAXILLUS INVOLUTUS
BROWN ROLLRIM
(BATSCH) FRIES

The Brown Rollrim is a very common woodland species, taking its English name from the cap margin which long remains inrolled. It has unusually soft gills, easily squashed, and bruising dark brown. The fruitbodies are widely eaten in eastern Europe, usually after boiling with a change of water, since they cause gastric upsets raw. However, the Brown Rollrim—also known as the Poison Pax—is potentially much more dangerous, producing an unpredictable and often lethal syndrome in people who have previously eaten it with impunity. It seems antigens within the fruitbodies can sometimes trigger an autoimmune reaction, causing the body to destroy its own blood cells.

SIMILAR SPECIES
Several closely related species have been distinguished and confirmed as distinct by recent molecular research. They include *Paxillus vernalis*, a North American associate of aspen and birch, and the European *P. rubicundulus*, an alder associate with reddish brown scales on the cap. *Tapinella atrotomentosa* may look similar, but grows on conifer wood.

Actual size

The Brown Rollrim forms caps that are convex at first, becoming flatter and often depressed, the margin long remaining incurved. The surface of the cap is smooth, finely downy, sticky when wet, and ocher-buff to olive-buff, becoming tan to brown. The decurrent gills are ocher-buff to brown (see photo right), bruising dark brown. The stem is smooth, cap-colored or paler.

FAMILY	Cortinariaceae
DISTRIBUTION	Eastern North America, Europe
HABITAT	In woodland
ASSOCIATION	Possibly ectomycorrhizal, with conifers
GROWTH FORM	In needle litter, often in troops
ABUNDANCE	Occasional
SPORE COLOR	Rusty brown
EDIBILITY	Not edible

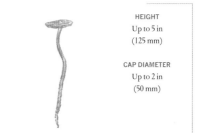

HEIGHT
Up to 5 in
(125 mm)

CAP DIAMETER
Up to 2 in
(50 mm)

259

PHAEOCOLLYBIA CHRISTINAE

CHRISTINA'S ROOTSHANK

(FRIES) R. HEIM

The small genus *Phaeocollybia* contains a distinctive group of rusty-spored agarics, many of which have conical caps that can often become sharply pointed, like a fairy-tale pixie's bonnet. They also have long, rather tough stems that appear to be rooting, extending deep into leaf litter and moss. Most *Phaeocollybia* species grow in northern conifer forests, though a few species can be found in montane areas much further south. Christina's Rootshank—named after his wife by nineteenth-century Swedish mycologist Elias Magnus Fries—is one of the more brightly colored species in the genus.

SIMILAR SPECIES

Several similar species of *Phaecollybia* have been described, but they are best distinguished microscopically. Species of *Hygrocybe* often have sharply conical caps, but all are white-spored. A few *Entoloma* species, such as *E. quadratum*, also have a similar shape, but have salmon-pink spores.

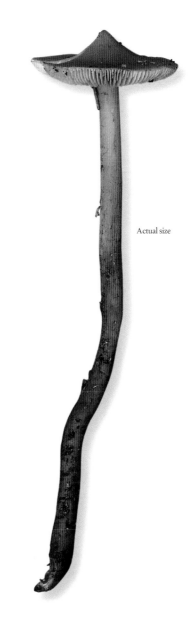

Actual size

The Christina's Rootshank forms caps that are conical, becoming sharply umbonate. The cap surface is smooth, slighty sticky when damp, orange-red to red-brown. The gills are yellowish, becoming rusty. The long stem is smooth and yellowish brown at the top, dark reddish brown toward the rooting base.

FAMILY	Agaricaceae
DISTRIBUTION	North America, Europe, northern Asia
HABITAT	In woodland and parkland
ASSOCIATION	With broadleaf trees (particularly alder in western North America), in rich soil
GROWTH FORM	On ground, in troops
ABUNDANCE	Occasional
SPORE COLOR	Ocher
EDIBILITY	Poisonous (to some), best avoided

HEIGHT
Up to 10 in
(250 mm)

CAP DIAMETER
Up to 12 in
(300 mm)

260

PHAEOLEPIOTA AUREA
GOLDEN BOOTLEG
(MATTUSCHKA) MAIRE

The Golden Bootleg is a giant relative of *Cystoderma* species and like them has a powdery-granular cap, together with a veil covering the lower stem like a boot or stocking. It is uncommon in lowland Europe, most frequently being found in rich soil with nettles. It is more common in montane and northern areas, particularly in Alaska (it has sometimes been called the Alaska Gold) where it typically occurs with alders. The Golden Bootleg is often listed as edible, but is known to cause gastric poisoning in some people and is therefore best avoided.

SIMILAR SPECIES

The Spectacular Rustgill (*Gymnopilus junonius*) has frequently been confused with the Golden Bootleg, but has a scaly-fibrous cap and typically grows in clusters on wood or at the base of trunks and stumps. The Gypsy (*Cortinarius caperatus*) is a much paler species, the stem usually whitish to buff in color.

Actual size

The Golden Bootleg forms caps that are convex to conical (see photo right), becoming flat to shallowly umbonate. The cap surface is granular, becoming smooth, ocher-yellow to tan, paling with age and with a fringed margin. The gills are yellowish to tawny-yellow. The stem is cap-colored, with a sheathlike granular veil on the lower part, topped by a conspicuous ring.

FAMILY	Inocybaceae
DISTRIBUTION	North America, Europe
HABITAT	In woodland
ASSOCIATION	With broadleaf trees, particularly willow
GROWTH FORM	On dead, attached twigs and branches
ABUNDANCE	Common
SPORE COLOR	Cinnamon-brown
EDIBILITY	Not edible

HEIGHT
Up to ½ in
(15 mm)

CAP DIAMETER
Up to ½ in
(15 mm)

PHAEOMARASMIUS ERINACEUS

HEDGEHOG SCALYCAP

(FRIES) SCHERFFEL EX ROMAGNESI

261

This little agaric can sometimes be spotted—usually by chance—on a dead, attached twig or branch. The Hedgehog Scalycap often occurs singly, making it especially easy to overlook. It usually prefers willow, but is occasionally reported on poplar, birch, and other broadleaf trees. The Latin epithet *erinaceus* means "hedgehog," and fruitbodies are densely woolly-spiny, the scales giving a shaggy fringe to the cap margin. It looks very much like a miniature *Pholiota* species, though it belongs in a quite different family.

SIMILAR SPECIES

Flammulaster erinaceellus and *F. muricatus* look rather similar, but can grow up to 1½ in (40 mm) across, occur in small groups on logs and fallen branches, and have more granular-powdery scales on their caps (less woolly than in the Hedgehog Scalycap). *Pholiota* species look similar, but are all much larger.

The Hedgehog Scalycap forms caps that are convex to shallowly umbonate. The cap surface is densely woolly-scaly, rusty-tawny to reddish brown. The gills are ocher-brown to cinnamon-brown. The stem is smooth and pale above the ring or ring-zone, cap-colored and scaly below.

Actual size

FAMILY	Strophariaceae
DISTRIBUTION	North America, Europe, northern Asia, Australia, New Zealand
HABITAT	In woodland and parkland
ASSOCIATION	With broadleaf trees, more rarely conifers
GROWTH FORM	At base of trunks, on stumps and logs, densely clustered
ABUNDANCE	Occasional
SPORE COLOR	Brown
EDIBILITY	Poisonous (to some), best avoided

HEIGHT
Up to 8 in
(200 mm)

CAP DIAMETER
Up to 8 in
(200 mm)

262

PHOLIOTA AURIVELLA
GOLDEN SCALYCAP
(BATSCH) P. KUMMER

The Golden Scalycap is one of a complex of large, cluster-forming *Pholiota* species that have slimy caps with deciduous scales. Though the fruitbodies may look attractive, the fungus can cause a trunk or butt rot of living trees. It is said to be edible and consumed in China and Russia, but some texts claim it can cause gastric poisoning in susceptible individuals. Since *Pholiota aurivella* is so difficult to distinguish from closely related species, and it is not clear which are edible and which are not, the whole group is best avoided for culinary purposes.

SIMILAR SPECIES
Several very similar, slimy-capped species, including *Pholiota limonella*, *P. adiposa*, and *P. cerifera*, can only be distinguished microscopically, if at all. The edible, Asian *P. nameko* would also be difficult to separate, if found in the field. The Shaggy Scalycap (*P. squarrosa*) has a dry, not slimy, cap.

Actual size

The Golden Scalycap forms caps that are hemispherical, becoming convex to umbonate, slimy, yellow to ocher, with loose, reddish brown scales that may wash off in rain. The gills are cream to ocher to brown. The stem is dry, with a cobwebby veil when young, yellowish but reddish brown toward the base, and covered in reddish brown scales.

FAMILY	Strophariaceae
DISTRIBUTION	North America, Europe, northern Asia
HABITAT	In woodland
ASSOCIATION	With conifers
GROWTH FORM	At base of trunks, on stumps, singly or clustered
ABUNDANCE	Common
SPORE COLOR	Brown
EDIBILITY	Poisonous (to some), best avoided

PHOLIOTA FLAMMANS

FLAMING SCALYCAP

(BATSCH) P. KUMMER

HEIGHT
Up to 4 in
(100 mm)

CAP DIAMETER
Up to 4 in
(100 mm)

263

The vivid colors make the Flaming Scalycap the most eye-catching of *Pholiota* species, so it is perhaps no surprise that fruitbodies are sought after by craft-dyers. The resulting dyes can color yarns and cloth a vibrant lemon-yellow, orange, or a greenish mustard, depending on the methods used. Fruitbodies of the Flaming Scalycap are not so densely clustered as in some other *Pholiota* species, but typically occur singly or in small groups on old stumps and logs. *Pholiota flammans* is a strict conifer associate and is locally common in native conifer forests, but rather less common in plantations.

SIMILAR SPECIES

The Golden Scalycap (*Pholiota aurivella*) also has a slimy cap, but it is less brightly colored, and has reddish brown scales. The Shaggy Scalycap (*P. squarrosa*) has larger, dry caps that are pale yellow to ocher with dark brown scales. Both normally grow on broadleaf trees, only rarely on conifers.

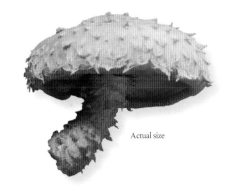

Actual size

The Flaming Scalycap forms caps that are hemispherical, becoming flat to weakly umbonate. The cap surface is slimy when damp, golden yellow to yellow-orange, with dry, erect, yellow scales. The gills are lemon-yellow becoming rusty brown. The stem is dry, with a fibrous ring when young, cap-colored, and covered in scales that are yellow at first, darkening to tan.

FAMILY	Strophariaceae
DISTRIBUTION	North America, Europe, northern Asia, Australia, New Zealand
HABITAT	In woodland and parkland
ASSOCIATION	With broadleaf trees, more rarely conifers
GROWTH FORM	At base of trunks, on stumps, densely clustered
ABUNDANCE	Common
SPORE COLOR	Brown
EDIBILITY	Poisonous (to some), best avoided

HEIGHT
Up to 8 in
(200 mm)

CAP DIAMETER
Up to 6 in
(150 mm)

264

PHOLIOTA SQUARROSA

SHAGGY SCALYCAP

(VAHL) P. KUMMER

Growing in large clusters, the Shaggy Scalycap is a fine-looking fungus, though its appearance at the base of living trees is a sign of trunk or butt rot. The species is eaten in China and eastern Europe, but has been reported as causing gastric poisoning in some people, so is not recommended. Like many wood-rotting fungi, the Shaggy Scalycap has been investigated for novel metabolites of possible pharmaceutical use. A polyketide compound called squarrosidine has been isolated from the fungus and may have some potential for improving cardiovascular health.

SIMILAR SPECIES

Pholiota squarrosoides is a very similar species with a slightly sticky cap, best distinguished microscopically by its smaller spores. The Flaming Scalycap (*P. flammans*) is smaller, more brightly colored with yellow to tan scales, and grows on conifers. The Golden Scalycap (*P. aurivella*) has a gelatinous cap with loose scales.

Actual size

The Shaggy Scalycap forms caps that are convex, becoming flat to weakly umbonate, dry, and pale yellow to pale ocher, with erect, dark brown scales. The gills are pale, greenish yellow, becoming rusty brown. The stem is dry, with a fibrous ring when young, whitish to yellowish but reddish brown toward the base, and covered in dark brown scales. The tough flesh is yellowish.

FAMILY	Boletaceae
DISTRIBUTION	North America, Central America
HABITAT	In woodland and parkland
ASSOCIATION	Ectomycorrhizal, with broadleaf trees, especially oak
GROWTH FORM	On ground, singly or in small groups
ABUNDANCE	Common
SPORE COLOR	Ocher
EDIBILITY	Edible

HEIGHT
Up to 4 in
(100 mm)

CAP DIAMETER
Up to 4 in
(100 mm)

PHYLLOPORUS RHODOXANTHUS

GILLED BOLETE

(SCHWEINITZ) BRESADOLA

265

This species is always a surprise, since seen from above it exactly resembles a bolete in the genus or subgenus *Xerocomus*—except that, once turned over, it has gills instead of pores. This is not just a coincidence. Recent molecular research shows that *Phylloporus* is so closely related to *Xerocomus* that the two genera may in future need to be combined. The Gilled Bolete is common in North America, but its European look-alike, *Phylloporus pelletieri* is unaccountably rare, featuring on the Red Lists of threatened fungal species in a dozen different countries. It has even been proposed for international protection under the Bern Convention.

SIMILAR SPECIES

The look-alike Golden Gilled Bolete (*Phylloporus pelletieri*) is a European and north Asian species which has been much confused with the American *P. rhodoxanthus*. Apart from geography, it is mainly distinguishable microscopically. Other North American species include *P. foliiporus*, which has bluing flesh when cut, and *P. arenicola*, which grows on the west coast with pines.

Actual size

The Gilled Bolete forms convex caps becoming flat, dry, smooth and slightly velvety, sometimes finely cracked with age, and dark red to reddish brown or brown, sometimes with olive tints. The gills are decurrent, widely spaced, and bright yellow to golden yellow. The stem is dry, and yellowish, becoming reddish to reddish brown.

FAMILY	Tricholomataceae
DISTRIBUTION	North America, Europe, Central America, northern Asia
HABITAT	In woodland
ASSOCIATION	With broadleaf trees and conifers
GROWTH FORM	On rotten wood, singly or in clusters or tiers
ABUNDANCE	Locally common
SPORE COLOR	Ocher-pink
EDIBILITY	Not edible

HEIGHT
Less than ⅛ in
(3 mm)

CAP DIAMETER
Up to 3 in
(75 mm)

266

PHYLLOTOPSIS NIDULANS
ORANGE MOCK OYSTER
(PERSOON) SINGER

The hairy cap surface and overall orange colors should distinguish the Orange Mock Oyster from the edible, true Oyster Mushrooms (*Pleurotus* species). The fruitbodies are also said to smell terrible—like a skunk, sewer gas, or rotten eggs, according to some authors—though occasional collections seem to be aroma-free or even pleasant. It is a common species in North America, on both broadleaf trees and conifers, but seems to be much less common, even locally rare, in Europe. The epithet *nidulans* means "nesting," since immature fruitbodies can look a little like miniature birds' nests.

SIMILAR SPECIES
The Oyster Rollrim (*Tapinella panuoides*) has orange gills, but is a brown-spored species with a smooth to velvety, brownish cap and is restricted to conifer wood. The Saffron Oysterling (*Crepidotus crocophyllus*) also has yellow-orange gills, but it too is brown-spored, and has a cream to brownish, scaly cap.

The Orange Mock Oyster forms fruitbodies that often form clusters or tiers and are laterally attached to wood. The fruitbodies are wide, shell-shaped, and soft. The caps are weakly convex to flat, orange to orange-buff, becoming pale ocher-yellow, with a densely hairy surface. The gills are cap-colored. The stem is absent.

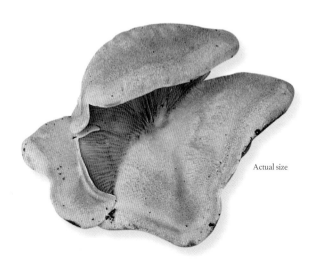

Actual size

FAMILY	Pleurotaceae
DISTRIBUTION	East Asia
HABITAT	In woodland
ASSOCIATION	With broadleaf trees
GROWTH FORM	On dead trunks and logs, densely clustered
ABUNDANCE	Occasional
SPORE COLOR	White
EDIBILITY	Edible

HEIGHT	Up to 4 in (100 mm)
CAP DIAMETER	Up to 3 in (75 mm)

PLEUROTUS CITRINOPILEATUS

GOLDEN OYSTER

SINGER

267

Originally described from the Russian Far East, this vividly colored oyster fungus is restricted to eastern Asia in the wild. It is edible, however, and is now widely cultivated both on a commercial scale and by grow-your-own enthusiasts. Apart from its color, the Golden Oyster is very similar to the much more widespread Branching Oyster (*Pleurotus cornucopiae*) which is typically whitish to pale brown. Indeed, the Golden Oyster is often treated as just a color form or variety of the Branching Oyster. Both form densely clustered fruitbodies with multiple caps arising from a single stem.

SIMILAR SPECIES

The yellow, funnel-shaped caps and white gills should be distinctive. The Branching Oyster (*Pleurotus cornucopiae*) has the same shape, but its caps are ivory to pale brown. The Honey Fungus (*Armillaria mellea*) grows in similar large clusters, but its caps are tawny-yellow with sparse scales, and its stems have a distinct ring.

The Golden Oyster produces funnel-shaped fruitbodies branching from a single base or basal stem. The caps are convex at first, becoming flat to funnel-shaped, smooth, and lemon-yellow. The gills are deeply decurrent and white. The stem is almost central and typically curved, smooth, and white.

Actual size

FAMILY	Pleurotaceae
DISTRIBUTION	Africa, Central and South America, southern and eastern Asia, Australia, New Zealand
HABITAT	In woodland
ASSOCIATION	With broadleaf trees
GROWTH FORM	On trunks, singly or densely clustered
ABUNDANCE	Occasional
SPORE COLOR	White
EDIBILITY	Edible

HEIGHT
Up to ½ in
(10 mm)

CAP DIAMETER
Up to 3 in
(75 mm)

268

PLEUROTUS DJAMOR
TROPICAL OYSTER
(RUMPHIUS) BOEDIJN

Pleurotus djamor is the tropical and subtropical counterpart of the ordinary, temperate Oyster Mushroom (*P. ostreatus*), occasionally found as far north as Japan and as far south as Argentina and New Zealand. Like the Oyster Mushroom, the Tropical Oyster is a good edible species and is widely cultivated and marketed as the eye-catching and exotic-looking Pink Oyster. This is something of a misnomer, however, since the Tropical Oyster—like its temperate counterpart—is variable in color. In the wild, the fruitbodies are most frequently white, but cultivated strains are usually taken from the less commonly occurring pink color form.

SIMILAR SPECIES

Pink forms of the Tropical Oyster should be unmistakable. White forms, however, may look very similar to white forms of the temperate Oyster Mushroom (*Pleurotus ostreatus*). In regions where both species occur, they are best differentiated microscopically. Several other white or whitish *Pleurotus* species also occur in the tropics.

The Tropical Oyster produces shell- or spoon-shaped fruitbodies that are laterally attached to wood. The caps are convex at first becoming flat to funnel-shaped, smooth, white, or less commonly pinkish to pink. The gills are decurrent, whitish to cap-colored. The stem is lateral, often very short or even absent, smooth, and cap-colored.

Actual size

FAMILY	Pleurotaceae
DISTRIBUTION	Southern Europe, North Africa, southwestern Asia
HABITAT	In scrub
ASSOCIATION	With field eryngo
GROWTH FORM	On ground, singly or clustered at the base of host stems
ABUNDANCE	Occasional
SPORE COLOR	White
EDIBILITY	Edible

HEIGHT
Up to 4 in
(100 mm)

CAP DIAMETER
Up to 6 in
(150 mm)

PLEUROTUS ERYNGII

ERYNGO OYSTER

(DE CANDOLLE) QUÉLET

269

Most oyster fungi grow on wood, but the Eryngo Oyster belongs to a group of species that are weak parasites on the roots of umbellifers. Its host is the thistlelike field eryngo (*Eryngium campestre*), a common plant in the Mediterranean area. It is a good edible species and is now widely cultivated under the commercial name of King Oyster. A related species, the critically endangered *Pleurotus nebrodensis*, is the only non-lichenized fungus on the global IUCN Red List of Threatened Species and is restricted to northern Sicily. It too is now cultivated—a fact that may save the species from extinction.

SIMILAR SPECIES

Other fungi in this group are very similar, but grow with different hosts, such as the giant fennel (*Ferula communis*), in southern Europe and central Asia. They are often treated as varieties of *Pleurotus eryngii* and are equally edible. The rare Sicilian *Pleurotus nebrodensis* is also similar, but has a whitish cap.

The Eryngo Oyster forms convex caps that become flat to funnel-shaped with age. The cap surface is smooth, and variously buff, beige, grayish brown, or purplish brown. The gills are decurrent and whitish to cream or buff. The stem is central or almost so, thick, smooth, and white.

Actual size

FAMILY	Pleurotaceae
DISTRIBUTION	North America, Europe, northern Asia
HABITAT	In woodland
ASSOCIATION	With broadleaf trees
GROWTH FORM	On trunks, in clustered tiers
ABUNDANCE	Common
SPORE COLOR	Whitish to pale lilac
EDIBILITY	Edible

HEIGHT
Up to ½ in
(10 mm)

CAP DIAMETER
Up to 6 in
(150 mm)

270

PLEUROTUS OSTREATUS

OYSTER MUSHROOM

(JACQUIN) P. KUMMER

Easily cultivated on wood, compacted straw, and other vegetable waste, the Oyster Mushroom has become one of most popular and widely marketed edible fungi around the world. Unlike most "exotic" fungi, *Pleurotus ostreatus* is not a recent introduction from the Far East, but was first cultivated in Germany as a subsistence measure during World War I. The fruitbodies resemble oysters in shape, rather than in taste, having a faint aroma of aniseed when fresh. They also contain the natural compound lovastatin, one of several statins now routinely synthesized and used to lower cholesterol levels.

SIMILAR SPECIES

The Pale Oyster (*Pleurotus pulmonarius*) grows earlier in the year, produces smaller fruitbodies, often has a distinct lateral stem, and has white to pale tan caps. In Europe, the Branching Oyster (*P. cornucopiae*) is also pale, but large, often funnel-shaped, and has a more central (not lateral) stem. Both are equally edible.

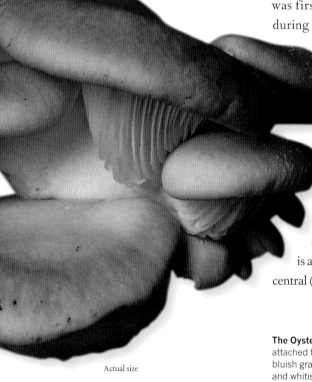

Actual size

The Oyster Mushroom forms fruitbodies in clusters or tiers, laterally attached to wood. The caps are convex at first, becoming flat, smooth, bluish gray to dark gray or pale to dark gray-brown. The gills are decurrent and whitish. The stem is usually absent, but if one is present it is lateral, short, and cap-colored.

FAMILY	Pluteaceae
DISTRIBUTION	North America, Europe, northern Asia, Australia, New Zealand
HABITAT	In woodland
ASSOCIATION	With conifers
GROWTH FORM	On dead wood, singly
ABUNDANCE	Common
SPORE COLOR	Pink
EDIBILITY	Not edible

HEIGHT
Up to 5 in
(125 mm)

CAP DIAMETER
Up to 5 in
(125 mm)

PLUTEUS ATROMARGINATUS

BLACK-EDGED SHIELD

(KONRAD) KÜHNER

271

Pluteus atromarginatus is a comparatively large species, distinguished by growing on conifer wood and by its smartly black-edged gills. Seen under a microscope, this edging comes from a layer of sterile cells lining the gill margins, each cell containing a dark brown pigment. The species was first described from France as late as the 1920s, but is actually much more widespread and not uncommon. It has probably been overlooked because of its similarity to the more familiar Deer Shield (*Pluteus cervinus*), of which it was originally thought to be a variety.

SIMILAR SPECIES

The very common Deer Shield (*Pluteus cervinus*) is similarly sized, but typically grows on broadleaf wood. It lacks the black margin to the gills, as does its conifer equivalent, *P. pouzarianus*. The Velvet Shield (*P. umbrosus*) has brown-edged gills, but grows on broadleaf wood and has a velvety-scaly cap.

The Black-Edged Shield forms caps that are convex, becoming flat to shallowly umbonate. The cap surface is smooth to finely silky-fibrous, dark to blackish brown at the center, paler brown toward the margin. The gills are whitish at first, becoming salmon, with a distinct blackish brown edge. The stem is smooth to fibrous and pale grayish brown.

Actual size

FAMILY	Pluteaceae
DISTRIBUTION	North America, Europe, northern Asia
HABITAT	In woodland and hedgerows
ASSOCIATION	With broadleaf trees, particularly elm
GROWTH FORM	On old trunks and stumps, singly or in small groups
ABUNDANCE	Occasional
SPORE COLOR	Pink
EDIBILITY	Not edible

HEIGHT
Up to 2 in
(50 mm)

CAP DIAMETER
Up to 2½ in
(60 mm)

272

PLUTEUS AURANTIORUGOSUS
FLAME SHIELD
(TROG) SACCARDO

The Flame Shield is the most brightly colored *Pluteus* species, all of which have salmon or pinkish spores that gradually color the gills. They are related to *Volvariella* species, but not to the equally pink-spored *Entoloma* group. Most *Pluteus* species grow on wood and the Flame Shield has a preference for elm. When the British Isles lost 20 million of its elm trees to Dutch Elm Disease, the fungus became briefly more common than usual, thanks to all the dead elm wood. Now, however, it has become much rarer and is met with only occasionally.

SIMILAR SPECIES

Older, faded fruitbodies might be confused with some of the yellow-capped *Pluteus* species, such as the European *P. leoninus* or the North American *P. admirabilis*. *Mycena* species with scarlet to orange caps have white spores, and are usually less fleshy. *Mycena leaiana* also has orange gills.

The Flame Shield forms caps that are convex at first, becoming flat to umbonate. The cap surface is smooth or somewhat wrinkled, bright scarlet at first, becoming orange to yellow-orange with age. The gills are whitish at first, becoming salmon. The stem is smooth, whitish at first, becoming yellow from the base upward.

Actual size

FAMILY	Pluteaceae
DISTRIBUTION	Europe, North Africa, northern Asia
HABITAT	In woodland and hedgerows
ASSOCIATION	With broadleaf trees
GROWTH FORM	On stumps and dead wood, singly or in small groups
ABUNDANCE	Occasional
SPORE COLOR	Pink
EDIBILITY	Not edible

HEIGHT
Up to 3 in
(75 mm)

CAP DIAMETER
Up to 2½ in
(60 mm)

PLUTEUS LEONINUS

LION SHIELD

(SCHAEFFER) P. KUMMER

273

The epithet *leoninus* means "lionlike," and the yellow caps of *Pluteus leoninus* typically have a golden or tawny tint. The species is quite widespread in Europe, but nowhere common, the similar Yellow Shield (*P. chrysophaeus*) being rather more frequent. Both occur on dead or fallen wood of broadleaf trees. Like all *Pluteus* species, *P. leoninus* has been given the name "shield" in English (presumably with reference to a Roman round shield) from the rather neat shape of the cap. *Pluteus* is said to mean "a movable penthouse," a description which is deeply puzzling.

SIMILAR SPECIES

A very similar, yellow-capped species, *Pluteus admirabilis*, occurs in North America. The Yellow Shield (*P. chrysophaeus*), though typically with more greenish yellow caps, is another look-alike and is best distinguished microscopically. *Mycena* species with yellowish caps have white spores, and are usually less fleshy.

Actual size

The Lion Shield forms caps that are convex, becoming flat to umbonate. The cap surface is smooth, silky, yellow to golden to tawny-yellow, often brownish at the center. The gills are whitish at first, becoming salmon. The stem is smooth, whitish becoming yellow from the base upward.

FAMILY	Pluteaceae
DISTRIBUTION	North America, Europe, North Africa, South America, northern Asia
HABITAT	In woodland
ASSOCIATION	With broadleaf trees
GROWTH FORM	On dead wood, singly or in small groups
ABUNDANCE	Occasional
SPORE COLOR	Pink
EDIBILITY	Not edible

HEIGHT
Up to 3 in
(75 mm)

CAP DIAMETER
Up to 2 in
(50 mm)

274

PLUTEUS THOMSONII
VEINED SHIELD
(BERKELEY & BROOME) DENNIS

This little, pink-spored agaric often has a curious veinlike network on the cap surface that helps distinguish it from similar gray-brown *Pluteus* species. Fruitbodies are typically solitary, only occasionally appearing in small groups, and are found on stumps, fallen branches, or buried wood, when they look as if they are growing in soil or leaf litter. *Pluteus thomsonii* was originally described in 1876 from Kent in England, where it was discovered by a Dr. Thomson. It appears to be a widespread species in the north temperate region, but has also been recorded as far south as Brazil.

SIMILAR SPECIES

The Wrinkled Shield (*Pluteus phlebophorus*) is a more red-brown species that also has a veined or wrinkled cap, though the network is usually finer and less prominent than in *P. thomsonii*. Smooth-capped collections of the Veined Shield can be distinguished from other gray-brown *Pluteus* species, but only microscopically.

Actual size

The Veined Shield forms caps that are convex, becoming flat to shallowly umbonate. The cap surface is smooth, or with a veinlike network, at the center particularly, and buff to brown or dark reddish brown. The gills are whitish at first, becoming salmon. The stem is pale grayish to brownish, smooth but dusted whitish.

FAMILY	Psathyrellaceae
DISTRIBUTION	North America, Europe
HABITAT	In woodland
ASSOCIATION	With conifers
GROWTH FORM	On or near stumps
ABUNDANCE	Rare
SPORE COLOR	Black
EDIBILITY	Not edible

HEIGHT
Up to 5 in
(125 mm)

CAP DIAMETER
Up to 2 in
(50 mm)

PSATHYRELLA CAPUT-MEDUSAE

MEDUSA BRITTLESTEM

(FRIES) KONRAD & MAUBLANC

275

The Medusa Brittlestem takes its odd name from the shaggy scales on the cap and stem. In some collections, these can become very prominent and spiky—though the likeness to the Gorgon's serpent-haired head (*caput-medusae*) is a little fanciful. In other collections, the scales are not so prominent and the fruitbodies may look like those of a pale *Pholiota* species. The Medusa Brittlestem grows in clusters on old, dead conifer wood and seems to be an uncommon to rare species, appearing on the national Red Lists of threatened fungal species in many European countries.

SIMILAR SPECIES

The Yellowfoot Brittlestem (*Psathyrella cotonea*) also grows in clusters on stumps, but lacks the prominent ring of the Medusa Brittlestem and typically has a yellowish base to the stem. Some paler species of *Pholiota* may look superficially similar, but they have rusty brown spores.

Actual size

The Medusa Brittlestem produces fruitbodies in clusters. The caps are convex to umbonate, smooth at first but breaking up into scales toward the margin, and whitish to pale brown, darker at the center, the scales similarly colored or with darker tips. The gills are brown to blackish brown. Individual stems are cap-colored, with a pendulous ring (see photo right), and darker scales toward the base.

FAMILY	Psathyrellaceae
DISTRIBUTION	North America, Europe, New Zealand
HABITAT	In woodland, gardens, parkland, roadsides
ASSOCIATION	With broadleaf trees
GROWTH FORM	On buried wood and dead roots
ABUNDANCE	Locally common
SPORE COLOR	Black
EDIBILITY	Not edible

HEIGHT
Up to 5 in
(125 mm)

CAP DIAMETER
Up to 1 in
(25 mm)

276

PSATHYRELLA MULTIPEDATA
CLUSTERED BRITTLESTEM
(PECK) A. H. SMITH

Though *Psathyrella* species are common as a group, they tend to look very similar and are not so easy to identify to species. *Psathyrella multipedata* is an exception, since its fruitbodies do not appear in ordinary troops and tufts, but arise in massive, densely packed clusters from a single, buried, root-like base. The epithet *multipedata* means "many footed," since the cluster is in effect a single large fruitbody with many caps and stems. The Clustered Brittlestem grows on buried wood or dead roots and typically appears in disturbed ground, often along roadsides or in gardens.

SIMILAR SPECIES

The Common Stump Brittlestem (*Psathyrella piluliformis*) also grows in clusters, but has larger, brown to ocher-brown caps and typically occurs on rotten stumps and logs. The Fairy Inkcap (*Coprinellus disseminatus*) produces large numbers of fruitbodies on rotten wood, but in dense swarms rather than in a single clump.

Actual size

The Clustered Brittlestem produces fruitbodies in dense clusters. The individual caps are convex, very thin-fleshed and fragile, smooth, striate at the margin, and pale gray-brown when damp, drying dingy cream to gray-cream. The gills are whitish at first, becoming black. Individual stems are whitish, smooth, and fragile.

FAMILY	Tricholomataceae
DISTRIBUTION	North America, Europe, northern Asia
HABITAT	In woodland
ASSOCIATION	With conifers and broadleaf trees
GROWTH FORM	On ground, singly or in small troops
ABUNDANCE	Common
SPORE COLOR	White
EDIBILITY	Edible, but best avoided

HEIGHT
Up to 5 in
(125 mm)

CAP DIAMETER
Up to 3 in
(75 mm)

PSEUDOCLITOCYBE CYATHIFORMIS

THE GOBLET

(BULLIARD) SINGER

277

The Latin epithet *cyathiformis* means "goblet-shaped," and this elegantly long-stemmed agaric with its funnel-shaped cap certainly looks the part. It is a litter-rotting species, typically producing its fruitbodies late in the season after many other agarics have disappeared. The Goblet was originally described from France, but seems to be widespread throughout the north temperate region. It is edible, but not much valued, and would need to be very carefully distinguished from poisonous *Clitocybe* species, some of which also have funnel-shaped caps.

SIMILAR SPECIES

Cantharellula umbonata is of similar shape and color, but is a moss-associated agaric with a distinct umbo (raised boss) at the cap center and cream gills that bruise reddish. The Clouded Funnel (*Clitocybe nebularis*) is usually a much larger species, paler gray, and also with whitish to cream gills.

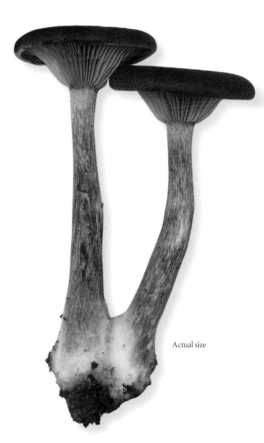

Actual size

The Goblet forms caps that are deeply depressed in the center, entirely funnel-shaped when old, smooth, dark purplish brown when moist, drying paler gray-brown. The gills are decurrent and pale grayish brown. The stem is smooth, swollen toward the base, and cap-colored, but with a fine, white, fibrous coating when young.

FAMILY	Strophariaceae
DISTRIBUTION	Southeastern North America, Central and South America, southern Asia, Australia
HABITAT	In pastures and manured grass
ASSOCIATION	With dung
GROWTH FORM	On dung, singly or in small groups
ABUNDANCE	Occasional
SPORE COLOR	Black
EDIBILITY	Poisonous (hallucinogenic)

HEIGHT
Up to 6 in
(150 mm)

CAP DIAMETER
Up to 3 in
(75 mm)

PSILOCYBE CUBENSIS
GOLD CAP
(EARLE) SINGER

278

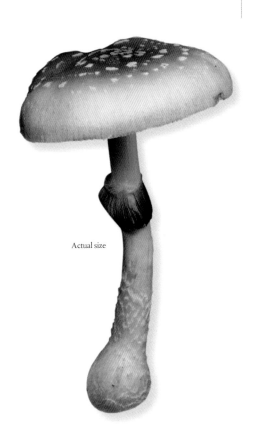

Actual size

Originally described from Cuba, the Gold Cap is a comparatively large, coprophilous (dung-loving) species, with a mainly tropical to subtropical distribution. Fruitbodies contain high levels of psilocybin, a psychoactive compound found in many *Psilocybe* species, including species used in mystic rituals by native peoples in Central America. The compound was first isolated in 1958 by Swiss scientist Albert Hoffman, the discoverer of LSD. Since then, the Gold Cap has been widely used as an hallucinogenic drug and has also been cultivated for this purpose, though in many countries such cultivation—or even possession of fruitbodies—is now illegal.

SIMILAR SPECIES
Psilocybe subcubensis has a similar distribution and is only distinguishable microscopically by its smaller spores. The Dung Roundhead (*Panaeolus semiovatus*) is a ringed species of similar size and habit, but has a more temperate distribution and has a paler, slimier cap, and mottled black gills.

The Gold Cap forms conical caps, becoming flat to shallowly umbonate. The cap surface is smooth, slimy when damp, cream to ocher to reddish brown, sometimes dotted with whitish veil remains. The gills are brown, becoming purple-black with a whitish edge. The stem is smooth, whitish to cap-colored, with a membranous ring. All parts may bruise dull bluish.

FAMILY	Strophariaceae
DISTRIBUTION	North America, Europe, northern Asia, Australia, New Zealand
HABITAT	In pastures and manured grass
ASSOCIATION	With grass and dung
GROWTH FORM	In grass, less commonly on dung, singly or in small troops
ABUNDANCE	Common
SPORE COLOR	Black
EDIBILITY	Poisonous (hallucinogenic)

HEIGHT
Up to 5 in
(125 mm)

CAP DIAMETER
Up to 1½ in
(35 mm)

PSILOCYBE SEMILANCEATA

LIBERTY CAP

(FRIES) P. KUMMER

279

This innocent-looking, little dung fungus has achieved notoriety in recent years, thanks to its reputation as an hallucinogen. Fruitbodies contain the psychoactive compound psilocybin. The English name Liberty Cap comes from the fungal cap's resemblance to the pointed Phrygian cap, adopted as a symbol of liberty during the French Revolution. The alternative name of the Magic Mushroom is also used for other psychoactive fungi. Although gathering Magic Mushrooms has become a popular ritual for enthusiasts, it is also now illegal in many countries, and possession of collected specimens may be regarded as a serious criminal offence.

SIMILAR SPECIES

Other small and rather similar *Psilocybe* species also grow in grassland, but lack the distinctively pointed cap of *P. semilanceata*. *Panaeolus* species are also similar, but have mottled black gills. Some grassland *Conocybe* species, like *Psilocybe semilanceata*, have pointed caps, but all have rusty brown spores and gills.

The Liberty Cap forms conical caps, usually with a sharply pointed umbo at the center. The cap surface is smooth, ocher to ocher-brown, and sometimes slimy when damp, drying buff. The gills are brownish, becoming dark gray to purple-black. The stem is smooth to finely fibrous, silvery white to cap-colored. All parts may bruise dull bluish.

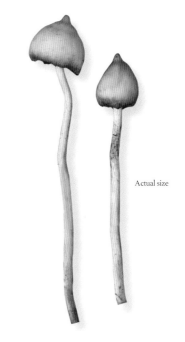

Actual size

FAMILY	Marasmiaceae
DISTRIBUTION	North America, Europe, North Africa, northern Asia
HABITAT	In woodland
ASSOCIATION	With conifers and broadleaf trees
GROWTH FORM	On ground, singly or in troops
ABUNDANCE	Very common
SPORE COLOR	Pale pinkish buff
EDIBILITY	Edible

HEIGHT	Up to 4 in (100 mm)
CAP DIAMETER	Up to 3 in (75 mm)

280

RHODOCOLLYBIA BUTYRACEA

BUTTER CAP

(BULLIARD) LENNOX

The Butter Cap takes its Latin and English names from the slippery, buttery feel to the cap surface when moist. It is very common, especially with conifers, continuing to produce fruitbodies late in the season. It is also very variable, partly because the caps are hygrophanous—changing color according to humidity—which often makes them appear two-toned, with a darker (moist) center and paler (drier) margins. In addition, the species is currently split between the standard reddish brown variety and the locally commoner ocher to gray-brown variety (var. *asema*).

SIMILAR SPECIES

The much less common *Rhodocollybia prolixa* var. *distorta* (and *R. badiialba* in western North America) is somewhat similar, but has a non-hygrophanous, reddish brown cap with a stem that often appears twisted. The common Russet Toughshank (*Gymnopus dryophilus*) is a much slimmer species, with a paler orange-russet to ocher-buff cap.

Actual size

The Butter Cap forms caps that are convex, becoming flat to shallowly umbonate. The cap surface is smooth, slippery, and hygrophanous so that when wet it is yellow-brown, gray-brown, or dark red-brown, and when dry it is buff or gray-buff, the center long remaining darker. The gills are whitish. The stem is smooth, swollen toward the base, and pale, becoming cap-colored.

FAMILY	Physalacriaceae
DISTRIBUTION	Eastern North America, Europe, northern Asia
HABITAT	In woodland
ASSOCIATION	With broadleaf trees, particularly elm
GROWTH FORM	On stumps or logs, singly or in small clusters
ABUNDANCE	Occasional
SPORE COLOR	White
EDIBILITY	Not edible

HEIGHT
Up to 2 in
(50 mm)

CAP DIAMETER
Up to 6 in
(150 mm)

RHODOTUS PALMATUS

WRINKLED PEACH

(BULLIARD) MAIRE

281

Rhodotus palmatus has a curious and distinctive cap that is gelatinous below the surface, so that just pressing it with a finger can cause it to wrinkle. It also wrinkles naturally, sometimes forming a network of veins. Though the fruitbodies smell fruity, they are bitter and inedible. The Wrinkled Peach typically grows on rotten elm wood, less frequently on other trees, and is widespread but seldom common. In some European countries it is on the Red List of threatened fungal species and in a few countries it is even protected by law.

SIMILAR SPECIES

There are no closely related species. Pink forms of *Pleurotus djamor* may be similarly colored, but have non-wrinkled caps and are tropical or subtropical. The Peeling Oysterling (*Crepidotus mollis*) and the Saffron Oysterling (*C. crocophyllus*) may sometimes feel gelatinous, but they are stemless and brown-spored.

The Wrinkled Peach forms caps that are convex, becoming flat. The cap surface is smooth to veined or wrinkled, the veins sometimes forming a raised network, pink to flesh-pink. The gills are pale cap-colored. The stem is often off-center or lateral, smooth, whitish to cap-colored or yellowish pink.

Actual size

FAMILY	Repetobasidiaceae
DISTRIBUTION	North America, Europe, North Africa, Central and South America, Antarctica, northern Asia, Australia, New Zealand
HABITAT	In mossy grassland, lawns, more rarely woodland
ASSOCIATION	With moss
GROWTH FORM	On ground, in scattered troops
ABUNDANCE	Very common
SPORE COLOR	White
EDIBILITY	Not edible

HEIGHT
Up to 2 in
(50 mm)

CAP DIAMETER
Up to ½ in
(15 mm)

RICKENELLA FIBULA
ORANGE MOSSCAP
(BULLIARD) RAITHELHUBER

282

Despite its small size, the Orange Mosscap is a familiar sight, thanks to its bright color and its habit of growing underfoot, in mossy lawns. The species is, in fact, intimately associated with mosses, the fungal hyphae penetrating the rhizoids (root-like hairs) of the moss. Whether the fungus is a parasite of the moss or whether the association is mutually beneficial is, as yet, unknown. The Orange Mosscap was formerly known as *Gerronema fibula*, which explains why cytotoxic compounds isolated from the fungus have been called gerronemins. It is possible they may prove useful in anticancer research.

SIMILAR SPECIES

The small size, orange caps, decurrent gills, and growth in moss should be distinctive. Waxcaps (*Hygrocybe* species) also grow with moss and may be similarly colored, but only a few have decurrent gills and almost all are larger. Many small *Galerina* species are also found in moss, but they have rusty brown gills and spores.

Actual size

The Orange Mosscap forms caps that are convex at first, becoming convex to flat with a central depression. The cap surface is smooth, strongly striate, pale yellow-orange to orange when damp, drying paler or buff. The gills are decurrent, rather thick, and whitish to pale cap-colored. The narrow stem is smooth and cap-colored.

FAMILY	Repetobasidiaceae
DISTRIBUTION	North America, Europe, New Zealand
HABITAT	In mossy grassland, lawns, more rarely woodland
ASSOCIATION	With moss
GROWTH FORM	On ground, in scattered troops
ABUNDANCE	Common
SPORE COLOR	White
EDIBILITY	Not edible

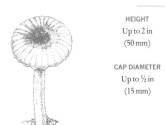

HEIGHT
Up to 2 in
(50 mm)

CAP DIAMETER
Up to ½ in
(15 mm)

RICKENELLA SWARTZII

COLLARED MOSSCAP

(FRIES) KUYPER

283

Apart from its color, the Collared Mosscap is similar to the Orange Mosscap and the two frequently occur together in mossy lawns and grassland. The Collared Mosscap seems, however, to be geographically more restricted than the world-spanning *Rickenella fibula*. Molecular research has shown that both these *Rickenella* species, together with a few similar moss associates, are very distant from most other agarics. They actually belong to the order Hymenochaetales, which includes many large bracket fungi, such as the Robust Bracket (*Phellinus robustus*).

SIMILAR SPECIES

Rickenella swartzii is distinguished by its small size, decurrent gills, growth in moss, and dark-centered cap. *Lichenomphalia umbellifera* is almost as small and has decurrent gills, but its cap is usually pale brown to buff throughout and it is a lichenized species, usually found on heaths and moors, rather than mossy lawns and grassland.

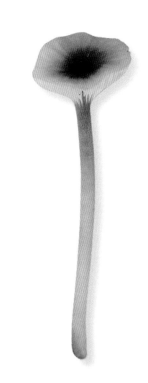

Actual size

The Collared Mosscap forms caps that are convex at first, becoming convex to flat with a central depression (see photo above). The cap surface is smooth, strongly striate, dark purple-brown to sepia at the center, pale brown toward the margin. The gills are decurrent, rather thick, and whitish. The narrow stem is smooth, dark brown at the top, paler toward the base.

FAMILY	Tricholomataceae
DISTRIBUTION	North America, Europe, North Africa, Central America, western Asia
HABITAT	In woodland
ASSOCIATION	With broadleaf trees and conifers
GROWTH FORM	On ground, singly or in troops
ABUNDANCE	Occasional
SPORE COLOR	Pale brown
EDIBILITY	Not edible

HEIGHT
Up to 2 in
(50 mm)

CAP DIAMETER
Up to 1½ in
(40 mm)

284

RIPARTITES TRICHOLOMA
BEARDED SEAMINE
(ALBERTINI & SCHWEINITZ) P. KARSTEN

Actual size

This odd little agaric was once referred to *Inocybe* and also to *Paxillus* because of its pale brownish spores and buff gills. In fact it is more closely related to white-spored species of *Tricholoma*, than to any of the brown-spored groups. It takes its peculiar English name from its almost spherical spores with peglike projections—fancifully reminiscent of an old-fashioned naval mine. The beard refers to the shaggy margin of the cap, but this is rather variable and tends to disappear with age.

The Bearded Seamine forms caps that are convex, becoming flat to weakly depressed. The cap surface is whitish, finely felted to distinctly hairy at first, especially at the margin, becoming smooth with age. The gills are weakly decurrent, buff to pinkish gray. The stem is almost smooth, whitish to buff or pinkish gray.

SIMILAR SPECIES

Ripartites is a small genus, but there are a few uncommon species that are similar, all of them best distinguished microscopically. Many species of *Clitocybe* are similarly shaped and several have pinkish to grayish, decurrent gills. They are typically smooth-capped, however, and their spore prints are never pale brown.

FAMILY	Mycenaceae
DISTRIBUTION	North America, Europe, northern Asia
HABITAT	In woodland, hedgerows, and scrub
ASSOCIATION	With broadleaf trees, conifers, and herbaceous plants
GROWTH FORM	On fallen leaf and needle litter, dead twigs and stems
ABUNDANCE	Common
SPORE COLOR	White
EDIBILITY	Not edible

HEIGHT	Up to 2 in (50 mm)
CAP DIAMETER	Up to ½ in (15 mm)

RORIDOMYCES RORIDUS

DRIPPING BONNET

(SCOPOLI) REXER

285

This little agaric can sometimes occur abundantly on fallen conifer needles, on dead bramble stems, and other small plant remains. The Latin *roridus* means "bedewed," and in damp weather, *Roridomyces roridus* is remarkable for the extraordinarily thick, slimy-gelatinous coating to the stem that often exceeds the width of the stem itself, as if it were encased in aspic. The Dripping Bonnet otherwise resembles a species of *Mycena* and was indeed placed in this genus until recently. Curiously, the fruitbodies produce luminous spores, one of several examples of bioluminescence in fungi.

SIMILAR SPECIES

The thick, slimy-gelatinous coating to the stem is distinctive, though similar species occur elsewhere. *Roridomyces austrororidus* is found in Australia and New Zealand and *R. lamprosporus* in the tropics, including southern Asia and South America. Both are distinguished by microscopic characters.

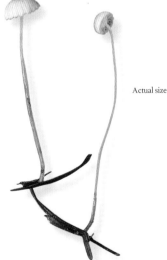

Actual size

The Dripping Bonnet forms caps that are convex to flat, sometimes with a central depression. The cap surface is smooth, becoming ridged, pale gray-brown at the center, whitish toward the margin. The gills are decurrent and whitish. The narrow stem is smooth, dark brown at the top, paler toward the base, and covered in a thick, gelatinous slime when damp.

FAMILY	Russulaceae
DISTRIBUTION	Europe, North Africa, northern Asia
HABITAT	In woodland
ASSOCIATION	Ectomycorrhizal, with broadleaf trees
GROWTH FORM	On ground, singly or in troops
ABUNDANCE	Occasional
SPORE COLOR	Ocher
EDIBILITY	Edible

HEIGHT
Up to 5 in
(125 mm)

CAP DIAMETER
Up to 4 in
(100 mm)

286

RUSSULA AUREA
GILDED BRITTLEGILL
PERSOON

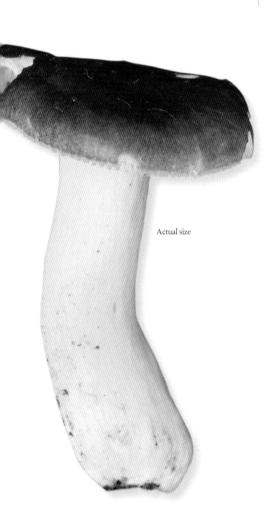

Actual size

The Latin epithet *aurea* means "golden," and the golden-yellow gills and yellow-flushed stem are distinctive features of this attractive *Russula* species. Though it typically associates with a range of familiar broadleaf trees—especially hazel, oak, and beech—the Gilded Brittlegill is not a common species and seems to become rarer in the northern part of its range. It occurs in Asia as well as Europe, and has even featured on postage stamps from Bhutan. The flesh is mild-tasting and fruitbodies are edible, though not greatly sought after.

SIMILAR SPECIES
Several other red-capped *Russula* species, such as the Sickener (*R. emetica*) and the Beechwood Sickener (*R. nobilis*), have a bitter or acrid taste and are not edible. Many have white gills, however, and none has the yellow-flushed stem that is seen in the Gilded Brittlegill.

The Gilded Brittlegill has caps that are hemispherical at first, becoming convex to flat. The cap surface is smooth, bright copper-red to rusty red. The gills are pale to deep yellow-ocher, the edges often brighter golden yellow. The stem is smooth and whitish, frequently with a bright yellow flush.

FAMILY	Russulaceae
DISTRIBUTION	North America, Europe
HABITAT	In woodland
ASSOCIATION	Ectomycorrhizal, with pine
GROWTH FORM	On ground, singly or in troops
ABUNDANCE	Common
SPORE COLOR	Pale ocher
EDIBILITY	Edible

HEIGHT
Up to 4 in
(100 mm)

CAP DIAMETER
Up to 3 in
(75 mm)

RUSSULA CAERULEA

HUMPBACK BRITTLEGILL

(PERSOON) FRIES

287

This is one of the commoner and more distinctive *Russula* species occurring with pines, and can be abundant in plantations as well as natural forests. It has been given its odd English name because of its typically umbonate cap (having a central hump or boss), which is unusual for a *Russula* species. The dark violet colors of the cap and its shiny or glossy surface are also distinctive. Fruitbodies of the Humpback Brittlegill are edible and mild, but the cap skin (which can be peeled off) is bitter.

SIMILAR SPECIES

The Purple Brittlegill (*Russula atropurpurea*) has a dark cap that is almost black at the center, but reddish to purple toward the margin. Though it occurs occasionally with pines, it is more frequent with oak. The North American *R. placita* is a conifer species with dark purple cap, but is thin-fleshed. Both these species lack the umbo of *R. caerulea*.

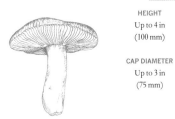

The Humpback Brittlegill has caps that are hemispherical at first, becoming umbonate when expanded. The cap surface is smooth, rather glossy, dark violet to brownish violet. The gills are pale to deep ocher (see photo above). The stem is white and smooth.

Actual size

FAMILY	Russulaceae
DISTRIBUTION	North America, Europe, northern Asia
HABITAT	In wet woodland
ASSOCIATION	Ectomycorrhizal, with birch
GROWTH FORM	On ground, amongst sphagnum moss, singly or in troops
ABUNDANCE	Common
SPORE COLOR	Pale ocher
EDIBILITY	Edible

HEIGHT
Up to 4 in
(100 mm)

CAP DIAMETER
Up to 5 in
(125 mm)

288

RUSSULA CLAROFLAVA

YELLOW SWAMP BRITTLEGILL

GROVE

This is a cheerful agaric to discover growing among sphagnum moss in wet woodland, marshes, swamps, and bogs where birch is present. Its bright yellow caps are conspicuous and can be common in the right habitat. Like a number of *Russula* species, fruitbodies of the Yellow Swamp Brittlegill tend to turn gray-black when bruised (sometimes turning reddish first), a color change that is especially noticeable in the gills and stem. *Russula claroflava* was first described from England, but is widespread throughout the north temperate zone. The fruitbodies are mild-tasting and edible, though rather thin-fleshed and not highly valued.

The Yellow Swamp Brittlegill has caps that are hemispherical, becoming convex to flat, sometimes weakly depressed, smooth, slightly sticky when moist, and bright lemon-yellow to yellow. The gills are whitish at first, becoming pale ocher. The stem is smooth and white. Gills and stem may turn slowly gray-black when bruised, or become grayish with age.

SIMILAR SPECIES

The Ocher Brittlegill (*Russula ochroleuca*) is probably the commonest of the yellow brittlegills, but has duller, more ocher-yellow caps and occurs in ordinary mixed woodland, not just in wet areas with birch. The uncommon *R. solaris* can have a bright yellow cap, but typically occurs in calcareous woodland with beech. Neither has flesh which turns gray-black.

Actual size

FAMILY	Russulaceae
DISTRIBUTION	North America, Europe, North Africa, Central America, northern Asia
HABITAT	In woodland
ASSOCIATION	Ectomycorrhizal, with broadleaf trees, less commonly conifers
GROWTH FORM	On ground, singly or in troops
ABUNDANCE	Very common
SPORE COLOR	White
EDIBILITY	Edible

HEIGHT
Up to 4 in
(100 mm)

CAP DIAMETER
Up to 4 in
(100 mm)

RUSSULA CYANOXANTHA

CHARCOAL BURNER

(SCHAEFFER) FRIES

289

The Charcoal Burner has a deceptive range of cap colors that may baffle beginners. Indeed, an older English name for the species was the Chameleon. Fortunately, it is a very common agaric and its typical palette of dull violets, purples, and gray-greens gradually becomes familiar. The curious name Charcoal Burner seems to derive from the French *Russule Charbonnière*, presumably referring to the rather smoky appearance of the fruitbodies—*charbonnière* being French for a charcoal burner. The unhelpful epithet *cyanoxantha* means "blue and yellow," two colors which are rarely, if ever, present. Once recognized, the Charcoal Burner is considered a good edible species.

SIMILAR SPECIES

Though the colors are variable, the gills of the Charcoal Burner are distinct, since they are supple and slightly greasy, not brittle as in most *Russula* species. A similar species, *R. variata*, occurs in eastern North America, mainly distinguished by its acrid taste.

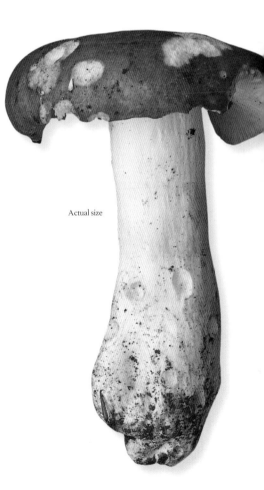

Actual size

The Charcoal Burner has caps that are hemispherical at first, becoming convex to flat or slightly depressed. The cap surface is smooth to finely veined, dull gray-violet or purple with gray-green tints, often with cream or pinkish discolored areas, occasionally entirely dull green. The gills are white and flexible (not brittle). The stem is smooth and white, sometimes flushed violet.

FAMILY	Russulaceae
DISTRIBUTION	North America, Europe, northern Asia
HABITAT	In woodland
ASSOCIATION	Ectomycorrhizal, with conifers, particularly pine
GROWTH FORM	On ground, singly or in troops
ABUNDANCE	Locally common
SPORE COLOR	Pale ocher
EDIBILITY	Edible

HEIGHT
Up to 5 in
(125 mm)

CAP DIAMETER
Up to 6 in
(150 mm)

290

RUSSULA DECOLORANS

COPPER BRITTLEGILL

(FRIES) FRIES

The Copper Brittlegill, which is also known as the Graying Russula, is a common species in northern and montane conifer forests, and seems to be particularly associated with pines. It is recognizable not only because of the copper-orange cap but also because it discolors gray to black with handling or with age. Even the flesh turns slowly gray when cut. Despite this rather off-putting characteristic, the Copper Brittlegill is an edible species with a mild taste—though there are some similar graying species which may be acrid or otherwise unpleasant.

SIMILAR SPECIES

The conifer associate *Russula paludosa* can be similarly colored, though typically it has a more reddish cap with a stem that is sometimes flushed pink. Cut flesh turns gray, but not black, and is somewhat bitter to acrid. *Russula vinosa* is another graying conifer species, but has a purplish cap.

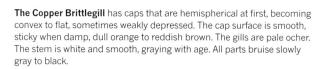

Actual size

The Copper Brittlegill has caps that are hemispherical at first, becoming convex to flat, sometimes weakly depressed. The cap surface is smooth, sticky when damp, dull orange to reddish brown. The gills are pale ocher. The stem is white and smooth, graying with age. All parts bruise slowly gray to black.

FAMILY	Russulaceae
DISTRIBUTION	North America, Europe, North Africa, Central America, northern Asia
HABITAT	In woodland
ASSOCIATION	Ectomycorrhizal, with conifers, especially pine
GROWTH FORM	On ground, singly or in troops
ABUNDANCE	Common
SPORE COLOR	White
EDIBILITY	Poisonous (said to be edible after processing)

HEIGHT
Up to 4 in
(100 mm)

CAP DIAMETER
Up to 4 in
(100 mm)

RUSSULA EMETICA

THE SICKENER

(SCHAEFFER) PERSOON

291

The Sickener is clearly not a good, edible species. The flesh is hot and acrid and, if consumed, causes gastroenteritic poisoning. Despite this, it used to be widely eaten in eastern Europe, Russia, and elsewhere after boiling (with a change of water) to remove most of the toxins, followed by salting or pickling—the same process used for the equally toxic *Lactarius torminosus*. This was presumably done out of winter necessity, rather than because the result tasted good. It is not recommended. The Sickener is a conifer associate, with a preference for damp or wet woodland. A similar and equally common species grows in beechwoods.

SIMILAR SPECIES

The Bloody Brittlegill (*Russula sanguinaria*) has a red cap and grows with conifers, but its stem is also flushed red. The Beechwood Sickener (*R. nobilis*) is very similar to *R. emetica*, but, as the name indicates, occurs with beech, not conifers. More than 100 additional, red-capped *Russula* species are known worldwide.

Actual size

The Sickener has caps that are hemispherical at first, becoming convex to flat, sometimes weakly depressed. The cap surface is smooth, scarlet to bright cherry-red, and peels easily almost to the center. The gills are white to pale cream. The stem is white and smooth to finely and irregularly ridged.

FAMILY	Russulaceae
DISTRIBUTION	North America, Europe, North Africa, Central America, northern Asia
HABITAT	In woodland
ASSOCIATION	Ectomycorrhizal, with broadleaf trees and conifers
GROWTH FORM	On ground, singly or in troops
ABUNDANCE	Very common
SPORE COLOR	White
EDIBILITY	Not edible, best avoided

HEIGHT
Up to 4 in
(100 mm)

CAP DIAMETER
Up to 8 in
(200 mm)

292

RUSSULA NIGRICANS
BLACKENING BRITTLEGILL
(BULLIARD) FRIES

Actual size

The Blackening Brittlegill belongs to a group of *Russula* species that have unusually solid, chunky fruitbodies that gradually blacken with age. These old, blackened fruitbodies can persist for weeks, sometimes providing a home for the Powdery Piggyback (*Asterophora lycoperdoides*), a small agaric that grows on the remains. The species is sometimes considered edible, but has been implicated in cases of gastroenteritic poisoning. It is also close to the lethally poisonous *Russula subnigricans*. On a more positive note, a compound called nigricanin has been isolated from fruitbodies and may have potential antitumor properties.

SIMILAR SPECIES
Russula subnigricans is an extremely poisonous species known from Eastern Asia and possibly present in southern North America. Its cut flesh reddens, but does not turn black. *Russula densifolia* is a widespread species, distinguished by having gills that are not widely spaced. *Russula albonigra* has flesh that turns slowly black (not red) when cut.

The Blackening Brittlegill has caps that are convex, becoming flatter and depressed with age. The cap surface is smooth, sordid whitish to cream with smoky, gray-brown patches, eventually becoming black. The gills are widely spaced, sordid white to cream, becoming gray-brown, then black. The stem is cap-colored. Cut flesh turns red (see photos left), then slowly gray to black.

FAMILY	Russulaceae
DISTRIBUTION	Europe; introduced in South Africa, southern South America
HABITAT	In woodland
ASSOCIATION	Ectomycorrhizal, with pine
GROWTH FORM	On ground, singly or in troops
ABUNDANCE	Common
SPORE COLOR	Pale yellow-ocher
EDIBILITY	Not edible

HEIGHT
Up to 4 in
(100 mm)

CAP DIAMETER
Up to 5 in
(125 mm)

RUSSULA SARDONIA

PRIMROSE BRITTLEGILL

FRIES

293

There are many *Russula* species with dark red to violet caps, but *R. sardonia* stands out from the crowd, thanks to its deeply colored stem and contrasting, primrose gills. It is typically associated with pine, perhaps exclusively with Scots pine—hence its comparatively restricted natural range. The epithet *sardonia* means "bitter" or "acrid" (as in the English word "sardonic"). As is often the case amongst *Russula* species, odd color forms occasionally occur (greenish and yellow, in the case of *R. sardonia*), which are difficult to identify without microscopic examination.

SIMILAR SPECIES

Russula torulosa is very similar, with a less acrid taste and slightly paler gills. The Fruity Brittlegill (*Russula queletii*) is also similar, but is associated with spruce, and has a red-purple cap and stem, with pale cream gills. The Bloody Brittlegill (*R. sanguinaria*) grows with conifers, but has a deep red cap and red-flushed stem.

The Primrose Brittlegill has caps that are hemispherical at first, becoming convex to flat. The cap surface is smooth, typically deep purple-violet, less commonly red-purple (greenish or yellow in two rare color forms). The gills are pale yellow-cream (see photo top right). The stem is smooth, flushed with the cap color.

Actual size

FAMILY	Russulaceae
DISTRIBUTION	North America, Europe, North Africa, northern Asia
HABITAT	In woodland
ASSOCIATION	Ectomycorrhizal, with broadleaf trees, rarely conifers
GROWTH FORM	On ground, singly or in troops
ABUNDANCE	Common
SPORE COLOR	White
EDIBILITY	Edible

HEIGHT
Up to 4 in
(100 mm)

CAP DIAMETER
Up to 4 in
(100 mm)

294

RUSSULA VESCA
THE FLIRT
FRIES

The caps of *Russula* species are covered in a thin, slightly elastic, skinlike cuticle that can often be peeled off from the margin. An unusual feature of *R. vesca* is that the cuticle frequently peels back from the margin of its own accord, revealing the whitish undersurface and petticoatlike or toothlike gill-edges below. This is the reason why the species has been given the odd English name of The Flirt, or, less coquettishly, the Bare-toothed Brittlegill. Under any name, it is a fairly common species, most frequently found with oak, often early in the season.

SIMILAR SPECIES
The ham- or baconlike cap color and the tendency (in older fruitbodies) for the cuticle to peel back from the cap margin help make this species recognizable. Many other species have pinkish caps, including the smaller and rather delicate *Russula gracillima*, which is common with birch, and the much more compact *R. faginea* with beech.

Actual size

The Flirt has caps that are hemispherical (see photo above), becoming convex to flat. The cap surface is smooth, and typically brownish pink (ham-colored) to pale purplish-buff. The gills are whitish to pale cream. The stem is smooth, white, rarely with a pinkish flush.

FAMILY	Russulaceae
DISTRIBUTION	Europe, North Africa, northern and southeastern Asia
HABITAT	In woodland
ASSOCIATION	Ectomycorrhizal, with broadleaf trees, rarely conifers
GROWTH FORM	On ground, singly or in troops
ABUNDANCE	Common
SPORE COLOR	White
EDIBILITY	Edible

HEIGHT
Up to 4 in
(100 mm)

CAP DIAMETER
Up to 4 in
(100 mm)

RUSSULA VIOLEIPES

VELVET BRITTLEGILL

QUÉLET

295

This oddly colored but attractive agaric can frequently be found with oak and beech, often quite early in the season. Like many other *Russula* species, the Velvet Brittlegill is very variable in color, with caps ranging from lemon-yellow to deep purple, sometimes with greenish, buff, olive, or bronze tints. This is one of the reasons why the brittlegills have earned themselves a reputation for being a "difficult" group to identify. In addition, there are a lot of different species—with well over 300 recorded from the Americas and nearly 150 in the British Isles alone.

SIMILAR SPECIES

The contrasting yellowish cap and purple-flushed stem should be distinctive, though the less common *Russula amoenicolor* is very similar and is best distinguished microscopically. Purple-capped forms of the Velvet Brittlegill are also similar to *R. amoena*, which again is best distinguished microscopically.

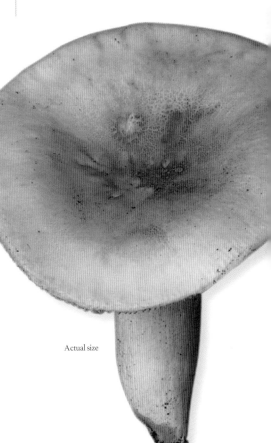

Actual size

The Velvet Brittlegill has caps that are hemispherical at first, becoming convex to flat. The cap surface is smooth, typically olive-yellow with purple tints at the center, less commonly wholly lemon-yellow or purple. The gills are pale cream. The stem is smooth, white, typically flushed (in part) red-purple or purple, and often tapering to the base (see photo above).

FAMILY	Russulaceae
DISTRIBUTION	North America, Europe, North Africa, Central America, northern and southeastern Asia
HABITAT	In woodland
ASSOCIATION	Ectomycorrhizal, with broadleaf trees, especially oak and beech
GROWTH FORM	On ground, singly or in troops
ABUNDANCE	Common
SPORE COLOR	White
EDIBILITY	Edible

HEIGHT
Up to 4 in
(100 mm)

CAP DIAMETER
Up to 4 in
(100 mm)

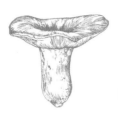

296

RUSSULA VIRESCENS
GREENCRACKED BRITTLEGILL
(SCHAEFFER) FRIES

The Greencracked Brittlegill is one of several *Russula* species in which the skin (or cuticle) of the cap breaks up as the fruitbodies expand, giving the surface a mosaic-like appearance, as if covered with a crust of small flakes or tiles. It is a fairly common species, typically growing with beech and oak. It is also widely eaten, especially in eastern Europe and eastern Asia, though care needs to be taken since the Death Cap (*Amanita phalloides*) is also green-capped, though its stem has a distinctive ring and sack-like volva at the base.

SIMILAR SPECIES

A number of closely related species have recently been identified in eastern North America, including the smaller, but otherwise similar, *Russula parvovirescens*. The Green Brittlegill (*R. aeruginea*) is a more widespread, green-capped species, but the cuticle does not crack, the cap surface often becomes brown-spotted, and fruitbodies are typically found with birch.

Actual size

The Greencracked Brittlegill has caps that are hemispherical at first, becoming convex to flat. The cap surface is smooth, but cracks into small, mosaic-like pieces with age, green to gray-green, fading to ocher-green. The gills are pale cream. The stem is smooth and white. The flesh is white and fairly dense.

FAMILY	Schizophyllaceae
DISTRIBUTION	North America, Europe, Africa, Central and South America, Asia, Australia, New Zealand
HABITAT	Woodland, grassland, farmland, and man-made habitats
ASSOCIATION	On woody debris of all kinds, from branches to straw bales
GROWTH FORM	Singly or more usually in large clusters
ABUNDANCE	Very common
SPORE COLOR	White
EDIBILITY	Edible

HEIGHT
Up to ¼ in
(5 mm)

CAP DIAMETER
Up to 1½ in
(40 mm)

SCHIZOPHYLLUM COMMUNE
SPLITGILL
FRIES

297

The Splitgill is one of the most widely distributed of all larger fungi, capable of utilizing many different food sources. The unusual, divided gills are an adaptation to arid climates, protecting the spore-producing surfaces in dry periods. The fungus can also tolerate high temperatures. These capabilities have led to (fortunately rare) medical reports of Splitgill infecting immunocompromised patients. On a more positive note, trials suggest it may improve survival rates for gastric and cervical cancer when used with chemotherapy. It is sold for medicinal purposes as a tea and in capsule form. Though tough, it is also widely used as food in the tropics.

SIMILAR SPECIES
No other group of fungi has grooved or split gills like *Schizophyllum*. *Plicaturopsis crispa* has a tough, hairy, wavy cap, but with veinlike gills underneath. Species of fan-shaped *Crepidotus* have narrow but normal gills with brown spores.

The Splitgill has beige-gray, fan-shaped brackets with a wavy edge, and a slighty hairy surface. In dry weather they shrivel and roll inward. The pinkish white gills radiate out from the point of attachment and have a distinct groove or split, the sides of which curl inward in dry weather and open up in wet. The thin, grayish white flesh is tough and leathery.

Actual size

FAMILY	Tricholomataceae
DISTRIBUTION	North America, continental Europe
HABITAT	In woodland
ASSOCIATION	On *Hebeloma mesophaeum*
GROWTH FORM	Parasitizing fruitbodies, singly or in clusters
ABUNDANCE	Rare
SPORE COLOR	White
EDIBILITY	Not edible

HEIGHT
Up to 1½ in
(40 mm)

CAP DIAMETER
Up to 2 in
(50 mm)

298

SQUAMANITA ODORATA
FRAGRANT STRANGLER
(COOL) IMBACH

Rarely-encountered *Squamanita* species mystified mycologists for many years, until it was realized that they were parasites on the fruitbodies of other agarics. Indeed, the strange, swollen "bulbs" at the base of *Squamanita* stems are the galled remains of the host. *Squamanita odorata* takes its Latin and English names from its sweet smell (which is said to be like artificial grape juice). DNA analysis shows that its host is a species of *Hebeloma*, specifically the common Veiled Poisonpie (*H. mesophaeum*). The Fragrant Strangler is anything but common, however, and is on the national Red Lists of threatened fungal species in many countries.

SIMILAR SPECIES
The Powdercap Strangler (*Squamanita paradoxa*) is similar, but emerges from the scaly remains of the Earthy Powdercap (*Cystoderma amianthinum*), and lacks the sweet smell. The Contorted Strangler (*S. contortipes*) is also similar, but grows on species of *Galerina*. Both occur in North America and Europe.

Actual size

The Fragrant Strangler forms caps that are hemispherical, becoming flat to weakly umbonate. The cap surface is scaly, gray-violet to gray-brown, the scales slightly darker. The gills are pale cap-colored. The stem is pale cap-colored, with darker scales toward the base, and arises from irregularly swollen, smooth, ocher-buff, bulb-like remains of the host.

FAMILY	Strophariaceae
DISTRIBUTION	North America, Europe, North Africa, South America, northern Asia, New Zealand
HABITAT	In woodland, also in woodchip mulch
ASSOCIATION	With broadleaf trees or conifers
GROWTH FORM	On ground, singly or in troops
ABUNDANCE	Common
SPORE COLOR	Dark purple-brown
EDIBILITY	Not edible

HEIGHT
Up to 3 in
(75 mm)

CAP DIAMETER
Up to 3 in
(75 mm)

STROPHARIA AERUGINOSA

VERDIGRIS AGARIC

(CURTIS) QUÉLET

299

This is an eye-catching species when young, with a cap and stem the color of weathered copper or bronze (verdigris). The extraordinary color fades with age, though it usually persists near the margin. Like most *Stropharia* species, the Verdigris Agaric prefers rich soils and has recently taken a liking to the woodchip mulch used in parks and gardens, where it can sometimes produce spectacular fruitings in large swarms. The species was first described from London in 1782 by naturalist William Curtis. It has a widespread distribution throughout north temperate regions and into South America, though it may be an exotic introduction in New Zealand.

SIMILAR SPECIES
The Verdigris Agaric is frequently confused with the related Blue Roundhead (*Stropharia caerulea*), which is commoner in grassland and has a poorly developed, nonpersistent ring. The Peppery Roundhead (*S. pseudocyanea*) is similar but drabber, with only weak, green to bluish tints in the cap.

Actual size

The Verdigris Agaric has caps that are convex, becoming flat to broadly umbonate. The cap surface is smooth, slimy when damp, and bright, deep turquoise when young with white veil remains near margin, fading with age to yellow-green or ocher. The gills are purplish gray to black. The stem is cap-colored, and is densely scaly below the persistent ring.

FAMILY	Strophariaceae
DISTRIBUTION	North America, Europe, North Africa, Central America, northern Asia, Australia, New Zealand
HABITAT	In pastures, lawns, and grassland
ASSOCIATION	With grass
GROWTH FORM	On ground, singly or in troops
ABUNDANCE	Common
SPORE COLOR	Dark purple-brown
EDIBILITY	Not edible, best avoided

HEIGHT
Up to 3 in
(75 mm)

CAP DIAMETER
Up to 3 in
(75 mm)

300

STROPHARIA CORONILLA
GARLAND ROUNDHEAD
(BULLIARD) QUÉLET

The Garland Roundhead is a species of pastures and turf, where it can often be mistaken—at least from a distance—for small specimens of the edible Field Mushroom (*Agaricus campestris*). *Stropharia coronilla* is said to be eaten and even sold in markets in Mexico, and fruitbodies are not known to contain any toxins. Nonetheless, it has been implicated in at least one case of gastroenteritic poisoning in North America, so is probably best avoided. The peculiar, grooved ring on the stem is distinctive, the grooves often highlighted by falling, purple-brown spores.

SIMILAR SPECIES
Stropharia melanosperma is a similar species, usually paler and more slender, but best distinguished microscopically. *Stropharia halophila* is salt-loving and is typically found in coastal dunes. The edible Field Mushroom (*Agaricus campestris*) has gills that are pinkish-red to chocolate-brown and "free" (not reaching the stem). It also lacks a distinctly grooved ring.

Actual size

The Garland Roundhead has caps that are convex, becoming flat. The cap surface is smooth, dull pale ocher to buff. The gills are pale brown to purplish black. The stem is whitish, tinged cap-color toward the base, with a persistent ring, grooved on the upper side.

FAMILY	Strophariaceae
DISTRIBUTION	North America, Europe, northern Asia
HABITAT	In woodland
ASSOCIATION	With conifers and broadleaf trees
GROWTH FORM	On very decayed, fallen wood, singly or in troops
ABUNDANCE	Locally common
SPORE COLOR	Dark purple-brown
EDIBILITY	Not edible

HEIGHT	Up to 6 in (150 mm)
CAP DIAMETER	Up to 6 in (150 mm)

STROPHARIA HORNEMANNII

CONIFER ROUNDHEAD

(FRIES) S. LUNDELL & NANNFELDT

301

This is one of the larger *Stropharia* species, but is confined
to northern and montane forests where it occurs predominantly
with conifers and can be locally common. It is sometimes
also found with broadleaf trees, mainly birch and more rarely
alder. Further south and in the lowlands, it becomes increasingly
rare and is unknown in countries such as
England and the Netherlands. It grows on
the decayed remains of fallen wood, but does
not yet seem to have colonized woodchip
mulch. The species was named in honor of
the Danish botanist Jens Wilken Hornemann, a friend
of Hans Christian Andersen.

SIMILAR SPECIES

The Wine Cap (*Stropharia rugosoannulata*) is of similar size
and appearance, but with a more distinctly red-toned cap, and a
lowland habit, typically on woodchip mulch. In western North
America, *S. ambigua* is another similar, lowland species, but has
a yellow-toned cap and lacks a well-defined ring.

The Conifer Roundhead has caps that are hemispherical
(see photo right), becoming convex to broadly umbonate.
The cap surface is smooth, slimy when damp, yellow-brown
to red-brown or purple-brown, with white veil remains at the
margin. The gills are whitish to gray-violet. The stem is whitish
at the top, yellow-brown toward the base, with a ring, and
dense scales below.

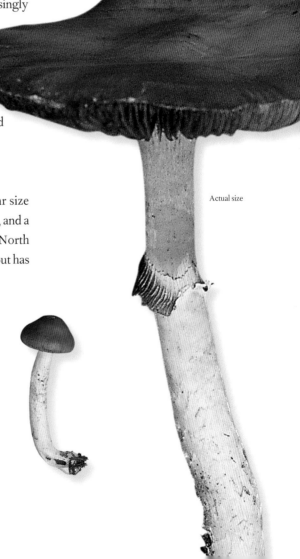

Actual size

FAMILY	Strophariaceae
DISTRIBUTION	North America, Europe, South America, northern Asia, Australia, New Zealand
HABITAT	In parkland, and gardens, often in woodchip mulch
ASSOCIATION	With broadleaf trees or conifers
GROWTH FORM	On ground or in woodchips, singly or in troops
ABUNDANCE	Locally common
SPORE COLOR	Dark purple-brown
EDIBILITY	Edible but best avoided

HEIGHT
Up to 8 in
(200 mm)

CAP DIAMETER
Up to 12 in
(300 mm)

STROPHARIA RUGOSOANNULATA
WINE CAP
FARLOW

The Wine Cap can grow to an impressive size, and is sometimes known as the King Stropharia or Garden Giant when grown in North America. The species was first described from rich, cultivated ground in Massachusetts, but its actual origin is unclear since it is nearly always found in gardens, arable fields, or (more recently) in woodchip mulch. In the 1960s, the Wine Cap was promoted as a garden crop in eastern Europe and it has since become a popular mushroom for home-growers (and some commercial growers) elsewhere, though it is said to cause gastroenteritic problems for a few people.

SIMILAR SPECIES

The Conifer Roundhead (*Stropharia hornemanii*) is similar, but typically grows on rotten, fallen wood in northern and montane conifer forests. True mushrooms (*Agaricus* species) may look superficially similar, but have pinkish to chocolate-brown gills that are "free"—not attached the stem, as in the Wine Cap.

The Wine Cap has caps that are convex, becoming flat to broadly umbonate. The cap surface is smooth to finely scaly, wine-red to purple-brown, sometimes yellow-brown (rarely entirely white), with white veil remains at the margin. The gills are pale gray, becoming purple-black. The stem is whitish to ocher, with a conspicuous double ring.

Actual size

FAMILY	Strophariaceae
DISTRIBUTION	North America, Europe, North Africa, Central and South America, northern Asia, Australia, New Zealand
HABITAT	In pastures
ASSOCIATION	On manured grass and dung
GROWTH FORM	On grass or dung, singly or in troops
ABUNDANCE	Very common
SPORE COLOR	Dark purple-brown
EDIBILITY	Not edible, best avoided

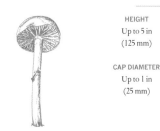

HEIGHT
Up to 5 in
(125 mm)

CAP DIAMETER
Up to 1 in
(25 mm)

STROPHARIA SEMIGLOBATA

DUNG ROUNDHEAD

(BATSCH) QUÉLET

303

Stropharia semiglobata is one of the commonest agarics associated with dung in pastures, appearing in damp weather at any time from spring to early winter. Its distribution is almost global, and it has been recorded on the dung of a wide range of domesticated and wild herbivores, from moose to wallabies. Though hardly appetizing, the Dung Roundhead is considered an edible species by some authorities. Others, however, list it as poisonous, so it is probably best avoided. It is typical for this species that the cap barely expands, but remains hemispherical, hence the epithet *semiglobata*.

SIMILAR SPECIES

Stropharia dorsispora is a look-alike species with a smell of flour, best distinguished microscopically. *Stropharia luteonitens* is similarly shaped and grows on dung, but has an umbonate cap with an orange-brown center. The Egghead Mottlegill (*Panaeolus semiovatus*) is typically much larger, and has a more bell-shaped, often wrinkled cap.

Actual size

The Dung Roundhead has caps that are hemispherical, barely expanding with age. The cap surface is smooth, sticky when damp, dull yellow to ocher or buff. The gills are pale olive-gray, becoming brown-black and mottled. The narrow stem is smooth, whitish and dry at the top, to ocher and sticky below, with a fragile ring often colored by the dark spores.

FAMILY	Tapinellaceae
DISTRIBUTION	North America, Europe, Central America, northern Asia
HABITAT	In woodland
ASSOCIATION	With conifers
GROWTH FORM	On stumps and at base of living or dead trunks
ABUNDANCE	Locally common
SPORE COLOR	Brown
EDIBILITY	Poisonous

HEIGHT
Up to 5 in
(125 mm)

CAP DIAMETER
Up to 10 in
(250 mm)

304

TAPINELLA ATROTOMENTOSA
VELVET ROLLRIM
(BATSCH) ŠUTARA

The Velvet Rollrim is a wood-rotting species, typically associated with conifers. Its velvety texture, decurrent gills, and general appearance are reminiscent of the Brown Rollrim (*Paxillus involutus*) and it was formerly placed in the same genus, though the two species are not closely related. The Velvet Rollrim is apparently eaten in parts of eastern Europe, but is bitter and has also been involved in poisoning cases, so is best left alone. Fruitbodies do have a use in craft-dyeing, however, producing a wide range of colors from violet to dark green and purplish black.

SIMILAR SPECIES

The related Oyster Rollrim (*Tapinella panuoides*) is much smaller and lacks a thick, velvety stem. The Brown Rollrim (*Paxillus involutus*) and related species have commonplace central stems and are ectomycorrhizal, typically growing on the ground with broadleaf trees, as well as with conifers.

The Velvet Rollrim forms caps that are convex, becoming flat to funnel-shaped with an inrolled margin. The cap surface is smooth and velvety, olive-brown to reddish brown, becoming darker with age. The gills are decurrent, pale ocher, and often developing rusty spots. The thick stem is off-center, velvety to woolly, and olive-brown to purplish brown, becoming blackish brown.

Actual size

FAMILY	Tapinellaceae
DISTRIBUTION	North America, Europe, North Africa, Central America, northern Asia, Australia, New Zealand
HABITAT	In woodland, occasionally on structural timber
ASSOCIATION	With conifers
GROWTH FORM	On stumps, fallen wood, woodchip mulch, and sawdust
ABUNDANCE	Common
SPORE COLOR	Brown
EDIBILITY	Not edible

HEIGHT
Up to ½ in
(10 mm)

CAP DIAMETER
Up to 5 in
(125 mm)

TAPINELLA PANUOIDES

OYSTER ROLLRIM

(BATSCH) E. -J. GILBERT

305

The Oyster Rollrim is a widespread fungus, always occurring on conifer wood in which it produces a brown, cubical rot. It can also rot softwood timber if it becomes sufficiently damp. In the eighteenth century, the great naturalist Alexander von Humboldt described *Tapinella panuoides* attacking pit props and mine timbers in Germany and, even today, the species is still occasionally referred to as the Mine Fungus. In buildings and timber yards, the Oyster Rollrim often occurs together with the Wet Rot Fungus (*Coniophora puteana*), since both species like the same conditions.

SIMILAR SPECIES

The Orange Mock Oyster (*Phyllotopsis nidulans*) is similarly shaped, but both cap and gills are orange, and it usually (but not always) grows on broadleaf wood. The Saffron Oysterling (*Crepidotus crocophyllus*) has yellow-orange gills with a cream to brownish, scaly cap, and also prefers broadleaf wood.

Actual size

The Oyster Rollrim forms caps that are fan-shaped with an inrolled margin, the surface smooth and velvety, ocher or buff to yellow-brown, sometimes with small, red-brown scales. The gills are decurrent, and pale orange to cap-colored. The stem is often absent, but when present is lateral and rudimentary, cap-colored or distinctly lilac.

FAMILY	Lyophyllaceae
DISTRIBUTION	Africa, Southeast Asia
HABITAT	In scrub, grassland, and woodland
ASSOCIATION	With termites
GROWTH FORM	On termitaries
ABUNDANCE	Common
SPORE COLOR	Pale pinkish
EDIBILITY	Edible

HEIGHT
Up to 8 in
(200 mm)

CAP DIAMETER
Up to 8 in
(200 mm)

306

TERMITOMYCES ROBUSTUS
ROBUST TERMITE-FUNGUS
(BEELI) R. HEIM

The Robust Termite-Fungus forms caps that are convex at first, flattening when expanded but sharply umbonate. The surface of the cap is often irregularly ridged or channeled, frequently splitting as it expands, and is ocher-brown to dark brown. The gills are white to pinkish cream. The stem is smooth, whitish to cream, and has a blackish, root-like base.

In the Old World tropics a remarkable association has evolved between certain species of termites and a genus of agarics called *Termitomyces*. The termites actively "farm" the fungi inside their mounds, using the mycelium to help break down and release nutrients from indigestible woody material. In return, the fungus is provided with its food resource, is protected from competitors, and is actively spread from mound to mound. Fruitbodies— including those of *T. robustus*—appear in the rainy season and are widely collected by local people for food, sometimes on a commercial scale in Southeast Asia.

SIMILAR SPECIES
Some *Termitomyces* species produce vastly larger fruitbodies, notably those of the African *T. titanicus* which may reach 40 in (1000 mm) across. The Robust Termite-Fungus, however, falls into the middle size-range. *Tricholoma fuliginosus*, which also has brownish fruitbodies and is known from both Africa and Asia, is generally regarded as a synonym.

Actual size

FAMILY	Marasmiaceae
DISTRIBUTION	Eastern North America, Central and South America, Eastern Asia
HABITAT	In woodland
ASSOCIATION	With broadleaf trees
GROWTH FORM	On fallen sticks, dead leaves, and detritus, in troops
ABUNDANCE	Common
SPORE COLOR	White
EDIBILITY	Not edible

HEIGHT
Up to 2 in
(50 mm)

CAP DIAMETER
Up to 1 in
(25 mm)

TETRAPYRGOS NIGRIPES
BLACKFOOT PARACHUTE
(SCHWEINITZ) E. HORAK

307

The Blackfoot Parachute looks like a species of *Marasmius*, and is indeed closely related, but is placed in the genus *Tetrapyrgos* thanks to its oddly shaped, triangular spores and other microscopic features. Like many *Marasmius* species, it is a leaf- and litter-rotter, appearing in troops on dead sticks and fallen leaves. It was originally described by the early American mycologist Lewis David von Schweinitz, and is common in eastern North America. The Latin epithet *nigri-pes* means "black-foot," though the conspicuous darkening of the stem only takes place as the fruitbodies age.

SIMILAR SPECIES

Marasmiellus candidus, a widespread north-temperate species originally described from England, also has a white cap and dark gray stem and looks very similar. It is best distinguished microscopically. Several other pale-capped *Marasmius* and *Marasmiellus* species are superficially similar, but have dark brown or polished stems.

Actual size

The Blackfoot Parachute forms convex caps, becoming flat or depressed at the center, often with a central pimple. The cap surface is smooth to finely wrinkled and entirely white. The gills are rather distant and white. The stem is white at first and finely hairy, gradually becoming dark gray to black from the base upward.

FAMILY	Tricholomataceae
DISTRIBUTION	North America, southern Europe, North Africa, Central America, southwestern Asia
HABITAT	In woodland
ASSOCIATION	Ectomycorrhizal, with pine
GROWTH FORM	On ground, in troops or rings
ABUNDANCE	Occasional
SPORE COLOR	White
EDIBILITY	Not edible

HEIGHT
Up to 4 in
(100 mm)

CAP DIAMETER
Up to 5 in
(125 mm)

308

TRICHOLOMA CALIGATUM
TRUE BOOTED KNIGHT
(VIVIANI) RICKEN

The epithet *caligatum* means "wearing boots," and certainly the fleecy, brownish stem base topped by a ring does make fruitbodies of this species look as if they are wearing shaggy socks, if not boots. *Tricholoma caligatum* was originally described from Italy and occurs with pine trees around the Mediterranean area. It has also been reported from North and Central America with a variety of host trees, but it is quite possible that American records represent one or more similar, but distinct, species. Fruitbodies are normally too bitter to be edible.

SIMILAR SPECIES
Tricholoma caligatum has frequently been confused with the commercially valuable Matsutake (*T. matsutake*), but is typically smaller and darker with a bitter taste and fruity smell. *Tricholoma focale*, a more northerly species that has been given the name Booted Knight, has a variegated, red-brown and yellowish brown cap and smells of meal or cucumber.

Actual size

The True Booted Knight forms caps that are convex, becoming flat to weakly depressed. The cap surface is broken into large, chocolate-brown scales on a pale brown to whitish background. The gills are white to cream. The stem is whitish at the top, with a distinct ring and bands of cap-colored scales below.

FAMILY	Tricholomataceae
DISTRIBUTION	North America, Europe, northern Asia
HABITAT	In woodland and dune slacks
ASSOCIATION	Ectomycorrhizal, with willow
GROWTH FORM	On ground, in troops or rings
ABUNDANCE	Occasional
SPORE COLOR	White
EDIBILITY	Not edible

HEIGHT
Up to 3 in
(75 mm)

CAP DIAMETER
Up to 2½ in
(60 mm)

TRICHOLOMA CINGULATUM

GIRDLED KNIGHT

(ALMFELT) JACOBASCH

309

The Girdled Knight is easily distinguished from similar gray
Tricholoma species by the presence of a distinct ring on the
stem (*cingulatum* means "girdled" or "belted"). The fungus is
a strict associate of willows and occurs throughout the northern
hemisphere. Curiously, it is sometimes parasitized by a flowering
plant called the Yellow Bird's-Nest or Dutchman's Pipe
(*Monotropa hypopitys*). The plant lacks chlorophyll and cannot
grow on its own, but instead taps into the mycorrhiza formed
by the Girdled Knight and its willow associate, helping itself to
carbon and nutrients.

SIMILAR SPECIES

The presence of a ring distinguishes the Girdled Knight from
similar gray *Tricholoma* species such as the Yellowing Knight
(*T. scalpturatum*, which—as the names indicates—also bruises
yellow) and the Gray Knight (*T. terreum*).

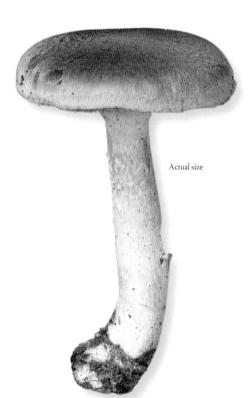

Actual size

The Girdled Knight forms caps that are conical,
becoming convex to umbonate. The cap surface
is finely scaly, the scales dark gray on a paler gray
background. The gills are white to pale gray (see
photo left), sometimes bruising yellowish with age.
The stem is smooth to fibrous, whitish to pale gray,
sometimes bruising yellowish, with a distinct ring.

FAMILY	Tricholomataceae
DISTRIBUTION	North America, Europe, North Africa, Central America, northern Asia
HABITAT	In woodland
ASSOCIATION	Ectomycorrhizal, with pine, occasionally beech
GROWTH FORM	On ground, in troops or rings
ABUNDANCE	Common
SPORE COLOR	White
EDIBILITY	Poisonous

HEIGHT
Up to 5 in
(125 mm)

CAP DIAMETER
Up to 5 in
(125 mm)

310

TRICHOLOMA EQUESTRE
YELLOW KNIGHT
(LINNAEUS) P. KUMMER

Actual size

Until recently, *Tricholoma equestre* (formerly also known as *T. flavovirens*) was considered a good edible species and was even traded commercially. It was traditionally reserved for the nobility in France (hence the reference to knights) and widely sold in local markets. Between 2001 and 2009, however, almost 20 poisoning cases—several of them fatal—were reported in France and Poland as a result of eating fruitbodies. All the victims suffered rhabdomyolysis (a breakdown of muscle tissue), though only after eating repeated meals of the fungus. Many older books say the Yellow Knight, which is also known as the Man on Horseback, is edible, but it is clearly best avoided.

SIMILAR SPECIES
The Sulfur Knight (*Tricholoma sulphureum*) is similarly colored, but lacks the sticky cap, and has a disagreeable smell of coal gas. *Tricholoma sejunctum* has a cap that is yellowish and sticky, at least when young, but its gills are whitish. Both usually occur with broadleaf trees.

The Yellow Knight forms caps that are convex at first, becoming flat to umbonate when expanded. The cap surface is smooth to fibrous, slimy when damp, yellow at first, becoming reddish brown to brown. The gills are yellow (see photo right). The stem is smooth to somewhat fibrous, whitish at the top, yellow below.

FAMILY	Tricholomataceae
DISTRIBUTION	North America, Central America
HABITAT	In woodland
ASSOCIATION	Ectomycorrhizal, with pine and oak
GROWTH FORM	On ground, in troops or rings
ABUNDANCE	Occasional
SPORE COLOR	White
EDIBILITY	Edible

HEIGHT
Up to 6 in
(150 mm)

CAP DIAMETER
Up to 10 in
(250 mm)

TRICHOLOMA MAGNIVELARE

AMERICAN MATSUTAKE

(PECK) REDHEAD

311

The Japanese fetish for the Matsutake (*Tricholoma matsutake*) has resulted in a booming export market for its American relative, *Tricholoma magnivelare*. Starting in the 1970s, successful collectors have earned large sums of money—particularly in the forests of the Pacific Northwest—in what has been dubbed "the white gold rush." There is also a substantial export trade from Mexico. Like the true Matsutake, the American Matsutake, or the Pine Mushroom, has a characteristic, spicy aroma. Freshly gathered fruitbodies are sent by air to Japan, since the valuable aroma disappears if the fungi are dried or preserved.

The American Matsutake forms caps that are convex, becoming flat to weakly depressed. The cap surface is broken into large, white scales that stain yellowish to orange-brown with age. The gills are white, spotted brown with age. The stem is whitish at the top, with a distinct ring and bands of cap-colored scales below.

SIMILAR SPECIES

Tricholoma magnivelare has also been called the White Matsutake, since it differs from the much darker, browner Japanese species in the white to pale scales of the cap. The True Booted Knight (*T. caligatum*) is also similar, but smaller, with even darker cap scales.

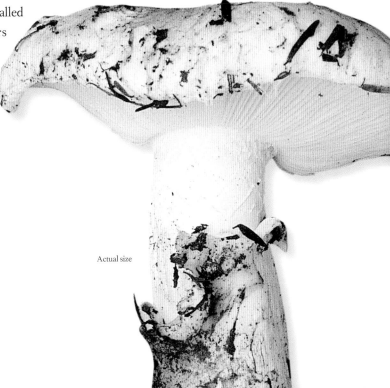

Actual size

FAMILY	Tricholomataceae
DISTRIBUTION	Continental Europe, northern Asia
HABITAT	In woodland
ASSOCIATION	Ectomycorrhizal, with pine and oak
GROWTH FORM	On ground, singly or in troops
ABUNDANCE	Locally common
SPORE COLOR	White
EDIBILITY	Edible

HEIGHT
Up to 6 in
(150 mm)

CAP DIAMETER
Up to 8 in
(200 mm)

312

TRICHOLOMA MATSUTAKE
MATSUTAKE
(S. ITO & S. IMAI) SINGER

Young, unexpanded fruitbodies of the Matsutake have a distinctive aroma when fresh that is highly esteemed in Japan—to such an extent that perfect specimens, often exchanged as gifts, can command fabulously high prices. This has led to an extraordinary import trade from neighboring countries, including Korea, China, and Tibet, where Matsutake-gathering has become an important part of some rural economies. Recent DNA research has shown that the fungus also occurs in Europe, where it is known by the older name of *Tricholoma nauseosum*—the Latin epithet showing that the aroma of the Matsutake is not to everyone's taste.

SIMILAR SPECIES
The American Matsutake (*Tricholoma magnivelare*) is a related species, also edible and exported to Japan, but differs in the white to pale scales of the cap. The True Booted Knight (*T. caligatum*) is also similar, but it is smaller, and has darker cap scales.

The Matsutake forms caps that are convex, becoming flat. The cap surface is broken into large, brown scales, the margin often with woolly veil remains. The gills are white to cream. The stem is whitish at the top, with a distinct ring and bands of cap-colored scales below.

Actual size

FAMILY	Tricholomataceae
DISTRIBUTION	North America, continental Europe, northern Asia
HABITAT	In woodland
ASSOCIATION	Ectomycorrhizal, with broadleaf trees and conifers
GROWTH FORM	On ground, in troops or rings
ABUNDANCE	Occasional
SPORE COLOR	White
EDIBILITY	Poisonous

HEIGHT
Up to 5 in
(125 mm)

CAP DIAMETER
Up to 6 in
(150 mm)

TRICHOLOMA PARDINUM
LEOPARD KNIGHT
QUÉLET

The Leopard Knight takes its English and Latin names from the patchwork scales on the cap, which are, rather fancifully, likened to a leopard's spots—if leopards were gray. It is a large species with a liking for calcareous, montane woodland, and has an unpleasant rancid-sweet smell. It is also toxic, causing severe gastric upsets. In places such as Switzerland, where other gray *Tricholoma* species are frequently collected for eating and the Leopard Knight is comparatively common, it is a major cause of poisoning as a result of mistaken identity.

SIMILAR SPECIES

The Leopard Knight causes problems when picked in mistake for the edible Gray Knight (*Tricholoma terreum*), a smaller and much commoner species with a conical cap and little or no smell. Several other gray *Tricholoma* species exist, and as a group they are best avoided for culinary purposes.

The Leopard Knight forms caps that are convex, sometimes becoming weakly umbonate. The cap surface is smooth and dark gray at first, splitting into scales on a paler background as it expands. The gills are whitish, sometimes tinted yellowish brown with age. The stem is fibrous, whitish, but often bruising yellowish gray toward the base.

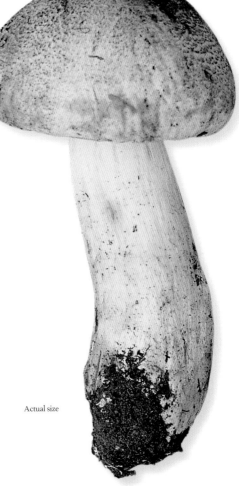

Actual size

FAMILY	Tricholomataceae
DISTRIBUTION	North America, Europe, Central America, northern Asia
HABITAT	In woodland
ASSOCIATION	Ectomycorrhizal, with broadleaf trees and conifers
GROWTH FORM	On ground, in troops or rings
ABUNDANCE	Common
SPORE COLOR	White
EDIBILITY	Probably poisonous, best avoided

HEIGHT
Up to 5 in
(125 mm)

CAP DIAMETER
Up to 6 in
(150 mm)

314

TRICHOLOMA SAPONACEUM
SOAPY KNIGHT
(FRIES) P. KUMMER

The odd English and Latin names for this species come from its distinctive smell—usually likened to cheap soap. In fact, the smell of the Soapy Knight is its most distinctive feature, since fruitbodies are highly variable and numerous forms and varieties have been described. It is quite possible that further research may show that *Tricholoma saponaceum* is actually a complex of closely related species. This may explain why the Soapy Knight is said to be edible by some authorities, but has also been blamed for causing severe gastric distress.

SIMILAR SPECIES

Because it is so variable in color and in scaliness, the Soapy Knight could easily be mistaken for several other *Tricholoma* species. The smell, however, should be diagnostic, as is the tendency to bruise reddish, especially at the base of the stem.

Actual size

The Soapy Knight forms caps that are convex at first, becoming flat to umbonate. The cap surface is smooth to scaly, typically olive to olive-brown or gray, but sometimes reddish-brown, yellow, or even bluish. The gills are pale yellowish green, sometimes with pinkish tints. The stem is smooth to scaly, whitish to pale cap-colored, often bruising reddish toward the base.

FAMILY	Tricholomataceae
DISTRIBUTION	North America, Europe, northern Asia, New Zealand
HABITAT	In woodland
ASSOCIATION	Ectomycorrhizal, with broadleaf trees, rarely conifers
GROWTH FORM	On ground, in troops or rings
ABUNDANCE	Common
SPORE COLOR	White
EDIBILITY	Not edible

HEIGHT
Up to 4 in
(100 mm)

CAP DIAMETER
Up to 3 in
(75 mm)

TRICHOLOMA SULPHUREUM

SULFUR KNIGHT

(BULLIARD) P. KUMMER

315

The Sulfur Knight takes its English and Latin names from its dull, sulfur-yellow color, but in fact its most striking feature is its smell. It reeks of old-fashioned coal gas—though according to Jean Baptiste Bulliard, who first described it from France in 1784, its taste is not so disagreeable (merely bitter). It is a common species, at least in Europe, where it most frequently occurs with oaks. A variety with a brownish cap can sometimes be found in calcareous meadows and pastures where it forms an association with rockroses (*Helianthemum* species).

SIMILAR SPECIES

The Yellow Knight (*Tricholoma equestre*) is similarly colored, but typically grows with conifers, has a sticky cap when damp, and lacks the distinctive smell of the Sulfur Knight. Other species with yellow cap and gills, such as the more brightly colored *Calocybe chrysenteron*, also lack the coal-gas smell.

The Sulfur Knight forms caps that are convex at first (see photo top right), becoming flat to umbonate when expanded. The cap surface is smooth, pale sulfur-yellow, sometimes with reddish brown or greenish gray tints. The gills are sulfur-yellow. The stem is smooth to finely fibrous and cap-colored.

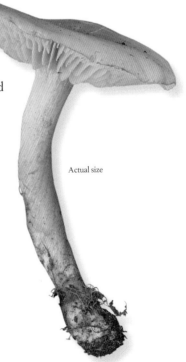

Actual size

FAMILY	Tricholomataceae
DISTRIBUTION	North America, Europe, northern Asia
HABITAT	In woodland
ASSOCIATION	Ectomycorrhizal, with conifers
GROWTH FORM	On ground, in troops or rings
ABUNDANCE	Locally common
SPORE COLOR	White
EDIBILITY	Not edible

HEIGHT
Up to 4 in
(100 mm)

CAP DIAMETER
Up to 4 in
(100 mm)

316

TRICHOLOMA VACCINUM
SCALY KNIGHT
(SCHAEFFER) P. KUMMER

Based on its Latin name, the Scaly Knight should really be called the Dun Cow Knight—since that is what *vaccinum* refers to. Its distinctive features are its red-brown color and coarsely hairy to scaly cap. It also has a cobwebby veil when young, wispy remnants of which are sometimes visible on the cap margin and upper stem. It is a locally common species with conifers, especially spruce and pine, but is rare in some places—like the British Isles—and possibly even extinct in the Netherlands.

SIMILAR SPECIES
The Matt Knight (*Tricholoma imbricatum*) is a similarly colored species that also grows with conifers. It has a smooth cap when young, only becoming scaly with age—when it is still much less hairy-scaly than the Scaly Knight.

Actual size

The Scaly Knight forms caps that are conical, becoming convex to umbonate. The surface of the cap is hairy-scaly, the scales dark reddish brown to pinkish brown on a paler background (see photo left). The gills are white to cream, sometimes bruising brown. The stem is fibrous to hairy, whitish at the top, reddish brown toward the base. The flesh becomes pinkish with age.

FAMILY	Tricholomataceae
DISTRIBUTION	North America, Europe, Central America, northern Asia
HABITAT	In woodland
ASSOCIATION	With conifers
GROWTH FORM	On fallen wood, stumps, and sawdust, usually clustered
ABUNDANCE	Locally common
SPORE COLOR	White
EDIBILITY	Not edible, best avoided

HEIGHT
Up to 4 in
(100 mm)

CAP DIAMETER
Up to 3 in
(75 mm)

TRICHOLOMOPSIS DECORA

PRUNES AND CUSTARD

(FRIES) SINGER

317

This attractive, speckled species is locally common on conifer wood, but in Europe at least tends to prefer montane areas, and is distinctly rare in some lowland countries. It takes its odd English name from its better-known relative, the Plums and Custard (*Tricholomopsis rutilans*), which has a plum-red and custard-yellow cap. The cap of *T. decora* is brown and yellow, hence the link to prunes. Despite these culinary references, the Prunes and Custard is not a good edible species and is said to have been the cause of a least one severe poisoning case in America. It has an alternative name of the Decorated Mop.

SIMILAR SPECIES

Several hard-to-distinguish species have been described from North America, including *Tricholomopsis sulfureoides*, which is said to have a less scaly cap and veil remains on the stem, at least when immature. Yellow-capped species of *Pholiota* have rusty brown spores.

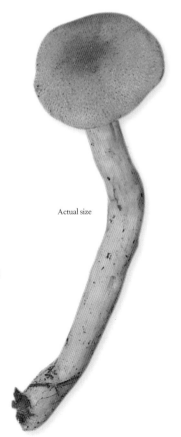

Actual size

The Prunes and Custard forms caps that are convex, becoming flat or depressed at the center. The cap surface is finely scaly, bright yellow to yellow-brown at the center, the small scales slightly darker, yellow-brown (see photo right). The gills are bright yellow. The stem is smooth and also bright yellow.

FAMILY	Tricholomataceae
DISTRIBUTION	North America, Europe, North Africa, Central America, northern Asia; introduced in Australia and New Zealand
HABITAT	In woodland
ASSOCIATION	With conifers
GROWTH FORM	On fallen wood, stumps, and sawdust, usually clustered
ABUNDANCE	Common
SPORE COLOR	White
EDIBILITY	Not edible

HEIGHT
Up to 4 in
(100 mm)

CAP DIAMETER
Up to 6 in
(150 mm)

318

TRICHOLOMOPSIS RUTILANS
PLUMS AND CUSTARD
(SCHAEFFER) SINGER

The contrasting purplish red scales and yellow gills make this a particularly handsome species, the colors mimicking a dishful of stewed plums and custard—true to its fanciful English name. It is a common species on conifer wood and seems equally at home in plantations as well as in native forests. The Plums and Custard, which is also known as the Variegated Mop, has probably been introduced in Australia and New Zealand. Sadly, the fruitbodies (though said to be edible by some) are not recommended for the table, despite their appetizing appearance. However, this species can be used for dyeing, producing a range of mustard-yellow to dark brown tones.

SIMILAR SPECIES

The contrasting colors should be distinctive, but *Gymnopilus dilepis*—a species that is increasing its range worldwide by growing in woodchip mulch—has very similar purplish red scales on a yellowish background. Its spores are rusty yellow, however, and it has a ring on the stem.

Actual size

The Plums and Custard forms caps that are convex, becoming flat or shallowly umbonate. The cap surface is finely scaly, the fine scales purplish red on a pale yellow background. The gills are pale to bright yellow (see photo right). The stem is covered in fine purplish red scales on a pale yellow background.

FAMILY	Inocybeaceae
DISTRIBUTION	Europe, North Africa
HABITAT	In woodland and scrub
ASSOCIATION	Typically with hawthorn, less commonly with cotoneaster and holly
GROWTH FORM	On ground, arising from old, fallen berries
ABUNDANCE	Common
SPORE COLOR	Ocher
EDIBILITY	Not edible

TUBARIA DISPERSA

HAWTHORN TWIGLET
(LINNAEUS) SINGER

HEIGHT
Up to 1½ in
(35 mm)

CAP DIAMETER
Up to 1 in
(25 mm)

319

At first sight, this looks like yet another little brown agaric—one of a large group of similar-looking species that usually require microscopic examination to identify. The Hawthorn Twiglet, however, is more interesting and easier to identify than most. It typically grows scattered under hawthorn trees and does so because it specializes in rotting down the woody pips of old, fallen, and often buried haws. It can sometimes be found doing the same thing with fallen berries of cotoneaster, holly, and other berry-bearing shrubs.

SIMILAR SPECIES

The habitat and the yellow-to-ocher gills distinguish the Hawthorn Twiglet from most other small, brown agarics. The Scurfy Twiglet (*Tubaria conspersa*) has a reddish brown to tan cap with white veil remains at the margin and similarly colored gills. It is a very common species growing in litter and grass, often late in the year.

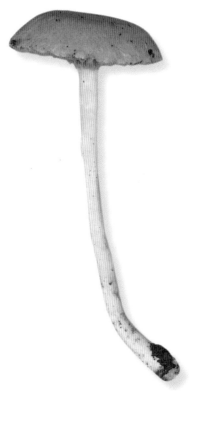

The Hawthorn Twiglet forms caps that are convex at first (see photo top right), becoming flat to shallowly depressed. The cap surface is finely felty, buff to ocher-buff when damp, drying paler. The gills are pale yellow, becoming ocher. The thin stem is smooth and whitish.

Actual size

FAMILY	Pluteaceae
DISTRIBUTION	North America, Europe, Africa, Central America, Asia
HABITAT	In woodland
ASSOCIATION	With broadleaf trees
GROWTH FORM	On dead and living trunks, singly
ABUNDANCE	Occasional
SPORE COLOR	Brownish pink
EDIBILITY	Edible

HEIGHT
Up to 8 in
(200 mm)

CAP DIAMETER
Up to 8 in
(200 mm)

320

VOLVARIELLA BOMBYCINA
SILKY ROSEGILL
(SCHAEFFER) SINGER

Though they may look superficially like *Amanita* species, which also possess a volva at the stem base, *Volvariella* species are pink-spored and are actually close relatives of *Pluteus* species. The Silky Rosegill is one of the largest, and is unusual in that it grows on wood, often in clefts and knotholes of dead or living trunks. It is an edible species, though frequently has an unpleasant, raw potato smell and is not much valued. Its relative, the Paddy Straw Mushroom (*V. volvacea*), is commercially cultivated, however, and is a major component of East Asian cuisine.

SIMILAR SPECIES
Volvariella caesiotincta is a less common species on wood, with a bluish gray cap. The mainly tropical Paddy Straw Mushroom (*V. volvacea*) is similar to the Silky Rosegill, but grows in rich, composted ground, as does the temperate Stubble Rosegill (*V. gloiocephala*). The latter has a smooth cap, sticky when damp, and a white volva.

The Silky Rosegill forms caps that are conical to convex, becoming flatter. The cap surface is silky-hairy, white to pale yellow, and the hair tips sometimes brownish. The gills are pale pinkish at first, becoming pinkish brown. The stem is whitish, with a large sack-like volva at the base, which is whitish, yellowish, or frequently mottled dark brown.

Actual size

FAMILY	Pluteaceae
DISTRIBUTION	North America, Europe, North Africa, New Zealand
HABITAT	In woodland
ASSOCIATION	With *Clitocybe nebularis*
GROWTH FORM	On caps of fruitbodies
ABUNDANCE	Occasional to rare
SPORE COLOR	Brownish pink
EDIBILITY	Not edible

HEIGHT
Up to 4 in
(100 mm)

CAP DIAMETER
Up to 3 in
(75 mm)

VOLVARIELLA SURRECTA

PIGGYBACK ROSEGILL

(KNAPP) SINGER

321

Like *Asterophora* species, the Piggyback Rosegill has made a peculiar niche for itself by growing on fruitbodies of other agarics—in this case the Clouded Funnel (*Clitocybe nebularis*). It appears to be a parasitic association, since the host fruitbody is often still intact and recognizable. The Piggyback Rosegill is quite rare, however, while the Clouded Funnel is extremely common, so there must be some factor that keeps the parasite in check. It may not be a rapid colonizer, since it tends to reappear in the same area from year to year.

SIMILAR SPECIES

The appearance on fruitbodies of the Clouded Funnel, together with the large, sack-like volva at the base of the stem, should make the Piggyback Rosegill unmistakable. Several other *Volvariella* species are of similar size and color, but are found in grass or in leaf litter.

Actual size

The Piggyback Rosegill forms caps that are convex, becoming flatter. The cap surface is smooth to silky-hairy and white. The gills are pale pinkish at first, becoming pinkish brown. The stem is white to pale buff, with a large, white, sack-like volva at the base.

FAMILY	Mycenaceae
DISTRIBUTION	North America, Europe, Central America, northern Asia
HABITAT	In woodland
ASSOCIATION	With conifers
GROWTH FORM	On trunks, stumps, and logs, in clusters
ABUNDANCE	Locally common
SPORE COLOR	White
EDIBILITY	Not edible

HEIGHT
Up to 2 in
(50 mm)

CAP DIAMETER
Up to 1 in
(25 mm)

322

XEROMPHALINA CAMPANELLA

PINEWOOD GINGERTAIL

(BATSCH) KÜHNER & MAIRE

Though originally described from Germany, the Pinewood
Gingertail appears to be commonest in North America, where
it appears in dense swarms on decaying conifer wood. In Europe
it is locally rare, seldom recorded in England (though more
frequent in Scotland) and on the Danish Red List of threatened
fungal species. *Campanella* means "little bell," while *omphalos* in
the genus name refers to the navel-like depression at the center
of the cap. A peculiar feature of the fruitbodies is the shaggy
ring of ginger mycelium at the base of their stems—hence the
alternative name of Fuzzy Foot.

SIMILAR SPECIES

There are several closely related species in North America.
Xeromphalina brunneola has darker, reddish brown caps and
is said to smell and taste unpleasant, *X. campanelloides* has
less decurrent gills and a bitter taste, and *X. kauffmanii* grows
on broadleaf wood. All are best distinguished microscopically.

Actual size

The Pinewood Gingertail forms convex caps that are centrally depressed.
The cap surface is smooth, striate, yellow to orange-brown, darker in the
center. The gills are decurrent, widely spaced, pale yellow to pale orange.
The stem is smooth and yellowish at the top, orange-brown toward the
base, which is hairy.

FAMILY	Physalacriaceae
DISTRIBUTION	North America, Europe, North Africa, Central America, Asia
HABITAT	In woodland
ASSOCIATION	With broadleaf trees
GROWTH FORM	On ground from buried wood, singly
ABUNDANCE	Locally common
SPORE COLOR	White
EDIBILITY	Edible

HEIGHT	Up to 8 in (200 mm)
CAP DIAMETER	Up to 4 in (100 mm)

XERULA RADICATA

ROOTING SHANK

(RELHAN) DÖRFELT

323

The Rooting Shank grows on dead tree roots and buried wood, to which the fruitbodies are attached by a long, subterranean stem—rather like the taproot of a plant. The stem is elongated above ground as well, giving the fungus a tall, stately appearance. It is related to the Porcelain Fungus (*Oudemansiella mucida*), which grows on branches and trunks, and has a rather similar, thin-fleshed cap with widely spaced gills. The Rooting Shank is common in Europe, but apparently rare in North America where other very similar species occur—some requiring microscopic examination to differentiate.

SIMILAR SPECIES

A few related species should be recognizable in the field. The European *Xerula longipes* has a velvety to finely hairy cap and stem, while the North American *X. furfuracea* has a smooth cap and velvety-hairy stem. *Xerula australis*, which is found in Australia, and the North American *X. rubrobrunnescens* both have stems that bruise brown.

The Rooting Shank forms thin-fleshed, convex caps that are flat to weakly umbonate or depressed when expanded. The surface is smooth, yellowish brown to brown, often sticky and radially wrinkled. The gills are white and rather distant. The stem is smooth, white at the top, yellow-brown below, and has a long, tapering, root-like base.

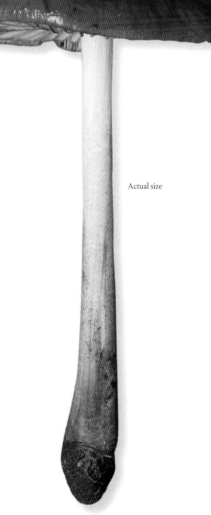

Actual size

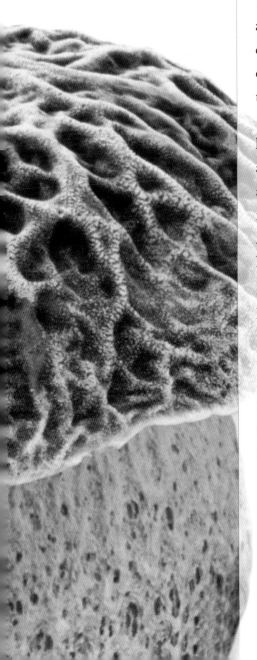

BOLETES

The boletes look like agarics, until you turn them over and discover they have spongelike pores beneath their caps. A closer look will show that the pores are the open ends of small tubes, and it is on the inner surface of these tubes that boletes produce their spores.

All these fungi were once placed in the genus *Boletus*, but it is now known that they are more diverse than that and belong in several different families—though they are all still distantly related to each other. A few bracket fungi with caps and stems, such as species of *Albatrellus*, *Boletopsis*, and *Polyporus* could be mistaken for a fleshy bolete—but most are woody or leathery.

The boletes are all either ectomycorrhizal or parasites of ectomycorrhiza (see Introduction), and as such are typically found in woodland and forests. It also means they cannot be cultivated, so that prized edible species, such as the Cep or Porcini (*Boletus edulis*), have to be collected by hand in the wild—which is why they are so expensive. A few boletes are bitter or poisonous, though none is known to contain any deadly toxins.

FAMILY	Boletaceae
DISTRIBUTION	East Asia, Australia
HABITAT	In woodland
ASSOCIATION	Ectomycorrhizal, with broadleaf trees
GROWTH FORM	On ground, singly or in small troops
ABUNDANCE	Occasional
SPORE COLOR	Dark brown
EDIBILITY	Not edible

HEIGHT
Up to 4 in
(100 mm)

CAP DIAMETER
Up to 3 in
(75 mm)

BOLETELLUS OBSCUROCOCCINEUS
RHUBARB BOLETE
(HÖHNEL) SINGER

The Rhubarb Bolete was originally described from Java in Indonesia, but is now known to occur throughout eastern Asia, from Japan and China southward, and has also been found in Australia. It takes its odd English name from the rhubarb-pink cap color, rather than its taste—which is said to be bitter. In Australia, the species forms mycorrhizal associations with eucalypts, but in Asia it occurs with oaks and other broadleaf trees. Though it may look like an ordinary *Boletus* species, the Rhubarb Bolete belongs to the genus *Boletellus*, which is distinguished microscopically by the fact that it produces spores decorated with ridges.

SIMILAR SPECIES

Boletellus rubrolutescens is a very similar African species that was initially misidentified as *B. obscurococcineus*. Similarly colored boletes—such as *Boletus rubellus*—occur in Europe and North America, but although they may have a crimson cap and yellow pores, they lack the scurfy-scaly stem of the Rhubarb Bolete.

Actual size

The Rhubarb Bolete forms caps that are hemispherical, becoming convex, dry, deep rose-red, smooth but finely cracked with age, showing yellowish flesh below. The pores are yellow. The stem is dry, yellowish at the top, cap-colored and scurfy-scaly below, whitish at the base.

FAMILY	Boletaceae
DISTRIBUTION	Eastern North America, Central America
HABITAT	In woodland
ASSOCIATION	Ectomycorrhizal, with broadleaf trees and conifers
GROWTH FORM	On ground, singly or in troops
ABUNDANCE	Occasional
SPORE COLOR	Olive-brown
EDIBILITY	Edible

HEIGHT
Up to 8 in
(200 mm)

CAP DIAMETER
Up to 5 in
(125 mm)

BOLETELLUS RUSSELLII

JAGGED-STEM BOLETE

(FROST) E. -J. GILBERT

327

The long, shaggy stem with its deep furrows and irregular ridges is a particular feature of this rather uncommon bolete, first described from New England in 1878. It was named after local mycologist and Unitarian minister John Lewis Russell, and is sometimes referred to as Russell's Bolete. Curiously, its microscopic spores are almost as deeply grooved and furrowed as the stem—a feature that places the species in the genus *Boletellus* rather than *Boletus*. The Jagged-Stem Bolete is edible, but is said to be soft and insipid, so is not much sought after for the kitchen.

SIMILAR SPECIES

The similar-looking Shaggy-Stalked Bolete (*Heimioporus betula*) occurs in the same area, but has a smooth, sticky, or shiny cap. Faded fruitbodies of Frost's Bolete (*Boletus frostii*) may also appear similar, but the pores—even when old—should retain some orange-red tints.

The Jagged-Stem Bolete forms caps that are hemispherical, becoming convex. The cap surface is dry and finely velvety at first, cracking into patches with age, and yellow-brown to reddish brown. The pores are yellow to greenish yellow. The stem is reddish to pinkish brown, with a coarse, shaggy network of grooves and ridges. The flesh is pale yellow.

Actual size

FAMILY	Boletaceae
DISTRIBUTION	North America, Europe, northern Asia
HABITAT	In woodland
ASSOCIATION	Ectomycorrhizal, with conifers, rarely with broadleaf trees
GROWTH FORM	On ground, singly or in troops
ABUNDANCE	Common
SPORE COLOR	Dark brown
EDIBILITY	Edible

HEIGHT
Up to 5 in
(125 mm)

CAP DIAMETER
Up to 6 in
(150 mm)

328

BOLETUS BADIUS
BAY BOLETE
(FRIES) FRIES

The Bay Bolete is considered one of the best edible species of *Boletus*, and is collected and exported on a commercial scale. It typically grows with conifers, but, unusually, can continue to produce fruitbodies in woodland where conifers once grew, suggesting it can sometimes form an association with broadleaf trees. Following the Chernobyl nuclear accident, it was found that a brown pigment in the Bay Bolete binds closely to radioactive cesium. This was bad news for mushroom hunters in eastern Europe, but it has been suggested that the fungus may be of future use as a bioremediation agent to clean up contaminated sites.

SIMILAR SPECIES

Some forms of the Cep (*Boletus edulis*) may be similarly colored, but its pores never bruise blue like those of the Bay Bolete. *Boletus subtomentosus* and related species have pores that sometimes bruise blue, but they have dry caps (usually paler, olive-brown or yellow-brown in *B. subtomentosus*), and typically narrower stems.

Actual size

The Bay Bolete forms caps that are hemispherical, becoming convex to flat, smooth, slimy when wet, bay-brown to chestnut-brown. The pores are pale yellow, bruising bluish (see photo left). The stem is dry and pale cap-colored. The cut flesh is white to pale yellow, flushing bluish at the top of the stem, purple-brown near the cap surface.

FAMILY	Boletaceae
DISTRIBUTION	North America, Europe, northern Asia
HABITAT	In woodland
ASSOCIATION	Ectomycorrhizal, with broadleaf trees, rarely conifers
GROWTH FORM	On ground, singly or in troops
ABUNDANCE	Common
SPORE COLOR	Olive-brown
EDIBILITY	Not edible

HEIGHT
Up to 5 in
(125 mm)

CAP DIAMETER
Up to 5 in
(125 mm)

BOLETUS CALOPUS
BITTER BEECH BOLETE
PERSOON

329

As the English name suggests, *Boletus calopus* is not generally considered an edible species, the taste being unpleasantly bitter. The compounds responsible for the bitterness have been identified as cyclocalopins, a previously unknown group of fungal metabolites. Despite this, the species is said to be eaten in Russia and the Ukraine, though it can hardly be pleasant. The English name also suggests that *B. calopus* is restricted to beech, but it also grows with oaks and other broadleaf trees, rarely with conifers. The epithet *calopus* means "beautiful foot," referring to the distinctive, crimson to scarlet stem covered with a fine, raised net.

SIMILAR SPECIES
In western North America, the Red-Stemmed Bitter Bolete (*Boletus rubripes*) is very similar, but lacks a network on the stem. In eastern North America, *Boletus roseipes* and *B. inedulis* are also similar, but the former grows only with hemlock, while the latter is smaller than *B. calopus* and has a paler, white to gray-white cap.

The Bitter Beech Bolete forms caps that are convex to flat, smooth, pale gray to pale brown. The pores are pale yellow (see photo left), bluish when bruised. The stem has a raised network and is pale yellow at the top, then bright crimson, becoming brownish toward the base. The cut flesh is pale yellow, flushing blue.

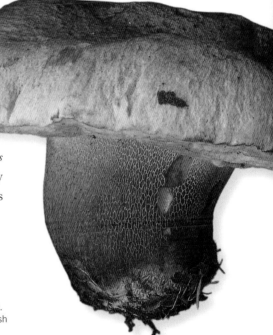

Actual size

FAMILY	Boletaceae
DISTRIBUTION	North America, Europe, North Africa, northern Asia, New Zealand
HABITAT	In woodland
ASSOCIATION	Ectomycorrhizal, with conifers, rarely broadleaf trees
GROWTH FORM	On ground, singly or in small groups
ABUNDANCE	Common
SPORE COLOR	Brown to pink-brown
EDIBILITY	Edible

HEIGHT
Up to 4 in
(100 mm)

CAP DIAMETER
Up to 5 in
(125 mm)

330

BOLETUS CHRYSENTERON

RED-CRACKING BOLETE

BULLIARD

Boletus (or *Xerocomus*) *chrysenteron* was once thought to be a widespread and easily recognized species, thanks to its cap skin cracking to reveal reddish flesh below. Recent research, however, has revealed a number of look-alike species some of which may actually be commoner than the true Red-Cracking Bolete. The real species has a preference for conifers, only occasionally occurring with beech and other broadleaf trees. The species is edible, but is said to be tasteless and soggy, so is not esteemed by bolete hunters—unless they are very, very hungry.

SIMILAR SPECIES

In Europe, *Boletus cisalpinus* is a look-alike, red-cracking species, only identifiable microscopically by its finely striped spores. It does, however, have a preference for broadleaf trees, especially oak. In North America, *B. truncatus* is another look-alike, distinguishable by its truncate spores. Brown-capped forms of the Ruby Bolete (*B. rubellus*) may also look similar.

Actual size

The Red-Cracking Bolete forms caps that are convex, becoming flatter. The cap surface is finely velvety, dark to grayish brown, cracking with age and revealing reddish flesh below. The pores are pale yellow-green, bruising bluish. Its stem is smooth, yellow at the top, and dark reddish below (see photo right). The flesh is pale yellow, reddish immediately below the cap, slowly bluing when cut.

FAMILY	Boletaceae
DISTRIBUTION	North America, Europe, North Africa, Central America, northern Asia; introduced in South Africa, South America, and New Zealand
HABITAT	In woodland
ASSOCIATION	Ectomycorrhizal, with broadleaf trees or conifers
GROWTH FORM	On ground, singly or in small groups
ABUNDANCE	Common
SPORE COLOR	Olive-brown
EDIBILITY	Edible

HEIGHT
Up to 9 in
(225 mm)

CAP DIAMETER
Up to 8 in
(200 mm)

BOLETUS EDULIS

CEP

BULLIARD

331

Often the shape and color of an old-fashioned penny loaf when young, the Cep—also known as the Porcini or the Penny Bun—is one of the best-known edible fungi. Since it is an ectomycorrhizal species, fruitbodies cannot be cultivated, but are widely collected on a commercial scale. Though apparently widespread (as well as being introduced with exotic trees in South Africa and New Zealand), the Cep is part of a complex of closely related species and its true distribution is uncertain. Bizarrely, the Cep contains amatoxins (the same compound found in the Death Cap, *Amanita phalloides*), but in such low quantities as to cause no reported ill effects.

SIMILAR SPECIES

In Europe, the Pine Bolete (*Boletus pinophilus*) has a purplish brown cap and grows with pines, while *B. aereus* is a broadleaf species with a dark cap and brown network on the stem. In western North America, the Spring King Bolete (*B. rex-veris*) occurs under conifers in spring, while the Queen Bolete (*B. regineus*) is dark-capped and similar to *B. aereus*.

Actual size

The Cep forms caps that are convex, becoming flatter. The cap surface is smooth to wrinkled, greasy or sticky when damp, buff to pale brown or reddish brown. The pores are white, becoming pale yellow-green. Its thick stem is whitish to buff, with a whitish network on the upper part. The flesh is white, with a wine-red flush in the cap.

FAMILY	Boletaceae
DISTRIBUTION	Eastern North America, Central America
HABITAT	In woodland
ASSOCIATION	Ectomycorrhizal, with broadleaf trees, especially oak
GROWTH FORM	On ground, singly or in troops
ABUNDANCE	Occasional
SPORE COLOR	Olive-brown
EDIBILITY	Not edible

| HEIGHT |
| Up to 5 in |
| (125 mm) |
| CAP DIAMETER |
| Up to 6 in |
| (150 mm) |

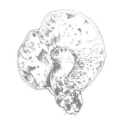

332

BOLETUS FIRMUS
FIRM BOLETE
FROST

The Firm Bolete has a rather unusual combination of cap and stem that bruise brown on handling and pores that bruise blue. The cap is pale, but otherwise rather variable in color, and the attractive pink tints on the stem fade with age. It is a species associated with broadleaf trees, particularly oak, and it is known from eastern Canada southward into Costa Rica and Belize. The taste is often rather bitter, so the Firm Bolete is not a species that is collected for eating.

SIMILAR SPECIES

The pale cap colors of the Firm Bolete, together with the red pores and pinkish stem, should be distinctive. The poisonous *Boletus eastwoodiae*, known from western North America (but not the east), is similar, but typically has a markedly bulbous stem with a more distinct red to purplish red network.

The Firm Bolete forms caps that are convex, the surface smooth to finely velvety, and whitish to grayish or pinkish buff, bruising brown. The pores are orange-red to red, bruising blue. The stem is yellowish at the top, sometimes with a fine reddish, raised network, and pink below, bruising brown. The flesh is pale yellow, turning slightly blue when cut.

Actual size

FAMILY	Boletaceae
DISTRIBUTION	Eastern North America
HABITAT	In woodland
ASSOCIATION	Ectomycorrhizal, with conifers
GROWTH FORM	On ground, singly or in troops
ABUNDANCE	Occasional
SPORE COLOR	Olive-brown
EDIBILITY	Not edible

HEIGHT
Up to 5 in
(125 mm)

CAP DIAMETER
Up to 5 in
(125 mm)

BOLETUS FLAMMANS

FLAME BOLETE

E. A. DICK & SNELL

333

The epithet *flammans* means "flaming," and the deep red colors and occurrence under conifers should make this eye-catching bolete easy to recognize. An additional diagnostic feature is that all parts of the fruitbody turn blue where bruised, scratched, or cut. The Flame Bolete seems to be confined to eastern North America, from Nova Scotia south to Georgia and west to Texas, and forms mycorrhizal associations with pine, hemlock, and spruce. Its edibility is unknown, however, so it is a species that is better admired than eaten.

SIMILAR SPECIES

Several similar species occur in eastern North America, but all are found under broadleaf trees, not conifers. *Boletus rubroflammeus* is somewhat darker red with a more pronounced network on the stem. *Boletus rhodosanguineus* has a stem that is more yellowish and a purplish red cap.

The Flame Bolete forms caps that are convex, the surface smooth, brick-red to dark red or red-brown. The pores are orange-red to red (see photo above). The stem is cap-colored, yellowish at the base, with a fine, raised network at the top. The flesh is yellow. All parts turn blue when bruised or cut.

Actual size

FAMILY	Boletaceae
DISTRIBUTION	North America, Central America
HABITAT	In woodland
ASSOCIATION	Ectomycorrhizal, with broadleaf trees, especially oak
GROWTH FORM	On ground, singly or in troops
ABUNDANCE	Locally common
SPORE COLOR	Pale to olive brown
EDIBILITY	Poisonous (to some), best avoided

HEIGHT
Up to 5 in
(125 mm)

CAP DIAMETER
Up to 5 in
(125 mm)

BOLETUS FROSTII

FROST'S BOLETE

J. L. RUSSELL

334

One of the most sumptuously colored of all the North American boletes, *Boletus frostii* is a handsome species with a wonderfully ornate stem. It was named in 1874 by New England mycologist John Lewis Russell for his friend, and fellow mycologist, Charles Frost. A few years later, Frost repaid the compliment by naming one of his new species *B. russellii*. Frost's Bolete, sometimes known as the Apple Bolete, is often listed as edible and is even sold in some markets in Mexico, but is suspected of causing stomach upsets in some people and is best avoided.

SIMILAR SPECIES

Boletus luridus (which occurs in Europe as well as America) is a poisonous, red-pored species that differs in its brownish cap and less deeply incised network on the stem. The equally poisonous *B. subvelutipes* is common in America, but has a stem that is mainly yellow, with little or no evidence of a network.

Actual size

Frost's Bolete forms caps that are hemispherical, becoming convex to flat. The cap surface is smooth, sticky when damp, dark red, developing yellowish areas with age. The pores are dark red, bruising blue. The stem is cap-colored, bruising blue, with a pronounced network of grooves and ridges. The flesh is lemon-yellow, turning blue when cut.

FAMILY	Boletaceae
DISTRIBUTION	Eastern North America, Central America, eastern Asia
HABITAT	In woodland
ASSOCIATION	Ectomycorrhizal, with broadleaf trees, occasionally conifers
GROWTH FORM	On ground, singly or in troops
ABUNDANCE	Common
SPORE COLOR	Olive-brown
EDIBILITY	Edible

HEIGHT	Up to 5 in (125 mm)
CAP DIAMETER	Up to 5 in (125 mm)

BOLETUS HORTONII

CORRUGATED BOLETE

A. H. SMITH & THIERS

335

The unusual corrugated or pitted cap surface is a characteristic feature of *Boletus hortonii*, a species named after the nineteenth-century American mycologist Charles Horton Peck. Similar caps are occasionally found in *Leccinum* species, and the Corrugated Bolete is known as *Leccinum hortonii* in Asia, despite lacking the scurfy stem typical of that group of boletes. It seems that its DNA will need to be sequenced in order to decide to which genus it really belongs. The Corrugated Bolete is considered to be edible, but not of any great culinary value.

SIMILAR SPECIES

The Corrugated Bolete was originally described by Peck as a variety of *Boletus* (or *Leccinum*) *subglabripes*, a species also found in eastern North America, Central America, and eastern Asia. It is similar in shape and color, but has a smooth cap surface and inconspicuously scurfy stem.

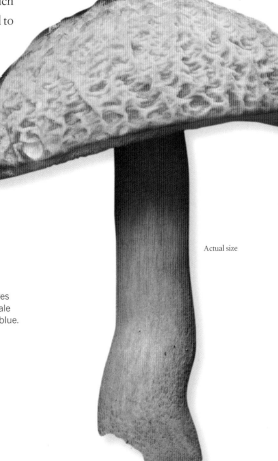

Actual size

The Corrugated Bolete forms caps that are convex, the surface deeply wrinkled or pitted, red-brown to cinnamon-brown or pale brown. The pores are pale yellow, sometimes slowly bruising bluish. The stem is smooth, pale yellow to pale brown. The cut flesh is whitish, sometimes slowly flushing blue.

FAMILY	Boletaceae
DISTRIBUTION	Eastern North America, Europe, North Africa, Central and northern South America, northern Asia
HABITAT	In woodland
ASSOCIATION	Ectomycorrhizal, with conifers and broadleaf trees, particularly oak
GROWTH FORM	On ground, usually singly
ABUNDANCE	Common
SPORE COLOR	Olive-brown
EDIBILITY	Edible

HEIGHT
Up to 4 in
(100 mm)

CAP DIAMETER
Up to 4 in
(100 mm)

336

BOLETUS PULVERULENTUS
INKSTAIN BOLETE
OPATOWSKI

Boletus pulverulentus is a rather drab species, often occuring singly and not immediately distinguishable in the field. Once touched, however, every part of the fruitbody—cap, pores, and stem—immediately bruises dark blue-black, hence the inkstain name. It was originally described from Europe by mycologist Wilhelm Opatowski, but appears to be widespread, though reports from western North America may refer to the similar but green-staining *B. rainisii*. Surprisingly, the Inkstain Bolete is an edible species, though not one that is greatly sought after.

SIMILAR SPECIES
In eastern North America, *Boletus oliveisporus* is a similar, staining species, occurring under conifers. It differs mainly in having a pinkish to reddish middle section of the stem. Another conifer species, *B. rainisii*, is found in the west of the continent, distinguished by its yellow stem and all parts staining greenish black when bruised.

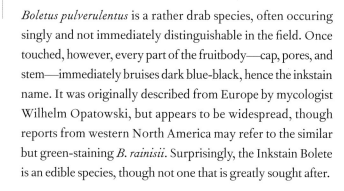

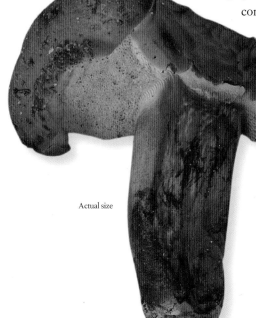

Actual size

The Inkstain Bolete forms caps that are convex, becoming flatter. The cap surface is smooth, pale to dark brown, sometimes flushed reddish or olive. The pores are deep yellow. The stem is yellow at the top, brown to purple-brown below. The flesh is pale yellow. All parts turn dark blue when bruised or cut (see photo top left).

FAMILY	Boletaceae
DISTRIBUTION	Europe, northern Asia
HABITAT	In calcareous woodland and parkland
ASSOCIATION	Ectomycorrhizal, with broadleaf trees, particularly oak
GROWTH FORM	On ground, singly or in clustered groups
ABUNDANCE	Common
SPORE COLOR	Olive-brown
EDIBILITY	Not edible

HEIGHT
Up to 6 in
(150 mm)

CAP DIAMETER
Up to 12 in
(300 mm)

BOLETUS RADICANS

ROOTING BOLETE

PERSOON

337

Many bolete species seem to prefer open woodland or parkland, rather than dense woodland or forest, and are often found growing with old, isolated trees or in long-established avenues or hedgebanks. The Rooting Bolete is just such a species, associating mainly with old oaks (occasionally beech and lime) on calcareous soils. It produces large, pale, bitter-tasting fruitbodies, with attractive lemon-yellow pores and a sky-blue bruising reaction. The species was long known as *Boletus albidus*, but *B. radicans* (*radicans* meaning "rooting") is an earlier name—even though fruitbodies only occasionally produce a short, root-like elongation of the stem.

SIMILAR SPECIES

The Rooting Bolete has sometimes been reported from eastern North America, but this may be in error for the local species, *Boletus inedulis*, which is similarly colored and has an equally bitter taste. The pale-capped Devil's Bolete (*Boletus satanas*) could look similar when seen from above, but has red pores and a red stem.

Actual size

The Rooting Bolete forms caps that are convex, becoming flatter. The cap surface is smooth, whitish to pale gray or buff. The pores are lemon-yellow, bruising pale blue. The stem is lemon-yellow at the top, buff below, occasionally flushed pink, with a whitish or pale network. The flesh is whitish to pale yellow, turning pale blue when cut.

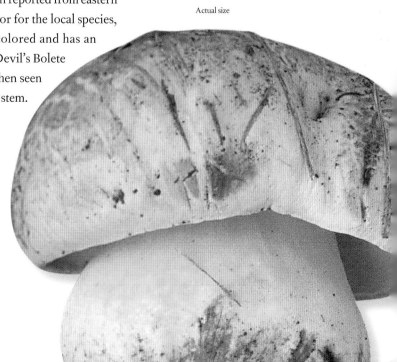

FAMILY	Boletaceae
DISTRIBUTION	Eastern Asia
HABITAT	In woodland and grassland
ASSOCIATION	Ectomycorrhizal, with conifers and sedges
GROWTH FORM	On ground, singly or in small groups
ABUNDANCE	Locally common
SPORE COLOR	Brown
EDIBILITY	Edible

HEIGHT
Up to 5 in
(125 mm)

CAP DIAMETER
Up to 5 in
(125 mm)

338

BOLETUS RETICULOCEPS
FISHNET BOLETE
(M. ZANG ET AL) Q. B. WANG & Y. J. YAO

The Latin epithet *reticuloceps* means "netted head," but the Fishnet Bolete not only has a raised, netlike surface to the cap, it also has an additional net on the stem. The result is a curious-looking and distinctive bolete. The species was originally described from China and is locally common in mountain areas such as Yunnan, where it is widely eaten. Unusually, it is said to form an ectomycorrhizal association with some of the sedges found in upland grasslands, as well as with firs and spruce.

SIMILAR SPECIES
The Tibetan Bolete (*Aureoboletus thibetanus*) occurs in the same area and also has a deeply veined cap. When damp, however, the cap is slimy, with gelatinous veil remnants, and the stem is smooth. Many other boletes have raised networks on the stem (including the Cep, *Boletus edulis*), but have caps that are smooth or shallowly wrinkled.

The Fishnet Bolete forms caps that are convex, becoming flatter. The surface of the cap is ocher to brown, covered in fine, granular scales, and deeply veined or ridged, the veins forming a netlike pattern. The pores are whitish, then yellow. The stem is brownish, with a whitish, raised network. The flesh is white.

Actual size

FAMILY	Boletaceae
DISTRIBUTION	Continental Europe
HABITAT	In calcareous woodland and parkland
ASSOCIATION	Ectomycorrhizal, with broadleaf trees, particularly oak
GROWTH FORM	On ground, singly or in small groups
ABUNDANCE	Occasional to rare
SPORE COLOR	Olive-brown
EDIBILITY	Poisonous

HEIGHT
Up to 6 in
(150 mm)

CAP DIAMETER
Up to 12 in
(300 mm)

BOLETUS RHODOXANTHUS
RUDDY BOLETE
(KROMBHOLZ) KALLENBACH

The Ruddy Bolete is a European species, first described by German-Czech mycologist Julius Vincenz von Krombholz in 1846. It belongs to a group of boletes with red pores, red stem, and pale to reddish caps, all of which are poisonous, causing gastroenteritic symptoms. None of them is common, most if not all being warmth-loving species (in Europe, they are typical of the Mediterranean region, becoming rarer northward) with a preference for chalk or limestone soils. They also seem to associate with old, long-established trees—which perhaps accounts for their rarity.

SIMILAR SPECIES

The Devil's Bolete (*Boletus satanas*) is similar, but lacks any pink tints on the cap and has a less pronounced bluing reaction. The Purple Bolete (*B. purpureus*) is more difficult to distinguish, but often develops a purple-red flush to the cap. Both are poisonous.

The Ruddy Bolete forms caps that are convex, becoming flatter. The cap surface is smooth, whitish yellow, but pink to rosy when touched, discoloring to buff with age. The pores are yellow at first, becoming red, bruising dark blue. The stem is yellow, becoming red toward the base, with a red, raised network, bruising dark blue. The flesh is white to pale yellow, turning deep blue when cut (see photo above).

Actual size

FAMILY	Boletaceae
DISTRIBUTION	Eastern North America, Europe, northern Asia, Australia, New Zealand
HABITAT	In woodland
ASSOCIATION	Ectomycorrhizal, with broadleaf trees, particularly oak
GROWTH FORM	On ground, singly or in small groups
ABUNDANCE	Common
SPORE COLOR	Olive-brown
EDIBILITY	Edible

HEIGHT
Up to 3 in
(75 mm)

CAP DIAMETER
Up to 3 in
(75 mm)

340

BOLETUS RUBELLUS
RUBY BOLETE
KROMBHOLZ

Boletus rubellus is an attractive little bolete—at least when young—thanks to its bright ruby cap and red-dotted stem. When older, the colors fade and it is then almost impossible to distinguish from other species often placed in the genus *Xerocomus*. Typical *Xerocomus* species have comparatively small fruitbodies with a dry, often felty cap that sometimes becomes finely cracked, yellowish pores often bruising bluish, and rather long, narrow stems. They are notoriously difficult to separate into species. Most, like the Ruby Bolete, are edible, but of poor taste and unappealing texture.

SIMILAR SPECIES

In Europe, *Boletus ripariellus* is a similar species, with a preference for wet woodland and a strongly blue-bruising stem. *Boletus armeniacus* may also look similar, but it has a bright apricot-orange cap when young. In North America, *B. campestris* (which is said to have a preference for open spaces) looks almost identical.

Actual size

The Ruby Bolete forms caps that are convex at first, becoming flatter. The cap surface is finely velvety, ruby at first, fading to pinkish red and finally olive-brown. The pores are yellow (see photo right) to pale yellow-green, bruising weakly bluish. The stem is smooth, dull yellow but, dotted with red. The flesh is pale yellow, purple-red immediately below the cap, slowly bluing in places when it is cut.

FAMILY	Boletaceae
DISTRIBUTION	Europe, North Africa
HABITAT	In calcareous woodland and parkland
ASSOCIATION	Ectomycorrhizal, with broadleaf trees, particularly oak
GROWTH FORM	On ground, singly or in small groups
ABUNDANCE	Rare
SPORE COLOR	Olive-brown
EDIBILITY	Poisonous

HEIGHT
Up to 6 in
(150 mm)

CAP DIAMETER
Up to 12 in
(300 mm)

BOLETUS SATANAS

DEVIL'S BOLETE

LENZ

341

Harald Othmar Lenz, who first described the species from Germany in 1831, believed he was made ill by vapors from the fruitbodies he was examining. He concluded that *Boletus satanas* was the most poisonous fungus of them all—hence his choice of name. In fact, despite its fearsome reputation, the Devil's Bolete causes nothing worse than gastroenteritic poisoning. Fruitbodies are seldom eaten, since they have a reputation for developing a repulsive, sickly-sweet smell, although it is quite pleasant and spicy when young. The Devil's Bolete is also quite rare and is on the national Red Lists of threatened fungal species in several European countries.

SIMILAR SPECIES

In California, *Boletus eastwoodiae* is locally called the Devil's Bolete. It is similarly colored, but often develops a curious, abruptly bulbous stem—rather like the stem of *Cortinarius sodagnitus* and similar Bigfoot Webcaps (*Cortinarius* species). It is said to be as poisonous as the real Devil's Bolete.

The Devil's Bolete forms caps that are convex, becoming flatter. The cap surface is smooth, whitish flushed with brown or buff (see photo above). The pores are red to orange, bruising bluish green. The stem is yellow-orange at the top, red below, and buff at the base, typically swollen above the base and with a partial netlike covering. The flesh is white to pale yellow, turning pale blue when cut.

Actual size

FAMILY	Boletaceae
DISTRIBUTION	Western North America, Central America
HABITAT	In woodland
ASSOCIATION	Ectomycorrhizal, with conifers, occasionally with broadleaf trees
GROWTH FORM	On ground, singly or in troops
ABUNDANCE	Common
SPORE COLOR	Olive-brown
EDIBILITY	Edible

HEIGHT
Up to 4 in
(100 mm)

CAP DIAMETER
Up to 4 in
(100 mm)

342

BOLETUS ZELLERI
ZELLER'S BOLETE
(MURRILL) MURRILL

The sharply contrasting colors and velvety cap make the Zeller's Bolete a handsome-looking bolete, though local mushroom hunters seem divided on its culinary merits. It was originally described as "slightly mucilaginous to the taste" and has more recently been dismissed as "slimy and tasteless." Others, however, esteem it highly and the Zeller's Bolete is commercially harvested and marketed in western Canada. The species—sometimes referred to as *Xerocomus zelleri*—was first collected in Seattle, Washington, by Professor Sanford Myron Zeller and was named in his honor by American mycologist William Murrill.

SIMILAR SPECIES
The very dark, often wrinkled cap (sometimes covered with a fine whitish bloom when young) should distinguish the Zeller's Bolete from more widespread, red-stemmed species such as *Boletus chrysenteron* and its allies. The latter group has smooth, brownish caps that often become finely cracked, showing reddish flesh below.

Actual size

The Zeller's Bolete forms caps that are convex to flat, the surface smooth to deeply wrinkled, velvety, and dark brown to black-brown. The pores are pale yellow, sometimes bruising bluish. The stem is smooth or slightly ribbed, pale yellow at the top, scarlet to crimson below. The cut flesh is pale yellow, sometimes slowly flushing blue.

FAMILY	Boletaceae
DISTRIBUTION	North America, Europe, Africa, Central and South America, northern Asia, Australia, New Zealand
HABITAT	In woodland
ASSOCIATION	Possibly ectomycorrhizal, with broadleaf trees and conifers
GROWTH FORM	On ground, singly or in small groups
ABUNDANCE	Common
SPORE COLOR	Brown to pink-brown
EDIBILITY	Not edible

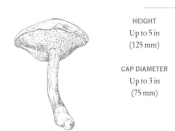

HEIGHT	Up to 5 in (125 mm)
CAP DIAMETER	Up to 3 in (75 mm)

CHALCIPORUS PIPERATUS

PEPPERY BOLETE

(BULLIARD) BATAILLE

343

As the name indicates, this is a hot little species, but opinion is divided as to its edibility. Some authorities suggest it can be used as a spice, others claim it is mildly poisonous—so it seems best to consider it as inedible and make do with chili instead. It does, however, produce a good range of dyes, including yellow, orange, and greenish brown. In the British Isles at least, the Peppery Bolete always seems to be associated with fruitbodies of the Fly Agaric (*Amanita muscaria*). It is possible that it is a parasite on the mycorrhiza of this species.

SIMILAR SPECIES

In North America, *Chalciporus piperatoides* is a similar species with pores bruising bluish. In continental Europe, the uncommon *C. amarellus* can be distinguished by its pinker pores and bitter (rather than peppery) taste. The equally uncommon *Rubinoboletus rubinus* is similarly shaped, but has red pores and red dots on the stem.

Actual size

The Peppery Bolete forms caps that are convex at first, becoming flatter. The cap surface is smooth, sticky when damp, buff to reddish brown (see photo near right). The decurrent pores are yellow-brown to red-brown. The stem is smooth, cap-colored, but with a bright yellow base. The flesh is yellow to pinkish in the cap, bright yellow in the stem (see photo far right).

FAMILY	Gyroporaceae
DISTRIBUTION	North America, Europe, North Africa, Central and South America, northern Asia, New Zealand
HABITAT	In woodland
ASSOCIATION	Ectomycorrhizal, with broadleaf trees, particularly oak
GROWTH FORM	On ground, singly or in small groups
ABUNDANCE	Locally common
SPORE COLOR	Pale yellow
EDIBILITY	Edible, but best avoided

HEIGHT
Up to 4 in
(100 mm)

CAP DIAMETER
Up to 4 in
(100 mm)

344

GYROPORUS CASTANEUS
CHESTNUT BOLETE
(BULLIARD) QUÉLET

The Chestnut Bolete is quite a distinctive species, placed (with other *Gyroporus* species) in its own separate family. It tends to have a less fleshy, and more brittle, feel than other boletes—the outer surface of the cap and stem may even crack and split—and the stem quickly becomes hollow. Originally described from France, it is a widespread fungus, though it was probably introduced in New Zealand and western North America. The Chestnut Bolete is considered to be edible and good, if slightly bitter, but in southwestern Europe the look-alike *G. ammophilus* is poisonous, so care must be taken.

SIMILAR SPECIES

Gyroporus ammophilus is a look-alike species known to cause gastroenteritic poisoning, but so far is only known from coastal dunes in southwestern Europe. In eastern North America and northern Asia, *Gyroporus purpurinus* is a similar species differing in its purple-red cap and stem.

Actual size

The Chestnut Bolete forms caps that are convex, becoming flat. The cap surface is smooth and chestnut-brown. The pores are white (see photo left), becoming pale yellowish. Its stem is smooth and cap-colored, becoming hollow with age. The flesh is white and fairly brittle.

FAMILY	Gyroporaceae
DISTRIBUTION	North America, Europe, North Africa, northern Asia, Australia
HABITAT	In woodland
ASSOCIATION	Ectomycorrhizal, with broadleaf trees, especially birch, and more rarely conifers
GROWTH FORM	On ground, singly or in small groups
ABUNDANCE	Locally common
SPORE COLOR	Pale yellow
EDIBILITY	Edible

GYROPORUS CYANESCENS

CORNFLOWER BOLETE

(BULLIARD) QUÉLET

HEIGHT
Up to 5 in
(125 mm)

CAP DIAMETER
Up to 6 in
(150 mm)

345

The Cornflower Bolete has pale, almost white, fruitbodies and may seem misnamed—until the fruitbodies are touched. The slightest handling will cause all parts to bruise immediately deep blue. *Gyroporus cyanescens* is sometimes referred to as the Bluing Bolete, but this can be a little misleading, since several other species—such as the Inkstain Bolete (*Boletus pulverulentus*)—exhibit a similar reaction. It is caused by a chemical compound within the fruitbodies called variegatic acid, which is colorless until exposed to oxygen by cutting or bruising.

SIMILAR SPECIES

A variety (var. *violaceotinctus*) occurs in eastern North America in which the bruising reaction is dark violet to indigo instead of blue. In southern North America and Central America, *Gyroporus phaeocyanescens* has a much smaller, yellow-brown cap and also bruises indigo, except for the pores (which do not react at all).

The Cornflower Bolete forms caps that are convex at first, becoming flat. The cap surface is coarsely velvety or almost scaly, ivory to pale ocher or buff. The pores are white, becoming pale yellowish. The stem is smooth and cap-colored, becoming hollow with age. The flesh is white and fairly brittle. All parts bruise immediately dark blue (see photo left).

Actual size

FAMILY	Boletaceae
DISTRIBUTION	Eastern North America, Central America, northern Asia
HABITAT	In woodland
ASSOCIATION	Ectomycorrhizal, with broadleaf trees and conifers
GROWTH FORM	On ground, singly or in troops
ABUNDANCE	Locally common
SPORE COLOR	Olive-brown
EDIBILITY	Edible

HEIGHT
Up to 8 in
(200 mm)

CAP DIAMETER
Up to 4 in
(100 mm)

346

HEIMIOPORUS BETULA
SHAGGY-STALKED BOLETE
(SCHWEINITZ) E. HORAK

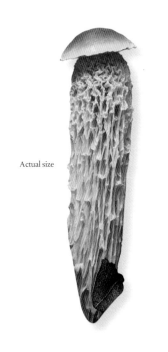

Actual size

Heimioporus betula has a quite extraordinary stem that is deeply ridged and furrowed. It is a feature that is particularly striking in immature fruitbodies, since the stem quickly develops to almost its full size, while the button-like cap is left behind—perched on top—to expand and catch up later. The epithet *betula* refers to birch, and confusingly the species has sometimes been called the Birch Bolete (a name more usually given to *Leccinum scabrum*), even though it is normally found with oak and pine.

SIMILAR SPECIES

The Jagged-Stem Bolete (*Boletellus russellii*) has a similar, deeply grooved, and lacerated stem, but its cap is brownish and dry (not sticky), often breaking up into scalelike patches. The Frost's Bolete (*Boletus frostii*) may also appear similar, but its pores are red to orange-red.

The Shaggy-Stalked Bolete forms caps that are hemispherical, becoming convex. The cap surface is smooth, sticky when damp, and yellow to orange, red, or reddish brown. The pores are yellow to greenish yellow. The stem is yellow to dull red, with a coarse, shaggy network of grooves and ridges. The flesh is greenish yellow to orange-yellow.

FAMILY	Boletaceae
DISTRIBUTION	North America, Europe, Central America, northern Asia
HABITAT	In woodland
ASSOCIATION	Ectomycorrhizal, with broadleaf trees, particularly oak and poplar
GROWTH FORM	On ground, singly or in troops
ABUNDANCE	Common
SPORE COLOR	Olive-brown
EDIBILITY	Edible

HEIGHT	Up to 9 in (225 mm)
CAP DIAMETER	Up to 8 in (200 mm)

LECCINUM AURANTIACUM

ORANGE OAK BOLETE

(BULLIARD) GRAY

347

Despite its English name, this large and imposing bolete is not restricted to oaks, but also occurs with poplars, or occasionally birches and limes. Until recently it was split into two species, the more orange *Leccinum aurantiacum* with poplars, and the slightly darker *L. quercinum* with oaks—but DNA sequencing has shown them to be identical. The species was originally described from France and is widespread in the northern hemisphere, though its status in North America is uncertain because of confusion with look-alike species. It is considered a good edible bolete and is commercially harvested in eastern Europe and China.

SIMILAR SPECIES

The Orange Birch Bolete (*Leccinum versipelle*) is similar, but is restricted to birch and has gray to blackish brown scales on the stem. The Foxy Bolete (*L. vulpinum*) is an orange-capped species with blackish stem-scales that grows with pines. It (or a look-alike conifer species) has been widely confused with *L. aurantiacum* in North America.

The Orange Oak Bolete forms caps that are hemispherical, becoming convex, the surface smooth, orange to rusty red or brick-red. The pores are whitish, bruising wine-red. The stem is white and scurfy-scaly, the scales whitish, becoming cap-colored to brown. The cut flesh is cream, flushing wine-red to purplish gray, sometimes also bluish in parts.

Actual size

FAMILY	Boletaceae
DISTRIBUTION	Eastern North America, Central America, Eastern Asia
HABITAT	In woodland
ASSOCIATION	Ectomycorrhizal, with conifers and broadleaf trees
GROWTH FORM	On ground, singly or in troops
ABUNDANCE	Common
SPORE COLOR	Pink
EDIBILITY	Poisonous

HEIGHT
Up to 5 in
(125 mm)

CAP DIAMETER
Up to 5 in
(125 mm)

348

LECCINUM EXIMIUM
LILAC-BROWN BOLETE
(PECK) SINGER

The epithet *eximium* means "excellent" or "distinguished," but it is not clear why New York mycologist Charles Peck thought so highly of this species when he first described it in 1887. Perhaps it was the violet-brown colors, which are quite attractive in a formal, nineteenth-century manner. Or possibly it was because the species was once considered edible and tasty. In the latter case, the Lilac-Brown Bolete has lost its excellence, having in recent years been implicated in several cases of gastroenteritic poisoning. It is now considered a toxic species, and best avoided.

SIMILAR SPECIES

Other North American species with similar colors include the bitter-tasting Violet-Gray Bolete (*Tylopilus plumbeoviolaceus*), with whitish pores and a smooth (not scurfy) stem, as well as *T. violatinctus* which is much the same, but has a slightly paler cap.

The Lilac-Brown Bolete forms caps that are convex, becoming flatter. The cap surface is smooth, violet-brown to gray-brown. The pores are chocolate to violet-brown. The stem is scurfy and cap-colored, or paler. The flesh is white, slowly turning lilac to grayish when cut.

Actual size

FAMILY	Boletaceae
DISTRIBUTION	North America, Europe, northern Asia
HABITAT	In woodland and bogs
ASSOCIATION	Ectomycorrhizal, with birch
GROWTH FORM	On ground, singly or in troops
ABUNDANCE	Occasional
SPORE COLOR	Pinkish ocher
EDIBILITY	Edible

HEIGHT	Up to 5 in (125 mm)
CAP DIAMETER	Up to 5 in (125 mm)

LECCINUM HOLOPUS

GHOST BOLETE

(ROSTKOVIUS) WATLING

349

Young fruitbodies of the Ghost Bolete are often pure white and sometimes remain so when mature. Occasionally, however, the caps become flushed with other colors—a tendency that has led to several variant species being described, though recent DNA research suggests they are all one and the same. Like many *Leccinum* species, the Ghost Bolete associates with birch and is at its commonest in wet woodland and boggy areas, typically among sphagnum moss. It is edible, but is said to be tasteless and pappy, so is not recommended.

SIMILAR SPECIES

Leccinum holopus var. *americanum*, reported with birch from North America, is a variety in which the cut flesh turns reddish and then sometimes gray. In eastern North America, *Leccinum albellum* is a similar-looking white species, but it is mycorrhizal with oak (not birch).

The Ghost Bolete forms caps that are convex. The cap surface is smooth, sometimes sticky when damp, and white at first, often developing buff, brownish, or gray-green tints. The pores are white, buff to slightly cinnamon with age. The stem is scurfy and cap-colored. The flesh is white, sometimes flushing pink when cut.

Actual size

FAMILY	Boletaceae
DISTRIBUTION	Eastern North America, Europe, northern Asia
HABITAT	In woodland and bogs
ASSOCIATION	Ectomycorrhizal, with hazel and hornbeam
GROWTH FORM	On ground, singly or in troops
ABUNDANCE	Occasional
SPORE COLOR	Ocher-brown
EDIBILITY	Edible

HEIGHT
Up to 5 in
(125 mm)

CAP DIAMETER
Up to 5 in
(125 mm)

350

LECCINUM PSEUDOSCABRUM
HAZEL BOLETE
(KALLENBACH) ŠUTARA

Comparatively few larger fungi are specifically associated with hazel or with hornbeam, but the Hazel Bolete is one such specialist. Together with the blackening flesh, its choice of tree partners should make it easy to distinguish from other brown *Leccinum* species. The Hazel Bolete was originally described from Germany and is widespread in Europe, though often overlooked. It has been reported from eastern North America, but it is not entirely clear that the reports refer to the same species, since the American fungus is said to be associated with oak.

SIMILAR SPECIES
The Hazel Bolete takes its Latin name from its similarity to *Leccinum scabrum*, the common Brown Birch Bolete. The latter has a similarly brown cap and scurfy stem, but does not turn black when cut or bruised. The Slate Bolete (*L. duriusculum*) has flesh that turns pinkish, then blackish, but occurs with poplars.

Actual size

The Hazel Bolete forms caps that are convex. The cap surface is smooth to wrinkled, often becoming cracked when dry, pale to dark brown. The pores are white to buff, bruising slowly purple-black. The stem is buff to ocher-buff, scurfy, the scales gray to dark gray-brown, bruising blackish. The flesh is whitish, gradually blackening when cut (see photo left).

FAMILY	Boletaceae
DISTRIBUTION	Eastern North America, Europe
HABITAT	In woodland
ASSOCIATION	With or on the Common Earthball (*Scleroderma citrinum*)
GROWTH FORM	Clustered around host fruitbodies
ABUNDANCE	Locally common
SPORE COLOR	Olive-brown
EDIBILITY	Edible, but best avoided

HEIGHT
Up to 2½ in
(60 mm)

CAP DIAMETER
Up to 2 in
(50 mm)

PSEUDOBOLETUS PARASITICUS

PARASITIC BOLETE

(BULLIARD) ŠUTARA

351

The Parasitic Bolete is small but easy to recognize, since it grows, often in clusters, at the base of the Common Earthball (*Scleroderma citrinum*). It has been suggested that it is not really a parasite, but simply fruits in association with the earthball. The earthball fruitbodies, however, do not look happy about this association and are frequently hollow or partly collapsed. It would seem more likely that the bolete is a parasite of the *Scleroderma* mycorrhiza. The Parasitic Bolete is said to be edible, but its host is certainly not.

SIMILAR SPECIES

No other bolete produces fruitbodies parasitic on earthballs, though a related species—*Pseudoboletus astraeicola*—occurs on fruitbodies of the Barometer Earthstar (*Astraeus hygrometricus*) in eastern Asia. Detached from its host, the Parasitic Bolete most closely resembles a small, brown Red-Cracked Bolete (*Boletus chrysenteron*) or similar species.

Actual size

The Parasitic Bolete forms caps that are convex, becoming flatter. The cap surface is smooth, olive-buff to tawny or grayish brown. The pores are yellow, becoming ocher to rusty (sometimes reddish). The stem is smooth to finely stippled and cap-colored. The flesh is pale yellow.

FAMILY	Boletaceae
DISTRIBUTION	North America, Central America, Eastern Asia
HABITAT	In woodland
ASSOCIATION	Ectomycorrhizal, with broadleaf trees and conifers
GROWTH FORM	On ground, singly or in troops
ABUNDANCE	Locally common
SPORE COLOR	Olive-brown
EDIBILITY	Not edible

HEIGHT
Up to 6 in
(150 mm)

CAP DIAMETER
Up to 5 in
(125 mm)

352

PULVEROBOLETUS RAVENELII
SULFUR BOLETE
(BERKELEY & M. A. CURTIS) MURRILL

The Sulfur Bolete is unusual in possessing a powdery, bright yellow veil that covers the fruitbody when young and when older leaves tatters of veil on the cap margin, and sometimes an irregular ring on the stem. The species was named after the nineteenth-century South Carolina mycologist Henry William Ravenel, who discovered many American fungi new to science. The Sulfur Bolete is sometimes said to be edible, but has a sour, unpleasant taste. It contains vulpinic acid (also found in many lichens) which is believed to deter grazing by invertebrates.

SIMILAR SPECIES

Younger fruitbodies that clearly show the sulfur-yellow veil or its remnants should be unmistakable. The veil may not be so obvious in older fruitbodies, however, leading to possible confusion with the duller, but similarly colored, fruitbodies of the Oak or Butter Bolete (*Boletus appendiculatus*) and other yellow-brown species.

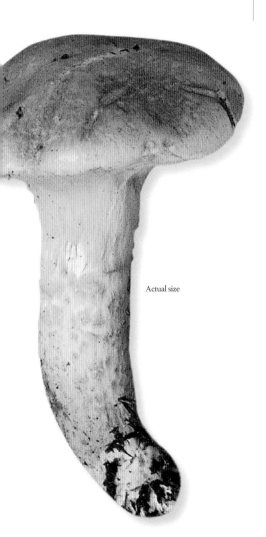

Actual size

The Sulfur Bolete forms caps that are convex, becoming flat. The cap surface is finely powdery at first, becoming finely fibrous-scaly, sulfur-yellow, becoming orange-brown from the center outward. The pores are bright yellow, bruising bluish. The stem is cap-colored, with an irregular ring or veil remains. The flesh is white to pale yellow, slowly turning pale blue when it is cut (see photo right).

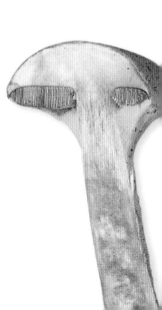

FAMILY	Boletaceae
DISTRIBUTION	North America, Europe, Central America, northern Asia
HABITAT	In woodland
ASSOCIATION	Mycorrhizal, with broadleaf trees, especially oak and beech
GROWTH FORM	On ground, singly or in troops
ABUNDANCE	Locally common
SPORE COLOR	Black
EDIBILITY	Edible

HEIGHT
Up to 5 in
(125 mm)

CAP DIAMETER
Up to 5 in
(125 mm)

STROBILOMYCES STROBILACEUS

OLD MAN OF THE WOODS

(SCOPOLI) BERKELEY

353

Strobilomyces species mainly occur in East Asia and the tropics, but the Old Man of the Woods is found throughout the northern hemisphere and is the only member of the genus in Europe, where its distribution is rather patchy and local. It takes its English name from its gray, unkempt appearance and its Latin name (*strobilaceus*) from its fancied resemblance to a pinecone. Fruitbodies are woodier than most boletes and tend to persist for some time in dry weather. The Old Man of the Woods is edible, but is said to be insipid.

SIMILAR SPECIES

In America and Asia, *Strobilomyces confusus* is a related species of similar color, but with smaller and more erect scales on the cap. *Strobilomyces mirandus* is an attractive East Asian species, known from Malaysia northward to Japan, that has a yellowish to orange scaly cap and stem.

The Old Man of the Woods forms caps that are convex, becoming flat. The surface of the cap is densely scaly, gray to dark brown, and finally black-brown, the scales overhanging the margin. The pores are white, becoming gray to black, bruising reddish. The stem is scaly and cap-colored, with a thick scaly ring. The flesh is white, turning reddish then black when cut (see photo below).

Actual size

FAMILY	Suillaceae
DISTRIBUTION	North America, Europe, northern Asia
HABITAT	In woodland
ASSOCIATION	Ectomycorrhizal, with larch
GROWTH FORM	On ground, singly or in troops
ABUNDANCE	Locally common
SPORE COLOR	Olive-ocher
EDIBILITY	Edible

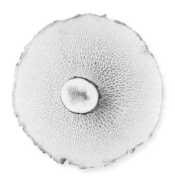

HEIGHT
Up to 4 in
(100 mm)

CAP DIAMETER
Up to 5 in
(125 mm)

354

SUILLUS CAVIPES
HOLLOW BOLETE

(OPATOWSKI) A. H. SMITH & THIERS

The Hollow Bolete is a larch associate, fairly common where the tree is native, but much less so in plantations—certainly when compared to the ubiquitous Larch Bolete (*Suillus grevillei*). The Latin *cavipes* means "hollow foot" (or "stem") and this is one of the distinguishing features of the species, though the contrast between the brownish cap and stem and the yellow-to-olive colored pores should be equally distinctive. The name *Suillus* means "pertaining to swine," perhaps because many *Suillus* species—including the Hollow Bolete—are edible and sought after by pigs.

SIMILAR SPECIES
The Rosy Larch Bolete (*Suillus ochraceoroseus*) has a more pinkish to brick-red cap and is restricted to western North America and Eastern Asia. The Painted Bolete (*S. pictus*) and the Western Painted Bolete (*S. lakei*) have browner caps, but occur with firs and pine rather than with larch.

The Hollow Bolete forms caps that are convex, becoming flat to broadly umbonate. The cap surface is fibrous-scaly, tawny to rusty or a reddish brown, the margin often with whitish veil remains. The pores are elongated, yellow to olive-ocher (see photo above). The hollow stem is yellow at the top, cap-colored and fibrous toward the base, with a whitish, often partial, ring. The flesh is yellowish.

Actual size

FAMILY	Suillaceae
DISTRIBUTION	North America, Europe, northern Asia; introduced in Australia and New Zealand
HABITAT	In woodland
ASSOCIATION	Ectomycorrhizal, with larch
GROWTH FORM	On ground, singly or in troops
ABUNDANCE	Very common
SPORE COLOR	Ocher to cinnamon-brown
EDIBILITY	Edible

HEIGHT
Up to 5 in
(125 mm)

CAP DIAMETER
Up to 5 in
(125 mm)

SUILLUS GREVILLEI

LARCH BOLETE

(KLOTZSCH) SINGER

355

Suillus grevillei is a strict associate of larch, so it is rather odd that it was first described from Scotland, where larch is not a native tree. It seems to travel well, however, since it has also been introduced in Australia and New Zealand. In wet weather, the fruitbodies are exceedingly slimy, but the caps become shiny when dry. They are edible if the slime is removed, but are not highly regarded. The Larch Bolete produces a good range of dyes from tan to burnt orange and is one of the ingredients of "Tendon-easing Powder" in Chinese medicine, said to benefit leg pain and lumbago.

SIMILAR SPECIES

The North American *Suillus clintonianus* is sometimes considered a distinct species, sometimes just a form of the Larch Bolete with a darker, reddish brown cap. The Slippery Jack (*S. luteus*) is an equally slimy species, but it grows under pines and usually has a darker, liver-colored cap and a whitish stem.

The Larch Bolete forms caps that are convex, becoming flatter. The cap surface is smooth, sticky when damp (see photo below left), golden yellow flushed rusty to red-brown with age. The pores are golden yellow, becoming rusty or red-brown. The stem is smooth, sticky when damp, and cap-colored, becoming red-brown toward the base, with a distinct ring. The flesh is lemon-yellow.

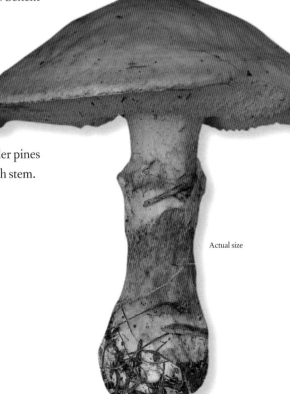

Actual size

FAMILY	Suillaceae
DISTRIBUTION	North America, Europe, Central America, northern Asia; introduced in Africa, South America, Australia, and New Zealand
HABITAT	In woodland
ASSOCIATION	Ectomycorrhizal, with pine
GROWTH FORM	On ground, singly or in troops
ABUNDANCE	Very common
SPORE COLOR	Pale brown to ocher-brown
EDIBILITY	Edible (after processing)

HEIGHT
Up to 5 in
(125 mm)

CAP DIAMETER
Up to 10 in
(250 mm)

356

SUILLUS LUTEUS
SLIPPERY JACK
(LINNAEUS) ROUSSEL

In damp weather the Slippery Jack lives up to its name, having an extremely slimy cap surface. Despite this, it is considered an edible species, drying well, and is even collected commercially in eastern Europe, China, and South America for processing and export. The gelatinous cap skin peels off quite easily, which is just as well—since it appears to be mildly toxic, causing gastroenteritic symptoms in some people. Originally described from Europe, the species is widespread and common in the northern hemisphere and has been introduced elsewhere with plantation pines.

SIMILAR SPECIES
Another pine associate that produces similarly colored, slimy-capped fruitbodies is *Suillus collinitus*, but it lacks a ring on the stem—as does the Weeping Bolete (*S. granulatus*), which has a pinkish to tawny cap. The Larch Bolete (*S. grevillei*) is slimy and does have a ring, but its cap is golden-yellow and it occurs with larch.

Actual size

The Slippery Jack forms caps that are convex at first, becoming flat. The cap surface is smooth, very slimy when damp, purplish brown, becoming rusty brown with age. The pores are lemon-yellow, becoming dull ocher. The stem is sticky when damp, and white to buff, stippled with darker dots, becoming purplish brown toward the base, with a distinct whitish to cap-colored ring. The flesh is white to lemon-yellow.

FAMILY	Suillaceae
DISTRIBUTION	Western North America, Eastern Asia
HABITAT	In woodland
ASSOCIATION	Ectomycorrhizal, with larch or (in Asia) pine
GROWTH FORM	On ground, singly or in troops
ABUNDANCE	Occasional
SPORE COLOR	Dark red-brown
EDIBILITY	Not edible

HEIGHT
Up to 5 in
(125 mm)

CAP DIAMETER
Up to 10 in
(250 mm)

SUILLUS OCHRACEOROSEUS

ROSY LARCH BOLETE

(SNELL) SINGER

357

The Rosy Larch Bolete is an attractively colored fungus, occurring mainly with larch in America's Rocky Mountains and Pacific Northwest, but also reported with pine in China and Taiwan. With its dry, fibrous-scaly cap, it is not closely related to the slimy, smooth-capped Larch Bolete (*Suillus grevillei*), despite the similarity of the English names. Indeed, *Suillus ochraceoroseus* is distinct enough to have been referred in the past to the separate genera *Boletinus* or *Fuscoboletinus*. Fruitbodies are sometimes said to be edible, but not worth eating because of their bitterness.

SIMILAR SPECIES

The Western Painted Bolete (*Suillus lakei*) occurs in the same area of North America and has a similar, but slightly duller, pinkish to reddish brown, fibrous-scaly cap. It associates with Douglas fir, however, rather than larch. The Painted Bolete (*S. pictus*) of eastern North America is a look-alike species growing with pine.

Actual size

The Rosy Larch Bolete forms caps that are convex, becoming flat. The cap surface is fibrous-scaly, bright pink to rose, brick-red with age. The pores are elongated and dark yellow to olive-ocher. The stem is yellowish, sometimes with red-brown stains toward the base. The whitish veil forms a partial ring or persists as tatters at the cap margin. The flesh is yellowish.

FAMILY	Suillaceae
DISTRIBUTION	North America, Europe, northern Asia
HABITAT	In woodland
ASSOCIATION	Ectomycorrhizal, with white pine
GROWTH FORM	On ground, singly or in troops
ABUNDANCE	Locally common
SPORE COLOR	Cinnamon-brown
EDIBILITY	Edible (after processing)

HEIGHT
Up to 5 in
(125 mm)

CAP DIAMETER
Up to 4 in
(100 mm)

358

SUILLUS PLACIDUS
SLIPPERY WHITE BOLETE
(BONORDEN) SINGER

Suillus placidus is a bolete that seems only to associate with certain species of white pine, principally the Arolla pine in alpine Europe and the eastern white pine in North America. Where these trees are native, it may be locally common—but elsewhere (in western North America, for example, or the British Isles) it is a rare associate of planted trees. Fruitbodies are edible, but—as with the Slippery Jack (*S. luteus*)—the gelatinous cap skin needs to be peeled off and discarded, since it may be mildly toxic.

SIMILAR SPECIES

In western North America, *Suillus pallidiceps* is an uncommon, white-capped species occurring with lodgepole pine. It lacks the red-brown stippling on the stem. The Ghost Bolete (*Leccinum holopus*) is white-capped, but is not slimy and has a stem that is scurfy-scaly, rather than stippled.

Actual size

The Slippery White Bolete forms caps that are convex at first, becoming flat (see photo right). The cap surface is smooth, sticky when damp, white to ivory, ocher-tinted with age. The pores are ocher-yellow. The stem is white, stippled with red-brown dots, becoming ocher-tinted with age. The flesh is white, becoming yellowish with age.

FAMILY	Boletaceae
DISTRIBUTION	Eastern North America, Central America, Eastern Asia
HABITAT	In woodland
ASSOCIATION	Ectomycorrhizal, with broadleaf trees, especially oak
GROWTH FORM	On ground, singly or in troops
ABUNDANCE	Common
SPORE COLOR	Pink
EDIBILITY	Edible

HEIGHT
Up to 5 in
(125 mm)

CAP DIAMETER
Up to 6 in
(150 mm)

TYLOPILUS ALBOATER

BLACK VELVET BOLETE

(SCHWEINITZ) MURRILL

359

This is a smart-looking species when young, the black cap and stem of the fruitbodies contrasting nicely with the white pores. Rather like the unrelated Blackening Brittlegill (*Russula nigricans*), the flesh of the Black Velvet Bolete turns reddish when cut, then slowly becomes gray to black—a chemical reaction that occurs when compounds within the fruitbodies are exposed to oxygen. Many *Tylopilus* species, such as *T. felleus*, are bitter, but the Black Velvet Bolete is mild and generally considered a good edible species.

SIMILAR SPECIES

Several related, North American species are similar. *Tylopilus atratus* is smaller and the flesh does not turn red when cut. *Tylopilus atronicotianus* has a smooth, olive-brown cap. *Tylopilus griseocarneus* has a distinct netlike pattern on the stem.

Actual size

The Black Velvet Bolete forms caps that are convex (see photo above), becoming flatter. The cap surface is smooth and velvety, dark gray-brown to black. The pores are white, aging to a dull pink, bruising reddish then slowly black. The stem is smooth and cap-colored. The flesh is white, becoming pink, and eventually black when cut.

FAMILY	Boletaceae
DISTRIBUTION	Eastern North America, Central America, Eastern Asia
HABITAT	In woodland
ASSOCIATION	Ectomycorrhizal, with broadleaf trees and conifers
GROWTH FORM	On ground, singly or in troops
ABUNDANCE	Common
SPORE COLOR	Pink-brown
EDIBILITY	Edible

HEIGHT
Up to 6 in
(150 mm)

CAP DIAMETER
Up to 6 in
(150 mm)

360

TYLOPILUS CHROMAPES
YELLOWFOOT BOLETE
(FROST) A. H. SMITH & THIERS

The Yellowfoot Bolete is a distinctive and attractive species, but is not so distinctive when it comes to selecting a genus in which to place it. The scurfy scales on the stem suggest it is a *Leccinum* species, albeit not a typical one. Recent molecular research agrees that it is close to *Leccinum*— but also close to *Tylopilus*. Either way, *Leccinum* or *Tylopilus chromapes* is a not uncommon species in eastern North America and is also considered edible and good by fungus-eating enthusiasts.

SIMILAR SPECIES

The epithet *chromapes* means "yellow foot," and the combination of rose-pink cap, scurfy stem scales, and yellow stem base is characteristic of the species. *Tylopilus cartagoensis* of Central America is similar, but smaller with a duller cap. *Tylopilus subchromapes* is one of several related Australian species.

Actual size

The Yellowfoot Bolete forms caps that are convex, becoming flatter. The cap surface is smooth, rose-pink when young, becoming pinkish tan with age. The pores are white, aging to a dull pink. The stem is finely scurfy, white to pinkish but with a bright yellow base. The flesh is white, but yellow in the stem base.

FAMILY	Boletaceae
DISTRIBUTION	Eastern North America, Europe, Central America, northern Asia
HABITAT	In woodland
ASSOCIATION	Ectomycorrhizal, with broadleaf trees and conifers
GROWTH FORM	On ground, singly or in troops
ABUNDANCE	Common
SPORE COLOR	Pink
EDIBILITY	Not edible

HEIGHT
Up to 9 in
(225 mm)

CAP DIAMETER
Up to 12 in
(300 mm)

TYLOPILUS FELLEUS

BITTER BOLETE

(BULLIARD) P. KARSTEN

361

Though not poisonous, the flesh of this large bolete can be intensely bitter, the Latin epithet *felleus* referring to "gall." Despite this, the Bitter Bolete is said to be eaten in parts of eastern Europe and Mexico—though presumably only in desperation. Fruitbodies may, however, have some potential use, since a polysaccharide called tylopilan has been extracted from the Bitter Bolete that is said to show potential antitumor activity. The species is widespread and fairly common, occurring particularly with beech and oak, but also with other broadleaf trees and conifers.

SIMILAR SPECIES

The Bitter Bolete is the only *Tylopilus* species found in Europe, where the pink pores and spores make it distinctive. The edible Cep (*Boletus edulis*) is otherwise rather similar, but has a whitish network on the stem, and, of course, lacks the bitter taste. In North America, *T. rubrobrunneus* has a purplish or purple-brown cap and is equally bitter.

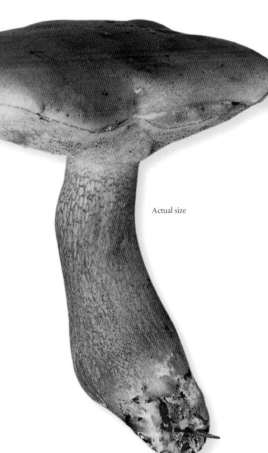

Actual size

The Bitter Bolete forms caps that are convex, becoming flatter. The cap surface is smooth and buff to brown. The pores are white, aging to a purplish pink, bruising brownish. The stem is white at the top, cap-colored or paler below, with a conspicuous, raised, dark brown network. The flesh is white, sometimes slightly pinkish when cut.

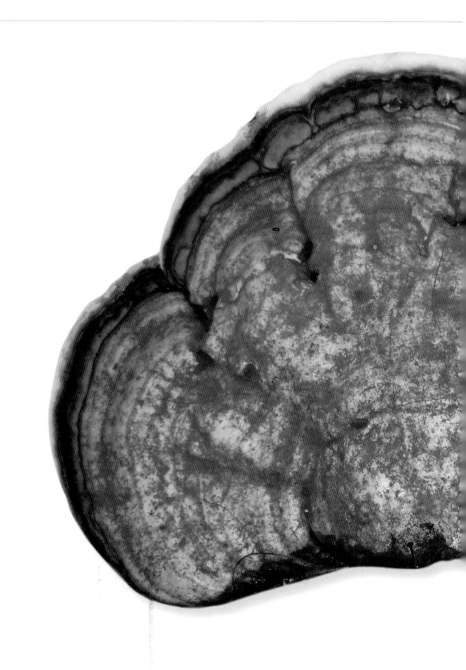

BRACKETS, CRUSTS & JELLY FUNGI

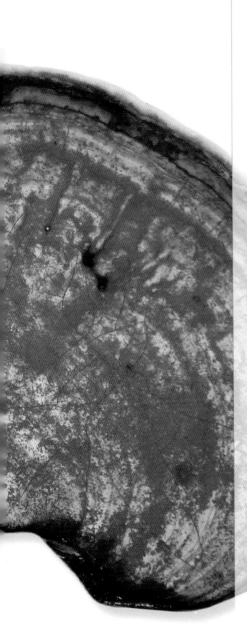

Most bracket fungi (or polypores) are wood-rotters, growing on trunks, dead branches, stumps, and fallen wood. They often form shelflike fruitbodies with a cap and pores that are sometimes fleshy, but frequently leathery or hard. The woody-hard fruitbodies are perennial, a new pore layer being added each year. Though they may all look rather similar, the bracket fungi are not closely related to each other. Most have evolved pores and tubes below the cap—an adaptation that helps prevent the spore-bearing surfaces from drying out. A few have teeth or spines instead of pores.

The crust (or corticioid) fungi are even more of a mixed bag. They, too, are also mostly wood-rotters, forming patches or crusts on the underside of branches or logs. The crust surface, on which the spores are formed, is usually smooth, but sometimes warted, wrinkled, or toothed. A few species have shelflike edges and look like thin bracket fungi.

Some of the jelly fungi (or heterobasidiomycetes) are wood-rotters, but others are ectomycorrhizal (see Introduction) or are parasites on other fungi. Their gelatinous fruitbodies are an alternative way of retaining moisture and prolonging the formation of spores. Many of them are capable of dehydrating in dry weather and reviving after rain.

FAMILY	Meruliaceae
DISTRIBUTION	North America, Europe, Africa, Central and South America, Asia, Australia, New Zealand
HABITAT	In woodland
ASSOCIATION	With broadleaf trees, rarely conifers
GROWTH FORM	On stumps or on the ground, often in grass
ABUNDANCE	Common
SPORE COLOR	White
EDIBILITY	Not edible

HEIGHT
Up to 2 in
(50 mm)

CAP DIAMETER
Up to 6 in
(150 mm)

364

ABORTIPORUS BIENNIS
BLUSHING ROSETTE
(BULLIARD) SINGER

The Blushing Rosette is often a tricky species to identify. Occasionally it behaves like a normal bracket fungus, and produces shelflike fruitbodies at the base of stumps. More commonly, it is found on the ground, probably arising from dead roots, where it forms circular caps or rosette-like clusters on a short stem. Just as frequently, however, it produces strangely distorted lumps, with pores and protuberances all over the place, which are full of chlamydospores (asexual spores). Whether bracket-like, rosette-like, or lumpy—the Blushing Rosette bruises pink when it is fresh, and exudes watery red droplets when it is damp.

The Blushing Rosette sometimes forms single or rosette-like clusters of caps, often on a stem, but just as frequently forms distorted fruitbodies with pores on the upper surface. When caps are present, they are flat to funnel-shaped, and pale pinkish to reddish brown, with a paler, feathery or wavy margin. The pores are pinkish white to pink-buff, as is the stem.

SIMILAR SPECIES
Distorted fruitbodies oozing red droplets are frequently confused with fruitbodies of the unrelated, but similarly colored, Devil's Tooth (*Hydnellum peckii*), which also exudes red droplets when damp. The latter species (which is much less common and widespread) has spines on the undersurface, not pores.

Actual size

FAMILY	Albatrellaceae
DISTRIBUTION	North America, northern Asia
HABITAT	In conifer woodland
ASSOCIATION	Ectomycorrhizal, particularly with hemlock
GROWTH FORM	On ground, often clustered and coalescing
ABUNDANCE	Rare
SPORE COLOR	White
EDIBILITY	Edible

HEIGHT
Up to 2½ in
(60 mm)

CAP DIAMETER
Up to 2½ in
(60 mm)

ALBATRELLUS CAERULEOPORUS

BLUE ALBATRELLUS

(PECK) POUZAR

365

DNA evidence shows that *Albatrellus* species are more closely related to gilled agarics in the genera *Russula* and *Lactarius* than to most other fungi with pores. They are not wood-rotters, but form associations with the roots of living trees. The distinctive Blue Albatrellus or Blue-Pored Polyphore was first described from the east coast of North America, where it is uncommon. More recently, separate populations have been found in western and northwestern forests, where it is rare and of conservation concern. Although reported as edible, the Blue Albatrellus is said to be tough. In Asia it has been used as a herbal medicine.

SIMILAR SPECIES

Most other *Albatrellus* species are differently colored. In western North America, however, there is another blue species, *Albatrellus flettii*. This is often larger, with a cap up to 8 in (200 mm) wide, and has pores that are whitish to pinkish buff. In China and Japan, *Albatrellus yasudai* has a greenish blue, but sticky (not dry), cap and whitish pores.

The Blue Albatrellus is a beautiful indigo or gray-blue when young, but quickly turns gray to gray-brown with age. The cap is often irregularly shaped, smooth or slightly scurfy, with an inrolled margin. The decurrent pores are similarly colored, as is the stem (see photo above), but the flesh when cut is cream to pale buff.

Actual size

FAMILY	Albatrellaceae
DISTRIBUTION	North America, continental Europe, northern Asia
HABITAT	In conifer woodland
ASSOCIATION	Ectomycorrhizal, particularly with spruce
GROWTH FORM	On ground, often in clusters
ABUNDANCE	Locally common
SPORE COLOR	White
EDIBILITY	Edible

HEIGHT
Up to 2½ in
(60 mm)

CAP DIAMETER
Up to 6 in
(150 mm)

366

ALBATRELLUS OVINUS
SHEEP POLYPORE
(SCHAEFFER) KOTLABA & POUZAR

The Sheep Polypore has a cream to buff cap, which becomes finely cracked and grayish brown or olive-green with age. The cap is an irregular funnel shape and the edge remains strongly inrolled even in age. The minute, decurrent pores are white to pale yellowish when fresh, and bruise lemon-yellow. The stout stem is often positioned off-center and is whitish to cream, as is the cut flesh.

This is one of the commonest and most widely distributed *Albatrellus* species, absent from the British Isles but otherwise occurring in spruce forests throughout the northern hemisphere. A character that helps distinguish the species is that the flesh turns bright yellow when a drop of dilute ammonia (or other alkali) is placed on it. In many parts of its range, the Sheep Polypore is common enough to be considered a good edible species, and is widely collected and even exported commercially. It has long been studied for its bioactive compounds, some of which are said to have shown promising antibacterial and other medicinal properties.

SIMILAR SPECIES

Albatrellus ovinus often grows together with *A. confluens*, which can be separated by its pinkish buff colors. Without using a microscope, *A. subrubescens* is more difficult to distinguish, but it typically grows with pine rather than spruce, and its pores bruise chrome-yellow to orange rather than lemon-yellow.

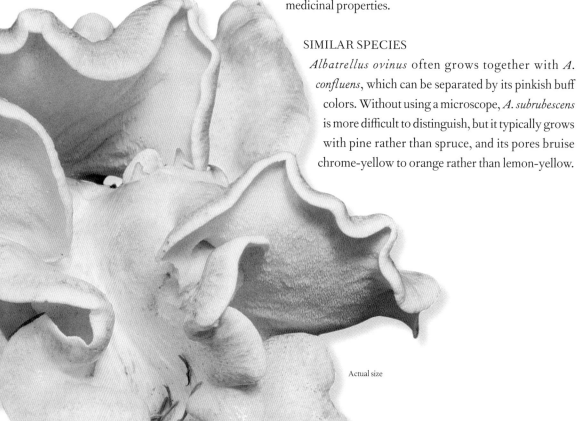

Actual size

FAMILY	Albatrellaceae
DISTRIBUTION	Eastern North America, Central America
HABITAT	In woodland
ASSOCIATION	With broadleaf trees, especially beech
GROWTH FORM	On ground
ABUNDANCE	Occasional
SPORE COLOR	White
EDIBILITY	Not edible

HEIGHT
Up to 2 in
(50 mm)

CAP DIAMETER
Up to 2 in
(50 mm)

ALBATRELLUS PECKIANUS

PECK'S POLYPORE

(COOKE) NIEMELÄ

367

The odd thing about *Albatrellus peckianus* is that it is not actually an *Albatrellus* species, according to recent DNA evidence, though for the moment it is still retained in the genus. While true *Albatrellus* species are ectomycorrhizal, the Peck's Polypore is a wood-rotter, producing fruitbodies on the ground that arise singly or in branched clusters from buried wood. It was named in honor of nineteenth-century New York mycologist Charles Horton Peck, and appears to be restricted to eastern North America and Central America, with reports from northern Asia referring to an as-yet-unnamed, look-alike species.

SIMILAR SPECIES

Albatrellus dispansus is another yellow, branched species, but was originally described from Japan and in North America is known only from the Rocky Mountains, where it is associated with conifers. *Albatrellus ellisii* occurs in eastern North America, but its cap is scaly and more yellowish green.

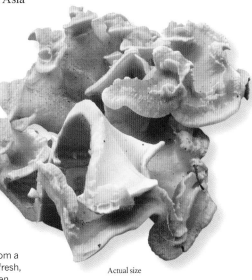

The Peck's Polypore may produce single caps or several branching from a single stem. The cap surface is smooth, often depressed, yellow when fresh, and becoming buff to yellowish brown. The pores are bright yellow when fresh. The stem is smooth, yellow to buff, as is the cut flesh.

Actual size

FAMILY	Ganodermataceae
DISTRIBUTION	Australia
HABITAT	In wet woodland
ASSOCIATION	On hardwoods
GROWTH FORM	On fallen trunks and logs
ABUNDANCE	Locally common
SPORE COLOR	Brown
EDIBILITY	Not edible

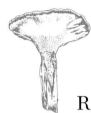

HEIGHT
Up to 6 in
(150 mm)

CAP DIAMETER
Up to 5 in
(125 mm)

368

AMAURODERMA RUDE
RED-STAINING STALKED POLYPORE
(BERKELEY) TORREND

The Red-Staining Stalked Polypore seems to be restricted to Australia, where it is typically found in rainforests. It belongs in the same group of fungi as the Artist's Bracket (*Ganoderma applanatum*) and shares the same intense bruising reaction. Scratch the whitish pores on the undersurface of the fruitbody and they turn bright blood-red. Unlike the brackets of *Ganoderma*, most fruitbodies of *Amauroderma* have a central stem. As a group, they are common in the tropics and subtropics, but more or less absent from temperate regions.

SIMILAR SPECIES

Amauroderma rude has sometimes been reported from South America, but it seems this is based on a misidentification of a similar species, *A. intermedium*. Reports of *A. rude* from Southeast Asia are based on another look-alike species, *A. rugosum*. Both have whitish pores that stain when bruised.

Actual size

The Red-Staining Stalked Polypore produces woody, perennial fruitbodies with a central stem. The cap is flat to depressed, the surface red-brown at first with a whitish margin, then becoming brown to black-brown, wrinkled and concentrically ridged, the margin becoming wavy or irregular. The pores are white, turning red then black where bruised. The stem is velvety and dark brown.

FAMILY	Polyporaceae
DISTRIBUTION	Australia, New Zealand; introduced in South America
HABITAT	In woodland
ASSOCIATION	With hardwoods, especially southern beech
GROWTH FORM	On living and dead trunks and logs
ABUNDANCE	Common
SPORE COLOR	White
EDIBILITY	Not edible

THICKNESS
Up to ½ in
(10 mm)

CAP DIAMETER
Up to 4 in
(100 mm)

AURANTIPORUS PULCHERRIMUS

STRAWBERRY BRACKET

(RODWAY) P. K. BUCHANAN & HOOD

369

Fresh fruitbodies of the Strawberry Bracket can be a shockingly bright color, typically an extravagant, eye-catching crimson. The Latin epithet *pulcherrimus* means "very beautiful," so it certainly appealed to Tasmanian mycologist Leonard Rodway when he first described it in 1922. The Strawberry Bracket is restricted to Australia and New Zealand, where it occurs on native southern beech and (in Australia) eucalypts. It has also been found on eucalypts in Brazil, where it is clearly an exotic introduction. Despite its tempting name, the Strawberry Bracket is not edible.

SIMILAR SPECIES

The Blood-Red Bracket (*Pycnoporus sanguineus*) also occurs in Australia and New Zealand, but its fruitbodies—though almost as brightly colored—are leathery to woody. The Curry Punk (*Piptoporus australiensis*) is a spongy, orange species on eucalypts, with—as the English name indicates—a strong curry-like smell.

The Strawberry Bracket produces fleshy, annual fruitbodies broadly attached to wood. The caps are irregular to lobed, the surface velvety-hairy, deep pink at first, becoming bright salmon to orange or crimson. The pores are cap-colored. The whole fruitbody becomes hard and resinous when dried.

Actual size

FAMILY	Meruliaceae
DISTRIBUTION	North America, Europe, Africa, Central and South America, Asia, Australia, and New Zealand
HABITAT	In woodland
ASSOCIATION	On broadleaf trees, rarely conifers
GROWTH FORM	On stumps, logs, and dead trees, in dense tiers
ABUNDANCE	Common
SPORE COLOR	White
EDIBILITY	Not edible

THICKNESS
Up to ½ in
(10 mm)

CAP DIAMETER
Up to 4 in
(100 mm)

370

BJERKANDERA ADUSTA
SMOKY BRACKET
(WILLDENOW) P. KARSTEN

Actual size

This is one of the commonest bracket fungi in the world, found on a wide variety of trees in every continent except Antarctica. The Smoky Bracket is an active parasite, attacking living trees as well as dead wood. It produces enzymes that are capable of breaking down lignin and, as a result, is one of several fungal species being tested in research laboratories to see what else their enzymes can tackle. The hope is that the Smoky Bracket can help to clean up long-lasting environmental pollutants such as pesticides and dyes. On a non-commercial basis, the Smoky Bracket has been used to make homemade craft paper.

SIMILAR SPECIES
The related and less common *Bjerkandera fumosa* is quite similar, but when checked underneath has paler, brownish pores. Another uncommon bracket, *Cerrena unicolor*, has grayish pores when older, but the pores are larger and become very irregular and toothlike.

The Smoky Bracket is easily distinguished by having small gray pores (see photo above) that contrast with its cream to buff cap. It is rather tough and leathery, and typically grows in dense, tiered clusters, the individual fruitbodies coalescing. If growing under logs, it sometimes forms effused fruitbodies which grow flat against the wood with little or no bracket-like cap.

FAMILY	Bankeraceae
DISTRIBUTION	North America, continental Europe, northern Asia
HABITAT	In dry pine woodland
ASSOCIATION	Ectomycorrhizal, with Scots pine
GROWTH FORM	On ground, singly or in troops
ABUNDANCE	Rare
SPORE COLOR	Pale brown
EDIBILITY	Not edible

HEIGHT
Up to 3 in
(80 mm)

CAP DIAMETER
Up to 6 in
(150 mm)

BOLETOPSIS GRISEA
GRAY FALSEBOLETE
(PECK) BONDARTSEV & SINGER

371

As its English name suggests, the Gray Falsebolete could be mistaken for a true bolete, but is actually more closely related to *Bankera* species, such as the Spruce Tooth (*B. violascens*), which have spines below the cap instead of pores. Like *Albatrellus* species, the Falseboletes are not wood-rotters but form mutually beneficial associations with tree roots. In Europe, the Gray Falsebolete is on the Red List of threatened fungal species in at least five countries and is one of the 33 fungi proposed for international protection under the Bern Convention.

SIMILAR SPECIES
There are several closely related species. *Boletopsis perplexa*, recently described from Scotland and known from North America, is darker, but otherwise almost indistinguishable from *B. grisea* in the field. *Boletopsis leucomelaena* is also very similar, but associates with spruce rather than pine.

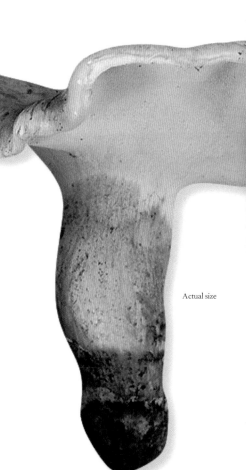

Actual size

The Gray Falsebolete has a large, smooth, fleshy cap that is pale grayish brown, and becomes somewhat cracked at the center with age. The margin remains inrolled, and the pores are white when fresh and are decurrent, running down the comparatively short, grayish brown stem.

FAMILY	Bondarzewiaceae
DISTRIBUTION	Western North America, continental Europe, northern Asia
HABITAT	In woodland
ASSOCIATION	With conifers
GROWTH FORM	At base or among roots of living trees
ABUNDANCE	Occasional
SPORE COLOR	White
EDIBILITY	Edible

HEIGHT
Up to 12 in
(300 mm)

CAP DIAMETER
Up to 10 in
(250 mm)

372

BONDARZEWIA MONTANA
BONDARTSEV'S POLYPORE
(QUÉLET) SINGER

This large and conspicuous polypore grows at the base of conifers and slowly rots away the heartwood in the butt and roots. It is quite widespread throughout the northern hemisphere, though not known in eastern North America or the British Isles. Microscopically it has very distinctive spores which show that it is related to gilled agarics in the genera *Russula* and *Lactarius*. It has a pleasantly nutty smell when fresh, and is said to be edible when very young, though the flesh becomes tough and bitter with age. The compound fruitbodies can reach 40 in (1000 mm) in diameter.

SIMILAR SPECIES

A related species, *Bondarzewia berkeleyi*, grows at the base of broadleaf trees in eastern North America and Asia. It typically has paler, tan to ocher caps. The common but unrelated *Meripilus giganteus* can look similar, but it also grows with broadleaf trees and all parts bruise black.

Actual size

The Bondartsev's Polypore is a large species that produces one or several fleshy caps on a central or lop-sided, branching stem. Multi-capped specimens can form giant, cabbage-like rosettes. The individual caps are smooth and purplish brown. The pores are cream and decurrent, running right down the stem.

FAMILY	Phanerochaetaceae
DISTRIBUTION	North America, eastern Europe, northern Asia, Australia, New Zealand
HABITAT	In woodland
ASSOCIATION	On broadleaf wood, more rarely conifers
GROWTH FORM	On the underside of fallen branches and logs
ABUNDANCE	Locally common
SPORE COLOR	White
EDIBILITY	Not edible

THICKNESS
Less than ⅛ in (1 mm)

DIAMETER
Up to 6 in (150 mm)

CERIPORIA TARDA

MAUVE WAXPORE

(BERKELEY) GINNS

Ceriporia species are more closely related to some of the crust-forming fungi than they are to most bracket fungi. The majority of species are white or cream, but several are brightly colored and can be various shades of pink, cinnamon, purple, red, orange, or even green. All are wood-rotters, mainly decaying dead, fallen wood. The Mauve Waxpore has a preference for hardwoods, but is occasionally found on conifer wood. The species, originally described from Australia, is widely distributed, though very rare in Europe.

SIMILAR SPECIES

Several related species, including *Ceriporia excelsa*, *C. purpurea*, *C. reticulata*, and *C. viridans*, have similar fruitbodies that are variable in color and can sometimes be pinkish or reddish purple. They are best distinguished from *C. tarda* microscopically.

Actual size

The Mauve Waxpore is a thin, soft, effused species, consisting of little more than a pore surface surrounded by a narrow, sterile margin. It typically grows in small patches that often coalesce to form larger fruitbodies. The color varies from cream to rose-pink, mauve or pinkish violet, becoming duller with age.

FAMILY	Phanerochaetaceae
DISTRIBUTION	Eastern North America, continental Europe, northern Asia
HABITAT	In woodland and roadsides
ASSOCIATION	With hardwoods, especially maple
GROWTH FORM	On living and dead trunks
ABUNDANCE	Common
SPORE COLOR	White
EDIBILITY	Not edible

THICKNESS
Up to 2 in
(50 mm)

CAP DIAMETER
Up to 12 in
(300 mm)

374

CLIMACODON SEPTENTRIONALIS
NORTHERN TOOTH FUNGUS
(FRIES) P. KARSTEN

The Northern Tooth Fungus produces shelflike clusters of fleshy, annual fruitbodies. Individual caps are felted to hairy, soft, cream to yellowish cream, becoming brownish (or greenish from algae) with age. The spines are up to 1 in (25 mm) long and are cap-colored.

Fruitbodies of *Climacodon septentrionalis* look just like a large cluster of bracket fungi, until closer inspection reveals they have toothlike spines instead of pores on their undersurface. They typically occur on the trunks of living trees in which they cause a rot of the inner heartwood. In time, this can lead to the tree becoming hollow—though when the fungus appears in garden and roadside trees, they are often felled for safety reasons. The epithet *septentrionalis* means "northern," and the species, first described from Scandinavia, seems to prefer cold or dry, continental climates.

SIMILAR SPECIES

The pale, bracket-like fruitbodies with teeth or spines should be distinctive. In Europe, the unrelated Tiered Tooth (*Hericium cirrhatum*) produces clusters of whitish fruitbodies with spines, but they are more rounded and less shelflike, often with small spines on the upper surface.

Actual size

FAMILY	Hymenochaetaceae
DISTRIBUTION	North America, Europe, Asia
HABITAT	In woodland
ASSOCIATION	Ectomycorrhizal, mainly with conifers
GROWTH FORM	On soil, often on burnt ground, in groups, sometimes coalescing
ABUNDANCE	Common
SPORE COLOR	Brown
EDIBILITY	Not edible

HEIGHT
Up to 3 in
(75 mm)

CAP DIAMETER
Up to 3 in
(75 mm)

COLTRICIA PERENNIS
TIGER'S EYE
(LINNAEUS) MURRILL

375

Coltricia species are related to some of the large, brown-spored brackets found on tree trunks, but have evolved a rather different form and lifestyle. All are mycorrhizal and grow on soil close to trees, so, instead of looking like brackets, they resemble miniature, woody boletes. Tiger's Eye, also known as the Brown Funnel Polypore, is one of the commonest species, widely distributed in the northern hemisphere. It is often found on old woodland fire sites, suggesting that fire may somehow stimulate or facilitate its growth.

SIMILAR SPECIES

Other *Coltricia* species are similar, but most are not so strikingly zoned or as common as the Tiger's Eye. *Coltricia cinnamomea* has a cinnamon to reddish brown cap which may be weakly zoned. The rarer *C. montagnei* is also reddish brown, but its cap is unzoned and the fruitbodies are larger and thicker-fleshed.

Actual size

The Tiger's Eye has a circular cap, often depressed at the center, which is beautifully zoned in different shades of brown with a narrow white band at the margin. The pores beneath are slightly decurrent, either pale or golden brown at first, darkening or becoming gray-brown with age. The stalk is slender, brown, and velvety (see photo right). The whole fungus is tough, leathery, and rather thin-fleshed.

FAMILY	Polyporaceae
DISTRIBUTION	North America, Asia
HABITAT	In woodland
ASSOCIATION	On conifers
GROWTH FORM	On recently dead conifer trunks, singly or in groups
ABUNDANCE	Common
SPORE COLOR	Pinkish
EDIBILITY	Not edible

THICKNESS	Up to 2 in (50 mm)
CAP DIAMETER	Up to 3 in (75 mm)

376

CRYPTOPORUS VOLVATUS
VEILED POLYPORE
(PECK) SHEAR

This is a curious species that may not be recognizable as a bracket fungus at first sight, since it superficially looks a little like a puffball. It has been suggested that the unusual veil covering the pores may have evolved to help prevent desiccation and maintain a moist microclimate ideal for spore growth and release (the veil develops one or two small holes with age). It has also been suggested that the veil helps trap small wood-boring beetles, which become coated with spores and subsequently help to spread the fungus to new trees. Indeed the Veiled Polypore is so often associated with beetle holes that is used by foresters as an indicator of bark beetle infection.

SIMILAR SPECIES

A related species, *Cryptoporus sinensis*, has recently been described from China but only differs microscopically, having slightly smaller spores. Otherwise, no other bracket fungus has a veil similar to that of *C. volvatus*.

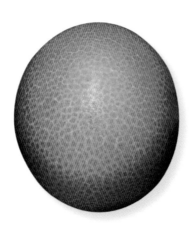

Actual size

The Veiled Polypore may be hoof-shaped or ball-like, smooth and whitish at first, with the upper half (the cap) becoming tan to ocher-brown on maturity, and developing a resinous crust. If the lower half (the veil) is cut open, the white to pinkish brown pores are revealed.

FAMILY	Fomitopsidaceae
DISTRIBUTION	North America, Europe, North Africa, Asia
HABITAT	In woodland
ASSOCIATION	On broadleaf wood, particularly oak
GROWTH FORM	On stumps and logs, singly or in small coalescing groups
ABUNDANCE	Common
SPORE COLOR	White
EDIBILITY	Not edible

THICKNESS
Up to 3 in
(75 mm)

CAP DIAMETER
Up to 8 in
(200 mm)

DAEDALEA QUERCINA

OAK MAZEGILL

(LINNAEUS) PERSOON

377

The generic name *Daedalea* is taken from the mythical Greek artificer Daedalus, who created the original labyrinth in which the minotaur was kept. His name was appropriately applied to this fungus because of its maze-like, or daedaleoid, pores which have also given it the English names of the Oak Mazegill and Thick-Walled Maze Polypore. In the past, fruitbodies have been used as natural curry-combs for grooming horses and, when set alight, to smoke out bees by beekeepers in England. Nowadays, small dried fruitbodies of *Daedalea quercina*, often brightly dyed, are a frequent component of decorative potpourri mixes.

SIMILAR SPECIES

Several other bracket fungi have similar maze-like pores, but none are quite so hard and thick as those of the Oak Mazegill. As its name suggests, *Daedaleopsis confragosa* is one such, but its fruitbodies are leathery and bruise red, eventually becoming entirely dark reddish. The fruitbodies of *Lenzites betulina* are much smaller and their pores are generally more gill-like.

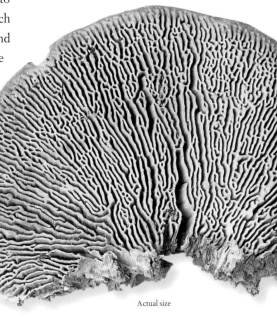

Actual size

The Oak Mazegill produces corky or woody, perennial brackets. The cap is brownish gray with an ocher margin and is smooth, though developing concentric ridges with each year's new growth. The distinctive maze-like pores are ocher to buff, and are quite thick, up to ⅛ in (3 mm) in width.

FAMILY	Polyporaceae
DISTRIBUTION	North America, Europe, Asia
HABITAT	In woodland
ASSOCIATION	On broadleaf wood, particularly willow
GROWTH FORM	On fallen branches and logs, singly or in small groups
ABUNDANCE	Very common
SPORE COLOR	White
EDIBILITY	Not edible

THICKNESS
Up to 1 in
(25 mm)

CAP DIAMETER
Up to 6 in
(150 mm)

378

DAEDALEOPSIS CONFRAGOSA
BLUSHING BRACKET
(BOLTON) J. SCHRÖTER

Old trees in willow carrs (wet or swampy woodland) are the best places to look for the Blushing Bracket, but it can also grow on a wide range of other broadleaf trees. Thanks to the reddening reaction that gives it its English name, this is one of the easiest bracket fungi to identify and it is widespread throughout north temperate woodlands. It has an alternative English name of Thin-Walled Maze Polypore. The species is one of several different brackets that have been used in the craft of ornamental paper-making, the fruitbodies being pulped and then dried to produce sheets of interesting texture and color.

SIMILAR SPECIES

Old, dark red specimens are sometimes confused with red *Pycnoporus* species, but the latter have more normal, circular pores. The Oak Mazegill (*Daedalea quercina*) has similar maze-like pores, but its fruitbodies are perennial and woody-hard, and they never bruise red.

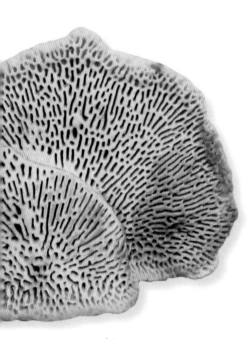

Actual size

The Blushing Bracket produces corky, annual fruitbodies with smooth or slightly hairy, buff to pale brown caps that are usually zoned and radially ridged. The pores are maze-like, sometimes almost gill-like, whitish at first, becoming pale brown. When touched, young fruitbodies bruise pinkish red and with age the whole bracket often turns dark reddish-brown.

FAMILY	Polyporaceae
DISTRIBUTION	North America, Europe, Asia
HABITAT	In woodland
ASSOCIATION	On broadleaf wood, particularly beech, rarely on conifers
GROWTH FORM	On fallen branches and logs, often coalescing
ABUNDANCE	Common
SPORE COLOR	White
EDIBILITY	Not edible

THICKNESS
Up to ¼ in
(5 mm)

CAP DIAMETER
Up to 7 in
(175 mm)

DATRONIA MOLLIS

COMMON MAZEGILL

(SOMMERFELT) DONK

379

This is a common and widespread species, typically found on the sides or undersides of fallen branches and logs, especially beech. The leathery fruitbodies are broadly attached and can often be peeled off the wood surface. Like many brackets, the Common Mazegill produces enzymes that break down the hard lignin component of wood, producing a "white rot" that turns it soft and stringy. In this way, fallen branches are gradually decomposed and recycled, becoming part of the woodland litter and eventually turning into humus and soil.

SIMILAR SPECIES

Many other species produce similarly shaped fruitbodies with narrow, ribbonlike caps and pores that are almost effused, but none has the same thick, maze-like pores and contrasting cap color of the Common Mazegill. *Antrodia albida* has maze-like but narrower pores, and a white cap surface. *Cerrena unicolor* also has a pale cap and its pores are pale brownish gray.

The Common Mazegill has tough, thin, leathery fruitbodies that are typically flattened against the wood and are sometimes entirely effused, with barely any cap and just a thick blackish brown margin. When caps are formed, they are narrow and ridge-like, often wavy, smooth, and dark brown to black. The contrasting whitish to pale buff pores are comparatively thick, angular, or maze-like.

Actual size

FAMILY	Echinodontiaceae
DISTRIBUTION	Western North America
HABITAT	In woodland
ASSOCIATION	On conifers, especially true firs and hemlock
GROWTH FORM	On standing trunks, singly or scattered
ABUNDANCE	Common
SPORE COLOR	White
EDIBILITY	Not edible

THICKNESS
Up to 12 in
(300 mm)

CAP DIAMETER
Up to 16 in
(400 mm)

380

ECHINODONTIUM TINCTORIUM
INDIAN PAINT FUNGUS
(ELLIS & EVERHART) ELLIS & EVERHART

The Indian Paint Fungus produces large, perennial, hooflike fruitbodies. The caps are dark brown and covered in matted hairs at first, but later become blackened, crusty, and fissured. The buff pores are highly irregular and quickly split, so that the undersurface appears to consist of flattened teeth. The flesh inside the fungus is brick-red.

Echinodontium tinctorium causes a heart rot of mature trees and inflicts substantial losses on conifers used in commercial forestry. It seems to be limited in its range to western North America, though it occurs from Alaska southward to Mexico. When the inner parts of fruitbodies are ground up, they produce a red pigment that was formerly used by some Native Americans as a face paint—hence the curious English name for the species. More recently the fungus has been used as a natural dye for wool and textiles producing a range of warm colors from orange to cinnamon.

SIMILAR SPECIES
A second American species, *Echinodontium ballouii*, used to occur on cedar in New Jersey but has not been seen since 1909 and may be extinct. *Echinodontium tsugicola* is similar to the Indian Paint Fungus but is only known from northern Japan.

Actual size

FAMILY	Polyporaceae
DISTRIBUTION	Southern North America, Africa, southern and Eastern Asia, Central and South America, Australia
HABITAT	In woodland
ASSOCIATION	On hardwoods
GROWTH FORM	On dead trees, logs, and fallen branches, singly or clustered
ABUNDANCE	Common
SPORE COLOR	White
EDIBILITY	Edible

THICKNESS
Up to 1 in
(25 mm)

CAP DIAMETER
Up to 5 in
(125 mm)

FAVOLUS TENUICULUS

TROPICAL WHITE POLYPORE

P. BEAUVOIS

381

The Tropical White Polypore was originally described from West Africa, but has since been found throughout the tropics and subtropics. It is very variable in cap shape and the extent to which it has a stem. This plasticity of form together with its wide distribution means that the Tropical White Polypore has been described as a new species over and over again, so that it now has at least 40 synonyms, mostly in the genera *Favolus* and *Polyporus*. It is said to be eaten by indigenous peoples in various parts of the world, but chewing it must be rather tough work.

SIMILAR SPECIES

Because of its variability, *Favolus tenuiculus* is not always easy to distinguish from other species of *Favolus* and *Polyporus*, but, when fresh, the comparatively thin, white to cream cap and rather large, angular pores are characteristic.

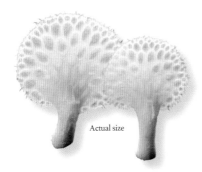

Actual size

The Tropical White Polypore produces fruitbodies with or without a stem. The thin cap is white to cream, buff when old, smooth or covered with raised bumps (mirroring the undersurface), and has a finely fringed margin when young. The rather large pores are decurrent, cap-colored, and hexagonal or elongated. The stem (when present) is central or lop-sided, and cap-colored.

FAMILY	Fistulinaceae
DISTRIBUTION	North America, Europe, Asia, Australia
HABITAT	In woodland
ASSOCIATION	On oak and chestnut
GROWTH FORM	On standing or fallen trunks, singly or in small clusters
ABUNDANCE	Common
SPORE COLOR	White
EDIBILITY	Edible

THICKNESS
Up to 2½ in
(60 mm)

CAP DIAMETER
Up to 8 in
(200 mm)

382

FISTULINA HEPATICA

BEEFSTEAK FUNGUS

(SCHAEFFER) WITHERING

Fistulina hepatica is a heart-rot species and one of the main fungi responsible for hollowing out old oaks and chestnuts, though in eastern North America it has become much less common since the advent of chestnut blight. The tannins produced by the fungus cause the wood to become a rich golden to reddish brown, making it highly valued by furniture makers. The Beefsteak Fungus, or Ox Tongue, is generally regarded as edible when young, but although widely eaten, some find it sour and disappointing. It is reported to have both antioxidant and antibacterial properties.

SIMILAR SPECIES

When young and fresh, the Beefsteak Fungus is unmistakable. It loses its color when old, but should still be recognizable by its watery, flabby consistency. A related species, *Pseudofistulina radicata*, occurs in eastern North America and South America, but is pale yellowish brown and has a distinct stem.

Actual size

The Beefsteak Fungus is entirely bright pinkish red when young, becoming blood-red when mature, and finally fading to a dull reddish yellow. The whole fungus is soft and rather gelatinous, oozing a watery blood-red liquid in damp weather. The cap is slightly scurfy, and the small round pores are easily separated into individual tubes.

FAMILY	Polyporaceae
DISTRIBUTION	North America, Europe, North Africa, Asia
HABITAT	In woodland
ASSOCIATION	On broadleaf trees, particularly birch
GROWTH FORM	On standing or fallen trunks, singly or scattered
ABUNDANCE	Common
SPORE COLOR	White
EDIBILITY	Not edible

THICKNESS
Up to 6 in
(150 mm)

CAP DIAMETER
Up to 6 in
(150 mm)

FOMES FOMENTARIUS

HOOF FUNGUS

(LINNAEUS) J. KICKX

Fomes fomentarius was the main source of amadou, a soft, felty substance made from the fibrous inner flesh of the fungus. Amadou, sometimes impregnated with saltpeter, was once widely used as tinder before the invention of matches. The ancient "Iceman," found frozen in an Alpine glacier, was carrying pieces of *F. fomentarius* with him, presumably to light fires. Amadou was also used by barber-surgeons as a styptic to stop bleeding. It is still occasionally used today by fly-fishermen for drying flies and (in eastern Europe) for making feltlike traditional hunting hats.

SIMILAR SPECIES

Old specimens of some *Ganoderma* species can develop a similar hard, gray surface to the cap, and can also become broadly hoof-shaped. Their pores are whitish, however, and their abundant spores are brown. *Fomitopsis pinicola* is likewise hoof-shaped, but has a conspicuous reddish margin to the cap. *Laricifomes officinalis* only occurs on conifers.

The Hoof Fungus produces hard, woody, perennial fruitbodies that over the years become hoof-shaped. The cap develops a smooth, gray crust, though the growing margin is pale brown. The pores are round and pale brown. The flesh is yellowish brown and fibrous.

Actual size

FAMILY	Fomitopsidaceae
DISTRIBUTION	North America, Europe, Asia
HABITAT	In woodland
ASSOCIATION	On conifer and, less commonly, broadleaf wood
GROWTH FORM	On dead trunks, stumps, and logs
ABUNDANCE	Common
SPORE COLOR	White
EDIBILITY	Not edible

THICKNESS
Up to 8 in
(200 mm)

CAP DIAMETER
Up to 16 in
(400 mm)

384

FOMITOPSIS PINICOLA
RED-BANDED POLYPORE
(SWARTZ) P. KARSTEN

The Red-Banded Polypore produces woody, perennial fruitbodies. When young, the cap surface has a sticky, reddish orange layer that persists as a band near the margin, which may be whitish. Over the years, new layers are added, the caps turn dark brown to grayish, and the fruitbodies become hoof-shaped. The pores are cream to yellowish, the flesh cream to buff.

Fomitopsis pinicola causes a brown, cubical rot that turns wood into a crumbly powder. In some northern conifer forests, the fungus is extremely common and is a major recycler of dead wood, rotting it down into humus. It is a weak pathogen and rarely attacks living trees. It has been used traditionally by the Canadian Cree in powdered and paste form to staunch wounds. Like many brackets, the species has been investigated for possible antifungal and antibacterial properties. It is even commercially harvested and sold by suppliers of herbal medicines for its supposed health-giving effects.

SIMILAR SPECIES

Fomes fomentarius is gray and hoof-shaped, but lacks the reddish margin, as do old specimens of brown-spored *Ganoderma* species. *Fomitopsis rosea* differs in its pale pinkish pores. *Laricifomes officinalis* also lacks the reddish margin and typically occurs on larch.

Actual size

FAMILY	Fomitopsidaceae
DISTRIBUTION	North America, Europe, northern Asia
HABITAT	In woodland, occasionally on cut timber
ASSOCIATION	On conifers, especially spruce and fir
GROWTH FORM	On living and dead trunks, stumps, and logs
ABUNDANCE	Locally common
SPORE COLOR	White
EDIBILITY	Not edible

THICKNESS
Up to 3 in
(75 mm)

CAP DIAMETER
Up to 6 in
(150 mm)

FOMITOPSIS ROSEA

ROSE POLYPORE

(ALBERTINI & SCHWEINITZ) P. KARSTEN

385

Most woody-hard, hooflike brackets are a rather dull gray or brown, so the pink pores of the Rose Polypore are quite startling. It is a not uncommon species in the conifer forests of North America, where it is even considered a pest, causing "brown top rot" of Douglas fir and other commercial trees. It can also occur as a rot in softwood timber, and (curiously) is only known in the British Isles from buildings. In European forests, however, it is an increasingly rare species of conservation concern, on national Red Lists of threatened fungal species in several countries.

SIMILAR SPECIES

Fomitopsis rosea belongs to a complex of species with pink pores. *Fomitopsis cajanderi* is common in North America, where it is a more southerly species, forming fruitbodies that are less hooflike and often growing in tiers or clusters. *Fomitopsis feei* is a species on broadleaf trees in the tropics and subtropics.

The Rose Polypore produces woody, perennial fruitbodies that become hoof-shaped. When young, the surface is velvety-hairy and pale pink, but with age becomes hard, crusty, dark brown to gray-black, and often cracked. The pores are pale pink to pink-brown, as is the flesh.

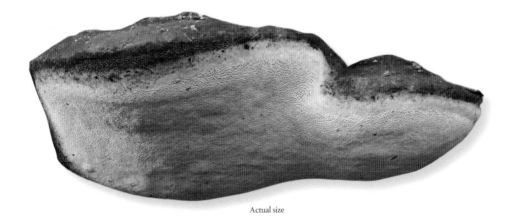

Actual size

FAMILY	Ganodermataceae
DISTRIBUTION	North America, Europe, northern Asia, Australia
HABITAT	In woodland
ASSOCIATION	On broadleaf wood , very rarely on conifers
GROWTH FORM	At base of dead and living trunks, also on stumps and logs
ABUNDANCE	Common
SPORE COLOR	Brown
EDIBILITY	Not edible

THICKNESS
Up to 2½ in
(60 mm)

CAP DIAMETER
Up to 24 in
(600 mm)

386

GANODERMA APPLANATUM
ARTIST'S BRACKET
(PERSOON) PATOUILLARD

Actual size

A peculiar feature of this fungus is the rapid browning of the white pore surface when scratched. The bruising is conspicuous and permanent, so that images can be drawn on the surface, hence the name Artist's Bracket. *Ganoderma applanatum* causes a white rot and can attack the butts and roots of living trees. The appearance of brackets often results in preventive felling for health and safety reasons, since the species attacks a wide range of garden and parkland trees. Traditionally it has been used not only in paper-making, but to produce hats and waistcoats. In Alaska it was burned to provide a mosquito repellent.

SIMILAR SPECIES
Ganoderma australe is a very similar but more southerly species, absent from North America. It tends to produce thicker fruitbodies, but is best distinguished microscopically by its larger spores. Most other common *Ganoderma* species have shiny or resinous, often reddish caps.

The Artist's Bracket produces woody, perennial fruitbodies. The cap surface is gray and smooth but unpolished, concentrically ridged by annual growth bands. The pores beneath are white, but immediately turn dark brown when bruised. When spores are produced, the abundant brown spores may visibly cover the cap surface and nearby vegetation.

FAMILY	Ganodermataceae
DISTRIBUTION	North America, Europe, South America, Asia
HABITAT	In woodland
ASSOCIATION	Weak parasite of broadleaf trees, especially oak, chestnut, and plum
GROWTH FORM	Singly or in groups on living and dead, standing, or fallen wood
ABUNDANCE	Occasional
SPORE COLOR	Brown
EDIBILITY	Not edible

THICKNESS
Up to 2 in
(50 mm)

CAP DIAMETER
Up to 12 in
(300 mm)

GANODERMA LUCIDUM
LACQUERED BRACKET
(CURTIS) P. KARSTEN

387

The Lacquered Bracket, known as Reishi in Japan and celebrated in China as the Mushroom of Immortality, is widely used in traditional oriental medicine. It is claimed to be effective against a wide range of illnesses, especially liver diseases, and is believed to prolong life. The Lacquered Bracket is too hard and bitter to be edible fresh, but is commonly taken dried as a tea or as a distinctive wine. Only in the last 20 years has it been possible to cultivate it commercially with a technique pioneered in Japan using plum tree sawdust. The Reishi industry is now thought to be worth in excess of 2.5 billion dollars a year.

SIMILAR SPECIES
Recent molecular research suggests that the Lacquered Bracket is part of a complex of difficult-to-distinguish species. These include *Ganoderma carnosum,* which occurs on conifers, especially yew, in Europe, and *G. tsuga*, which is found on conifers, mainly hemlock, in northeastern America.

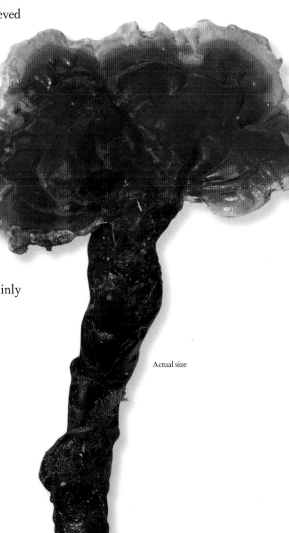

Actual size

The Lacquered Bracket is an attractive, reddish brown bracket with a hard, grooved, varnish-like cap. It often arises from a similarly colored, erect, off-center stalk up to 10 in (250 mm) high. As it ages, it can become dark purple-brown to blackish. The underside has tiny circular white pores, which mature to brown and darken on bruising.

FAMILY	Gloeophyllaceae
DISTRIBUTION	North America, Europe, Asia, Australia, New Zealand
HABITAT	In woodland
ASSOCIATION	On conifers and less commonly broadleaf wood
GROWTH FORM	On fallen wood, often on worked timber
ABUNDANCE	Common
SPORE COLOR	White
EDIBILITY	Not edible

THICKNESS
Up to ¼ in
(5 mm)

CAP DIAMETER
Up to 5 in
(120 mm)

388

GLOEOPHYLLUM SEPIARIUM

CONIFER MAZEGILL

(WULFEN) P. KARSTEN

Actual size

The Conifer Mazegill produces tough but flexible fruitbodies, often coalescing. The cap surface is distinctly hairy and zoned in bands of bright yellowish, rusty, or reddish brown, becoming duller and darker with age. The undersurface is usually a paler yellow-brown, the pores rather wide and highly irregular, maze-like to gill-like (see photo below).

The Conifer Mazegill, or Yellow-Red Gill Polypore, looks attractive, but causes a brown, cubic rot and is one of the most active decayers of untreated conifer timber, including not only poles and fences, but damp structural and other timber in buildings. It has even been called the Wooden-Window Fungus by timber specialists because it is so common on untreated softwood window sills. In the past, it used to be a dangerous destroyer of pit-props in mines. Curiously, an extremely dilute essence of Conifer Mazegill is commercially available and is said to alleviate traumatic memories and activate positive energies.

SIMILAR SPECIES

Several other *Gloeophyllum* species are similar, but they are generally less common and widespread. *Gloeophyllum abietinum* is a duller brown and has no pores but only thick, wavy gills on the undersurface. The tropical and subtropical species *G. striatum* has a similar undersurface. *Gloeophyllum trabeum* has finer, denser, maze-like pores.

FAMILY	Meripilaceae
DISTRIBUTION	Eastern North America, Europe, northern Asia
HABITAT	In woodland
ASSOCIATION	Parasitic on broadleaf trees, especially oak, beech, and ash
GROWTH FORM	At the base of living or decaying trees
ABUNDANCE	Common
SPORE COLOR	White
EDIBILITY	Edible

HEIGHT
Up to 24 in
(600 mm)

DIAMETER
Up to 24 in
(600 mm)

GRIFOLA FRONDOSA
HEN OF THE WOODS
(DICKSON) GRAY

389

This is reputedly an excellent edible species, now widely available in gourmet outlets since it was first cultivated commercially in 1979. Marketed in Japan under the name Maitake, and somewhat misleadingly known as the "dancing mushroom" (though it is not known to be hallucinogenic), some 8,000 tons were being grown each year in the 1990s. It has a range of reported medical properties including boosting the immune system and working as an antiviral. Its derivative Maitake D-fraction is under clinical trial in the USA for the treatment of advanced breast and prostate cancer. It is widely sold in powdered form or as tablets. Inoculated logs are also sold for home-growing.

SIMILAR SPECIES

The North American *Bondarzewia berkeleyi* has a similar appearance but is a lighter cream-tan and grows on conifers. The widespread *Meripilus giganteus* turns black with age or bruising. *Polyporus umbellatus* has smaller, umbrella-like caps perched on central, rather than lateral, stems.

The Hen of the Woods can form a huge, compound mound of fused and overlapping straplike or spoon-shaped caps attached laterally to a thick, branching stalk. The caps are gray-brown to dark brown, zoned and streaked. The stalk is whitish or cream, as are the tiny pores. The flesh is fairly tough and white, and does not darken or bruise with age.

Actual size

FAMILY	Polyporaceae
DISTRIBUTION	North America, Europe, northern Asia
HABITAT	In woodland
ASSOCIATION	On broadleaf wood, occasionally conifers
GROWTH FORM	On fallen or standing, decaying wood
ABUNDANCE	Occasional
SPORE COLOR	White
EDIBILITY	Poisonous

THICKNESS
Up to 1½ in
(40 mm)

CAP DIAMETER
Up to 4 in
(100 mm)

390

HAPALOPILUS NIDULANS
CINNAMON BRACKET
(FRIES) P. KARSTEN

The Cinnamon Bracket is renowned as "mushroom dyer's gold," capable of producing spectacular violet colors when used with strong alkaline mordants (fixatives). The terphenylquinones responsible for the coloration have also been found to have antimicrobial properties. *Hapalopilus nidulans* has recently been reported as causing some unpleasant neurotoxic poisoning when mistakenly eaten by a family in Germany. The symptoms, which appeared after about 12 hours, included nausea, impaired motor function, visual impairment, and liver and renal failure. Rather alarmingly, the urine of all three victims temporarily turned violet. All made a full recovery. The compound thought to be responsible was polyporic acid, present in high concentrations in this fungus.

SIMILAR SPECIES
Two fungi commonly collected for consumption which could be confused with Cinnamon Bracket are the Beefsteak Fungus (*Fistulina hepatica*) and Chicken of the Woods (*Laetiporus sulphureus*). The former is a soft blood-red bracket that oozes reddish juice, while the latter is bright sulfur yellow, fading paler. Both commonly occur on broadleaf trees.

Actual size

The Cinnamon Bracket is a vibrant cinnamon-orange-brown when young, and the kidney-shaped brackets are soft and watery with a slightly velvety texture. As they age, they become harder and more brittle. The flesh is also cinnamon. The tiny ocher to brown pores are slightly angular, and the whole fungus smells pleasant and sweetish. Any strong alkali (such as caustic soda or bleach) causes a diagnostic bright violet color change.

FAMILY	Marasmiaceae
DISTRIBUTION	North America, Europe, Central America, Asia, New Zealand
HABITAT	In woodland
ASSOCIATION	On broadleaf trees, more rarely conifers
GROWTH FORM	On stumps and fallen wood
ABUNDANCE	Common
SPORE COLOR	White
EDIBILITY	Not edible

HEIGHT
Up to ⅛ in
(2.5 mm)

DIAMETER
Less than ⅛ in
(1 mm)

HENNINGSOMYCES CANDIDUS

WHITE TUBELET

(PERSOON) KUNTZE

391

This unusual little fungus is easy to overlook, but can be quite conspicuous when growing in swarms on the undersurface of old logs or fallen wood. It is placed here because its fruitbodies look almost as if they were detached tubes and pores from the undersurface of a bracket fungus. In fact, the White Tubelet is one of the cyphelloid fungi—relatives of the agarics that have evolved disc- or cup-shaped fruitbodies. It actually belongs in the same family as *Marasmius* species, most of which have more conventional fruitbodies with cap, gills, and stem.

SIMILAR SPECIES

Henningsomyces candidus is the commonest member of the genus, but a few other species are known, notably *H. puber,* which is similar but minutely hairy if examined under a magnifying lens. Fruitbodies of *Rectipilus* species—a related group of cyphelloid fungi—can also be tubelike, though often more cup-shaped.

Actual size

The White Tubelet produces small, tubelike fruitbodies, usually growing gregariously; they are sometimes densely packed together, sometimes sparsely scattered. Individual tubes are cylindrical, whitish, and smooth, with a round, pore-like opening at the top.

FAMILY	Bondarzewiaceae
DISTRIBUTION	North America, Europe, northern Asia
HABITAT	In woodland
ASSOCIATION	Parasitic on conifers, occasionally on broadleaf trees
GROWTH FORM	Singly, or in groups, at the base of living or dead trees
ABUNDANCE	Very common
SPORE COLOR	White
EDIBILITY	Not edible

THICKNESS
Up to 1 in
(25 mm)

CAP DIAMETER
Up to 8 in
(200 mm)

392

HETEROBASIDION ANNOSUM

ROOT ROT

(FRIES) BREFELD

Root Rot is a serious root pathogen of conifers causing substantial losses in commercial forestry. It is an aggressive colonizer of wounds or cut stumps, and once established can spread to healthy trees nearby. However, using a fungal biocontrol method pioneered in Britain, it can be successfully contained by painting or spraying newly cut stumps with a preparation of the fungus *Phlebiopsis gigantea*. The *Phlebiopsis* is harmless, but prevents colonization by the Root Rot. More positively, *Heterobasidion annosum* has been used to make paper and, in folk medicine, to treat cancer and cauterize snake bites. It is known to contain the antibacterial compound fomannosin.

SIMILAR SPECIES

The Red-Banded Polypore (*Fomitopsis pinicola*) is a common weak parasite on conifers, and when young is quite similar to Root Rot, but has a thick resinous crust on its cap. *Antrodia serialis* seldom forms proper brackets, but can resemble cushionlike growths of Root Rot. It is creamy white throughout, and, although leathery, is easy to peel from the tree.

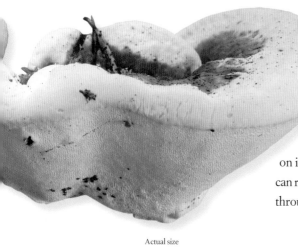

Actual size

Root Rot can vary in appearance from uneven, cushionlike growths to well-formed, sizable brackets. When present, the cap is lumpy and uneven with concentric grayish to reddish brown zones and a white margin. The white to cream pores are minute, hardly visible without a lens. The flesh is whitish cream and leathery, with a strong, sweetish, fungal smell.

FAMILY	Polyporaceae
DISTRIBUTION	Southern North America, Africa, Central and South America
HABITAT	In woodland
ASSOCIATION	On broadleaf wood
GROWTH FORM	On fallen branches, logs, and stumps
ABUNDANCE	Common
SPORE COLOR	White
EDIBILITY	Not edible

THICKNESS	Up to 1 in (25 mm)
CAP DIAMETER	Up to 8 in (200 mm)

HEXAGONIA HYDNOIDES

HAIRY HEXAGON

(SWARTZ) M. FIDALGO

393

Originally described from Jamaica, the Hairy Hexagon is a common wood-rotting species in Africa, and in tropical and subtropical America as far north as Florida and the Gulf Coast. When young, its cap is smartly hirsute, but with age it looks more like a boot brush that has seen better days—the coarse, black bristles gradually falling away. The rather angular, often hexagonal pores are a feature of the genus, but in the Hairy Hexagon the pores are small and often look conventionally round.

SIMILAR SPECIES

A second bristle-capped species, *Hexagonia hirta*, occurs in Africa, but its pores are much larger than those of *H. hydnoides* and are conspicuously angular. In southern Asia and Australia, *H. apiaria* also has a bristly cap when young, but its pores are even larger.

Actual size

The Hairy Hexagon has stemless fruitbodies that are leathery at first, becoming hard and rigid. When young, the dark brown to blackish caps are densely covered in concolorous hairs or bristles, up to ½ in (10 mm) long, which are shed when old. The small pores are circular to slightly angular, yellowish, brown becoming brownish gray.

FAMILY	Meripilaceae
DISTRIBUTION	Southern North America, Central and South America
HABITAT	In woodland
ASSOCIATION	With broadleaf trees
GROWTH FORM	On stumps and on ground from buried wood
ABUNDANCE	Common
SPORE COLOR	White
EDIBILITY	Edible

HEIGHT
Up to 3 in
(75 mm)

CAP DIAMETER
(cluster)
Up to 5 in
(125 mm)

394

HYDNOPOLYPORUS FIMBRIATUS

PORETOOTH ROSETTE

(FRIES) D. A. REID

This frondlike species sometimes forms single fruitbodies, but more typically grows in rosette-like clusters. It belongs in the same family as the Giant Polypore (*Meripilus giganteus*), which also produces frondlike caps, but on a vaster scale. Unlike other rosette-formers—such as the Wine-Glass Fungus (*Podoscypha petalodes*)—the Poretooth Rosette is not always smooth on the undersurface, but develops various projections resembling pegs, spines, teeth, or pores. It was first described from Brazil, but its range extends northward at least as far as Louisiana and the Gulf Coast.

SIMILAR SPECIES

Rosette-forming *Podoscypha* species have smooth undersurfaces. The Aromatic Earthfan (*Sistotrema confluens*), however, forms whitish, straplike fruitbodies that sometimes have pores, sometimes teeth. It is mainly north temperate, but is known as far south as Costa Rica. It is not normally clustered, grows in litter and soil rather than on wood, and has a sweetish smell.

Actual size

The Poretooth Rosette produces clusters or rosettes of frondlike, fibrous fruitbodies. The caps are finely velvety, becoming smooth, white or with yellowish or pinkish tints, and usually with a deeply cut, feathery margin. The underside is cap-colored and highly variable, smooth or with slot-like pores, or irregular teeth, or spines.

FAMILY	Hymenochaetaceae
DISTRIBUTION	North America, Europe, North Africa, northern Asia
HABITAT	In woodland
ASSOCIATION	On broadleaf wood, particularly ash and oak
GROWTH FORM	On living trees, singly or in scattered groups
ABUNDANCE	Common
SPORE COLOR	Brown
EDIBILITY	Not edible

THICKNESS
Up to 4 in
(100 mm)

CAP DIAMETER
Up to 12 in
(300 mm)

INONOTUS HISPIDUS

SHAGGY BRACKET

(BULLIARD) P. KARSTEN

395

The Shaggy Bracket causes canker rots of host trees, resulting in large, vertical wounds surrounded by callused margins. Fruitbodies often appear at the edge of these cankers. Ash is the commonest host in Europe while in North America the Shaggy Bracket appears on a range of broadleaf trees including oak, walnut, mulberry, and willow. More beneficially, *Inonotus hispidus* was the original source of the medically important metabolites hispidin and hispolon. Subsequent research has shown these fungal metabolites to have potentially useful antiviral and antioxidant properties. The fungus has also been used to dye fabrics a range of colors from yellow to greenish gold.

SIMILAR SPECIES

Most related species lack the densely bristled upper surface of the Shaggy Bracket. Fruitbodies of *Inonotus cuticularis* have woolly or fibrillose brackets when young, but are smaller, thinner, and often grow in clusters. The unrelated *Phaeolus schweinitzii* may look similar, but typically grows on the ground or at the base of conifers.

Actual size

The Shaggy Bracket produces large, annual fruitbodies with densely hairy or bristled caps that are bright reddish to orange-brown at first with a paler margin; they gradually become dark reddish brown, and eventually black. The pores are pale yellow brown at first, gradually darkening to reddish brown, and finally black.

FAMILY	Hymenochaetaceae
DISTRIBUTION	North America, Europe, northern Asia
HABITAT	In woodland
ASSOCIATION	On broadleaf trees, particularly birch
GROWTH FORM	Conks on living trees, fruitbodies on fallen trunks
ABUNDANCE	Locally common
SPORE COLOR	Brown
EDIBILITY	Not edible

THICKNESS
(of fruitbody)
Up to ½ in
(10 mm)

DIAMETER
(of fruitbody)
Up to 12 in
(300 mm)

396

INONOTUS OBLIQUUS
CHAGA
(ACHARIUS EX PERSOON) PILÁT

Actual size

Chaga causes canker rots of host trees, with masses of clinker-like fungal tissue visibly emerging from the cankers—hence its alternative name of Clinker Polypore. In parts of northern Russia, folk medicine associated this fungus with cancer and tea-like infusions of Chaga were taken as a cure. In the old Soviet Union, Chaga was used quite widely, as noted in Solzhenitsyn's novel *Cancer Ward*, and subsequent research has shown it may have genuinely beneficial properties. It has also been used to treat tuberculosis, as well as liver, stomach, and heart disease. Chaga is now widely sold as an alternative medicine.

SIMILAR SPECIES

Many other effused (capless) species of *Inonotus* and *Phellinus* produce fruitbodies of similar shape and color that can only be distinguished microscopically. If found on fallen birch, however, fruitbodies of *Inonotus obliquus* should be accompanied by the much more conspicuous, cindery black conks on nearby trees.

Chaga is most often seen as sterile conks (irregular masses of hard, blackened, gall-like tissue) erupting from trunks of host trees. Fruitbodies only form when the tree falls. They have no caps, but are effused, dark reddish brown, with a surface of circular pores. They are short-lived and often appear under loose bark, so are less frequently encountered than conks.

FAMILY	Fomitopsidaceae
DISTRIBUTION	North America, Europe, northern Asia
HABITAT	In woodland
ASSOCIATION	With conifers
GROWTH FORM	On stumps and logs
ABUNDANCE	Common
SPORE COLOR	White
EDIBILITY	Not edible

THICKNESS
Up to 1 in
(25 mm)

CAP DIAMETER
Up to 6 in
(150 mm)

ISCHNODERMA BENZOINUM

BENZOIN BRACKET

(WAHLENBERG) P. KARSTEN

397

The Benzoin Bracket changes its character as it gets older. Immature fruitbodies are brown and velvety, but the velvet wears away, revealing resinous—almost tarry—black zones. Eventually the whole fruitbody becomes hard and blackish, at which time the spores mature and are released. Though inedible, the fungus is of some potential interest to the food industry, since research shows it contains enzymes that can break down other compounds to create benzaldehyde—the flavor component of almonds—"naturally," rather than synthetically.

SIMILAR SPECIES

In Europe, cultural tests indicate that an uncommon, look-alike species, *Ischnoderma resinosum*, grows on broadleaf trees. Similar tests in North America, however, indicate that collections on both conifer and broadleaf trees are one and the same species—all of which is a bit of a puzzle that has yet to be sorted out.

The Benzoin Bracket produces fruitbodies that are soft at first, but become hard and dense. The caps are flat, velvety, and brown at first, later developing concentric, black, resinous zones, eventually becoming entirely black, wrinkled, and hard. The underside is whitish at first, bruising brown, later becoming brown to dark brown.

Actual size

FAMILY	Fomitopsidaceae
DISTRIBUTION	Eastern North America, Europe, Africa, Asia
HABITAT	In woodland
ASSOCIATION	On broadleaf trees, more rarely conifers, particularly yew
GROWTH FORM	On trunks and stumps of living or dead trees
ABUNDANCE	Very common
SPORE COLOR	White
EDIBILITY	Widely eaten when young, but toxic to some people; best avoided

THICKNESS
Up to 1 in
(25 mm)

CAP DIAMETER
Up to 20 in
(500 mm)

398

LAETIPORUS SULPHUREUS
CHICKEN OF THE WOODS
(BULLIARD) MURRILL

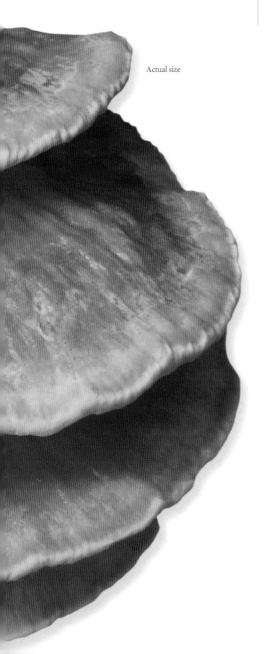

Actual size

Common and widely distributed, *Laetiporus sulphureus* is a wood-rotting species, producing a brown or cubic butt rot that can hollow out a trunk and sometimes cause its collapse. It is particularly common on oak, but also occurs on a range of other trees. It has been given the curious name of the Chicken of the Woods because it is widely considered a good edible species, and the cooked flesh of young specimens resembles chicken. Unfortunately, however, it causes rapid-onset nausea and vomiting in some people, possibly as an allergic reaction. It has an alternative English name of Sulfur Shelf.

SIMILAR SPECIES

Recent research has distinguished several very closely related species in North America, including *Laetiporus cincinnatus* with white pores, *L. conifericola* on conifers in the west, and *L. gilbertsonii* on broadleaf trees also in the west. They are all currently regarded as edible with caution. Otherwise the large size and vivid colors of *L. sulphureus* should make this bracket fungus unmistakable when fresh.

The Chicken of the Woods
typically forms overlapping clusters of annual fruitbodies. When young they are soft, orange-yellow, and rounded, but expand to become yellow and plate-like in maturity, with small yellow pores on the undersurface. They fade to buff with age, when they become crumbly and then disintegrate.

FAMILY	Polyporaceae
DISTRIBUTION	North America, Europe, northern Asia
HABITAT	In woodland
ASSOCIATION	On broadleaf trees, particularly birch, more rarely on conifers
GROWTH FORM	On fallen branches, logs, and stumps
ABUNDANCE	Common
SPORE COLOR	White
EDIBILITY	Not edible

THICKNESS
Up to ¼ in
(5 mm)

CAP DIAMETER
Up to 2 in
(50 mm)

LENZITES BETULINA

BIRCH MAZEGILL

(LINNAEUS) FRIES

399

This is a common species, but may be overlooked as washed-out Turkeytail (*Trametes versicolor*) unless the underside is examined. The two are often found together and this is no coincidence, since it has been shown that the Birch Mazegill—also known as the Gilled Polypore—is a parasite of the Turkeytail. The latter colonizes dead wood first, but the Birch Mazegill may take over, attacking and killing off the resident fungus. This strategy is called secondary resource capture and is probably common among fungi. The Birch Mazegill is one of the best species for making paper because of its particular cellular structure, giving tough, flexible sheets that take ink well.

SIMILAR SPECIES

From above, this species closely resembles pale specimens of the common *Trametes versicolor* and its relatives, but the gilled underside of *Lenzites betulina* is distinctive. *Daedalea quercina* also has gills, but is a larger, woodier species and the gills are much thicker.

The Birch Mazegill has leathery fruitbodies with finely hairy caps, zoned in grays and creams. Older fruitbodies often attract algae and appear greenish. The undersurface does not have pores, but instead has irregular gills, often splitting or joining together (see photo top right). These are white at first, becoming cream to ocher.

Actual size

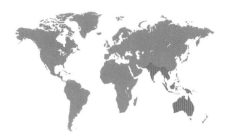

FAMILY	Polyporaceae
DISTRIBUTION	Southern Asia, Australia
HABITAT	In woodland
ASSOCIATION	With broadleaf trees
GROWTH FORM	On ground or very decayed, fallen wood
ABUNDANCE	Occasional
SPORE COLOR	White
EDIBILITY	Not edible

HEIGHT	Up to 12 in (300 mm)
CAP DIAMETER	Up to 6 in (150 mm)

400

LIGNOSUS RHINOCEROTIS

TIGER'S MILK FUNGUS

(COOKE) RYVARDEN

This imposing, long-stemmed species arises from a large, underground sclerotium—an irregular mass of dense fungal tissue that grows in the buried remains of fallen trunks and logs. Several fruitbodies may arise from a single big sclerotium. The species was first described from the Malayan peninsula, where it has traditionally been used as a cure-all folk medicine, applied to everything from asthma to food poisoning. Local belief had it that it grew from fallen drops of tiger's milk, since fruitbodies sometimes follow the line of a buried tree, as if along a trail.

SIMILAR SPECIES

A related and similar-looking species, *Lignosus sacer*, occurs in Africa. Tropical species of *Amauroderma*, such as *A. rude*, are of similar shape but are brown-spored and lack sclerotia. In Australia, species of *Laccocephalum* arise from underground sclerotia (edible sclerotia in the case of *L. mylittae*), but all are comparatively short-stemmed.

Actual size

The Tiger's Milk Fungus produces caps that are shallowly convex to flat, almost circular, but sometimes lobed or fused with adjacent caps. The surface is finely velvety when young, but becomes smooth, hard, often wrinkled, and dark brown, eventually blackish. The pores are white, but cap-colored when old. The woody stem is finely velvety at first, then smooth and cap-colored.

FAMILY	Meripilaceae
DISTRIBUTION	North America, Europe, northern Asia
HABITAT	In woodland
ASSOCIATION	With broadleaf trees, particularly beech, rarely with conifers
GROWTH FORM	At base of living trees and among roots, singly or in troops
ABUNDANCE	Common
SPORE COLOR	White
EDIBILITY	Edible

HEIGHT
Up to 12 in
(300 mm)

DIAMETER
(whole fruitbody)
Up to 30 in
(800 mm)

401

MERIPILUS GIGANTEUS
GIANT POLYPORE
(PERSOON) P. KARSTEN

This is one of the largest annual bracket fungi, and it can be quite a spectacular sight when growing in troops and clusters around the base of living, or recently felled, trees. It is another species that causes a butt and root rot, and the appearance of its fruitbodies on garden and parkland trees usually leads to preventive felling. The Giant Polypore—also known as the Black-Staining Polypore— is considered edible by some, but is not known to be good. North American collections have been referred to the look-alike *Meripilus sumstinei*, but further research is required to see if this is really a distinct species.

SIMILAR SPECIES
Other bracket fungi with compound fruitbodies at the base of trees include *Bondarzewia montana* and related species, whose pores do not bruise black. The mainly tropical *Laetiporus persicinus* is very similar but the pores bruise brownish, if at all. *Grifola frondosa* produces smaller fruitbodies with grayer, strap-like caps, and also does not bruise black.

The Giant Polypore forms very large, compound, rosette-like fruitbodies with multiple caps that branch from a single central stem. The caps are fleshy, smooth, and brown with cream margins when fresh. The pores are small, whitish to cream, and quickly bruise dark brown to black.

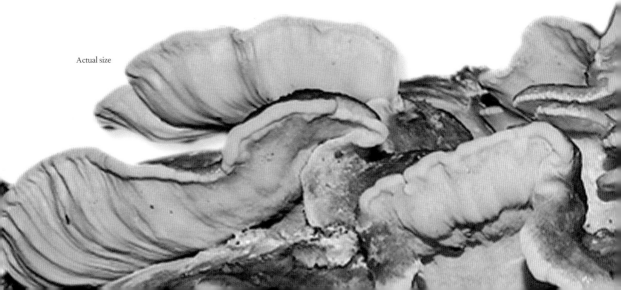

Actual size

FAMILY	Polyporaceae
DISTRIBUTION	Africa, southern Asia, Australia
HABITAT	In woodland
ASSOCIATION	On broadleaf trees
GROWTH FORM	On fallen branches, logs, and stumps
ABUNDANCE	Very common
SPORE COLOR	White
EDIBILITY	Not edible

HEIGHT
Up to 2½ in
(60 mm)

CAP DIAMETER
Up to 4 in
(100 mm)

402

MICROPORUS XANTHOPUS
YELLOW-STEMMED MICROPORE
(FRIES) KUNTZE

This is a very common and attractive species in tropical Africa, Asia, and Australia. The fruitbodies are tough and long-lasting, and have a preference for growing on fallen wood in open places, the fungus being particularly tolerant of heat and desiccation. Dried specimens of the Yellow-Stemmed Micropore keep their shape and color and the species is imported for decorative use in potpourri mixes. It has also featured on postage stamps from several tropical countries.

SIMILAR SPECIES

Coltricia perennis has a zoned cap and central stem, but grows on the ground and has normal-size pores. In the tropics, other less common *Microporus* species also occur on wood, but have unzoned, finely hairy, or differently colored caps with stems that are usually not yellow.

Actual size

The Yellow-Stemmed Micropore has a smooth cap concentrically zoned in shades of ocher and brown, and is normally depressed at the center, often deeply so. The pores on the underside are cream to pale buff, and so small that the surface appears smooth unless examined under a lens. The stem is central and covered with a hard yellow to yellowish brown cuticle.

FAMILY	Hymenochaetaceae
DISTRIBUTION	North America, continental Europe, northern Asia
HABITAT	In woodland
ASSOCIATION	With conifers
GROWTH FORM	At base of living trees, singly or in scattered groups
ABUNDANCE	Locally common
SPORE COLOR	Brown
EDIBILITY	Not edible

HEIGHT
Up to 3 in
(75 mm)

CAP DIAMETER
Up to 5 in
(125 mm)

ONNIA TOMENTOSA

WOOLLY VELVET POLYPORE

(FRIES) P. KARSTEN

403

Onnia tomentosa is a relative of the Shaggy Bracket (*Inonotus hispidus*) and was formerly referred to as *I. tomentosus*. Unlike most *Inonotus* species, however, it forms its fruitbodies on the ground. The fungus grows on the roots of conifers in which it causes a disease known as tomentosus root rot. This can be commercially damaging in stands of spruce, pine, and larch, sometimes killing young trees outright. The Woolly Velvet Polypore is widespread and locally common in northern conifer forests, but absent from some areas, such as the British Isles.

SIMILAR SPECIES

The widespread Dyer's Mazegill (*Phaeolus schweinitzii*) also occurs on the ground at the base of trees, but is usually much larger, often has bright yellow colors in the cap when young, and has pores that are typically greenish yellow. *Onnia triquetra* is a related species with a somewhat more southerly distribution, best distinguished microscopically.

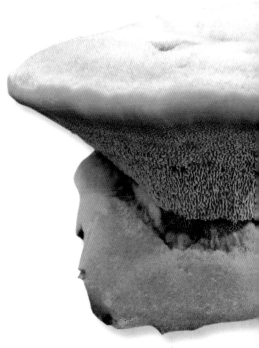

Actual size

The Woolly Velvet Polypore produces annual fruitbodies with a more or less central stem. The cap is typically circular but often lobed or irregular, flat to depressed, soft and velvety, yellowish brown to rusty brown, sometimes in concentric zones. The pores are decurrent, buff to gray-buff, becoming brown, and darkening when bruised. The stem is short, velvety, and cap-colored or darker.

FAMILY	Fomitopsidaceae
DISTRIBUTION	North America, Europe
HABITAT	In woodland
ASSOCIATION	Parasitic on conifers
GROWTH FORM	On the ground at the base of standing trees or old stumps
ABUNDANCE	Common
SPORE COLOR	White
EDIBILITY	Not edible

HEIGHT
Up to 4 in
(100 mm)

CAP DIAMETER
Up to 12 in
(300 mm)

404

PHAEOLUS SCHWEINITZII
DYER'S MAZEGILL
(FRIES) BREFELD

The Dyer's Mazegill—also known as the Velvet Top—has long been a favorite with those engaged in home-dyeing, producing a splendid range of colors from bright yellows to rusty browns. It has recently been shown to have the greatest dye potential from among 14 fungi tested. It is named after Lewis David von Schweinitz (1780–1834), renowned as the founder of American mycology, who was born in Bethlehem (Pennsylvania), trained in Nazareth (Pennsylvania), and became a minister in the Moravian church. *Phaeolus schweinitzii* contains antioxidants and shows antibacterial action. One enterprising business is marketing it as a tumor-inhibiting tonic tea, though some reports describe it as a stimulant and mild hallucinogenic, or even possibly poisonous.

SIMILAR SPECIES

Onnia tomentosa also grows parasitically at the base of conifers and looks superficially similar, but is smaller, tends to grow singly rather than overlapping, and lacks any green in the pore surface. *Gloeophyllum sepiarium* is a much smaller bracket, and although it is initially velvety, has yellow-brown pores that are much larger and more slot-like.

The Dyer's Mazegill starts as a bright yellow, furry mound and develops into a large, irregular to circular, lumpy, reddish brown, velvety bracket with a yellow margin and a short central or an off- center stem. The pore surface is a greenish yellow, maze-like labyrinth that bruises brown. The flesh is blackish brown, soft but bitter. Brackets often merge together and engulf nearby debris.

Actual size

FAMILY	Hymenochaetaceae
DISTRIBUTION	Southern North America, Europe, Africa, Central and South America, Asia, Australia, New Zealand
HABITAT	In woodland
ASSOCIATION	On broadleaf trees, particularly oak
GROWTH FORM	On old living trees
ABUNDANCE	Occasional
SPORE COLOR	Brown
EDIBILITY	Not edible

THICKNESS
Up to 8 in
(200 mm)

CAP DIAMETER
Up to 10 in
(250 mm)

PHELLINUS ROBUSTUS
ROBUST BRACKET
(P. KARSTEN) BOURDOT & GALZIN

405

Despite occurring in almost every continent, the Robust Bracket is generally rather uncommon, with a preference for old-growth forest or veteran trees. In Europe and North America, it becomes rarer northward. In England, it is known only from a few ancient oak trees, one of which was growing along Queen Anne's Drive in Windsor Great Park, owned by the Crown Estate. In the 1990s an order was made to fell some of these trees, but after mycologists protested that this would destroy one of the few sites for the Robust Bracket, the order was happily reversed in a landmark decision for fungal conservation.

SIMILAR SPECIES

Phellinus robustus is very widely distributed and over its range there are many similar-looking species that can be distinguished only microscopically. *Phellinus tremulae* looks similar, but is a more northern species typically growing on aspen. *Phellinus pomaceus* is also similar, but it is usually found growing on hawthorn, plums, and other fruit trees.

Actual size

The Robust Bracket produces large, perennial, hard and woody fruitbodies that can become hoof-shaped with age. The cap is often rather small in relation to the pore surface. It is dark brown at first, turning blackish and crusty, smooth but often cracked, and forming concentric ridges of annual growth. The pores below are small and circular, and yellowish to grayish brown.

FAMILY	Fomitopsidaceae
DISTRIBUTION	North America, Europe, northern Asia
HABITAT	In woodland
ASSOCIATION	On birch
GROWTH FORM	Single or in groups on standing or fallen trees or wood
ABUNDANCE	Very common
SPORE COLOR	White
EDIBILITY	Not edible

THICKNESS
Up to 3 in
(75 mm)

CAP DIAMETER
Up to 10 in
(250 mm)

406

PIPTOPORUS BETULINUS
BIRCH POLYPORE
(BULLIARD) P. KARSTEN

The Birch Polypore is a very versatile fungus. As the alternative common name Razorstrop suggests, strips were used to sharpen cut-throat razors and, more recently in Switzerland to polish watch parts. It was shredded for tinder and is still used to smoke bees. In Germany it was made into charcoal for drawing, and it can also be ground to make fine-grade white paper. Medicinally it has been used to treat stomach ailments, and trials were made in Bohemia to treat rectal cancer. Its use dates back more than 5,000 years: the Otzi "iceman"—a naturally mummified corpse found preserved in a glacier in the Alps—was carrying pieces, probably for medicinal purposes.

SIMILAR SPECIES
Phellinus igniarius can also be found on birch. It is superficially similar when young but develops into a woody, gray-brown, hoof-shaped bracket. Several whitish *Postia* species can grow on birch but these form small, soft, and often watery brackets.

Actual size

The Birch Polypore emerges from bark as a round, grayish ball, and develops into a large kidney-shaped, cream to grayish brown bracket. The smooth cap has a rounded margin that rolls over to the cream pores underneath. The pores are very small but visible with a lens, and do not change color on bruising. The texture is firm but spongy, and the flesh is white.

FAMILY	Fomitopsidaceae
DISTRIBUTION	Europe, Asia
HABITAT	In woodland, parkland, and wood pasture
ASSOCIATION	On very old oak trees
GROWTH FORM	On exposed heartwood of living trees and fallen wood
ABUNDANCE	Very rare
SPORE COLOR	White
EDIBILITY	Not edible

THICKNESS
Up to 2 in
(50 mm)

CAP DIAMETER
Up to 8 in
(200 mm)

PIPTOPORUS QUERCINUS

OAK POLYPORE

(SCHRADER) P. KARSTEN

407

The Oak Polypore only fruits on old oaks more than 250 years old, where it causes a brown, cubical, heartwood rot, hollowing out the trunks. It is regarded as endangered in Japan, Germany, Norway, and Poland. In Britain it is protected by law and has its European stronghold in ancient deer parks such as Windsor Great Park. Considerable conservation effort has been made not only to search for new sites but also to investigate its ecological requirements. DNA primers have now been developed that could allow its detection in oak without the need for the presence of fruitbodies.

SIMILAR SPECIES

Immature *Ganoderma resinaceum* has a very similar texture and yellowish color. It has tough brown flesh, however, and a lens shows that the yellow is part of a resinous cuticle on the cap surface. The Chicken of the Woods (*Laetiporus sulphureus*), especially when old and faded, can be mistaken for *Piptoporus quercinus*, and the two are then best distinguished microscopically.

The Oak Polypore produces annual fruitbodies that are white, soft, and juicy when young, the cap gradually darkening to rusty brown with concentric brown and gold zones, bruising reddish purple, and becoming dry and tough. Its surface is initially velvety, becoming smooth and skinlike. The flesh is whitish, flushed with magenta and yellow. The small pores are also whitish, becoming yellow-brown.

Actual size

FAMILY	Amylocorticiaceae
DISTRIBUTION	North America, Europe, Central America, northern Asia
HABITAT	In woodland
ASSOCIATION	On broadleaf wood, particularly beech and hazel
GROWTH FORM	On dead trunks and dead attached branches, often in dense clusters or troops
ABUNDANCE	Common
SPORE COLOR	White
EDIBILITY	Not edible

THICKNESS
Up to ¼ in
(5 mm)

CAP DIAMETER
Up to 1 in
(25 mm)

408

PLICATUROPSIS CRISPA
CRIMPED GILL
(PERSOON) D. A. REID

Actual size

The Crimped Gill is an odd little fungus, now shown to be more closely related to species of crust-forming fungi (which do not have caps) than to the majority of bracket fungi. It is a wood-rotting species, appearing throughout the year, with an ability to become crisp when dry, and revive again on wetting. In the Netherlands, this rather southerly, continental species has been cited as an example of an organism responding to global warming. From the 1980s onward, records show that the Crimped Gill has been expanding its range northward, possibly as a result of warmer winters.

SIMILAR SPECIES
The oddly pleated, gill-like undersurface of the Crimped Gill is also found on a white species, *Plicatura nivea*, which lacks bracket-like caps and normally grows on alder. From above, fruitbodies of the Crimped Gill may resemble those of *Stereum hirsutum*, which has a smooth, ocher undersurface.

The Crimped Gill produces small, thin, hairy to velvety brackets, whitish at first, becoming ocher to brown and weakly zoned, with undulating or crimped margins. The undersides are white (see photo above), and distinctively folded or pleated into gill-like ridges. The fruitbodies are soft and pliable when fresh, but quickly become brittle when dried.

FAMILY	Polyporaceae
DISTRIBUTION	Europe, northern Asia
HABITAT	In woodland
ASSOCIATION	On broadleaf trees, rarely conifers
GROWTH FORM	On dead trees, logs, and fallen branches, singly or scattered
ABUNDANCE	Common
SPORE COLOR	White
EDIBILITY	Not edible

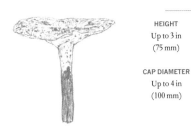

HEIGHT
Up to 3 in
(75 mm)

CAP DIAMETER
Up to 4 in
(100 mm)

POLYPORUS CILIATUS

FRINGED POLYPORE

FRIES

409

The Fringed Polypore is one of several *Polyporus* species that
have a central stem and look rather like a bolete, but are tough,
leathery, and grow on wood—though sometimes the wood
can be buried, so that fruitbodies appear to be growing out of
the ground. It is far too tough to be edible. The species occurs
in temperate Eurasia and typically produces its fruitbodies in
spring and early summer—so much so that in German it is
known as the Mai-Porling (May Polypore).

SIMILAR SPECIES

Many other *Polyporus* species produce bolete-like fruitbodies
with a central stem, but only a few have a distinctly fringed cap.
The temperate *Polyporus brumalis* has rather larger pores and
produces its fruitbodies in winter. The widespread tropical
and subtropical *Polyporus arcularius* is even more fringed and
has even larger pores.

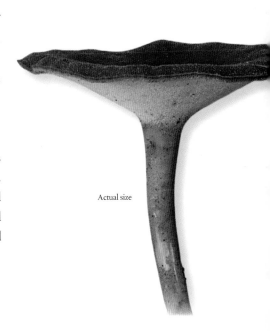

Actual size

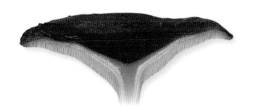

The Fringed Polypore produces fruitbodies with a cap and central stem.
The cap is convex, becoming flat or weakly depressed (see photo above),
smooth to finely scaly, pale brown to brown, and usually has a fringed
margin, at least when young. The pores are cream. The stem is central,
smooth to velvety, and pale ocher to pale brownish.

FAMILY	Polyporaceae
DISTRIBUTION	Eastern North America, Europe, Africa, Asia
HABITAT	In woodland
ASSOCIATION	With broadleaf trees
GROWTH FORM	On trunks or fallen wood, singly or in overlapping groups
ABUNDANCE	Common
SPORE COLOR	White
EDIBILITY	Edible

THICKNESS
Up to 2 in
(50 mm)

CAP DIAMETER
Up to 18 in
(450 mm)

410

POLYPORUS SQUAMOSUS
DRYAD'S SADDLE
(HUDSON) FRIES

Actual size

Polyporus squamosus takes its common names of the Dryad's Saddle and the Pheasant-back Polypore from its saddle-shaped appearance, supposedly fit for a wood nymph, and its striking markings resembling pheasant feathers. Although reported as a good edible species when young, it should be well-cooked as it contains lectins, natural insecticides that, if uncooked, can cause gastric upset. Like the Birch Polypore (*Piptoporus betulinus*), the Dryad's Saddle was traditionally dried in strips and used as a sharpening strop for cut-throat razors. More recently it has been used in craft paper-making. Its metabolites have been shown to absorb iron from solution, making it of potential use in heavy metal bioremediation.

SIMILAR SPECIES

Other species of *Polyporus* could be confused with young or small Dryad's Saddle's, but are generally much smaller, thinner, and less scaly. *Polyporus mori* has a slightly scaly cap with lateral stem but is smaller and more reddish orange, while *P. craterellus* is far less scaly and has a longer tapering stem. Both are reportedly edible.

The Dryad's Saddle is a large, kidney-shaped bracket with dark, blackish to reddish brown, concentric, feathery scales on a cream to yellowish ocher background. The white honeycomb-like pores run down the stem, which is usually off-center, and short, tough, and stout with a blackish base. The flesh is soft and whitish when young, with a sweetish, mealy smell.

FAMILY	Polyporaceae
DISTRIBUTION	North America, Europe, Asia
HABITAT	In woodland
ASSOCIATION	With broadleaf trees
GROWTH FORM	At base of living trees or among roots, especially oak and beech
ABUNDANCE	Rare
SPORE COLOR	White
EDIBILITY	Edible

HEIGHT
Up to 20 in
(500 mm)

DIAMETER
(whole fruitbody)
Up to 20 in
(500 mm)

POLYPORUS UMBELLATUS
UMBRELLA POLYPORE
(PERSOON) FRIES

411

This widespread but rare species arises from a large, underground sclerotium—a mass of thick-walled tissue that is the fungal equivalent of a plant tuber. The fruitbodies are annual, but the sclerotium overwinters and produces new fruitbodies the following year. Though the fruitbodies are edible, the Umbrella Polypore is so uncommon that it is best not to pick it for the pot. Under the name Zhu Ling, the sclerotium is used in Chinese medicine as a diuretic and to treat urinary problems. Sclerotia are cultivated in China, using inoculated logs buried in sawdust around the roots of suitable trees, and are exported in dried or powdered form.

SIMILAR SPECIES

No other species quite resembles the Umbrella Polypore. Most other big, compound bracket fungi at the base of trees have much larger individual caps that are fanlike or straplike without central stems. *Grifola frondosa* has smaller caps and might be confused at a distance, but its caps are also straplike when examined more closely.

Actual size

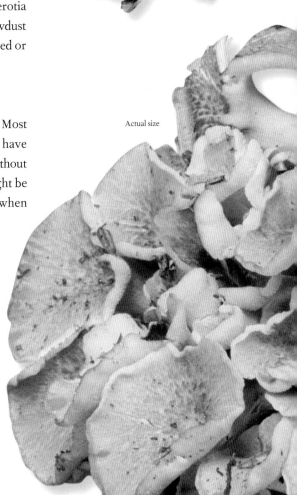

The Umbrella Polypore produces large, compound fruitbodies with multiple caps arising from a central stem. The caps are gray-brown, smooth, and almost circular, each about 2 in (50 mm) across with its own central stem, resembling a mass of miniature fruitbodies. The pores are white to cream, and strongly decurrent. The hard black sclerotium is buried in the ground.

FAMILY	Fomitopsidaceae
DISTRIBUTION	North America, Europe, northern Asia
HABITAT	In woodland
ASSOCIATION	With conifers
GROWTH FORM	On fallen branches and logs
ABUNDANCE	Common
SPORE COLOR	White
EDIBILITY	Not edible

THICKNESS
Up to ½ in
(15 mm)

CAP DIAMETER
Up to 2½ in
(60 mm)

412

POSTIA CAESIA
CONIFER BLUING BRACKET
(SCHRADER) P. KARSTEN

This is a common species on dead conifer branches, distinctive because of its unusual coloration. Molecular research has shown it to be part of a species complex, a group of species genetically distinct but so closely related that they may be difficult or impossible to distinguish visually, even when examined microscopically. Such complexes are common in fungi, especially when species have a wide geographic or host range. The Conifer Bluing Bracket, also known as the Blue-cheese Polypore, sometimes plays host to a parasitic jelly fungus called *Tremella polyporina*. Its almost-invisible fruitbodies occur in the pores of the bracket fungus.

SIMILAR SPECIES
Related species of *Postia* are mostly white or pinkish, but one other bluing species, *P. subcaesia*, is recognized. It is indistinguishable from *P. caesia* in the field, but has a preference for broadleaf trees, rather than conifers.

The Conifer Bluing Bracket produces soft, sappy, annual fruitbodies that are mostly white at first (see photo top left) but have blue or blue-gray patches, and bruise slowly bluish. Old fruitbodies may be entirely watery blue-gray. The caps are almost smooth, the pores similarly colored to the cap.

Actual size

FAMILY	Fomitopsidaceae
DISTRIBUTION	Europe
HABITAT	In woodland
ASSOCIATION	With conifers
GROWTH FORM	On stumps and logs
ABUNDANCE	Common
SPORE COLOR	White
EDIBILITY	Not edible

THICKNESS
Up to 2 in
(50 mm)

DIAMETER
Up to 3 in
(75 mm)

POSTIA PTYCHOGASTER
POWDERPUFF BRACKET
(F. LUDWIG) VESTERHOLT

413

It may not look much like a bracket fungus, but this odd, powdery-fluffy cushion on rotting conifer wood is the most visible stage in the life cycle of *Postia ptychogaster*. The cushion is a mass of chlamydospores—asexual spores of the fungus that allow it to propagate widely and colonize new wood resources. Many other bracket fungi—like the Blushing Rosette (*Abortiporus biennis*)—also produce chlamydospores, but usually they do so in a less conspicuous way. The true pore-bearing fruitbody of the Powderpuff Bracket is rather nondescript and typically occurs half-hidden at the base of the cushion.

SIMILAR SPECIES
Related species of *Postia* mostly form conventional brackets, but *P. rennyi* is another north-temperate conifer-rotter that forms a powdery-fluffy chlamydospore stage—distinguished by being pale lemon-yellow. These chlamydospore cushions may be mistaken for fruitbodies of slime molds (not fungi, despite their name) that also become powdery with age.

The Powderpuff Bracket produces both an imperfect (asexual) and a perfect fruitbody. The imperfect stage forms a white, fleecy cushion that becomes pale brown and powdery, gradually disintegrating. The perfect stage develops later at the cushion base or on nearby wood. It is typically effused, but may have a narrow, white cap. The pores are white.

Actual size

FAMILY	Hymenochaetaceae
DISTRIBUTION	North America, Europe, northern Asia
HABITAT	In woodland
ASSOCIATION	On broadleaf trees, particularly oak, rarely also on firs
GROWTH FORM	Near base of living trees
ABUNDANCE	Common
SPORE COLOR	Brown
EDIBILITY	Not edible

THICKNESS
Up to 6 in
(150 mm)

CAP DIAMETER
Up to 30 in
(750 mm)

414

PSEUDOINONOTUS DRYADEUS
OAK BRACKET
(PERSOON) T. WAGNER & M. FISCHER

This is a large and attractive species when young, but like many brackets found at the base of living trees it causes a butt and root rot that may prove fatal. Its appearance on urban and garden trees usually leads to preventive felling. Though the Latin name *dryadeus* refers to oak trees, the species can very occasionally occur on other hardwoods, and is even known on firs in southern Europe and western North America. The distinctive droplets exuded by the fruitbodies are said to have antibiotic properties, and this species has an alternative English name of the Weeping Conk.

The Oak Bracket has large, rather fleshy, annual fruitbodies, with buff to darker brown caps, sometimes with a whitish or paler margin, and pale buff pores. When fresh, the fungus typically exudes droplets of amber-brown liquid that dot the whole fruitbody and are a distinctive feature of this species.

SIMILAR SPECIES
Another bracket fungus that exudes droplets is *Abortiporus biennis*, but its fruitbodies are typically pale pink (never brownish) and the droplets are red. Species of *Inonotus* and *Phellinus* related to the Oak Bracket do not, or only rarely, form droplets and are usually rusty to dark brown, tough or woody, and on a variety of different hosts.

Actual size

FAMILY	Polyporaceae
DISTRIBUTION	Southern North America, Africa, Central and South America, Asia, Australia, New Zealand
HABITAT	In woodland
ASSOCIATION	On broadleaf wood
GROWTH FORM	On fallen branches and logs
ABUNDANCE	Very common
SPORE COLOR	White
EDIBILITY	Not edible

THICKNESS
Up to ¼ in (5 mm)

CAP DIAMETER
Up to 3 in (80 mm)

PYCNOPORUS SANGUINEUS

BLOOD-RED BRACKET

(LINNAEUS) MURRILL

415

This striking species is one of the commonest, and certainly one of the most conspicuous, brackets in the tropics and subtropics. It seems able to grow on exposed fallen wood, despite high temperatures and desiccation. In West Africa the species was traditionally used to create orange and brown dyes, but nowadays the Blood-Red Bracket has been widely tested as a source of metabolites to do just the opposite—break down and remove dyes. The fungus has also been used in traditional medicine and modern research has confirmed that cinnabarin, a compound produced by the fungus, has some potentially useful antibacterial and antiviral properties.

SIMILAR SPECIES

The very similar *Pycnoporus cinnabarinus* is a less common but widespread temperate species. Its fruitbodies are said to be thicker than those of *P. sanguineus*. *Pycnoporus coccineus*, common in Australia and New Zealand, differs mainly in being bright orange-red, but further research is needed to assess whether these species are really distinct.

Actual size

The Blood-Red Bracket produces leathery to woody, annual fruitbodies that are bright orange-red at first, gradually deepening to blood-red. The caps are smooth, the small pores similarly colored to the cap.

FAMILY	Meripilaceae
DISTRIBUTION	North America, Europe, Central America, northern Asia
HABITAT	In woodland
ASSOCIATION	On broadleaf wood and conifers
GROWTH FORM	On fallen wood
ABUNDANCE	Common
SPORE COLOR	White
EDIBILITY	Not edible

THICKNESS
Up to ¼ in
(5 mm)

DIAMETER
Up to 8 in
(200 mm)

416

RIGIDOPORUS SANGUINOLENTUS
BLEEDING PORECRUST
(ALBERTINI & SCHWEINITZ) DONK

Rigidoporus sanguinolentus is a woodland-litter fungus, not only breaking down branches that fall to the ground, but any kind of plant debris. It can often been found running through fallen leaves and needles, fusing them loosely together, and sometimes produces fruitbodies on the undersides of mossy clumps or on overhanging clay or soil. The species was originally described from Germany, but is widespread throughout the northern hemisphere. Analysis has shown that extracts from the Bleeding Porecrust act as antifungal agents and can inhibit the growth of the economically destructive bracket *Heterobasidion annosum*.

SIMILAR SPECIES
Rigidoporus vitreus is a very similar, related species, but fresh fruitbodies have a watery bluish tint and the bruising reaction, which is less intense and immediate, is brownish red or sometimes absent. No other effused fungus with white pores has this kind of red-bruising reaction.

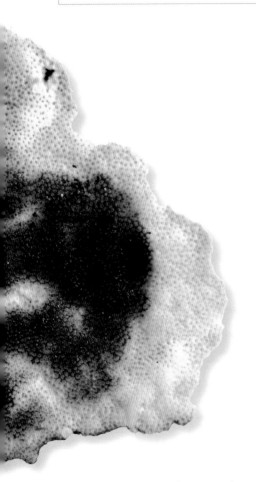

The Bleeding Porecrust produces encrusting fruitbodies, often coalescing to cover the undersides of fallen wood and surrounding woodland litter. These crusts are soft to cartilaginous, and watery white with small, round pores. Where bruised, the fruitbodies turn bright blood-red to rusty red, changing to gray or black when dried.

Actual size

FAMILY	Meripilaceae
DISTRIBUTION	North America, Europe, Africa, Central and South America, Asia
HABITAT	In woodland
ASSOCIATION	On broadleaf trees, particularly elm
GROWTH FORM	On trunks and stumps of living or dead trees
ABUNDANCE	Occasional
SPORE COLOR	White
EDIBILITY	Not edible

THICKNESS
Up to 20 in
(500 mm)

CAP DIAMETER
Up to 60 in
(1500 mm)

RIGIDOPORUS ULMARIUS

GIANT ELM BRACKET

(SOWERBY) IMAZEKI

417

In the 1990s a specimen of the Giant Elm Bracket was featured in the *Guinness Book of Records* as the largest fungal fruitbody on the planet, measuring over 16 ft (nearly 5 m) in circumference. It was growing over an old elm stump at the Royal Botanic Gardens, Kew, England, right next to the old Mycology Building. Not all specimens grow as large as this, but most are pretty big and solid. The species causes a butt and root rot of its host tree that can lead to preventive felling if the tree is near a public place.

SIMILAR SPECIES

Perenniporia fraxinea is very similar when young, though the pores are whitish. Old caps turn gray to black. *Oxyporus populinus* is usually smaller, but also has a cap that becomes overgrown with algae and moss. Its pores are small and whitish.

The Giant Elm Bracket produces tough, leathery-woody, perennial fruitbodies. The cream to pale ocher cap is smooth but rather knobbly and irregular, often growing around and incorporating bits of twigs and litter. Old caps may become greenish with algae and moss. The pores are pale pinkish to pinkish orange when fresh, becoming duller with age.

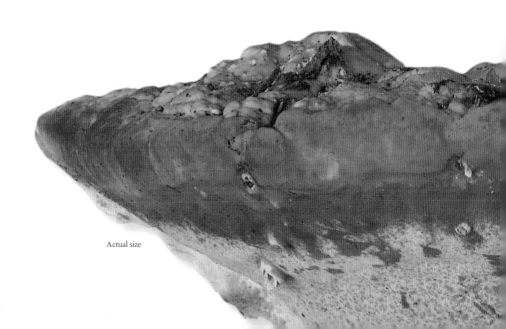

Actual size

FAMILY	Schizoporaceae
DISTRIBUTION	North America, Europe, Africa, Central and South America, Antarctic islands, Asia, Australia, New Zealand
HABITAT	In woodland
ASSOCIATION	On broadleaf trees and conifers
GROWTH FORM	On dead trees, logs, and branches
ABUNDANCE	Very common
SPORE COLOR	White
EDIBILITY	Not edible

THICKNESS
Up to ¼ in
(5 mm)

DIAMETER
Up to 12 in
(300 mm)

418

SCHIZOPORA PARADOXA
SPLIT PORECRUST
(SCHRADER) DONK

Schizopora paradoxa does not produce bracket-like caps, but—like one of the crust fungi—forms patches on the undersurface of dead attached or fallen branches. These patches can be extensive, sometimes covering the entire underside of fallen trunks. It is an extremely common species in north temperate woodlands, but has also been reported in the tropics and south temperate regions, as far as the sub-Antarctic island of South Georgia. Once seen, the rather ragged or split, angular pores of the Split Porecrust are distinctive.

SIMILAR SPECIES
Recent research suggests some records of the Split Porecrust are actually referable to *Schizopora radula*, a look-alike relative, not easy to distinguish even microscopically. *Schizopora flaviporia*, particularly common in the tropics, has more conventional, rounded pores.

The Split Porecrust produces effused fruitbodies, without a cap, of almost indefinite size. The pores are cream to pale ocher-buff, becoming darker with age, thin, rather irregular, ragged, split, and often toothlike, especially when fruitbodies are formed on a sloping surface.

Actual size

FAMILY	Polyporaceae
DISTRIBUTION	North America, Europe, Africa, Central and South America, Antarctic islands, Asia, Australia, New Zealand
HABITAT	In woodland
ASSOCIATION	On broadleaf trees, rarely conifers
GROWTH FORM	On stumps, branches, and logs, and worked timber
ABUNDANCE	Very common
SPORE COLOR	White
EDIBILITY	Not edible

THICKNESS
Up to ½ in
(10 mm)

CAP DIAMETER
Up to 1½ in
(40 mm)

TRAMETES VERSICOLOR

TURKEYTAIL

(LINNAEUS) LLOYD

419

This is probably the most common and widespread species of bracket fungus in the world. Fruitbodies are always markedly zoned and have been given their English name from a fancied resemblance to a wild turkey's tail. Recent research has shown that enzymes produced by *Trametes versicolor* to rot wood are also extremely effective in breaking down long-lasting colors in artificial dyes. This may mean it has a future role as a natural bioremediation agent, helping clear up chemical pollution. In East Asia, extracts of the Turkeytail—sometimes taken as a tea—have also been promoted for their supposed health benefits.

SIMILAR SPECIES

The False Turkeytail (*Stereum ostrea*) is easily distinguished by having a smooth undersurface without pores. The Hairy Bracket (*Trametes hirsuta*) is a less-common species with a hairier cap, zoned in shades of gray with a brownish margin. *Trametes pubescens* has a velvety, cream to buff cap without marked zones.

The Turkeytail produces fruitbodies in tiers and clusters, sometimes in rosettes if growing on the upper surfaces of stumps and logs. Individual caps are leathery but thin, concentrically zoned, the zones velvety or smooth, in various shades of gray, brown, slate, dark red, orange, olive, and buff, with a whitish margin. The pores are small and cream to pale gray.

Actual size

FAMILY	Polyporaceae
DISTRIBUTION	North America, Europe, Asia
HABITAT	In woodland
ASSOCIATION	On conifers
GROWTH FORM	On dead trees, logs, and fallen branches, often coalescing
ABUNDANCE	Common
SPORE COLOR	White
EDIBILITY	Not edible

THICKNESS
Up to ⅛ in
(3 mm)

CAP DIAMETER
Up to 3 in
(80 mm)

420

TRICHAPTUM ABIETINUM
PURPLEPORE BRACKET
(DICKSON) RYVARDEN

This is one of the commonest decomposers of recently fallen or felled conifer wood in the northern hemisphere. Although small, the Purplepore Bracket—or Violet-pored Bracket—can often dominate a logpile, covering it in fruitbodies. Curiously, it seems to provide a home for a second bracket fungus called *Skeletocutis carneogrisea*, which has small whitish caps and pinkish pores. Examining the undersides of old fruitbodies of the Purplepore Bracket sometimes reveals the *Skeletocutis* hiding underneath. Whether it is a parasite replacing the initial wood-rotter, or just a harmless associate, is unclear.

Actual size

The Purplepore Bracket grows in tiers or shelves of fruitbodies that typically coalesce and can cover large areas. The individual brackets are quite small and thin, the caps gray to gray-brown, smooth to slightly hairy, often colonized by algae, and appearing greenish. These dull caps contrast with the bright purple pore surface that often spreads over the wood below.

SIMILAR SPECIES
The Purplepore Bracket is quite distinctive and is only likely to be confused with other *Trichaptum* species, many of which are very similar and difficult to distinguish. Some, however, have caps which are distinctly hairy, or have irregular teeth or gills on the undersurface instead of pores.

FAMILY	Stereaceae
DISTRIBUTION	North America, Europe, northern Asia
HABITAT	In woodland
ASSOCIATION	On firs and spruce
GROWTH FORM	On dead, attached branches
ABUNDANCE	Locally common
SPORE COLOR	White
EDIBILITY	Not edible

THICKNESS
Less than ⅛ in
(1 mm)

DIAMETER
Up to 2 in
(50 mm)

ALEURODISCUS AMORPHUS

ORANGE DISCUS

RABENHORST

421

The Orange Discus is a wood-rotting species that has an interesting way of keeping off unwanted predators such as mites. When fruitbodies are injured, they release hydrocyanic acid—a so far unique defense system among the fungi. This does not, however, prevent *Aleurodiscus amorphus* being parasitized by two jelly fungi, *Tremella mycetophiloides* and *T. simplex*, whose tiny, reddish, gelatinous fruitbodies are frequently found growing on their host. One of the first people to study the Orange Discus was the famous children's author and illustrator Beatrix Potter, a keen amateur mycologist in her day.

SIMILAR SPECIES

In western North America and Japan there is a very similar species, *Aleurodiscus grantii*, that can only be distinguished microscopically. Otherwise, the Orange Discus is distinct, though its shape could lead to confusion with a number of bright orange *Lachnellula* species that grow on conifers. These, however, are much smaller and belong to the true cup fungi.

The Orange Discus takes its name from its disc-shaped fruitbodies that often remain separate, but sometimes coalesce in twos and threes. The surface is smooth, finely granular, and pinkish orange, becoming duller with age or in dry weather. The margins are distinct, often upturned, finely woolly, and whitish.

Actual size

FAMILY	Cyphellaceae
DISTRIBUTION	North America, Europe, Africa, Central and South America, Asia, Australia, New Zealand
HABITAT	In woodland
ASSOCIATION	On broadleaf wood
GROWTH FORM	On dead or living branches and trunks, often tiered or clustered
ABUNDANCE	Common
SPORE COLOR	White
EDIBILITY	Not edible

THICKNESS
Up to ⅛ in
(3 mm)

CAP DIAMETER
Up to 1 in
(25 mm)

422

CHONDROSTEREUM PURPUREUM
SILVERLEAF FUNGUS
(PERSOON) POUZAR

Chondrostereum purpureum may be attractively colored, but it can be a serious pest in orchards. It normally rots dead wood but it can also be a pathogen, attacking trees by infecting wounds. It can be a big problem for fruit trees, particularly plums, since it can establish itself through pruning cuts. The fungus damages leaf cells, turning them silvery, causing leaf loss, and eventually tree death. Good pruning practice helps prevent spread and another fungus, a *Trichoderma* species, has been trialed as a biocontrol. Oddly, a preparation of the Silverleaf Fungus is available commercially to control "weed" tree species in forestry.

SIMILAR SPECIES
The thin but tough caps, and smooth, purplish undersurfaces are distinctive. Fruitbodies that lack caps and are entirely crust-forming may be mistaken for similarly colored *Peniophora* species, but the Silverleaf Fungus usually has a finely hairy, whitish margin.

Actual size

The Silverleaf Fungus typically produces thin but tough brackets with finely hairy caps. These are whitish at first, becoming weakly zoned in shades of gray to purple-brown, the margins undulate and whitish. The undersides are smooth though rather knobbly, and are purple to purple-brown, growing over the wood below the caps, and often coalescing with other fruitbodies.

FAMILY	Coniophoraceae
DISTRIBUTION	North America, Europe, Africa, Central and South America, Asia, Australia, New Zealand
HABITAT	In woodland
ASSOCIATION	On broadleaf and conifer wood
GROWTH FORM	On dead branches, stumps, and trunks, also on structural timber
ABUNDANCE	Common
SPORE COLOR	Brown
EDIBILITY	Not edible

THICKNESS
Up to ⅛ in
(3 mm)

CAP DIAMETER
Up to 20 in
(500 mm)

CONIOPHORA PUTEANA

WET ROT FUNGUS

(SCHUMACHER) P. KARSTEN

423

Coniophora puteana is a common and extremely widespread wood-rotting species, typically found on the underside of logs and fallen trunks where it can spread almost indefinitely. It causes a brown, cubical rot that can be a serious problem, since it is one of the commonest fungi that attacks structural timber. The wood has to be wet for the fungus to establish itself (hence the name Wet Rot Fungus), but this can often happen in damp cellars, steamy rooms, or places where water has been leaking. Affected wood has to be cut out and the source of dampness removed to prevent further problems.

SIMILAR SPECIES

Other *Coniophora* species produce similar fruitbodies, the commonest being *C. arida*, which is normally thinner and lacks the olive tints. They can only be distinguished with confidence by microscopic examination.

The Wet Rot Fungus is an effused, crust-forming species, often covering large areas of damp wood. The surface is smooth, but shallowly warty when well developed, yellowish brown when young, then olive-brown to brown. The margins are yellowish white and cottony.

Actual size

FAMILY	Meruliaceae
DISTRIBUTION	Africa, southern Asia (also China and Japan), Australia, New Zealand
HABITAT	In woodland
ASSOCIATION	On broadleaf trees
GROWTH FORM	On dead trunks, branches, and logs
ABUNDANCE	Locally common
SPORE COLOR	White
EDIBILITY	Not edible

HEIGHT
Up to 5 in
(125 mm)

CAP DIAMETER
Up to 8 in
(200 mm)

424

CYMATODERMA ELEGANS
LEATHERY GOBLET
JUNGHUHN

This handsome species, originally described from Indonesia, occurs throughout tropical Africa and Asia, extending into temperate areas in Australia, New Zealand, China, and Japan. Curiously, it seems to have two forms, one with a smooth undersurface and another with a ridged, almost gill-like, undersurface. They were once considered separate species, but appear to be varieties of the same fungus. Despite its toughness, the Leathery Goblet is reported as being eaten by some indigenous peoples. Polysaccharides derived from this fungus have been shown to have potential anticarcinogenic properties.

SIMILAR SPECIES
Several other species of *Cymatoderma* occur in the tropics (including South America) and are best distinguished microscopically. Many tropical species of *Podoscypha* are similarly goblet-shaped, but are thinner and have smooth (not ridged) caps and undersurfaces.

Actual size

The Leathery Goblet produces stalked, funnel-shaped fruitbodies. The caps are finely hairy, concentrically zoned in pinkish to pale brown, becoming distinctly ridged. The center is irregular and often open, while the margins are wavy to frayed, sometimes tinted violet when young. The cream to gray undersurface is either smooth or ridged. The brown, often shaggy stem is extremely tough.

FAMILY	Corticiaceae
DISTRIBUTION	North America, Europe, northern Asia
HABITAT	In woodland
ASSOCIATION	On willows
GROWTH FORM	On dead attached twigs and branches
ABUNDANCE	Locally common
SPORE COLOR	White
EDIBILITY	Not edible

THICKNESS
Up to ¼ in
(5 mm)

CAP DIAMETER
Up to 1 in
(25 mm)

CYTIDIA SALICINA
SCARLET SPLASH
(FRIES) BURT

425

The bright scarlet fruitbodies make this an eye-catching species in willow thickets and damp woodland. Curiously, it was only known in the British Isles from two old specimens collected in Scotland, the last in 1900. Then, a century later, it was rediscovered near its old haunts and in northern England—a millennial event that received widespread press coverage and even an editorial in the London *Times*. Elsewhere, the Scarlet Splash can be a much more common and familiar species although seeming to be restricted to fairly cool northern or alpine climates. The color comes from the pigment cortisalin, a fungal metabolite originally extracted from *Cytidia salicina*.

Actual size

SIMILAR SPECIES
Some *Peniophora* species are also reddish orange, but are more typically found on trees other than willow. *Peniophora aurantiaca*, for example, grows on alders, while *P. laeta* grows on hornbeams. *Peniophora incarnata* may occasionally be found on willow, but is usually thinner, less gelatinous, and orange rather than scarlet.

The Scarlet Splash produces fruitbodies that are smooth and disc-shaped at first, but typically coalesce to become widely effused, often covering the undersides of branches. The margins are usually uplifted, and sometimes fruitbodies may remain cup- or ear-shaped. In damp weather, they are waxy-gelatinous and pliable, but become horny and hard when dry. They are bright scarlet when young, darkening when older.

FAMILY	Hygrophoraceae
DISTRIBUTION	Southeastern North America (Florida), Central and South America
HABITAT	On trees and on ground
ASSOCIATION	Lichenized, with cyanobacteria
GROWTH FORM	In clusters
ABUNDANCE	Common
SPORE COLOR	White
EDIBILITY	Not edible

THICKNESS
Up to ¼ in
(5 mm)

CAP DIAMETER
Up to 20 in
(500 mm)

426

DICTYONEMA GLABRATUM
ZONED SHELF LICHEN
(SPRENGEL) D. HAWKSWORTH

The handsome Zoned Shelf Lichen may be locally common in wet, often mountainous areas, in the neotropics—even colonizing road banks and other disturbed areas. It is one of several basidiolichens that have evolved their specialist lifestyle quite independently of the majority of species, which belong in the Ascomycota. It may look like a typical lichen, with the greenish tints coming from its cyanobacterial partner, but surprisingly it is more closely related to the waxcaps (*Hygrocybe* species) than to superficially similar species, such as the Gray Crottle (*Parmelia saxatilis*).

SIMILAR SPECIES
Several similar species of *Dictyonema* are known, though they lack the smooth, zoned surface of *D. glabratum*. Also in the neotropics, unrelated *Coenogonium* species (lichens in the Ascomycota) produce shelflike thalli, but they are typically bright grass-green with a hairy-felty surface.

The Zoned Shelf Lichen forms thalli with clustered, flattened, shelflike lobes. The upper surface is smooth, pale gray to green-gray, with distinct concentric zones. The undersurface is smooth and pale grayish. Spores are formed on the undersurface of the thallus.

Actual size

FAMILY	Hymenochaetaceae
DISTRIBUTION	North America, Europe, Africa, Central and South America, Asia, Australia, New Zealand
HABITAT	In woodland
ASSOCIATION	On broadleaf trees, particularly hazel, rarely on conifers
GROWTH FORM	On dead attached branches
ABUNDANCE	Common
SPORE COLOR	Brown
EDIBILITY	Not edible

THICKNESS
Less than ⅛ in
(1 mm)

CAP DIAMETER
Up to 20 in
(500 mm)

HYMENOCHAETE CORRUGATA

GLUE CRUST

(FRIES) LÉVEILLE

427

Hymenochaete species are common rotters of dead attached branches and are related to bracket fungi such as *Phellinus robustus*, but have smooth not poroid undersurfaces. *Hymenochaete corrugata* is one of the commonest and most widespread species in the north temperate zone, and also occurs, rather less commonly, in the tropics and southern hemisphere. It is called the Glue Crust or the Bondage Fungus because it produces pads of sterile fungal tissue that can quite firmly "glue" or bond to neighboring dead branches and twigs, locking them together, and thereby allowing the fungus to spread directly from branch to branch and tree to tree.

SIMILAR SPECIES

Hymenochaete rubiginosa is an equally common species on oak and chestnut, but is dark brown, very hard and brittle, and has a distinct wavy cap. Other *Hymenochaete* species are often differently colored, from red to yellow-brown, but otherwise are best distinguished microscopically.

The Glue Crust forms smooth, but often finely cracked, hard crusts on the undersides of dead but still attached branches. Young fruitbodies are small and disc-shaped, but quickly coalesce. The color is typically grayish brown to cinnamon brown with purplish to reddish tints. Under a magnifying lens, microscopic setae (thornlike sterile cells) can be seen covering the surface like tiny brown hairs.

Actual size

FAMILY	Meruliaceae
DISTRIBUTION	North America, Europe, North Africa, South America, Asia
HABITAT	In woodland
ASSOCIATION	On broadleaf trees and conifers
GROWTH FORM	On dead branches, stumps, and trunks, in large coalescing clusters
ABUNDANCE	Common
SPORE COLOR	White
EDIBILITY	Not edible and best avoided

THICKNESS
Up to ⅛ in
(3 mm)

CAP DIAMETER
Up to 3 in
(75 mm)

428

MERULIUS TREMELLOSUS
JELLY ROT
SCHRADER

This is a common and widespread species that produces a white rot of dead wood. It is sometimes mistaken for one of the jelly fungi, but is not at all closely related. The peculiar netlike undersurface on which the spores are formed occurs in a variety of other fungi and is termed merulioid after this species. *Merulius tremellosus* was the original source of several novel metabolites, known as merulidial and merulinic acids, which have potential antibiotic properties. Conversely, Jelly Rot—also known as the Trembling Merulius—can actually infect people with severe immunodeficiency and has been the cause of at least one fatality.

SIMILAR SPECIES
The color, consistency, hairy cap, and netlike underside of the Jelly Rot are distinctive. The patch-forming fungus *Phlebia rufa* is similarly colored with a rather gelatinous, netlike surface, but it never forms brackets. The jelly fungus *Auricularia mesenterica* has a more open, netlike undersurface that is brown to purplish brown.

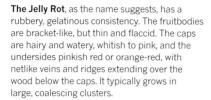

The Jelly Rot, as the name suggests, has a rubbery, gelatinous consistency. The fruitbodies are bracket-like, but thin and flaccid. The caps are hairy and watery, whitish to pink, and the undersides pinkish red or orange-red, with netlike veins and ridges extending over the wood below the caps. It typically grows in large, coalescing clusters.

Actual size

FAMILY	Meruliaceae
DISTRIBUTION	North America, continental Europe, northern Asia
HABITAT	In woodland
ASSOCIATION	On hardwoods and conifers
GROWTH FORM	On stumps, fallen branches, and logs
ABUNDANCE	Locally common
SPORE COLOR	White
EDIBILITY	Not edible

THICKNESS
Less than ⅛ in
(0.5 mm)

DIAMETER
Up to 12 in
(300 mm)

PHLEBIA COCCINEOFULVA

SCARLET WAXCRUST

SCHWEINITZ

429

The Scarlet Waxcrust is one of the brightest species in the genus *Phlebia*, a common and widespread group of crust fungi that have waxy fruitbodies. This waxy texture has probably evolved to help the fruitbodies retain moisture, allowing them to persist through short dry periods and resume their production of spores when rain returns. The Scarlet Waxcrust was originally described from the United States and is locally common in North America. In Europe, however, it is very rare and only known from a few localities.

SIMILAR SPECIES

The Red Waxcrust (*Phlebia rufa*) is a common species with a duller red or pinkish red fruitbody, the surface of which is so deeply veined and folded that it appears almost pore-like. The equally common Wrinkled Crust (*P. radiata*) is similar, but has a deeply wrinkled and furrowed surface, and is often more purple-red to gray-violet.

The Scarlet Waxcrust forms effused patches of indefinite size on the underside of fallen wood or on stumps. The fruitbodies are waxy, smooth to wrinkled or with shallow, irregular bumps, scarlet to blood-red in the fertile surface layers, yellow below (hence sometimes appearing orange), becoming darker and duller with age.

Actual size

FAMILY	Meruliaceae
DISTRIBUTION	Europe, Asia
HABITAT	In woodland and parkland
ASSOCIATION	With oak trees
GROWTH FORM	On ground among roots
ABUNDANCE	Occasional
SPORE COLOR	White
EDIBILITY	Not edible

HEIGHT
Up to 6 in
(150 mm)

DIAMETER
Up to 20 in
(500 mm)

430

PODOSCYPHA MULTIZONATA
ZONED ROSETTE
(BERKELEY & BROOME) PATOUILLARD

Actual size

Podoscypha species are common in the tropics, but this curious species has a very strange distribution. It is known only from Europe and Asia, with the majority of records (estimated at over 50 percent of the known world population) coming from Britain, especially southeastern England, with an additional stronghold in France. It grows on the roots of old oak trees, particularly those found in open parkland, and can reach quite an impressive size. Because of its restricted distribution and vulnerable habitat, it has become one of 33 fungal species proposed for international protection under the Bern Convention.

SIMILAR SPECIES

Large specimens of the Zoned Rosette are quite distinctive, but smaller ones can easily be confused with rosettes of the uncommon *Cotylidia pannosa*, which often has a bright reddish margin when young. They can be distinguished microscopically. Large bracket fungi with a similar habit are easily distinguished by having pores on the undersurface of their frondlike caps.

The Zoned Rosette forms large, dense, annual rosettes of leathery fronds arising from a common base. Each frond is incurved, smooth to ridged, and weakly zoned in shades of beige-pink to red-brown, with a wavy margin that is whitish when young. The underside is smooth and similarly colored. The whole fungus becomes browner with age.

FAMILY	Meruliaceae
DISTRIBUTION	Central and South America, Australia, New Zealand
HABITAT	In woodland
ASSOCIATION	With broadleaf trees
GROWTH FORM	On logs or buried wood, singly or in clusters
ABUNDANCE	Common
SPORE COLOR	White
EDIBILITY	Not edible

HEIGHT
Up to 3 in
(75 mm)

CAP DIAMETER
Up to 2 in
(50 mm)

PODOSCYPHA PETALODES
WINE GLASS FUNGUS
(BERKELEY) PATOUILLARD

431

The Wine Glass Fungus was first described from the Dominican Republic and is widespread in the Caribbean and the neotropics, but also occurs in Australia and New Zealand. When fruitbodies are formed singly, they are often wine-glass or goblet-shaped. When they grow together, they form dense, concentric clusters—which is why *Podoscypha petalodes* has also been called the Rosette Fungus. The species has potential pharmaceutical interest, since a compound called podoscyphic acid has been extracted from the mycelium that shows some antiviral properties.

SIMILAR SPECIES

The similar-looking Zoned Rosette (*Podoscypha multizonata*) occurs in Europe and northern Asia. Other *Podoscypha* species are mainly tropical or subtropical. Several species look similar to *P. petalodes* (as do some species of *Cotylidia*), but as a group they are best distinguished microscopically.

The Wine Glass Fungus forms thin, leathery, frondlike fruitbodies, the fronds sometimes curling inward and appearing almost cup-shaped. Clustered fruitbodies form dense rosettes. The upper surface is smooth to wrinkled, often concentrically zoned, and pale pink to pinkish brown or ocher-brown. The undersurface is smooth and similarly colored or paler. The stem (when present) is narrow and finely velvety.

Actual size

FAMILY	Amylocorticiaceae
DISTRIBUTION	Australia, New Zealand
HABITAT	In woodland
ASSOCIATION	With broadleaf trees
GROWTH FORM	Near or on rotten fallen wood
ABUNDANCE	Occasional
SPORE COLOR	White
EDIBILITY	Not edible

HEIGHT
Up to 4 in
(100 mm)

DIAMETER
Up to 2 in
(50 mm)

432

PODOSERPULA PUSIO

PAGODA FUNGUS

(BERKELEY) D. A. REID

The aptly named Pagoda Fungus is a wonderful curiosity. It produces up to a dozen caps in tiers from a central stem—a unique form of fruitbody not known in any other species. It seems to be restricted to Australia and New Zealand and is a wood-rotter, favoring very decayed fallen logs. Its closest relatives are some rather nondescript, crust-forming fungi, plus a few oddballs such as the north-temperate Crimped Gill (*Plicaturopsis crispa*), which has a similar type of undersurface, and *Irpicodon pendulus*, a small bracket-fungus with coarse, flattened teeth.

SIMILAR SPECIES

No other species is quite like the Pagoda Fungus. Some *Thelphora* species, such as the Carnation Earthfan (*T. caryophylla*), may produce a series of two or three semicircular caps on a central stem, but the effect is more like a rosette than a pagoda.

Actual size

The Pagoda Fungus produces caps in tiers from a central stem. Each fanlike cap is joined at one edge to the main stem, and the surface of the cap is flat or depressed, smooth, and pale ocher to buff or orange-brown, with a wavy margin. The undersurface is irregularly folded or wrinkled, pimpled, and pink. The stem is smooth and similarly pink.

FAMILY	Tapinellaceae
DISTRIBUTION	North America, Europe, northern Asia
HABITAT	In woodland
ASSOCIATION	On conifers
GROWTH FORM	On stumps, fallen branches, and logs
ABUNDANCE	Occasional
SPORE COLOR	Brown
EDIBILITY	Not edible

THICKNESS
Less than ⅛ in
(1 mm)

CAP DIAMETER
Up to 8 in
(200 mm)

PSEUDOMERULIUS AUREUS

ORANGE NETCRUST

(FRIES) JÜLICH

433

The Orange Netcrust has what is termed a merulioid spore-bearing surface—with ridges or folds forming a netlike pattern that in places may look like angular pores. The fruitbody margin is usually distinct and is often lifted away from the wood so that it forms a wavy edge or a series of small, caplike projections. In shape and color, these marginal caps look rather like fruitbodies of the Oyster Rollrim (*Tapinella panuoides*)—and recent molecular research has shown that the two species are indeed closely related.

The Orange Netcrust forms effused patches of indefinite size on the underside of fallen wood or on stumps. The fruitbodies are waxy, the surface with netlike folds, orange-yellow to orange, becoming duller yellow-brown with age. The margin is distinct and often lifted away from the wood in caplike lobes, the caps velvety and cream to orange-buff.

Actual size

SIMILAR SPECIES

Serpula himantoides has a similar netlike surface, but is a duller yellow-brown and has a cobwebby-cottony, often lilac-tinted margin. The infamous Dry Rot (*Serpula lacrymans*) is also similar, but with a rusty brown surface. *Leucogyrophana mollusca* has a brighter, rusty yellow, netlike surface, but also has a cobwebby margin.

FAMILY	Meruliaceae
DISTRIBUTION	North America, Europe, northern Asia
HABITAT	In orchards, gardens, and woodland
ASSOCIATION	On apples, more rarely other broadleaf trees
GROWTH FORM	On trunks and branches
ABUNDANCE	Rare
SPORE COLOR	White
EDIBILITY	Not edible

THICKNESS
Up to ½ in
(15 mm)

DIAMETER
Up to 4 in
(100 mm)

434

SARCODONTIA CROCEA
APPLE TOOTH
(SCHWEINITZ) KOTLABA

The Apple Tooth used to be fairly common on old apple trees in orchards, but since most of these old orchards have been felled, it has now become increasingly rare. In several countries it has been placed on the Red List of endangered fungal species. It causes a rot of dead heartwood that eventually hollows out the tree, but does not kill it. When young and fresh, the Apple Tooth is said to smell of pineapple, though the smell becomes rather sickly with age and is then often described as unpleasant.

SIMILAR SPECIES

Several common species of *Mycoacia* have waxy, yellow fruitbodies with spines, but all are much thinner, the spines are smaller, and they grow on a wide range of trees, usually on the undersides of branches. *Steccherinum* species are similarly shaped but are not waxy, and are cream to ocher rather than yellow. None has the distinctive fruity smell.

The Apple Tooth forms fruitbodies that are effused, but typically grow in cracks and crevices and then appear lumpy and irregular. The surface is partly covered in waxy, conical spines, but may also have non-spiny sterile areas and a wide margin. When young, the fruitbodies are yellow, but often discolor reddish with age.

Actual size

FAMILY	Serpulaceae
DISTRIBUTION	Western North America, central Europe, Asia (Himalayas); cosmopolitan in buildings
HABITAT	In woodland and in buildings
ASSOCIATION	On conifers and softwood timber
GROWTH FORM	Locally on dead branches, stumps, and trunks; more widely on structural timber in buildings
ABUNDANCE	Common in buildings
SPORE COLOR	Brown
EDIBILITY	Not edible

THICKNESS
Up to ½ in
(12 mm)

CAP DIAMETER
Up to 15 in
(400 mm)

SERPULA LACRYMANS
DRY ROT
(WULFEN) J. SCHRÖTER

435

This fungus is famously responsible for substantial losses and expense in buildings by causing a cubic brown rot that can turn structural and other timber to dust. It is able to attack wood with a comparatively low water content compared to that required by *Coniophora puteana* and other "wet" rots, though it still requires damp conditions to grow. When formed, fruitbodies produce vast numbers of spores that can cause asthmatic or allergic reactions in some people. The fungus has a restricted natural distribution, but has adapted itself to the human environment and now occurs in buildings far outside its former range.

SIMILAR SPECIES
The related *Serpula himantioides* has a very similar, brown, netlike surface, but never forms brackets and is normally found in woodland, only occasionally on structural timber. *Leucogyrophana pulverulenta* is also similar and is sometimes found on structural timber. It, too, lacks caplike brackets.

The Dry Rot sometimes forms soft, fleshy brackets that are smooth and whitish to grayish. Frequently, however, fruitbodies are entirely effused with thick, whitish margins. The underside of the bracket or effused fruitbody is yellow-brown at first, becoming rusty brown to dark brown, and has a deeply veined or wrinkled, netlike to pore-like surface. This pore surface can extend over the wood or other substrate almost indefinitely.

Actual size

FAMILY	Sparassidaceae
DISTRIBUTION	Eastern North America, Europe
HABITAT	In woodland
ASSOCIATION	With conifers, especially pine
GROWTH FORM	At base of living trees
ABUNDANCE	Common
SPORE COLOR	White
EDIBILITY	Edible

HEIGHT
Up to 20 in
(500 mm)

DIAMETER
Up to 20 in
(500 mm)

436

SPARASSIS CRISPA
WOOD CAULIFLOWER
(WULFEN) FRIES

Actual size

Sparassis crispa is a common wood-rotting species, typically growing on the ground at the base of pine trees or among their roots. It looks rather like a cauliflower and is certainly edible, but it tastes more like a mushroom—though it is not an easy fungus to clean when collected in the wild. In recent years, however, the Wood Cauliflower has been introduced into cultivation. The species (or possibly its East Asian relative, *Sparassis latifolia*) is already commercially grown in Japan and Korea and is sold in local supermarkets, as well as being dried and exported.

SIMILAR SPECIES

A very similar species, *Sparassis radicata*, occurs with conifers in western North America. In eastern North America, *S. spathulata* grows at the base of broadleaf trees and it has flatter, more upright, zoned fronds. Its uncommon counterpart in Europe is *S. brevipes*, also found with broadleaf trees, more rarely with firs.

The Wood Cauliflower produces densely branched fruitbodies, the branches flattened, thin, and frondlike. Each frond is smooth with a wavy or crisped margin, pale cream to buff, becoming ocher-brown with age. The underside is smooth and similarly colored.

FAMILY	Stereaceae
DISTRIBUTION	North America, Europe, Africa, Central and South America, Asia, Australia, New Zealand
HABITAT	In woodland
ASSOCIATION	On broadleaf trees, rarely conifers
GROWTH FORM	On dead attached and fallen branches, logs, stumps, and trunks
ABUNDANCE	Common
SPORE COLOR	White
EDIBILITY	Not edible

THICKNESS
Less than ⅛ in
(2 mm)

CAP DIAMETER
Up to 1½ in
(40 mm)

STEREUM HIRSUTUM

HAIRY CURTAIN CRUST

(WILLDENOW) PERSOON

437

Since its fruitbodies are common, perennial, and often grow in large swarms, *Stereum hirsutum* is one of the most conspicuous of woodland fungi throughout the year. It is a white-rot fungus that uses enzymes to break down cellulose and lignin, leaving the wood white, soft, and stringy. It can run rampant through piles of cut logs, entering the wood as spores through mutually beneficial insect activity and aggressively outcompeting other fungi . The bright yellow jelly fungus *Tremella aurantia* is a parasite of its fruitbodies, while the brown *T. foliacea* parasitizes its hyphae in the wood.

SIMILAR SPECIES

Stereum ostrea is similar, but its brackets are larger and oyster- or fan-shaped. The brackets of *Stereum complicatum* are smaller and often grow fused together along attached branches and twigs. *Trametes versicolor* may look similar from above, but it has white to cream pores on the underside.

Actual size

The Hairy Curtain Crust produces thin, leathery, bracket-like fruitbodies, the caps of which are finely hairy at first, and zoned in shades of gray, ocher, brown, or red-brown, sometimes green-tinted by algae. The margins are typically wavy and individual caps often fuse with their neighbors. The undersides are smooth and ocher to orange, often continuing over the wood in effused patches.

FAMILY	Stereaceae
DISTRIBUTION	North America, Africa, Central and South America, Asia, Australia, New Zealand
HABITAT	In woodland
ASSOCIATION	On broadleaf trees
GROWTH FORM	On dead attached and fallen branches, logs, stumps, and trunks
ABUNDANCE	Common
SPORE COLOR	White
EDIBILITY	Not edible

THICKNESS
Less than ⅛ in
(2 mm)

CAP DIAMETER
Up to 4 in
(100 mm)

438

STEREUM OSTREA
FALSE TURKEYTAIL
(BLUME & T. NEES) FRIES

The False Turkeytail, or the Golden Curtain Crust, is a common pantropical species, originally described from Java, Indonesia, but extending into the subtropics and North America. Over its range *Stereum ostrea* is extremely variable in shape and color, and future research may show that it is a complex of closely related species. The species epithet *ostrea* means "oyster" and refers to the typical shape of the fruitbodies. In Australia at least, it is said to release cyanide gas and have a faint smell of bitter almonds. Experiments have shown that it produces significant amounts of laccase, which is an economically important enzyme that is used in bioremediation to break down dyes and other pollutants.

SIMILAR SPECIES

Stereum hirsutum is similar, but its brackets are smaller, normally wavy at the margin, and often fuse together. The brackets of *Stereum complicatum* are even smaller, and also tend to grow fused. The true Turkeytail (*Trametes versicolor*) is somewhat similar from above, but has pores on the underside.

The False Turkeytail forms thin, leathery, bracket-like fruitbodies that are typically fanlike or oystershell-shaped. They grow in large troops or clusters, but do not normally fuse together. The caps are smooth, and variously zoned in shades of yellow, ocher, orange, brown, dark red, or gray, often green-tinted by algae. The undersides are smooth and yellow to ocher or pale grayish brown.

Actual size

FAMILY	Stereaceae
DISTRIBUTION	North America, Europe, South America, Asia, Australia, New Zealand
HABITAT	In woodland
ASSOCIATION	On conifer
GROWTH FORM	On dead attached and fallen branches, logs, stumps, and trunks
ABUNDANCE	Common
SPORE COLOR	White
EDIBILITY	Not edible

THICKNESS
Less than ⅛ in
(2 mm)

CAP DIAMETER
Up to 4 in
(100 mm)

STEREUM SANGUINOLENTUM

BLEEDING CONIFER CRUST

(ALBERTINI & SCHWEINITZ) FRIES

439

Stereum sanguinolentum is widespread in north-temperate regions and may have been introduced elsewhere in conifer plantations. It causes problems in commercial forestry since it is a rapid colonizer of recently felled wood or standing trees that have been damaged, either by deer and forest animals or by brash-cutting and other forestry operations. The "wound rot" it causes is often accompanied by the presence of fruitbodies, and affected wood has a distinctive, red-striped appearance as it becomes dyed red by the products of lignin decomposition. The jelly fungus *Tremella encephala* is an occasional parasite of its fruitbodies.

SIMILAR SPECIES

No other *Stereum* species on conifers has the bleeding reaction of *S. sanguinolentum* when scratched with a fingernail. On broadleaf trees, however, both *S. rugosum* and *S. gausapatum* have a similar reaction.

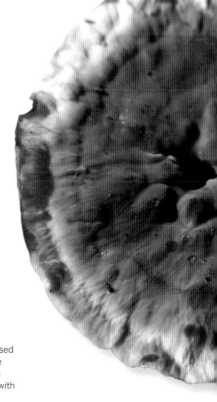

The Bleeding Conifer Crust produces effused fruitbodies that often, but not always, have narrow, ribbonlike caps. When present, the caps are zoned in grayish white to brown, with wavy margins. They often fuse together in strips or clusters. The undersides or effused areas are smooth or shallowly wrinkled, pinkish ocher to gray-brown with white margins, and turn intense blood-red when scratched.

Actual size

FAMILY	Phanerochaetaceae
DISTRIBUTION	North America, Europe, Africa, Central and South America, Asia, Australia, New Zealand
HABITAT	In woodland
ASSOCIATION	On broadleaf wood, more rarely conifers
GROWTH FORM	On fallen twigs, branches, logs, and stumps
ABUNDANCE	Locally common
SPORE COLOR	White
EDIBILITY	Not edible

THICKNESS
Les than ⅛ in
(2 mm)

DIAMETER
Up to 8 in
(200 mm)

440

TERANA CAERULEA
COBALT CRUST
(LAMBOTTE) KUNTZE

This attractive species is one of the few patch-forming fungi that can be confidently identified in the field, thanks to its eye-catching color. It seems to be a litter fungus, forming fruitbodies over the undersides of fallen wood and branches, but often spreading over surrounding leaf litter and mosses. The Cobalt Crust occurs throughout the tropics and subtropics, well into the temperate zone. In Europe it has a westerly distribution and seems to prefer mild, damp climates. The fungus produces a metabolite called cortalcerone that has been shown to have antibiotic properties.

SIMILAR SPECIES

Blue is a rare color among the crust-forming fungi and no other species is such a bright, deep blue as the Cobalt Crust. The uncommon *Byssocorticium pulchrum* and related species are pale greenish blue, and several rare *Amaurodon* species are similarly colored or a duller gray-blue.

The Cobalt Crust produces effused fruitbodies that are smooth to shallowly warty, soft, and velvety. Young fruitbodies are small and almost circular, but quickly amalgamate to produce large, irregular sheets. Fresh, actively growing specimens are bright, deep blue with white, cottony margins, but older fruitbodies may become a duller gray-blue, though often still bright near the margins.

Actual size

FAMILY	Thelephoraceae
DISTRIBUTION	North America, Europe, Asia
HABITAT	In woodland
ASSOCIATION	Ectomycorrhizal, with conifers and broadleaf trees
GROWTH FORM	On ground at base of trees, among roots
ABUNDANCE	Locally common
SPORE COLOR	Brown
EDIBILITY	Not edible

HEIGHT
Up to 2 in
(50 mm)

CAP DIAMETER
Up to 2 in
(50 mm)

THELEPHORA CARYOPHYLLEA

CARNATION EARTHFAN

EHRHART

441

The Carnation Earthfan takes its name from the caps, which often produce secondary, partial caps from the center, rather like a double-flowered carnation. It is an ectomycorrhizal species, associating mainly with the roots of living trees. In the Mediterranean area, however, it is particularly common in areas dominated by shrubby rockroses (*Cistus* species), which are known to be ectomycorrhizal associates. Early evidence suggests that the Carnation Earthfan may be a useful bioindicator for soil pollution by heavy metals, which it appears to actively accumulate. Its close relative *Thelephora vialis* is a powerful antioxidant and is used in traditional Chinese medicine as an anti-inflammatory agent.

SIMILAR SPECIES

The Earthfan, *Thelephora terrestris*, typically produces more irregular, coalescing fruitbodies without a central stem. Fruitbodies of *Coltricia perennis* are of similar shape to the Carnation Earthfan, but have pores on the undersurface.

Actual size

The Carnation Earthfan has leathery fruitbodies, rather like rosettes with central stems. The caps are irregularly round, often with additional partial caps. The surface is smooth to slightly hairy, ridged, and zoned in shades of brown. In young specimens the margin is whitish, and may be feathery. The undersurface is smooth and purplish brown, the stem narrow and whitish to purple-brown.

FAMILY	Thelephoraceae
DISTRIBUTION	North America, Europe, Africa, Central and South America, Asia, Australia, New Zealand
HABITAT	In woodland
ASSOCIATION	Ectomycorrhizal, with conifers and, less commonly, broadleaf trees
GROWTH FORM	On ground at base of trees, among roots
ABUNDANCE	Common
SPORE COLOR	Brown
EDIBILITY	Not edible

HEIGHT
Up to 2 in
(50 mm)

CAP DIAMETER
Up to 2 ½ in
(60 mm)

442

THELEPHORA TERRESTRIS

EARTHFAN

EHRHART

The Earthfan is a common and very widespread species, but its cryptic coloring means that it is often overlooked when growing among roots in leaf or needle litter. It is an ectomycorrhizal fungus, associating with living trees, particularly (but not exclusively) conifers. The irregular fruitbodies often attach themselves to and grow around fallen twigs, sticks, and stones, and even seedling plants. In conifer nurseries, this can be a problem and the Earthfan has been given the name of the Smothering Fungus because it can smother young seedlings.

SIMILAR SPECIES

Other *Thelephora* species may be difficult to distinguish from the Earthfan. *Thelephora caryophyllea* produces neater, less irregular fruitbodies with a central stem. Fruitbodies of *T. penicillata* are very feathery and spiny with no true caps, while *T. palmata* looks more like a coral fungus and has a strong unpleasant smell.

Actual size

The Earthfan produces multiple, small, irregular, leathery brackets that are often intricately coalesced. Each individual bracket has a purplish to gray-brown cap that is ridged and often coarsely hairy, with a paler to whitish margin that is hairy, feathery, or spiny. The undersurface is smooth but ridged, and is purplish brown. The stem, if present, is small and irregular.

FAMILY	Auriculariaceae
DISTRIBUTION	North America, Europe, northern Asia
HABITAT	In woodland
ASSOCIATION	On hardwoods, especially elder
GROWTH FORM	On dead trunks and branches, singly or clustered
ABUNDANCE	Very common
SPORE COLOR	White
EDIBILITY	Edible

THICKNESS
Up to ¼ in
(5 mm)

CAP DIAMETER
Up to 3 in
(75 mm)

AURICULARIA AURICULA-JUDAE

JELLY EAR

(BULLIARD) QUÉLET

443

Better known as the Jew's Ear, *Auricularia auricula-judae* is
particularly common on elder and takes its odd name from
the old Christian legend that Judas Iscariot hanged himself on
an elder tree. Why simulacra of his ears should appear on the
tree ever afterward is a mystery, except to the medieval mind.
Together with the Wood Ear (*A. cornea*), the Jelly Ear has long
been cultivated and eaten in China and more recently has been
marketed in the West. It is even an ingredient in "woodland
mushroom" instant soup.

SIMILAR SPECIES

The Jelly Ear is very similar to the more tropical and subtropical
Wood Ear (*Auricularia cornea*), differing mainly in having
sparser and shorter hairs on the cap surface. The Amber
Jelly (*Exidia recisa*) can look similar, but its fruitbodies are
more orange-brown, it typically grows on willow, and has a
smooth, not hairy, cap.

Actual size

The Jelly Ear produces thin, rubbery-gelatinous brackets. The caps are
smooth, but finely hairy, with a slightly downy appearance when dry, and
brown to pinkish brown or purple-brown (rarely unpigmented and white).
The undersides are smooth and cap-colored, and may sometimes have
sparse, irregular veins.

FAMILY	Auriculariaceae
DISTRIBUTION	Africa, South America, southern Asia (also China and Japan), Australia, New Zealand
HABITAT	In woodland
ASSOCIATION	On broadleaf wood
GROWTH FORM	On dead and fallen branches and logs, singly or clustered
ABUNDANCE	Common
SPORE COLOR	White
EDIBILITY	Edible

THICKNESS
Up to ¼ in
(5 mm)

CAP DIAMETER
Up to 4 in
(100 mm)

444

AURICULARIA CORNEA
WOOD EAR
EHRENBERG

Though they may not look particularly edible, Wood Ears have been cultivated for food in China for at least the last 1,400 years. They are particularly popular in stir-frys and soups, having a firm texture and pleasant, if mild, flavor. Better known under their synonym, *Auricularia polytricha*, they are now widely exported in dried form and also grown commercially elsewhere in the world, most commonly on logs or sawdust blocks. They are also valued for their reputed health-giving properties. Traditionally used to aid blood circulation, Wood Ears have now been shown to contain a blood-clotting inhibitor that could help reduce arteriosclerosis and stroke risk.

The Wood Ear produces thin, rubbery-gelatinous brackets. The caps are smooth, but densely covered in small hairs, giving them a whitish to grayish, downy appearance. The undersides are smooth, brown to pinkish or purplish brown, sometimes with sparse, irregular veins.

SIMILAR SPECIES
The Wood Ear is frequently confused with the temperate Jelly Ear, *Auricularia auricula-judae*, which lacks the densely hairy cap surface. Confusingly both species are sold as "Wood Ears," the name being used fairly interchangeably, while *A. cornea* is also marketed as "Cloud Ears," "Tree Ears," or similar names. *Auricularia mesenterica* has a much hairier, zoned cap surface and is not cultivated for food.

Actual size

FAMILY	Auriculariaceae
DISTRIBUTION	North America, Europe, Africa, Central and South America, Asia, Australia
HABITAT	In woodland
ASSOCIATION	On broadleaf wood, particularly elm
GROWTH FORM	On stumps, fallen branches, and logs, in clusters
ABUNDANCE	Locally common
SPORE COLOR	White
EDIBILITY	Edible

THICKNESS
Up to ⅜ in
(8 mm)

CAP DIAMETER
Up to 4 in
(100 mm)

AURICULARIA MESENTERICA

TRIPE FUNGUS

(DICKSON) PERSOON

445

Like other *Auricularia* species, the Tripe Fungus is a wood-rotter, typically found covering the sides of old stumps. The coalescing brackets can form large compound fruitbodies resembling intestinal animal tripe, from which it gets both its Latin and its common name. Although reported as inedible in many books, it is eaten by native peoples in Mexico and Nepal. It is also a favorite species for the small South American Goeldi's Monkey, which is currently the only known primate to consume mainly fungi rather than fruit and nuts. The Tripe Fungus is also occasionally used in China for its supposed medicinal value.

SIMILAR SPECIES

From above, the Tripe Fungus may look like a hairy, zoned, leathery bracket fungus such as *Trametes versicolor*, but the rubbery-gelatinous texture and lack of pores on the underside are distinctive. The related *Auricularia cornea* also has a hairy cap, but the hairs are much less dense, more bloomlike, and never form zones.

The Tripe Fungus produces rubbery-gelatinous brackets with densely hairy, wavy caps, zoned in shades of gray and brown (often tinged green with algae), with a white margin. The undersides are smooth, pale grayish to purplish brown, and irregularly veined, the veins sometimes joining to form an open, netlike surface. Fruitbodies are clustered and coalesce, the undersurfaces often forming effused sheets over the wood.

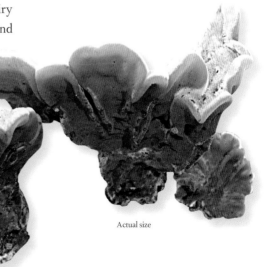

Actual size

FAMILY	Dacrymycetaceae
DISTRIBUTION	North America, Europe, Africa, Central and South America, Asia, Australia, New Zealand
HABITAT	In woodland
ASSOCIATION	On broadleaf and conifer wood
GROWTH FORM	On stumps, dead and fallen branches, and logs, in troops
ABUNDANCE	Very common
SPORE COLOR	White
EDIBILITY	Not edible

HEIGHT
Up to ½ in
(15 mm)

DIAMETER
Less than ⅛ in
(2 mm)

446

CALOCERA CORNEA
SMALL STAGSHORN
(BATSCH) FRIES

Actual size

The Small Stagshorn produces troops of rubbery-gelatinous fruitbodies that are normally unbranched and simple, though a few may be slightly forked at the pointed tip. Fruitbodies can grow singly from the wood or in small clusters. The color varies from watery yellowish to a bright orange-yellow when drying.

This species is cosmopolitan and is often seen on dead and fallen wood, especially after rain when the gelatinous fruitbodies are easily visible. It typically grows in troops, sometimes in large swarms, and favors barkless wood, often appearing on built structures such as untreated benches and gates. The spores are produced over the surface of each simple fruitbody on microscopic cells shaped like tuning forks. The basal part of the fruitbody (often whitish) is sterile, as are the pointed tips. The species epithet *cornea* means "horny," probably with reference to the shape, rather than the texture, though like all *Calocera* species the fruitbodies become tough and hard when dried.

SIMILAR SPECIES

The related *Calocera viscosa* has much larger, branching fruitbodies. *Calocera pallidospathulata* and tropical *Dacryopinax* species have a similar trooping habit, but are larger and the tips are not pointed but fan-shaped or spatulate. Several smaller but rarer *Calocera* species also have swollen or forking tips.

FAMILY	Dacrymycetaceae
DISTRIBUTION	North America, Europe, Central America, Asia, Australia
HABITAT	In woodland
ASSOCIATION	On conifers
GROWTH FORM	On stumps, fallen branches and logs
ABUNDANCE	Common
SPORE COLOR	White
EDIBILITY	Not edible

HEIGHT
Up to 4 in
(100 mm)

DIAMETER
Up to 3 in
(75 mm)

CALOCERA VISCOSA

YELLOW STAGSHORN

(PERSOON) FRIES

447

This species is only found on conifer wood, typically on old stumps but occasionally on buried wood or roots when it may appear as if it is growing from the soil. The bright color comes from carotene-like pigments, which are found in all this family of fungi. Rarely, however, unpigmented, white fruitbodies are formed. These were once given the name *Calocera cavarae*, but are not actually a separate species. The Yellow Stagshorn keeps it bright orange color well when dried, and is sometimes used as a colorful addition to natural, decorative table-arrangements and occasionally in potpourri mixes.

SIMILAR SPECIES

The related *Calocera cornea* produces much smaller fruitbodies that are simple or occasionally shortly forked at the tip. Branching, yellow *Ramaria* species are not gelatinous or rubbery, grow in woodland soil, and are never so brightly colored as the Yellow Stagshorn. The same is true of *Clavulinopsis corniculata*, another ocher-yellow, branching species that grows in grass or on the ground in woodlands.

The Yellow Stagshorn produces rubbery-gelatinous, coralloid fruitbodies branching repeatedly from a short, central stem. The tips of the branches are normally pointed and often shortly forked (see photo above). Fresh specimens are a bright egg-yolk yellow, drying a deep orange. The whole fruitbody becomes hard and tough when dry.

Actual size

FAMILY	Dacrymycetaceae
DISTRIBUTION	North America, Europe, Africa, Central America, Asia, Australia, New Zealand
HABITAT	In woodland
ASSOCIATION	On conifers
GROWTH FORM	On dead and fallen branches, trunks, and logs
ABUNDANCE	Locally common
SPORE COLOR	White
EDIBILITY	Not edible

HEIGHT
Up to 2 in
(50 mm)

DIAMETER
Up to 2½ in
(60 mm)

448

DACRYMYCES CHRYSOSPERMUS
ORANGE JELLY
BERKELEY & M. A. CURTIS

Though widely distributed, this is generally an uncommon species except in parts of North America where it is frequently encountered on conifers and is often incorrectly referred to as *Dacrymyces palmatus* (an illegitimate name). It is a saprotrophic, wood-rotting species occurring on barkless wood and, like many other gelatinous species, is capable or rehydration after dry spells. It is one of the largest *Dacrymyces* species, most being much smaller and disc-shaped or cushion-shaped, though still gelatinous and similarly colored.

SIMILAR SPECIES

Its comparatively large size means the Orange Jelly is unlikely to be mistaken for the many smaller species of *Dacrymyces*, such as the common *D. stillatus*, which often grows in swarms on conifer wood. It is more likely to be confused with bright yellow *Tremella* species, particularly *T. aurantia* and *T. mesenterica*. Neither of these species normally grows on conifer, however, and both are quite different microscopically.

The Orange Jelly, as its name suggests, is a bright chrome-yellow to orange, rubbery-gelatinous species that may be cushion-shaped when young, but becomes convoluted, brainlike, or with large lobes when older, sometimes with a thick, short stem. Fruitbodies may coalesce to form larger masses.

Actual size

FAMILY	Dacrymycetaceae
DISTRIBUTION	North America, Africa, Asia, Central and South America, Australia, New Zealand
HABITAT	In woodland
ASSOCIATION	On broadleaf and conifer wood
GROWTH FORM	On dead and fallen branches, trunks, and logs, in troops
ABUNDANCE	Common
SPORE COLOR	White
EDIBILITY	Edible

HEIGHT
Up to 1 in
(25 mm)

CAP DIAMETER
Up to ½ in
(10 mm)

DACRYOPINAX SPATHULARIA

FAN-SHAPED JELLY

(SCHWEINITZ) G. W. MARTIN

449

The Fan-Shaped Jelly is a very widely distributed species, common throughout the tropics and most temperate areas except Europe. Like other members of the family, it rots down dead wood. It is considered to have medicinal properties in China and is sold commercially as an extract "to nourish stomach, cure lung, and reduce sputum." It is also occasionally eaten as food in China and by indigenous peoples elsewhere. Its Chinese name is Guihua Er (which means "sweet osmanthus ear") and it is sometimes included in the traditional New Year vegetarian dish, Buddha's Delight, alongside other symbolic edible fungi such as the Wood Ear and the Shiitake.

SIMILAR SPECIES

In Britain, the locally common *Calocera pallidospathulata* is a very similar species, though typically paler and softer. In the Americas, *Dacryopinax elegans* is a browner species whose fruiting bodies are more cup-shaped than fan-shaped. Several other less common *Dacryopinax* species occur in the tropics, and are best distinguished microscopically.

The Fan-Shaped Jelly produces yellow-orange, rubbery-gelatinous fruitbodies that are fan- or spatula-shaped at the top, with a gelatinous or cartilaginous stalk. The species is very variable in shape and size, often growing particularly large in the tropics.

Actual size

FAMILY	Auriculariaceae
DISTRIBUTION	North America, Europe, Asia
HABITAT	In woodland
ASSOCIATION	On broadleaf trees, particularly oak and hazel
GROWTH FORM	On dead attached branches
ABUNDANCE	Common
SPORE COLOR	White
EDIBILITY	Not edible

HEIGHT
Up to 1½ in
(40 mm)

CAP DIAMETER
Up to 2½ in
(60 mm)

450

EXIDIA GLANDULOSA
WITCHES' BUTTER
(BULLIARD) FRIES

The gelatinous fruitbodies of *Exidia glandulosa* (and the related *E. nigricans*) have long been known as the Witches' Butter, a name used in one of the earliest English books on fungi published in 1741. At a witchcraft trial in Wales in 1656, it was part of the evidence that the Witches' Butter grew on the accused's doorpost. It was believed that witches produced this unpleasant-looking black matter and that stabbing or burning the fungus would harm the witch herself. In North America, the bright yellow *Tremella mesenterica* is sometimes called the Yellow Witch's Butter.

SIMILAR SPECIES
Exidia nigricans is a closely related species that has more effused fruitbodies that coalesce and then appear irregularly lobed. The unrelated *Bulgaria inquinans* produces similar black, gelatinous fruitbodies on oak, but its surfaces are never warted and its abundant spores are black, discoloring skin or paper if rubbed.

Actual size

The Witches' Butter produces blackish brown, rubbery-gelatinous fruitbodies that are shaped like an old-fashioned top or inverted cone. When old or soaked with rainwater, they often become lax and pendant. The upper surface is glossy and sparsely covered with small warts or pegs. The undersurface is matt and smooth at first, then covered with tiny, almost invisible spines or pegs.

FAMILY	Auriculariaceae
DISTRIBUTION	North America, Europe, northern Asia
HABITAT	In woodland
ASSOCIATION	On willows, rarely on other broadleaf trees
GROWTH FORM	On dead attached twigs and branches
ABUNDANCE	Locally common
SPORE COLOR	White
EDIBILITY	Not edible

HEIGHT
Up to 1½ in
(40 mm)

CAP DIAMETER
Up to 1½ in
(40 mm)

EXIDIA RECISA
AMBER JELLY
(DITMAR) FRIES

451

This attractive jelly fungus is locally common on dead twigs of willows still attached to the tree and often quite high off the ground. As in many other jelly fungi, the gelatinous flesh stores rainwater and allows the production of spores to continue for some time after the weather turns dry. Also, as in other jelly fungi, it can quickly rehydrate again once wet. This is a useful adaptation for fungi growing on exposed, dead, attached branches, but less successful for fungi on fallen wood. Perhaps as a result, the Amber Jelly does not persist for long when its host twigs fall to earth.

SIMILAR SPECIES
Exidia repanda is a closely related species that is similarly colored, but has fruitbodies that are more button-shaped and never become pendant. It tends to grow on birches, never on willows. The brownish black Witches' Butter *(Exidia glandulosa)* is similar to the Amber Jelly in shape, but has small warts on the surface and usually grows on oaks.

Actual size

The Amber Jelly produces orange-brown or amber-colored, rubbery-gelatinous fruitbodies that are shaped like an inverted cone when young. When older, they become lax, pendant, and (in wet weather) translucent. The upper surface is smooth and glossy, the underside smooth but matt.

FAMILY	Auriculariaceae
DISTRIBUTION	North America, Europe, Central and South America, Asia
HABITAT	In woodland
ASSOCIATION	With conifers
GROWTH FORM	On soil (with buried wood) and on wood chips and sawdust
ABUNDANCE	Locally common
SPORE COLOR	White
EDIBILITY	Edible

HEIGHT
Up to 4 in
(100 mm)

CAP DIAMETER
Up to 2 in
(50 mm)

452

GUEPINIA HELVELLOIDES
SALMON SALAD
(DE CANDOLLE) FRIES

Few people would imagine that the Salmon Salad and the Apricot Jelly could be one and the same thing, but the common names of this species refer to its color rather than to its taste. It is considered edible but insipid, and is used more as a colorful garnish than as a meal in itself. It is a saprotroph of well-rotted, small-size conifer wood and, unusually, seems to like disturbed sites, especially where logs have been sawn or chipped. In the British Isles at least, *Guepinia helvelloides* is slowly increasing its range by spreading into such places in timber plantations. It may also be appearing more frequently on conifer chips used in horticulture.

SIMILAR SPECIES
Few jelly fungi occur on the ground and none resembling *Guepinia helvelloides*. In shape and texture, species of the ascomycete genus *Otidea* are closest. The North American *O. auricula* is rabbit-ear-shaped and reddish brown on its inner surface, while the north-temperate *O. onotica* is similarly shaped, but ocher, often with a salmon-pink cast. Both are more brittle than *G. helvelloides*.

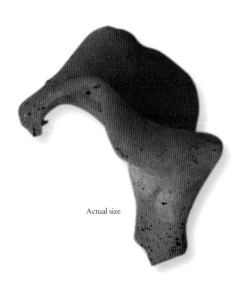

Actual size

The Salmon Salad produces erect fruitbodies that are almost trumpet-shaped, but are split and open along one side (see photo right). They are smooth or shallowly wrinkled, gelatinous to cartilaginous, clustered or coalescing, and typically pinkish to orange-red when fresh, becoming duller and more yellowish with age.

FAMILY	Auriculariaceae
DISTRIBUTION	North America, Europe, Central and South America, Asia, Australia, New Zealand
HABITAT	In woodland
ASSOCIATION	On conifers
GROWTH FORM	On dead trunks, stumps, and logs
ABUNDANCE	Common
SPORE COLOR	White
EDIBILITY	Edible

HEIGHT
Up to 1 in
(25 mm)

CAP DIAMETER
Up to 2½ in
(60 mm)

PSEUDOHYDNUM GELATINOSUM

JELLY TOOTH

(SCOPOLI) P. KARSTEN

453

The Jelly Tooth is an easy species to recognize, since there seems to be no other fungus that it closely resembles. It is said to be edible and has even been offered dried for export by one Chinese company (though the accompanying photographs suggested a completely different species), but eating it can hardly be worthwhile. It is variously described as "watery," "tasteless," and "best candied or marinated," presumably to give it some semblance of flavor. *Pseudohydnum* ("false hydnum") means it has a toothed undersurface like a *Hydnum* species, but the real Wood Hedgehog (*Hydnum repandum*) is an altogether different beast.

SIMILAR SPECIES

No other jelly fungus has a cap with spines on the undersurface. Several bracket-like fungi, including the north-temperate *Climacodon septentrionalis* and *Sarcodontia pachyodon*, are white and toothed below, but are much larger and not at all gelatinous.

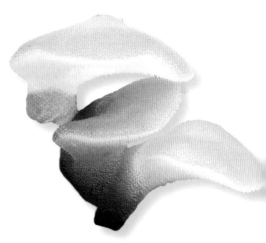

Actual size

The Jelly Tooth has bracket-like or tongue-shaped, rubbery-gelatinous fruitbodies with spines on the undersurface. The cap itself is watery grayish to brownish, smooth or slightly wrinkled. The spines below are whitish and soft. It often produces a distinct, and sometimes quite long, lateral stem, especially if growing on the top of stumps.

FAMILY	Sebacinaceae
DISTRIBUTION	North America, Europe, Central and South America, Asia
HABITAT	In woodland
ASSOCIATION	Ectomycorrhizal, with broadleaf and conifer trees
GROWTH FORM	Encrusting soil and leaf litter
ABUNDANCE	Common
SPORE COLOR	White
EDIBILITY	Not edible

HEIGHT
Up to ½ in
(10 mm)

DIAMETER
Up to 8 in
(200 mm)

454

SEBACINA INCRUSTANS
ENVELOPING CRUST
(PERSOON) TULASNE & C. TULASNE

Until recently, the Enveloping Crust was thought to belong in the same jelly fungus family as *Exidia* species since it has some microscopic features in common. Molecular research, however, has now shown that *Sebacina* is a very distant relative. It has also shown that the genus is ectomycorrhizal, its species forming associations with the roots of living trees. The Enveloping Crust is very variable in form and color, and it now seems probable that it represents a complex of closely related species that may prove difficult to distinguish.

SIMILAR SPECIES

The related *Sebacina epigaea* also encrusts earth, but is more gelatinous and bluish gray, only turning opaque and whitish in dry weather. It does not climb and encrust living plants in the way that *S. incrustans* does. Many unrelated crust-forming fungi also envelop fallen litter, but are typically soft and cobwebby, not rubbery to cartilaginous.

Actual size

The Enveloping Crust has effused fruitbodies that spread over the soil, enveloping and encrusting stones, fallen twigs, and living plants. The fruitbodies are sordid white to cream or ocher, and are rubbery to cartilaginous. They are smooth, but very irregular, and sometimes produce spiny or feathery projections, especially when growing upward, or take on the underlying shape of the litter and plants they are encrusting.

FAMILY	Sebacinaceae
DISTRIBUTION	Eastern North America
HABITAT	In woodland
ASSOCIATION	Ectomycorrhizal, with broadleaf trees, especially oak
GROWTH FORM	In soil and leaf litter
ABUNDANCE	Locally common
SPORE COLOR	White
EDIBILITY	Not edible

HEIGHT
Up to 4 in
(100 mm)

DIAMETER
Up to 4 in
(100 mm)

SEBACINA SPARASSOIDEA

WHITE CORAL JELLY

(LLOYD) P. ROBERTS

455

The White Coral Jelly was formerly known as *Tremella reticulata*, but is quite unrelated to the true *Tremella* species, none of which occurs on the ground. Instead, it is a relative of the crust-forming *Sebacina* species and false corals such as *Tremellodendron schweinitzii*, all of which form mutually beneficial associations with the roots of living trees. The species epithet *sparassoidea* means "like *Sparassis*," the Wood Cauliflower (*Sparassis crispa*), while *reticulata* means "netlike" since the branches of the White Coral Jelly often fuse together in a loose net.

SIMILAR SPECIES

Also in eastern North America, *Tremellodendron* species form fruitbodies of similar shape and color, but they are much more leathery and have branches that are flattened and fanlike. *Sebacina concrescens* can be similar, but its fruitbodies are more lobed than branched and tend to be much more irregular and encrusting.

The White Coral Jelly produces firm-gelatinous fruitbodies with erect, hollow lobes or branches arising from a common base. The branches are white and frequently fuse together, giving the species a netlike appearance. The branch tips are variously rounded or pointed, sometimes with fine feathery projections.

Actual size

FAMILY	Carcinomycetaceae
DISTRIBUTION	North America, Central America
HABITAT	In woodland
ASSOCIATION	Parasitic on *Gymnopus dryophilus*
GROWTH FORM	On fruitbodies
ABUNDANCE	Occasional
SPORE COLOR	White
EDIBILITY	Not edible

HEIGHT
(galls)
Up to ½ in
(15 mm)

DIAMETER
(galls)
Up to 1 in
(25 mm)

456

SYZYGOSPORA MYCETOPHILA
TOUGHSHANK BRAIN
(PECK) GINNS

This peculiar jelly fungus is a parasite on fruitbodies of the common Russet Toughshank (*Gymnopus dryophilus*). It induces pustular to brainlike, semigelatinous galls on the cap, stem, or gills—sometimes small, sometimes so large they almost envelop the host. The Toughshank Brain's own spores are formed on the gall surfaces. It was originally thought that these galls were teratological growths (monstrous malformations) of a kind that can cause agarics to develop oddly, until it was realized that *Syzygospora* species, relatives of *Tremella*, were responsible.

SIMILAR SPECIES

Two additional species—*Syzygospora effibulata* and *S. tumefaciens*—occur on the same host in North America and in Europe, but they are only distinguishable with a microscope. The latter species has also been recorded on the Butter Cap (*Rhodocollybia butyracea*). Other species parasitize *Marasmius pallidocephalus* in North America.

Actual size

The Toughshank Brain induces galls in the host tissue. These galls are pustular, but may proliferate and become convoluted and brainlike, appearing on cap, gills, or stem. The fruitbody of the parasite consists of a thin, colorless, gelatinous film on the surface of these galls.

FAMILY	Tremellaceae
DISTRIBUTION	North America, Europe, Asia, Australia
HABITAT	In woodland
ASSOCIATION	Parasitic on *Stereum sanguinolentum* on conifers
GROWTH FORM	On dead trunks, branches, and logs
ABUNDANCE	Occasional
SPORE COLOR	White
EDIBILITY	Not edible

HEIGHT
Up to 1¼ in
(30 mm)

DIAMETER
Up to 1¼ in
(30 mm)

TREMELLA ENCEPHALA

CONIFER BRAIN

WILLDENOW

457

The Conifer Brain has a pink, gelatinous exterior and, when cut open, a harder, white core. As a result, for well over a century, the fungus was placed in a separate genus (*Naematelia*) specially described for gelatinous fungi with hard cores, until it was realized that the core was the remains of a *Stereum sanguinolentum* fruitbody that the Conifer Brain had parasitized and engulfed. Now it seems obvious, since the fungus is always found growing alongside fruitbodies of its host, but this parasite-host connection was not discovered until the 1960s.

SIMILAR SPECIES

In North America there is a related, small, brainlike species, *Tremella tremelloides*, which is yellowish and grows with *Stereum* species on broadleaf trees. The unrelated *Exidia nucleata* may look superficially similar, but is normally softer, whitish (rarely, with a pinkish tint), lacks the hard central core, and also grows on broadleaf trees.

The Conifer Brain produces pale pink, gelatinous fruitbodies that are round or cushion-shaped, compact, and densely folded in a brainlike way. Older or water-soaked specimens may lose their color and become yellowish to buff with no more than a pinkish tint.

Actual size

FAMILY	Tremellaceae
DISTRIBUTION	North America, Europe, Central and South America, Asia, Australia
HABITAT	In woodland
ASSOCIATION	Parasitic on *Stereum* species on broadleaf and conifer wood
GROWTH FORM	On dead trunks, branches, and logs
ABUNDANCE	Common
SPORE COLOR	White
EDIBILITY	Edible

HEIGHT
Up to 4 in
(100 mm)

DIAMETER
Up to 8 in
(200 mm)

458

TREMELLA FOLIACEA
LEAFY BRAIN
PERSOON

This is one of the largest and most conspicuous *Tremella* species, often producing mounds of seaweedlike growth on stumps and logs. It is a parasite of bracket-like *Stereum* fungi, though unlike *Tremella aurantia* and *T. encephala* it does not parasitize the fruitbodies of its host but the host hyphae hidden in the wood. Often the Leafy Brain—also known as the Jelly Leaf—can be found fruiting on the top of a branch, while the *Stereum* is fruiting on the underside. *Tremella foliacea* is very variable across its range and may well prove to be a complex of closely related species.

SIMILAR SPECIES

There are many similar species in the tropics and subtropics, including *Tremella wrightii* with orange-brown, crisped, almost hornlike fronds, and *T. coffeicolor*, which is best distinguished microscopically by its larger spores. In temperate areas, coalesced fruitbodies of *Exidia saccharina* on conifers may look similar, but they are lobed not leafy. The rare *T. steidleri* on *Stereum hirsutum* is dull brown, but has dense, brainlike folds.

Actual size

The Leafy Brain has brown to purplish or blackish brown, gelatinous fruitbodies that are seaweedlike, producing a mass of thin to thickish fronds and folds. When fresh, these may be erect, but when old, or in dry weather, they become lax.

FAMILY	Tremellaceae
DISTRIBUTION	Southern North America, Africa, Central and South America, southern Asia, Australia, New Zealand
HABITAT	In woodland
ASSOCIATION	Parasitic on *Hypoxylon archeri* on broadleaf wood
GROWTH FORM	On dead trunks, branches, and logs
ABUNDANCE	Common
SPORE COLOR	White
EDIBILITY	Edible

HEIGHT
Up to 3 in
(75 mm)

DIAMETER
Up to 3 in
(75 mm)

TREMELLA FUCIFORMIS

SILVER EAR

BERKELEY

459

The Silver Ear, which is also known as the Snow Fungus, was originally described from Brazil and is a common species throughout the tropics and subtropics. It is parasitic on *Hypoxylon archeri*, a crusty, black, ascomycetous fungus that grows on dead broadleaf branches. Silver Ears are edible, and are widely grown in China using mixed cultures of the parasite and host on enriched sawdust. They are eaten for their supposed medicinal value, ranging from a tonic to boost the immune system to a cure for freckles, as well as for their texture and appearance. Unusually for a fungus, they are often consumed in syrup as a dessert. *Tremella fuciformis* is now widely available in the West, dried and packeted.

SIMILAR SPECIES

Tremella olens is another white, tropical species, but its fruitbodies are irregularly lobed and never rosette-like. In North America the unrelated *Sebacina sparassoidea* can produce gelatinous, white, branching fruitbodies rather similar to those of the Silver Ear, but growing on the ground.

Actual size

The Silver Ear has white, gelatinous fruitbodies that are seaweedlike (fuciform), producing a rosette of thin, wavy fronds, often branched and crisped toward the outer margin. Cultivated specimens are often very large, and look almost like decorative white pom-poms.

FAMILY	Tremellaceae
DISTRIBUTION	North America, Europe, Africa, Central and South America, Antarctic islands, Asia, Australia
HABITAT	In woodland
ASSOCIATION	Parasitic on *Peniophora* species on broadleaf trees, very rarely conifers
GROWTH FORM	On dead attached or recently fallen twigs and branches
ABUNDANCE	Common
SPORE COLOR	White
EDIBILITY	Edible

HEIGHT Up to 2 in (50 mm)	
DIAMETER Up to 3 in (75 mm)	

TREMELLA MESENTERICA
YELLOW BRAIN
RETZIUS

460

The Yellow Brain is a parasite of the mycelium of crust-forming *Peniophora* species, and is usually found close to the purplish-gray or reddish fruitbodies of its host, typically on dead attached branches and twigs. In North America, the species is also called the Yellow Witch's Butter—the gelatinous fruitbodies having once been associated with witchcraft. It is an extremely widespread fungus, found from the tropics to the Antarctic islands. Despite (or perhaps because of) its texture, it is said to be eaten in China —though it is not highly esteemed.

SIMILAR SPECIES

Tremella mesenterica has frequently been confused with the Golden Ear (*T. aurantia*). The latter species has a matt surface and is parasitic on fruitbodies of the Hairy Curtain Crust (*Stereum hirsutum*). It has also been confused with the unrelated Orange Jelly (*Dacrymyces chrysospermus*), common in North America, which grows on conifers in bright yellow, gelatinous clusters.

Actual size

The Yellow Brain produces bright yellow to yellow-orange, gelatinous fruitbodies that are shiny to greasy when young, pustular at first, becoming lobed and sometimes irregularly frondlike. The fruitbodies shrink in dry weather, becoming crisp and deep orange, swelling again when it rains.

FAMILY	Sebacinaceae
DISTRIBUTION	Eastern North America, Central and South America
HABITAT	In woodland
ASSOCIATION	Ectomycorrhizal, with broadleaf trees
GROWTH FORM	In soil and leaf litter
ABUNDANCE	Common
SPORE COLOR	White
EDIBILITY	Not edible

HEIGHT
Up to 5 in
(120 mm)

DIAMETER
Up to 6 in
(150 mm)

TREMELLODENDRON SCHWEINITZII

JELLIED FALSE CORAL

(PECK) G. F. ATKINSON

461

This is a common species in eastern North America, where it is often still referred to as *Tremellodendron pallidum*, an old illegitimate name. Though it looks like a true coral fungus, the Jellied False Coral is closely related to crust-forming *Sebacina* species and is microscopically almost indistinguishable. As in *Sebacina* species, the fruitbodies are indeterminate, forming their branches slowly (sometimes growing around and incorporating bits of litter and debris) and often changing their shape quite markedly over the course of time.

SIMILAR SPECIES

Other *Tremellodendron* species can be difficult to distinguish, but usually have narrower branches with more pointed tips. The related White Coral Jelly (*Sebacina sparassoidea*) can form similar fruitbodies, but they are more gelatinous and have branches that are lobed rather than flattened and fanlike. Similarly shaped fruitbodies of the Stinking Earthfan (*Thelephora palmata*) can be distinguished by being purplish brown with only the tips whitish.

The Jellied False Coral has rather tough, rubbery-cartilaginous fruitbodies that form a dense rosette of branches from a common base. The branches are whitish at first, often developing pinkish or reddish tints with age, and are usually flattened or fanlike, frequently fusing together. The tips are wedge-like, though sometimes can be feathery or incised.

Actual size

TOOTH FUNGI, CHANTERELLES, CLUBS & CORALS

The tooth (or hydnoid) fungi have spine- or toothlike projections on their undersurface instead of pores or gills—a type of fruitbody that has evolved in several unrelated groups. They include species that form associations with trees, have caps and stems, and may look like ordinary agarics from above, as well as some wood-rotters that grow on trunks and logs. A few of these look so bracket-like that you will find them included in the previous section.

Chanterelles are celebrated for their edibility, though a few look-alike species (such as the Woolly Chanterelle) may be poisonous. Most grow in woodlands and look a little like agarics, but never have true, paper-thin gills. Their spore-producing undersurfaces are smooth to wrinkled or veined—the veins often imitating gills, but always much thicker.

The clubs and corals (or clavarioid fungi) produce their spores on the surface of mostly upright, simple or branched fruitbodies. This is another shape that has evolved many different times and some clublike fungi, such as the earthtongues, belong in the Ascomycota. Many of the clubs and corals featured here are woodland tree associates; others (at least in Europe) are more typical of mossy grassland.

FAMILY	Auriscalpiaceae
DISTRIBUTION	North America, Europe, Central America, Asia
HABITAT	In conifer woodland
ASSOCIATION	Mainly with pine, occasionally spruce
GROWTH FORM	On fallen or buried cones
ABUNDANCE	Very common
SPORE COLOR	White
EDIBILITY	Not edible

HEIGHT
Up to 1 in
(25 mm)

CAP DIAMETER
Up to 1 in
(25 mm)

464

AURISCALPIUM VULGARE
EARPICK FUNGUS
GRAY

Careful search in any conifer woodland is likely to reveal this small but distinctive species, which, although it may appear to grow directly on the ground, has a specialized habitat niche as a wood-rotter of fallen and buried cones or cone debris. Several fruiting bodies can sometimes be found growing from one cone, and unlike many fungal species it can be found throughout the year. Its common name derives from its similarity in appearance to the right-angled device used by ancient Romans as an ear scraper. In the north temperate zone it is the sole known representative of the genus.

The Earpick Fungus has a small, irregular, kidney-shaped, reddish brown cap with a velvety to smooth texture, and a tall, dark, lateral stem bristling with tiny hairs. It has short, pale grayish, pointed spines up to ⅛ in (3 mm) long beneath the cap, and the whole fungus is quite rigid, tough, and leathery. The flesh is pale and mild-tasting without a particular smell.

SIMILAR SPECIES

A number of common and widespread cap-and-stem fungi also occur on fallen cones of conifers and may superficially resemble the Earpick Fungus. These include *Baeospora myosura* and members of the genus *Strobilurus,* all of which on closer inspection have gills underneath the cap rather than spines. The neotropical species *Auriscalpium villipes* is smaller in stature with a paler stem and acrid taste.

Actual size

FAMILY	Bankeraceae
DISTRIBUTION	North America, Europe
HABITAT	In conifer woodland
ASSOCIATION	Ectomycorrhizal, with spruce
GROWTH FORM	On ground, singly or in groups among spruce litter
ABUNDANCE	Occasional
SPORE COLOR	White
EDIBILITY	Not edible

HEIGHT
Up to 1 in
(25 mm)

CAP DIAMETER
Up to 6 in
(150 mm)

BANKERA VIOLASCENS
SPRUCE TOOTH
(ALBERTINI & SCHWEINITZ) POUZAR

465

The Spruce Tooth, sometimes called the Violet Tooth, is one of a group of species collectively known as the tooth fungi. They include members of the genera *Bankera*, *Hydnellum*, *Phellodon*, and *Sarcodon*, many of which are mycorrhizal with conifers, some with broadleaf trees. In parts of Europe they are of conservation concern, mainly as a result of habitat loss or degradation. Like all *Bankera* species, the Spruce Tooth has a very strong smell of curry when dried, which can permeate an herbarium collection and last for decades. *Bankera violascens* with its purplish tones and distinctive habitat and smell is relatively easy to distinguish.

SIMILAR SPECIES
There are a number of medium to large cap-and-stem fungi with spines, but most are brown-spored. Those with white spores like *Bankera violascens* include *Phellodon* and *Hydnum* species. *Phellodon* species have zoned flesh when cut, while *Hydnum* species are softer and more crumbly. *Bankera fuligineoalba* is more whitish and only occurs with pines.

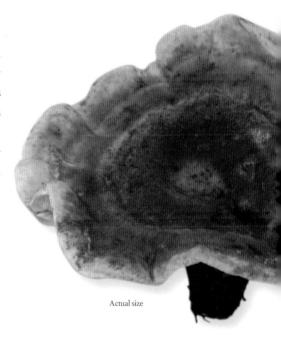

Actual size

The Spruce Tooth has a smooth, then scaly, irregularly lobed cap, which is whitish at first becoming purplish brown with age. The spines below are whitish to gray and ¼ in (6 mm) long (see photo left). The stem is brownish purple, though white at the very top, and normally tapers to the base. The flesh is tinted lilac in the cap, and darker purplish brown in the stem.

FAMILY	Pterulaceae
DISTRIBUTION	Africa, Central and South America, southern Asia
HABITAT	In woodland
ASSOCIATION	With broadleaf trees
GROWTH FORM	On wood
ABUNDANCE	Occasional
SPORE COLOR	White
EDIBILITY	Not edible

HEIGHT
Up to 1 in
(25 mm)

DIAMETER
Up to 1 in
(25 mm)

466

DEFLEXULA SUBSIMPLEX
PENDANT CORAL
(HENNINGS) CORNER

Originally described from Brazil, the Pendant Coral is a species of both the new and old world tropics. Fruitbodies may be simple or slightly branched, but always hang downward on trunks or logs. Though individually they may be small, they tend to grow in troops, making them more conspicuous. *Deflexula* species closely resemble species of *Pterula*, to which they are related, the only real difference being their pendant, rather than upright, habit. Fruitbodies may look delicate and fragile, but they contain thick-walled hyphae and are actually quite tough.

SIMILAR SPECIES

Several similar species occur in the tropics, but they are best distinguished microscopically. *Deflexula fascicularis* is a southern Asian species that extends beyond the tropics into Japan, Australia, and New Zealand. *Mucronella* species are also pendant, but have much softer, white to yellow fruitbodies.

The Pendant Coral typically produces a cluster of pendant spines arising from a thin disc attached to wood. The spines are narrow, simple or weakly branched, tapering toward the tips, and whitish to buff, sometimes with flesh-pink tints.

Actual size

FAMILY	Hericiaceae
DISTRIBUTION	North America, Europe, northern Asia
HABITAT	In broadleaf woodland
ASSOCIATION	On fallen and dead standing beech, ash, and birch
GROWTH FORM	Singly or in tiered groups
ABUNDANCE	Rare
SPORE COLOR	White
EDIBILITY	Edible, but too rare to collect from the wild

HEIGHT
Up to 16 in
(400 mm)

DIAMETER
Up to 10 in
(250 mm)

HERICIUM CORALLOIDES
CORAL TOOTH
(SCOPOLI) PERSOON

467

The Coral Tooth—also known as the Comb Tooth—is one of the few highly prized, edible fungi in commercial production, thus considerably reducing pressures on increasingly rare, wild populations. It can be grown on sterile hardwood sawdust, often supplemented with rice bran, in wide-mouthed, plastic bottles. It is particularly prized in Asia, where its medicinal attributes are promoted and it can be bought gift-wrapped in flamboyant packages. Like a spectacular marine coral with its elegant spines, it is one of eight or so species of *Hericium* known globally.

SIMILAR SPECIES

In eastern North America *Hericium americanum* grows on broadleaf trees including maple, and occasionally on conifers. It has longer spines arranged in clusters on the ends of branches, rather than comblike below the branches, and also has larger spores. *Hericium alpestre* and *H. abietis* are also similar, but the former is only found on fir trees in central Europe, the latter on conifers in western North America.

Actual size

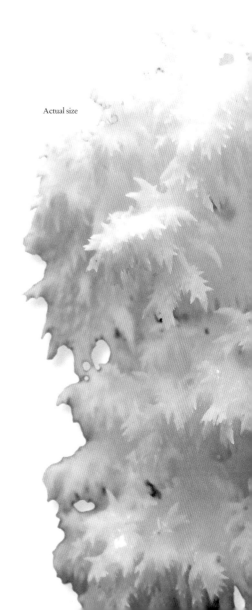

The Coral Tooth forms a shelflike clump of ramifying, creamy white branches emerging from a fleshy, lateral base. White, pointed spines up to ½ in (10 mm) long hang below these branches. The white flesh is soft but brittle, becoming pinkish beige to brown with age. It tastes and smells pleasant.

FAMILY	Hericiaceae
DISTRIBUTION	North America, Europe, northern Asia
HABITAT	In broadleaf woodland
ASSOCIATION	Especially with older beech, maple, and oak
GROWTH FORM	On cut or fallen logs or high up in standing trees
ABUNDANCE	Occasional
SPORE COLOR	White
EDIBILITY	Edible, but too rare to collect from the wild

HEIGHT
Up to 8 in
(200 mm)

DIAMETER
Up to 12 in
(300 mm)

468

HERICIUM ERINACEUS
LION'S MANE
(BULLIARD) PERSOON

Actual size

The Lion's Mane—or Bearded Tooth—is an important commercially grown gourmet species with a sweet flavor like lobster. It is especially popular in Asia where it is marketed as Monkey Head and grown on a variety of substrates, including cotton waste and sugar cane culms packed in huge polypropylene bags. It is under scrutiny for a range of medicinal properties from cancer inhibition to enhancing the immune system, is taken in pill form for gastric ulcers, and is even available as a canned tonic drink. In Europe it is rare in the wild, on Red Lists in 23 countries and proposed for international protection under the Bern Convention.

SIMILAR SPECIES

Other *Hericium* species are soft-fleshed with a spiny appearance, but all are branched, rather than forming a single ball-like cluster, and none has such remarkably long spines. Another large spiny bracket fungus growing on broadleaf trees is *Climacodon septentrionalis* but this has a tough fibrous texture, shelflike layers with short spines, and flesh that is clearly zoned when cut.

The Lion's Mane forms a spectacular whitish cushion of tiered clusters of pendant spines or teeth, which can be as long as 3 in (80 mm), and look very like a beard or mane. The fruitbody is soft and white when young, sometimes with flesh-colored tints, becoming yellowish, then dirty brown when bruised or with age. It is normally broadly attached to the tree, with at most only a rudimentary stem.

FAMILY	Bankeraceae
DISTRIBUTION	North America, Europe, northern Asia
HABITAT	In woodland
ASSOCIATION	Ectomycorrhizal, mainly with conifers and occasionally broadleaf trees
GROWTH FORM	On ground, singly or in groups, often fused
ABUNDANCE	Occasional
SPORE COLOR	Brown
EDIBILITY	Not edible

HEIGHT
Up to 1½ in
(40 mm)

CAP DIAMETER
Up to 5 in
(125 mm)

HYDNELLUM CAERULEUM
BLUE TOOTH
(HORNEMANN) P. KARSTEN

469

The Blue Tooth is a fairly hard, fibrous fungus, rendering it inedible despite its pleasant mealy smell. It has been used traditionally for dyeing silk and wool both in North America and Scandinavia, providing a range of colors including tan, blue, and dark forest-green depending on the mordants (fixatives)used. More recently it has been investigated for its potential as a cancer inhibitor. In Europe, the Blue Tooth and related species of *Hydnellum*, *Bankera*, *Phellodon*, and *Sarcodon* are causing increased conservation concern, their decline being linked to airborne nitrogen eutrophication (an increase in soil nutrients) to which they may be particularly sensitive.

SIMILAR SPECIES
Hydnellum suaveolens has blue tones when young but these occur in both the stem and the cap, and it has a distinctive sweet smell a little like aniseed. Another blue *Hydnellum* species is *H. regium*, which occurs in western North America and is a dark violaceous black with brownish spines and a notably fragrant smell.

Actual size

The Blue Tooth has beautiful bright blue to blue-gray tones in the cap when young, contrasting with the white spines underneath and the orange-brown stem. The cap is velvety and lumpy, and like all *Hydnellum* species can engulf debris and fuse with adjacent fruitbodies. It becomes dull with age, but, when cut, the flesh remains bluish in the cap and orange in the stem.

FAMILY	Bankeraceae
DISTRIBUTION	North America, Europe
HABITAT	In woodland
ASSOCIATION	Ectomycorrhizal, with conifers, especially pine and spruce
GROWTH FORM	On ground, singly or in small groups
ABUNDANCE	Occasional
SPORE COLOR	Brown
EDIBILITY	Not edible

HEIGHT
Up to 2 in
(50 mm)

CAP DIAMETER
Up to 5 in
(120 mm)

470

HYDNELLUM PECKII
DEVIL'S TOOTH
BANKER

The Devil's Tooth takes its common name from the macabre appearance of bloodlike droplets that ooze from it and that also led to its former scientific name of *Hydnellum diabolus*. Now, however, this exudate has proved to be not only benign, but beneficial since it contains an anticoagulant atromentin and has also shown antibacterial properties. Traditionally the Devil's Tooth has been used for dyeing, producing a range of grays, browns, olives, and greens. But, as with other tooth fungi, it is better not to collect it since it is now of conservation concern and declining, probably as a result of atmospheric nitrogen pollution.

SIMILAR SPECIES

Some other *Hydnellum* species can also exude reddish brown droplets. However, both *H. ferrugineum*, found mainly with conifers, and *H. spongiosipes*, found with broadleaf trees, smell distinctly mealy and have a mild taste. The Blushing Rosette (*Abortiporus biennis*) can also "bleed" in damp conditions, but has pores not teeth underneath.

Actual size

The Devil's Tooth is whitish and velvety when young, with a flattened, funnel-shaped fruitbody that is corky and becomes furrowed with age. The cap gradually turns brown to reddish brown. The short spines or teeth are whitish, becoming the color of red wine, and there is a short, tapering, velvety stem. The flesh is pinkish brown with darker zones, and smells sweetly resinous but with an acrid taste.

FAMILY	Hydnaceae
DISTRIBUTION	North America, Europe, northern Asia, Australia
HABITAT	In woodland
ASSOCIATION	Ectomycorrhizal, with broadleaf trees and conifers
GROWTH FORM	On ground, singly or in troops
ABUNDANCE	Common
SPORE COLOR	White
EDIBILITY	Edible

HEIGHT
Up to 4 in
(100 mm)

CAP DIAMETER
Up to 6 in
(150 mm)

HYDNUM REPANDUM

WOOD HEDGEHOG

LINNAEUS

471

The Wood Hedgehog is easily recognized by its chunky fruitbodies with pale caps and teeth or spines on the underside. Most other ground-dwelling, toothed fungi belong in the Thelephoraceae and tend to be uncommon or even endangered, but the Wood Hedgehog is a distant relative of the Chanterelle (*Cantharellus cibarius*) and is not only common, but edible. It is collected on a commercial scale in Europe, and is usually marketed under its French name, Pied-de-Mouton. In parts of North America the Wood Hedgehog is called the Sweet Tooth, even though it is sometimes said to have a bitter taste.

SIMILAR SPECIES

In Europe, the Terracotta Hedgehog (*Hydnum rufescens*) is similar, but slimmer and more strongly colored (pale reddish buff). In North America, the White Hedgehog (*H. albidum*) is white to pale yellowish gray, bruising yellow to orange, while the Giant Hedgehog (*H. albomagnum*) is pale and very large.

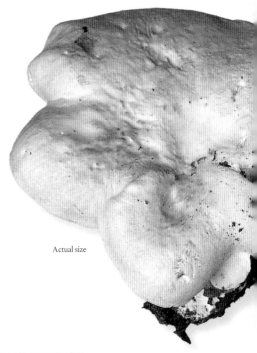

Actual size

The Wood Hedgehog forms caps that are convex, becoming irregularly flat to depressed. The surface of the cap is smooth, velvety, often irregular, lobed, or split, cream to pale pinkish buff. The undersurface is toothed or spiny, and cap-colored (see photo left). The stem is central or excentric, smooth but often irregular (see photo left), and pale cap-colored.

FAMILY	Clavariaceae
DISTRIBUTION	North America, Europe, North Africa, South America, northern Asia, New Zealand
HABITAT	In woodland
ASSOCIATION	With broadleaf trees and conifers
GROWTH FORM	On stumps and fallen wood
ABUNDANCE	Common
SPORE COLOR	White
EDIBILITY	Not edible

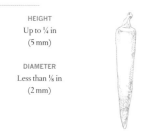

HEIGHT
Up to ¼ in
(5 mm)

DIAMETER
Less than ⅛ in
(2 mm)

472

MUCRONELLA CALVA
SWARMING SPINE
(ALBERTINI & SCHWEINITZ) FRIES

The Swarming Spine is a common and widespread species, particularly on the undersides of rotten logs and fallen branches, but occasionally running down the sides of old stumps. It makes up for its small size by frequently growing in large swarms that sometimes resemble continuous sheets—though a closer look reveals that the spines emerge from the wood individually and are not visibly connected. Occasionally it grows in small, or more scattered, groups, and is then a lot more difficult to find.

SIMILAR SPECIES
The Icicle Spine (*Mucronella pendula*) is rather larger and has a distinct stem. Other smallish, white to yellow *Mucronella* species, however, are difficult to distinguish—to the extent that it is not clear if many of them are really separate species, or just variations of the Swarming Spine.

The Swarming Spine typically produces single, pendant spines in dense swarms. The spines are simple, sometimes with an inconspicuous stem, and taper to a point. They are soft, fleshy, white to yellow, and easily detached from the surface.

Actual size

FAMILY	Clavariaceae
DISTRIBUTION	Western North America, Australia, New Zealand
HABITAT	In woodland
ASSOCIATION	With conifers
GROWTH FORM	On wood
ABUNDANCE	Occasional
SPORE COLOR	White
EDIBILITY	Not edible

HEIGHT
Up to ½ in
(10 mm)

DIAMETER
Up to ⅛ in
(3 mm)

MUCRONELLA PENDULA

ICICLE SPINE

(MASSEE) R. H. PETERSEN

473

The Icicle Spine is easily missed since it is by no means a large
fungus and occurs half-hidden on the underside of logs and
fallen trunks. Though fruitbodies appear singly, more rarely in
twos and threes, they usually occur in dense or scattered groups
which may make them a little easier to spot. The Icicle Spine was
originally described from Tasmania, but is also known from
New Zealand and western North America, where it is said to
grow principally or exclusively on conifers.

SIMILAR SPECIES

Most other *Mucronella* species, such as *M. calva*, lack a distinct
stem. In appearance, the Icicle Spine is much closer to unrelated
species of *Gloeomucro*—some of which occur in eastern North
America—and was at one time placed in the same genus as them.
Fruitbodies of *Gloeomucro* species have a distinctly gelatinous
texture, however, besides differing microscopically.

Actual size

The Icicle Spine typically produces single, pendant spines with a small,
but distinct, stem. The spines are simple, cone-like and tapering to a point,
whitish, but becoming watery yellowish with age. The stem is gelatinous,
but firm, and pale ocher to yellowish.

FAMILY	Bankeraceae
DISTRIBUTION	North America, Europe, northern Asia
HABITAT	In woodland
ASSOCIATION	Ectomycorrhizal, with conifers and broadleaf trees
GROWTH FORM	On ground, often in coalescing groups
ABUNDANCE	Occasional
SPORE COLOR	White
EDIBILITY	Not edible

HEIGHT
Up to 1½ in
(40 mm)

CAP DIAMETER
Up to 2 in
(50 mm)

PHELLODON NIGER
BLACK TOOTH
(FRIES) P. KARSTEN

474

Phellodon species are related to *Bankera* and have the same distinctive smell of fenugreek or curry powder when dried. They differ from *Bankera* in having caps that grow indeterminately outward as the fruitbodies mature, often engulfing twigs and leaves, and coalescing with caps of neighboring fruitbodies. A troop of Black Tooth can therefore look like one big, irregular cap with a lot of separate stems. They are generally not common and are considered to be endangered in many parts of the world. Traditionally fruitbodies have been used in small quantity for craft-dyeing, producing gray-blues and green tones.

SIMILAR SPECIES

Molecular research has recently shown the Black Tooth to be a complex of closely related species, not yet fully distinguished. A less closely related species, *Phellodon melaleucus*, can become gray to black, but is separated by having a smooth stem. *Hydnellum* species are similarly shaped, but have brown spores, rarely have blackish fruitbodies, and lack the spicy smell.

Actual size

The Black Tooth forms tough, corky, irregular fruitbodies that frequently coalesce. Its finely hairy cap becomes flat to slightly funnel-shaped. It is white at first, then darkens from the center to become brownish gray to black, but retains a white margin. The undersurface is gray and toothed, the stem is finely hairy, and similarly colored to the cap.

FAMILY	Bankeraceae
DISTRIBUTION	North America, continental Europe, northern Asia
HABITAT	In woodland
ASSOCIATION	Ectomycorrhizal, with spruce
GROWTH FORM	On ground among roots
ABUNDANCE	Locally common
SPORE COLOR	Brown
EDIBILITY	Edible

HEIGHT
Up to 4 in
(100 mm)

CAP DIAMETER
Up to 12 in
(300 mm)

SARCODON IMBRICATUS

SCALY TOOTH

(LINNAEUS) P. KARSTEN

475

Many different fungi have long been used for dyes, and the Scaly Tooth has been especially valued for its greenish blue pigment. It was said, however, that collections from pine woods were best for dyeing, while gatherers of edible species preferred spruce collections. This prompted some molecular research, which has now cleared up this minor mystery. It appears that there are two closely related species: *Sarcodon imbricatus* with spruce and *S. squamosus* with pine. As an edible fungus, the Scaly Tooth is particularly popular in Tibet where it is collected in large numbers and sold in markets, as well as exported to China.

SIMILAR SPECIES

As noted above, the closely related *Sarcodon squamosus* is associated with pine tree rather than spruce. It has a darker cap with a center that is rarely depressed and a margin that remains incurved. The spines below are often slightly decurrent and grayish or bluish gray. *Sarcodon scabrosus*, mainly with broadleaf trees, has a bluish stem base and a bitter taste.

The Scaly Tooth forms large fleshy fruitbodies with very scaly, brown caps that are typically depressed at the center, sometimes becoming almost funnel-shaped with age. The dense spines on the underside are whitish when young, becoming brown to grayish brown. The solid stem is brownish, and the flesh throughout is white to cream.

Actual size

FAMILY	Cantharellaceae
DISTRIBUTION	North America, Europe, Africa, Central America, northern Asia
HABITAT	In woodland
ASSOCIATION	Ectomycorrhizal with broadleaf trees and conifers
GROWTH FORM	On ground, in troops
ABUNDANCE	Common
SPORE COLOR	White
EDIBILITY	Edible

HEIGHT
Up to 4 in
(100 mm)

CAP DIAMETER
Up to 5 in
(125 mm)

476

CANTHARELLUS CIBARIUS
CHANTERELLE
FRIES

The Chanterelle, also known as the Golden Chanterelle, is one of the best-known and most highly prized edible fungi. Fortunately it is a common species, since it is collected on a commercial scale in many northern countries and exported worldwide. All *Cantharellus* and *Craterellus* species are collectively known as chanterelles, so other species are sometimes marketed under this name. There is even a thriving trade in collecting African species, such as the reddish *Cantharellus miniatescens*, for export to European markets. In North America, several species previously thought to be *C. cibarius* are now known to be distinct—but all are equally edible.

SIMILAR SPECIES
In North America, the Pacific Golden Chanterelle (*Cantharellus formosus*) is one of several look-alike species—all edible. In Europe, the rare Orange Chanterelle (*C. friesii*) is smaller, with a more orange cap and pink-tinted undersurface. The False Chanterelle (*Hygrophoropsis aurantiaca*) is also orange, but has true, thin gills on the undersurface.

Actual size

The Chanterelle has caps that are convex at first, becoming depressed or funnel-shaped. The cap surface is smooth, with a wavy or lobed margin, egg-yolk-yellow to ocher. The undersurface has thick, decurrent, gill-like ridges that are cap-colored (see photo left). The stem is smooth and cap-colored, but sometimes whitish at the base.

FAMILY	Cantharellaceae
DISTRIBUTION	Eastern North America, Central America, northern Asia
HABITAT	In woodland
ASSOCIATION	Ectomycorrhizal, with broadleaf trees
GROWTH FORM	On ground, in troops
ABUNDANCE	Common
SPORE COLOR	White
EDIBILITY	Edible

HEIGHT
Up to 3 in
(75 mm)

CAP DIAMETER
Up to 3 in
(75 mm)

CANTHARELLUS CINNABARINUS

CINNABAR CHANTERELLE

(SCHWEINITZ) SCHWEINITZ

477

The eye-catching color of the Cinnabar Chanterelle makes it
one of the most attractive species in the group, especially when
growing in large troops in woodland litter. Individual fruitbodies
are small, however, and though edible are not collected on
a commercial scale. *Cantharellus cinnabarinus* was first described
from North Carolina by the pioneering American mycologist
Lewis David von Schweinitz. It is widespread in eastern North
America and the Caribbean, as well as in China and east Asia.
Its colorful fruitbodies have featured on postage stamps from
Canada and several Caribbean nations.

SIMILAR SPECIES

The size and color of the Cinnabar Chanterelle should make
it easy to distinguish within its geographic range. A similarly
colored species, *Cantharellus concinnus*, occurs in Australia and
was once thought to be a variety of *C. cinnabarinus*. Several
red chanterelles, including the commercially harvested
C. miniatescens, occur in central Africa.

Actual size

The Cinnabar Chanterelle has caps that are convex at first,
becoming depressed or funnel-shaped (see photo left).
The cap surface is smooth, with a wavy or lobed margin,
deep coral-pink to orange-red or red. The undersurface
has thick, decurrent, gill-like ridges that are pale cap-
colored. The stem is smooth and cap-colored but
sometimes whitish at the base.

FAMILY	Cantharellaceae
DISTRIBUTION	Eastern North America, Central America
HABITAT	In woodland
ASSOCIATION	Ectomycorrhizal, with broadleaf trees and conifers
GROWTH FORM	On ground, in troops
ABUNDANCE	Common
SPORE COLOR	Pale salmon-pink
EDIBILITY	Edible

HEIGHT
Up to 3 in
(75 mm)

CAP DIAMETER
Up to 2 in
(50 mm)

478

CANTHARELLUS IGNICOLOR
FLAME CHANTERELLE
R. H. PETERSEN

Though one of the smaller species in the group, the Flame Chanterelle's conspicuous yellow-orange colors more than make up for its size. *Cantharellus ignicolor* (the epithet means "flame-colored") was first described from Tennessee, but is widespread in eastern North America and as far south as Costa Rica. Recent DNA research suggests it may be better placed in the related genus *Craterellus*, alongside the Trumpet Chanterelle (*C. tubaeformis*). As well as being edible, fruitbodies of the Flame Chanterelle are used in craft-dyeing, producing a range of yellow colors.

SIMILAR SPECIES

The Small Chanterelle (*Cantharellus minor*) also occurs in eastern North America and is similarly colored, but somewhat smaller and with a smooth not scurfy cap. The widespread true Chanterelle (*C. cibarius*) is a larger, chunkier species that has a solid stem.

Actual size

The Flame Chanterelle has caps that are convex at first, becoming depressed or funnel-shaped. The cap surface is finely scurfy, with a wavy margin, yellow-orange to orange, becoming dull yellow with age. The undersurface has decurrent, gill-like ridges that are cap-colored (see photo near left) but develop pink tints with age. The stem is smooth, cap-colored, and hollow.

FAMILY	Cantharellaceae
DISTRIBUTION	Europe
HABITAT	In woodland
ASSOCIATION	Ectomycorrhizal, with broadleaf trees
GROWTH FORM	On ground, in troops
ABUNDANCE	Rare
SPORE COLOR	Cream
EDIBILITY	Edible, but too rare to collect from the wild

HEIGHT
Up to 4 in
(100 mm)

CAP DIAMETER
Up to 4 in
(100 mm)

CANTHARELLUS MELANOXEROS

BLACKENING CHANTERELLE

DESMAZIÈRES

479

The Blackening Chanterelle's color change when bruised, together with its ocher and lilac color combinations, should make it a fairly easy species to identify—if you are fortunate enough to find any fruitbodies. The species is restricted to Europe, where it is widespread (mainly in the west) but distinctly rare. It features on the national Red Lists of threatened fungal species in at least nine countries and is also one of 33 fungal species proposed for international protection under the provisions of the Bern Convention.

SIMILAR SPECIES

The Chanterelle (*Cantharellus cibarius*) is similar in shape, and is also yellow to ocher, but lacks any pink or violet tints on the undersurface. The uncommon Amethyst Chanterelle (*C. amethysteus*) has lilac tints in the cap, but not on the undersurface. Neither blackens when bruised.

Actual size

The Blackening Chanterelle has caps that are convex at first, becoming depressed or funnel-shaped. The cap surface is scurfy to fibrous, with a wavy margin, pale dull yellow to ocher, sometimes flushed lilac. The undersurface has decurrent, gill-like ridges that are lilac-pink to pale gray-violet. The stem is smooth, deep yellow or cap-colored. All parts blacken slowly on bruising.

FAMILY	Cantharellaceae
DISTRIBUTION	North America, Europe, Central America, northern Asia
HABITAT	In mossy woodland
ASSOCIATION	Ectomycorrhizal, with broadleaf trees and conifers
GROWTH FORM	On ground, in clusters or troops
ABUNDANCE	Common
SPORE COLOR	White
EDIBILITY	Edible

HEIGHT
Up to 4 in
(100 mm)

CAP DIAMETER
Up to 3 in
(75 mm)

480

CRATERELLUS CORNUCOPIOIDES
HORN OF PLENTY
(LINNAEUS) PERSOON

The French call this species *trompette de la mort* (death trumpet), a sinister name for such a highly prized, edible fungus. It was once collected in England and sold at Covent Garden Market in London—a rare compliment in the days when the English were deeply suspicious of "poisonous toadstools." The shape of the fruitbodies is rather unusual, since they are hollow—like the cornucopia or Horn of Plenty after which they are named—and thin-fleshed. The funereal colors make the fruitbodies hard to spot, but once found they often occur in large clusters and troops.

SIMILAR SPECIES

In North and Central America, the Black Trumpet (*Craterellus fallax*) is a locally common, closely related species—recently shown by DNA analysis to be distinct—with salmon-buff spores that color the undersurface of older fruitbodies. The Fragrant Black Trumpet (*C. foetidus*) has a veined undersurface and a sweetish aroma.

The Horn of Plenty forms thin-fleshed caps that are funnel- or trumpet-shaped. The surface is felty to scurfy-scaly, with a deeply incurved margin, and gray-brown to black (rarely yellow). The center is typically hollow. The decurrent underside is smooth to slightly wrinkled, and brown to gray or cap-colored. The hollow stem is smooth and cap-colored.

Actual size

FAMILY	Cantharellaceae
DISTRIBUTION	North America, Europe, northern Asia
HABITAT	In woodland
ASSOCIATION	Ectomycorrhizal, with broadleaf and conifer trees
GROWTH FORM	On ground, in troops
ABUNDANCE	Common
SPORE COLOR	White
EDIBILITY	Edible

HEIGHT
Up to 3 in
(80 mm)

CAP DIAMETER
Up to 2½ in
(60 mm)

CRATERELLUS TUBAEFORMIS
TRUMPET CHANTERELLE
(FRIES) QUÉLET

481

The Latin epithet *tubaeformis* means "trumpet-shaped" which well describes this hollow chanterelle. It is a good edible species that grows late in the season, giving it the alternative names of Autumn Chanterelle or Winter Chanterelle. It often appears in large troops, typically (but not exclusively) in conifer woodland. Since it is ectomycorrhizal, it cannot be grown commercially, but has to be collected from the wild. This in part explains the high prices charged for "fresh" specimens in supermarkets and delicatessens.

SIMILAR SPECIES

A similar and frequently confused species is *Craterellus lutescens*, which differs in having an undersurface that is yellow and smooth to weakly veined. It is equally edible, but possibly less common. The related *C. cornucopioides* is also trumpet-shaped, but entirely black with a smooth undersurface.

The Trumpet Chanterelle has a funnel- or trumpet-shaped cap that is thin-fleshed, smooth at first, becoming slightly scaly, and variously yellow-brown to olive- or gray-brown. The margin is wavy and the center is often hollow. The underside has thick, decurrent, gill-like ridges, pale yellow at first, becoming pale gray. The hollow stem is smooth but often grooved or compressed, yellow to tawny.

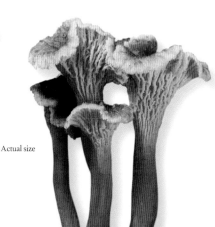

Actual size

FAMILY	Gomphaceae
DISTRIBUTION	North America, Europe, Central America, northern Asia
HABITAT	In woodland
ASSOCIATION	Ectomycorrhizal, with conifers, more rarely broadleaf trees, especially beech
GROWTH FORM	On ground, singly or in troops
ABUNDANCE	Locally common
SPORE COLOR	Ocher-brown
EDIBILITY	Edible

HEIGHT
Up to 7 in
(175 mm)

CAP DIAMETER
Up to 6 in
(150 mm)

482

GOMPHUS CLAVATUS
PIG'S EAR
(PERSOON) GRAY

The English name of the Pig's Ear seems rather unfair to what is quite an attractive and unusual-looking fungus. The species is locally common in parts of North America and in a few areas of central Europe, but is rare and of conservation concern elsewhere in Europe. It is one of the fungi proposed for international conservation under the Bern Convention. In the British Isles it is believed to be extinct, not having been seen in its former beechwood localities for more than 80 years. Where it is common, it is considered a good edible species—though rather prone to maggots.

SIMILAR SPECIES

If it is a separate species, *Gomphus crassipes*—known from Spain and North Africa—can be distinguished only microscopically. Some *Cantharellus* and *Craterellus* species also have violet tints, but most are much smaller than *G. clavatus* and have white, rather than ocher-brown, spores.

Actual size

The Pig's Ear frequently produces several caps from a single stem. The cap is flat to depressed or funnel-shaped, smooth, finely velvety, ocher to pale tan, often with violet tints. The undersurface is strongly wrinkled and violet-pink to violet, becoming violet-brown. The short stem is smooth, violet to brown.

FAMILY	Gomphaceae
DISTRIBUTION	North America, Asia
HABITAT	In woodland
ASSOCIATION	Ectomycorrhizal, with conifers
GROWTH FORM	On ground, singly or in troops
ABUNDANCE	Locally common
SPORE COLOR	Ocher-brown
EDIBILITY	Edible, but can cause gastric upsets

HEIGHT
Up to 8 in
(200 mm)

CAP DIAMETER
Up to 6 in
(150 mm)

GOMPHUS FLOCCOSUS
WOOLLY CHANTERELLE
(SCHWEINITZ) SINGER

483

Though its common name is the Woolly or Scaly Chanterelle, this attractive species is not a true chanterelle, but has ocher-brown spores and is more closely related to coral fungi in the genus *Ramaria*. It is even more unlike the true chanterelles in being a species to avoid in terms of edibility, since it contains an enzyme-blocking acid: in susceptible individuals it can cause nausea and gastrointestinal upsets after 8–14 hours. Others appear to be able to eat it with impunity and the Woolly Chanterelle is said to be relished by the Khasi peoples of northeastern India.

SIMILAR SPECIES

In western North America, *Gomphus kauffmanii* is a similar but larger species with very scaly, pale orange to pale brown caps. It also causes gastric upset in some. *Gomphus flabellatus* from Japan and Southeast Asia is also similar, but much smaller. The Japanese *G. fujisanensis* is best distinguished microscopically by its smaller spores.

The Woolly Chanterelle is almost cylindrical when young, but gradually expands to become deeply, and then more shallowly, funnel-shaped. The cap is bright orange or orange-red at first, turning darker with age, smooth then finely scaly. The undersurface is yellow-cream then buff, densely veined and wrinkled, running almost to the base of the fruitbody.

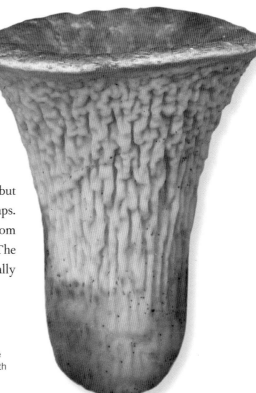

Actual size

FAMILY	Repetobasidiaceae
DISTRIBUTION	North America, continental Europe, northern Asia
HABITAT	In woodland
ASSOCIATION	With conifers
GROWTH FORM	On ground, in dense clusters or troops
ABUNDANCE	Locally common
SPORE COLOR	White
EDIBILITY	Said to be edible

HEIGHT
Up to 6 in
(150 mm)

DIAMETER
Up to ⅜ in
(8 mm)

484

ALLOCLAVARIA PURPUREA
PURPLE SPINDLES
(O. F. MÜLLER) DENTINGER & D. J. MCLAUGHLIN

This species is unusual among the larger club fungi since it grows in conifer woods, and also has some microscopic features not found in other species. Recent molecular research has discovered why. It seems that the Purple Spindles—also known as the Purple Fairy Club—is not remotely related to other club fungi, but belongs in the same order as the little Orange Mosscap agaric (*Rickenella fibula*) and the large Shaggy Bracket (*Inonotus hispidus*). It may also prove to be an ectomycorrhizal species, forming an association with the living roots of conifers.

SIMILAR SPECIES

The Purple Spindles has frequently been confused with *Clavaria incarnata*, a club fungus normally found singly or in small groups in grassland. The latter is usually dull pink, but sometimes has wine-colored tints and is microscopically distinct. *Clavaria fumosa* grows in clusters in grassland and is usually a very pale, smoky gray-brown, but can also develop additional pale pinkish or purplish tints.

Actual size

The Purple Spindles has smooth to wrinkled, tubular or slightly flattened, unbranched fruitbodies with pointed tips. They normally grow gregariously in clusters or dense troops. As the name suggests, they are typically deep or dull purple, fading to purplish gray or brown.

FAMILY	Auriscalpiaceae
DISTRIBUTION	North America, continental Europe, Central America, northern Asia
HABITAT	In woodland
ASSOCIATION	On broadleaf wood
GROWTH FORM	On logs and fallen trunks
ABUNDANCE	Locally common
SPORE COLOR	White
EDIBILITY	Edible, but can cause gastric upsets

HEIGHT
Up to 5 in
(125 mm)

DIAMETER
Up to 4 in
(100 mm)

ARTOMYCES PYXIDATUS

CANDELABRA CORAL

(PERSOON) JÜLICH

485

This attractive species, previously known as *Clavicorona pyxidata*, is locally common in some parts of North America, but is absent from the west coast and is equally absent from some western parts of Europe, including the British Isles. A recent study has shown that there are three distinct populations, one in Eurasia, one in northeastern North America, and another in southern North America and Central America—but all appear to be the same species. The Candelabra Coral, which has an alternative common name of the Crown Coral, is considered edible by many, but apparently can cause stomach upsets in some people. It has a very hot peppery taste when raw, but this usually disappears on cooking.

SIMILAR SPECIES

The crownlike branch tips and occurrence on wood should distinguish the Candelabra Coral from other coral fungi. Pinkish specimens might resemble *Ramaria stricta*, which also grows on wood, but the latter species is more deeply colored, has simple, pointed branch tips, and is brown-spored.

Actual size

The Candelabra Coral has densely but finely branched fruitbodies, white to yellowish cream, sometimes with a pinkish tint. The crownlike tips of the branches, with several short projections in a circle, are a distinctive feature of the species. The flesh is also whitish and fairly elastic rather than brittle.

FAMILY	Clavariaceae
DISTRIBUTION	North America, Europe, northern Asia, Australia
HABITAT	In unimproved grassland or in woodland litter
ASSOCIATION	With moss and grass or in leaf litter
GROWTH FORM	On ground, usually in dense clusters
ABUNDANCE	Common
SPORE COLOR	White
EDIBILITY	Edible

HEIGHT
Up to 5 in
(120 mm)

DIAMETER
Up to ¼ in
(5 mm)

CLAVARIA FRAGILIS
WHITE SPINDLES
HOLMSKJOLD

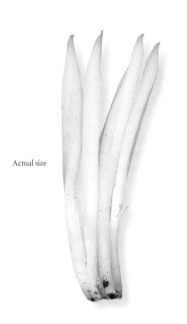

Actual size

The Latin epithet *fragilis* refers to the very brittle fruitbodies that make White Spindles hard to collect without breaking into small pieces. It has an alternative English name of Fairy Fingers. The species was previously known as *Clavaria vermicularis*, the epithet referring to "little worms." In Europe it is normally found in old, unimproved, mossy grassland, but in North America and elsewhere it seems more frequent in mixed woodland. White Spindles is said to be edible, though insubstantial and tasteless.

SIMILAR SPECIES

This species should be distinctive when growing in large clusters. *Clavaria fumosa* has a similar habit, but is pale smoky brown or pinkish brown. *Clavaria rubicundula* is also similar, but is pale pinkish and less widespread. *Clavaria acuta* is white, but smaller and it usually has a distinct, translucent white stem. It never forms large clusters, but grows singly or in small groups.

White Spindles produces smooth, tubular or slightly flattened, unbranched fruitbodies with pointed tips. They normally grow gregariously in large clusters. As the common name indicates, they are white, sometimes yellowing or browning at the tips when old.

FAMILY	Clavariaceae
DISTRIBUTION	North America, Europe, northern Asia
HABITAT	In unimproved grassland or in woodland litter
ASSOCIATION	With moss and grass or in leaf litter
GROWTH FORM	On ground, usually in dense clusters
ABUNDANCE	Common
SPORE COLOR	White
EDIBILITY	Not edible

HEIGHT
Up to 5 in
(120 mm)

DIAMETER
Up to ¼ in
(5 mm)

CLAVARIA FUMOSA

SMOKY SPINDLES

PERSOON

487

Like the closely related White Spindles, *Clavaria fumosa* (the epithet means "smoky") is extremely fragile and falls into pieces unless handled with caution. The smoky color has also led to an alternative English name of the Grayish Fairy Club. In Europe it is considered an indicator species of old, mossy, unimproved grasslands, which are an increasingly endangered habitat. The Smoky Spindles can still be found in traditional pastures which have not been resown or heavily fertilized, but in some intensely farmed areas there are few such places left.

SIMILAR SPECIES

Clavaria fragilis has a similar habit, but is entirely white. *Clavaria rubicundula* is also similar, but is pale pinkish (without the additional smoky brown tints of *C. fumosa*) and is restricted to North America and New Zealand. *Clavulinopsis umbrinella* can be similarly smoky brown and grows in similar habitats, but is a branched species.

The Smoky Spindles has smooth, tubular or slightly flattened, unbranched fruitbodies with pointed tips. They normally grow gregariously in large clusters, and are a pale brownish gray, sometimes with additional pinkish or purplish tints, becoming dark brown to black when old.

Actual size

FAMILY	Clavariaceae
DISTRIBUTION	Africa, southern Asia, Australia, New Zealand
HABITAT	In woodland
ASSOCIATION	In moss and leaf litter
GROWTH FORM	On ground, usually in troops
ABUNDANCE	Common
SPORE COLOR	White
EDIBILITY	Not edible

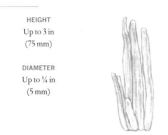

HEIGHT
Up to 3 in
(75 mm)

DIAMETER
Up to ¼ in
(5 mm)

488

CLAVARIA PHOENICEA
SUNSET SPINDLES
ZOLLINGER & MORITZI

Originally described from Java, the Sunset Spindles' bright pink, red, and orange shades make it an eye-catching species, even when half-hidden among forest litter and moss. Scarlet and carmine specimens are most likely to be found in tropical Africa and Asia. In Australia and New Zealand collections are more apricot-orange to bright pink-orange and have been referred to a separate variety (*Clavaria phoenicea* var. *persicina*). DNA research will be needed to see whether the Sunset Spindles is a single, variable species or a mix of close relatives.

SIMILAR SPECIES
Clavaria miniata is a handsome, bright red species described from South Africa and occurring in Australia, where it has been called the Flame Fungus. In North America, the Orange Spindles (*Clavulinopsis aurantiocinnabarina*) looks very similar to the orange variety of *Clavaria phoenicea*, but is microscopically distinct from it.

The Sunset Spindles produces smooth, tubular or slightly flattened, unbranched fruitbodies with pointed tips and an indistinct stem. They are deep coral pink to bright red (pink-orange or apricot in var. *persicina*), paler toward the base.

Actual size

FAMILY	Clavariaceae
DISTRIBUTION	North America, Europe, northern Asia
HABITAT	In unimproved, calcareous grassland or in woodland litter
ASSOCIATION	With moss and grass or leaf litter
GROWTH FORM	On ground, singly or in small clusters
ABUNDANCE	Occasional to rare
SPORE COLOR	White
EDIBILITY	Not edible

HEIGHT
Up to 2 in
(50 mm)

DIAMETER
Up to ¼ in
(5 mm)

CLAVARIA ROSEA

ROSE SPINDLES

FRIES

489

Though widespread throughout the north temperate region, this brightly colored species is distinctly rare and appears on the national Red Lists of threatened fungal species in several European and Asian countries. As with many other club fungi, it is typically found in old, unimproved, mossy grassland in Europe but often appears in late summer—rather earlier than most other grassland species. Elsewhere, it may be more frequent in mossy woodland. It tends to grow in small groups, rather than the big clusters that are typical of White Spindles (*Clavaria fragilis*) and Smoky Spindles (*C. fumosa*).

SIMILAR SPECIES

The species has frequently been confused with the commoner but duller Pink Spindles (*Clavaria incarnata*) which has flesh-colored to pinkish fruitbodies and differs microscopically. In North America and New Zealand, *C. rubicundula* is another, rather commoner, pale pink species often found in clusters.

Actual size

Rose Spindles produces smooth, tubular or flattened, unbranched fruitbodies that have pointed tips and an indistinct stem. They are bright rose-pink, paler or whitish toward the base. The flesh is hollow and very fragile.

FAMILY	Clavariaceae
DISTRIBUTION	North America, Europe, Asia, Australia, New Zealand
HABITAT	In grassland and woodland
ASSOCIATION	Often with mosses in grass and leaf litter
GROWTH FORM	On ground, singly or in small groups
ABUNDANCE	Occasional
SPORE COLOR	White
EDIBILITY	Not edible

HEIGHT
Up to 4 in
(100 mm)

DIAMETER
Up to 2½ in
(60 mm)

490

CLAVARIA ZOLLINGERI
VIOLET CORAL
LÉVEILLE

Most of the larger coral-shaped fungi belong to the brown-spored genus *Ramaria*, but this fine-looking species is white-spored and actually belongs with the club fungi, despite its densely branched shape. In Britain and Europe it is typically found in old, unimproved pasture and lawns, often in the same area as waxcaps (*Hygrocybe* species), and is generally uncommon. Elsewhere, particularly in North America and Australasia, it is a woodland fungus and may be more frequent.

SIMILAR SPECIES
The species has been much confused with *Clavulina amethystina*, an uncommon grayish coral with pinkish or lilac tints, easily distinguished microscopically. The diminutive *Ramariopsis pulchella* is bright violet, but its fruitbodies rarely exceed 1¼ in (30 mm) in height. Several *Ramaria* species have dull violet tints, and the southern European *R. fennica* var. *violacea* is bright violet. All, however, have deep ocher spores.

Actual size

The Violet Coral forms fruitbodies that are repeatedly branched, with each branch being rounded to somewhat flattened, slightly wrinkled, and very brittle. The base of the main stem may be whitish, but otherwise the whole fruitbody is bright violet to purple, though older specimens may fade considerably, becoming first gray and then eventually paling to a sordid yellowish white.

FAMILY	Clavariadelphaceae
DISTRIBUTION	Eastern North America, Europe, North Africa, northern Asia
HABITAT	In calcareous woodland
ASSOCIATION	Ectomycorrhizal, with broadleaf trees, especially beech
GROWTH FORM	On ground, singly or in troops
ABUNDANCE	Common
SPORE COLOR	White
EDIBILITY	Edible

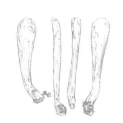

HEIGHT
Up to 12 in
(300 mm)

DIAMETER
Up to 3 in
(75 mm)

CLAVARIADELPHUS PISTILLARIS

GIANT CLUB

(LINNAEUS) DONK

491

The German name for this species is *Herkuleskeule*—Hercules'
Club—and it is certainly one of the largest of the club fungi,
though actually more closely related to species of *Gomphus* than
to most smaller clubs. The Giant Club is principally a species
of beech woodland, forming ectomycorrhiza with the roots of
living trees. It has a pleasant smell but a rather bitter taste, so
although it is edible, it is seldom collected for that purpose. It is
probably of more interest to craft-dyers, who obtain a range of
colors—beige, green, and purple—from its fruitbodies.

SIMILAR SPECIES

In western North America, *Clavariadelphus occidentalis* is a
similar species, but paler and usually associating with conifers.
In eastern North America and Central America, *C. americanus*
is another look-alike, associating with oak and pine. The
widespread *C. truncatus* is also similar, but it has a flattened
or truncated top.

The Giant Club has fruitbodies that are smooth to wrinkled, and as
the name implies, broadly club-shaped. The surface is yellowish to
ocher when young, becoming brown to red-brown or purplish brown
with age, staining dark purple when bruised. The stem is indistinct,
but whitish at the base.

Actual size

FAMILY	Clavulinaceae
DISTRIBUTION	North America, Europe, Central America, northern Asia
HABITAT	In woodland
ASSOCIATION	Ectomycorrhizal, with broadleaf trees
GROWTH FORM	On ground
ABUNDANCE	Very common
SPORE COLOR	White
EDIBILITY	Not edible

HEIGHT
Up to 4 in
(100 mm)

DIAMETER
Up to 4 in
(100 mm)

492

CLAVULINA CORALLOIDES
CRESTED CORAL
(LINNAEUS) J. SCHRÖTER

Actual size

Clavulina species are woodland fungi, forming ectomycorrhizal associations with living tree roots. The Crested Coral is one of the commonest species, though rather variable in color and shape. Older books refer to it as *C. cristata*, the tips of the branches often being "cristate"—feathery or crested—hence the English name. Fruitbodies are quite frequently parasitized by a specialized member of the flask fungi called *Helminthosphaeria clavariarum*. It gradually turns the Crested Coral gray and its own miniature fruitbodies can sometimes be seen under a magnifying lens as small black dots.

SIMILAR SPECIES

The species is difficult to distinguish from the Gray Coral (*Clavulina cinerea*), which is equally common and grows in similar situations. It tends to have more consistently gray fruitbodies without cristate branch tips. The Wrinkled Club (*C. rugosa*) is white, but usually simple or very sparsely branched.

The Crested Coral forms fruitbodies that are repeatedly branched. When young, the branches are dull whitish and crested or feathery at the tips, but with age the branches may become gray-tinted (sometimes as a result of being parasitized) and the tips more rounded. The surface may be smooth or wrinkled, and the white, brittle flesh is normally solid.

FAMILY	Clavariaceae
DISTRIBUTION	North America, Europe, northern Asia
HABITAT	In grassland, more rarely woodland
ASSOCIATION	With moss and grass
GROWTH FORM	On ground, often in scattered troops
ABUNDANCE	Common
SPORE COLOR	White
EDIBILITY	Edible, but best avoided

HEIGHT
Up to 3 in
(80 mm)

DIAMETER
Up to 2 in
(50 mm)

CLAVULINOPSIS CORNICULATA

MEADOW CORAL

(SCHAEFFER) CORNER

493

The Meadow Coral is often a common species in unimproved pastures and lawns, with a particular fondness for very short, rabbit-grazed, coastal turf where it can grow very low and stunted, keeping the same height as the grass. It is also sometimes found in woodlands, where the fruitbodies can be taller and less densely branched. Most related species in *Clavaria* and *Clavulinopsis* produce simple spindle- or club-shaped fruitbodies. It is said to be edible, but is hardly worthwhile, and needs to be carefully distinguished from poisonous *Ramaria* species.

SIMILAR SPECIES

The Meadow Coral is easily mistaken for a species of *Ramaria*, many of which are of similar shape and color. They are rarely found in grassland, however, and have ocher-brown rather than white spores, so can always be distinguished by a spore print or microscopic examination. *Clavulinopsis umbrinella* is a less common, similarly shaped, branched species found in grassland, but its fruitbodies are pale brownish and never yellow.

The Meadow Coral has a repeatedly branching fruitbody that is pale yellow to ocher with a whitish base. In short turf it can grow very small and densely branched, but in longer grass and woodland it can be taller and more open. Its flesh is similarly colored, tough, and elastic, often with a mealy smell.

Actual size

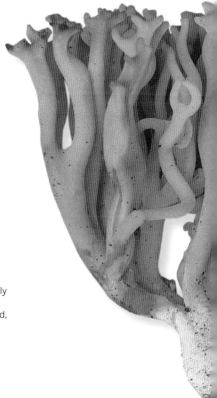

FAMILY	Clavariaceae
DISTRIBUTION	North America, Europe, northern Asia
HABITAT	In grassland, more rarely woodland
ASSOCIATION	With moss and grass
GROWTH FORM	On ground, often in scattered troops
ABUNDANCE	Common
SPORE COLOR	White
EDIBILITY	Not edible

HEIGHT
Up to 5 in
(120 mm)

DIAMETER
Up to ¼ in
(5 mm)

494

CLAVULINOPSIS FUSIFORMIS
GOLDEN SPINDLES
(SOWERBY) CORNER

Actual size

A large cluster of the Golden Spindles is an eye-catching sight on a dull day in fall. The species is related to the White and the Smoky Spindles (*Clavaria fragilis* and *C. fumosa*). Like them, it is a saprotroph, an organism that lives on dead and decaying matter, in this case the leaf litter of woodlands or the thatch and moss of grasslands. The Golden Spindles was originally described and illustrated by the English botanist and mycologist James Sowerby, who found it "not very rare" on Hampstead Heath in London in the 1790s. It probably still grows there today.

SIMILAR SPECIES
There are several other simple, spindle- or club-shaped fungi with yellow to orange fruitbodies. *Clavaria amoenoides* is similarly sized and grows in large clusters, but is pale yellow and much less common. *Clavulinopsis helvola*, *C. laeticolor*, and *C. luteoalba* are very common and bright orange-yellow, but are usually not so tall and grow singly or in small clusters, often in scattered troops.

The Golden Spindles has smooth, tubular or often somewhat flattened, unbranched fruitbodies with pointed tips. They normally grow gregariously in large clusters, and are bright orange-yellow when fresh.

FAMILY	Lachnocladiaceae
DISTRIBUTION	South America
HABITAT	In woodland
ASSOCIATION	With broadleaf trees
GROWTH FORM	On ground or very rotten wood, singly or in troops
ABUNDANCE	Occasional
SPORE COLOR	White
EDIBILITY	Not edible

HEIGHT
Up to 3 in
(75 mm)

DIAMETER
Up to 3 in
(75 mm)

LACHNOCLADIUM DENUDATUM

SMOOTH LEATHER-CORAL

CORNER

495

Lachnocladium species are common in the tropics, but absent from most of the temperate zones. All have fruitbodies that are leathery and long-lasting, extensively branched, and colored pale buff to brown. The commonest species is the tongue-defying *L. schweinfurthianum*, but species are difficult to tell apart and have not been well researched. It is quite possible that the Smooth Leather-Coral—originally described from Brazil—is just a form of *L. schweinfurthianum*, from which it is said to differ mainly by its smoother, rounder, less-flattened branches.

SIMILAR SPECIES

Other tropical *Lachnocladium* species look similar and can only be distinguished microscopically. Fruitbodies of *Ramaria* species may be similarly shaped, but are usually softer and more brittle, and have ocher to brown (not white) spores.

The Smooth Leather-Coral forms strongly branched, rather tough to leathery fruitbodies. The branches are slender, tubular, or slightly compressed, narrowing toward the tips, and the surface smooth to wrinkled, ocher to pale yellow-brown, becoming more reddish brown. The short stem is smooth, with root-like rhizomorphs at the base.

Actual size

FAMILY	Typhulaceae
DISTRIBUTION	North America, Europe, northern Asia
HABITAT	In woodland
ASSOCIATION	With broadleaf trees
GROWTH FORM	On dead attached or fallen branches, singly or in troops
ABUNDANCE	Common
SPORE COLOR	White
EDIBILITY	Not edible

HEIGHT
Up to 12 in
(300 mm)

DIAMETER
Up to ⅜ in
(8 mm)

496

MACROTYPHULA FISTULOSA

PIPE CLUB

(HOLMSKJOLD) R. H. PETERSEN

Fruitbodies of *Macrotyphula fistulosa* look a little like slender versions of the Giant Club (*Clavariadelphus pistillaris*) and the two species were once placed in the same genus, though it is now known that they are not closely related. The Pipe Club, however, typically grows in troops on fallen branches, rather than on the ground. Quite frequently, it produces contorted fruitbodies which have sometimes been treated as a separate variety (*M. fistulosa* var. *contortus*). These fruitbodies are often clustered, usually flattened, sometimes twisted, forked, or fan-shaped and can be very puzzling when first encountered.

SIMILAR SPECIES

The Slender Club (*Macrotyphula juncea*) is equally tall but extremely thin, less than ⅛ in (1 mm) wide, and grows in leaf litter in wet woodland areas, often attached to tiny twigs. *Typhula phacorrhiza* is similar, but its fruitbodies arise from a hard, lentil-like sclerotium of compacted fungal tissue.

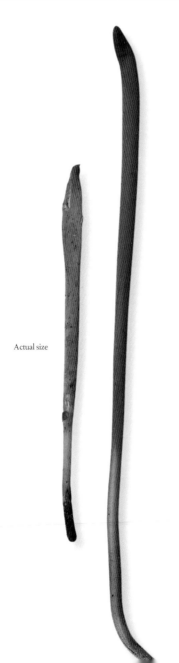

Actual size

The Pipe Club forms club-shaped, often hollow fruitbodies on wood, which are either long and slender, or contorted and compressed with short projections. The surface is smooth and yellowish brown, becoming reddish or purplish brown.

FAMILY	Physalacriaceae
DISTRIBUTION	North America
HABITAT	In woodland
ASSOCIATION	On broadleaf wood
GROWTH FORM	On fallen branches and logs, sometimes in leaf litter
ABUNDANCE	Locally common
SPORE COLOR	White
EDIBILITY	Not edible

HEIGHT
Up to ¾ in
(20 mm)

CAP DIAMETER
Up to ½ in
(12 mm)

PHYSALACRIA INFLATA

BLADDER STALKS

(SCHWEINITZ) PECK

497

Physalacria inflata has been described as looking like a miniature balloon on a stick, and its peculiar shape has meant that its relationships to other fungi have long been debated. Many mycologists suggested it belonged with the club and coral fungi, others with the gilled agarics. Now molecular research has clearly shown that the latter is true and that the Bladder Stalks is most closely related to gilled agarics such as the Porcelain Fungus (*Oudemansiella mucida*) and the Wrinkled Peach (*Rhodotus palmatus*).

SIMILAR SPECIES

Similar species of *Physalacria* occur in Australia, New Zealand, and the tropics. Most are smaller than the Bladder Stalks, but are best distinguished microscopically. *Caripia montagnei* also has bladderlike fruitbodies, but they are top- or drum-shaped with brownish stems.

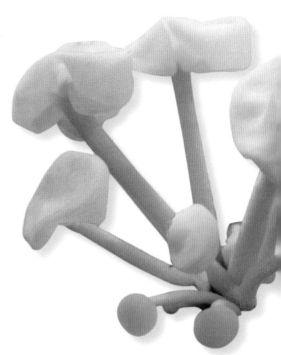

Actual size

The Bladder Stalks produces clusters or swarms of small fruitbodies on rotten wood or leaf litter. Each fruitbody consists of a smooth to somewhat wrinkled, white to cream, bladderlike head that is typically ball-shaped, but easily dented, collapsing and flattening with age. The stems are slender, smooth, and white to cream.

FAMILY	Pterulaceae
DISTRIBUTION	North America, Europe, Asia
HABITAT	In woodland and gardens
ASSOCIATION	With broadleaf trees and conifers
GROWTH FORM	On ground, or on woodland litter and decaying vegetation
ABUNDANCE	Occasional
SPORE COLOR	White
EDIBILITY	Not edible

HEIGHT
Up to 2½ in
(60 mm)

DIAMETER
Up to 2½ in
(60 mm)

498

PTERULA SUBULATA
ANGEL-HAIR CORAL
FRIES

This delicate-looking species, perhaps better known under its synonym *Pterula multifida*, is one of the more conspicuous members of the genus, most of which are either tiny or tropical. It can occur sparsely, or even singly, on pieces of rotting vegetation, but is usually found growing in dense, interlocking tufts or troops that may look as if they are one large fruitbody. In South America, relatives of the Angel-Hair Coral are cultivated for food by certain fungus-farming ants.

SIMILAR SPECIES

Many similar species occur in the tropics, often on rotting wood. The Angel-Hair Coral is north temperate, however, and should be distinct. *Thelephora penicillata* can be similarly colored and has finely pointed branches, but the branches are short, arise in flattened fronds, and are seldom erect. *Artomyces pyxidatus* is also finely branched, but can be distinguished by the distinctively crownlike branch tips.

Actual size

The Angel-Hair Coral typically produces a mass of small fruitbodies that become densely entangled and may be difficult to separate. Each fruitbody consists of thin, erect, filiform (almost hairlike) branches with finely pointed tips arising from an equally thin stem. Fruitbodies are tougher than they look, and vary from white with pinkish tints to entirely pinkish brown.

FAMILY	Gomphaceae
DISTRIBUTION	Western North America, Central America
HABITAT	In woodland
ASSOCIATION	Ectomycorrhizal, with broadleaf trees and conifers
GROWTH FORM	On ground, singly or in troops
ABUNDANCE	Locally common
SPORE COLOR	Ocher
EDIBILITY	Edible

HEIGHT
Up to 5 in
(125 mm)

DIAMETER
Up to 4 in
(100 mm)

RAMARIA ARAIOSPORA
RED CORAL
MARR & D. E. STUNTZ

499

In many areas—including the British Isles—large, ectomycorrhizal *Ramaria* species are decidedly uncommon and infrequently encountered, but a few places seem to be hot spots for coral fungi. The Pacific Northwest of America is one such, with a large number of distinctive species, many of which are not found elsewhere. The magnificent Red Coral—originally described from Washington—is just one example of the richness of this coastal region. The species mainly associates with western hemlock and tanoak and can also be found farther south, from California into Mexico and Guatemala.

SIMILAR SPECIES

In the same area, *Ramaria stuntzii* is a look-alike, bright red coral, though it typically has an irregular band of yellow at the base of the main branches. Otherwise, the fresh colors of the Red Coral should be distinctive. When faded to coral-pink or orange, however, there are many other look-alike species.

Actual size

The Red Coral forms densely branched fruitbodies arising from a main stem. The branches are bright red to coral-red at first, fading to pink or orange with age. The branch tips may be red or yellowish. The main stem is whitish toward the base. Spores may color old, faded fruitbodies ocher.

FAMILY	Gomphaceae
DISTRIBUTION	North America, Europe, northern Asia
HABITAT	In woodland
ASSOCIATION	Ectomycorrhizal, with broadleaf trees, especially beech
GROWTH FORM	On ground, singly or in troops
ABUNDANCE	Locally common
SPORE COLOR	Ocher
EDIBILITY	Edible (with caution)

HEIGHT
Up to 6 in
(150 mm)

DIAMETER
Up to 6 in
(150 mm)

500

RAMARIA BOTRYTIS
ROSSO CORAL
(PERSOON) RICKEN

An alternative name for the Rosso Coral is the Cauliflower Coral, which aptly describes its shape. It almost always has a massive main stem and lower branches, topped by a mass of small, stubby branchlets. Other *Ramaria* species are similarly shaped, however, so the resemblance to a cauliflower is not in itself diagnostic. The species was originally described from Europe where it forms an association with beech or oak. Records with conifers probably refer to one or more look-alike species. The Rosso Coral is edible, but is said to have a laxative effect on some people.

SIMILAR SPECIES

The purplish pink branch tips of *Ramaria botrytis* are usually distinctive, but there are several less-common *Ramaria* species—including *R. subbotrytis*, *R. botrytoides*, *R. rubrievanescens*, and *R. rubripermanens*—that can be similarly colored. The individual species are best distinguished microscopically.

Actual size

The Rosso Coral produces densely branched fruitbodies, the main stem and basal branches up to 2 in (50 mm) wide, the terminal branchlets often stubby or spine-like. The branches are whitish to cream with a rose-pink flush, the tips darker, deep rose-pink to wine-red. Spores may color old, faded fruitbodies ocher.

FAMILY	Gomphaceae
DISTRIBUTION	North America, Europe, northern Asia
HABITAT	In woodland
ASSOCIATION	Ectomycorrhizal, with broadleaf trees, especially beech
GROWTH FORM	On ground, singly or in troops
ABUNDANCE	Locally common
SPORE COLOR	Ocher
EDIBILITY	Poisonous

HEIGHT
Up to 6 in
(150 mm)

DIAMETER
Up to 8 in
(200 mm)

RAMARIA FORMOSA

SALMON CORAL

(PERSOON) QUÉLET

501

The epithet *formosa* means "beautiful," and the Salmon Coral is
certainly a handsome species when young and fresh, the salmon-
pink branches contrasting with the yellow tips. The species was
originally described from Europe where it mainly occurs as an
ectomycorrhizal associate of beech or chestnut. Reports of it
growing with conifers probably refer to one of several look-alike
species. Despite its attractive colors, the Salmon Coral is known
to cause gastroenteritic poisoning. Since *Ramaria* fruitbodies are
often difficult to identify to species, the whole group is probably
best avoided for culinary use.

SIMILAR SPECIES

The salmon-pink branches with yellow tips are distinctive but
not diagnostic, since there are several other *Ramaria* species—
including *R. neoformosa*, *R. raveneliana*, and *R. leptoformosa*—
that can be similarly colored. Some occur with conifers, but they
are best distinguished microscopically.

Actual size

The Salmon Coral produces densely branched fruitbodies, the main stem
and basal branches up to 1½ in (35 mm) wide, the terminal branchlets
short and often spine-like. The branches are flesh-pink to salmon-ocher,
the tips yellow. The main stem is whitish toward the base and sometimes
bruises violet. Spores may color old, faded fruitbodies ocher.

FAMILY	Gomphaceae
DISTRIBUTION	Western North America
HABITAT	In woodland
ASSOCIATION	Ectomycorrhizal, with conifers, especially western hemlock
GROWTH FORM	On ground, singly or in troops
ABUNDANCE	Locally common
SPORE COLOR	Ocher
EDIBILITY	Unknown

HEIGHT
Up to 7 in
(175 mm)

DIAMETER
Up to 4 in
(100 mm)

502

RAMARIA LONGISPORA

LONGSPORED ORANGE CORAL

MARR & D. E. STUNTZ

This is another brightly colored coral from the Pacific Northwest of America, where it is typically found growing in association with western hemlock (*Tsuga heterophylla*). The fungus has also been reported on rare occasions from continental Europe, but it seems likely that such reports refer to a look-alike species. A microscope is needed to see its longer-than-usual spores, but, when fresh, the Longspored Orange Coral also has an irregular band of yellow around the top of the main stem, which may help to distinguish it from other orange *Ramaria* species. Its edibility is unknown.

SIMILAR SPECIES

In the same area, the Golden Coral (*Ramaria largentii*) is a look-alike, with orange branches that have no yellow band at their base. It, too, has been reported from Europe. Other orange-branched species from western North America include *R. sandaracina*, *R. gelatiniaurantia*, and *R. aurantiisiccescens*—and they are all best distinguished microscopically.

The Longspored Orange Coral forms densely branched fruitbodies arising from a main stem. The branches are orange to orange-red, but yellow toward the main stem. The branch tips may also be yellow when young, but later become orange. The base of the main stem is whitish and the base has conspicuous, whitish, root-like rhizomorphs. Spores may color old, faded fruitbodies ocher.

Actual size

FAMILY	Gomphaceae
DISTRIBUTION	North America, Europe, Central America, northern Asia
HABITAT	In woodland
ASSOCIATION	With broadleaf trees and conifers
GROWTH FORM	On or attached to very rotten wood, singly or in troops
ABUNDANCE	Common
SPORE COLOR	Ocher-brown
EDIBILITY	Not edible

HEIGHT
Up to 6 in
(150 mm)

DIAMETER
Up to 5 in
(125 mm)

RAMARIA STRICTA
UPRIGHT CORAL
(PERSOON) QUÉLET

503

The Upright Coral is probably the commonest of the north temperate *Ramaria* species, though recent molecular research suggests it may not actually belong in the genus. True *Ramaria* species are ectomycorrhizal, but *R. stricta* belongs in a small group of similar-looking wood-rotters. White, root-like, mycelial strands found at the base of fruitbodies are always attached to nearby (sometimes buried) woody remains, even if the fruitbodies themselves do not seem to be growing on wood. Fruitbodies are very variable in size—sometimes quite small, sometimes forming massive clumps—and this may be related to the size of their wood resource.

SIMILAR SPECIES
A very similar species, *Ramaria moelleriana*, grows on rotten wood in the tropics and is best distinguished microscopically. *Ramaria gracilis* is a paler species that grows on conifer wood and has a distinct aniseed smell when fresh. Most other *Ramaria* species grow on the ground and lack the pinkish purple colors of the Upright Coral.

Actual size

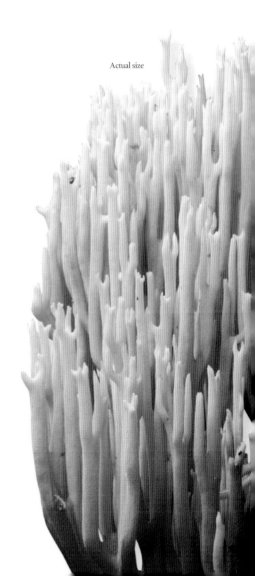

The Upright Coral produces densely branched fruitbodies, the branches thin, vertical, and closely packed together. The branches are typically pale, dusty pink, pale yellow at the tips when young, purplish pink toward the base. The whole fruitbody may bruise dull purplish on handling. With age, the spores gradually color the branches ocher.

FAMILY	Clavariaceae
DISTRIBUTION	North America, Europe, northern Asia
HABITAT	In grassland or woodland
ASSOCIATION	With moss and grass or leaf litter
GROWTH FORM	On ground, singly or in scattered troops
ABUNDANCE	Common
SPORE COLOR	White
EDIBILITY	Edible

HEIGHT
Up to 3 in
(80 mm)

DIAMETER
Up to 3 in
(80 mm)

504

RAMARIOPSIS KUNZEI
IVORY CORAL
(FRIES) CORNER

The Ivory Coral was first described in 1821 by Elias Fries, son of a Swedish priest who rose to become professor of botany, and is now regarded as the founding father of modern fungal taxonomy. It is quite common and widespread, but a good example of a fungus about which we still know very little. Big rosette-like fruitbodies can occasionally be found in pastures, taller fruitbodies in woodland, and much smaller and more delicate collections in both grassland and woodland. All are branched, white, and seem the same microscopically. Careful DNA analysis will be required to determine whether they represent a single variable species or several closely related ones.

SIMILAR SPECIES

Ramariopsis kunzei belongs in a complex of similar, but mostly smaller, species that are difficult to distinguish, even microscopically. Larger specimens may be confused with *Clavulina coralloides*, which has rather irregular branches with feathery or spiny tips. In eastern North America, some *Tremellodendron* species may also look similar, but their fruitbodies are tough and rubbery.

Actual size

The Ivory Coral is very variable, but is always branched and white (rarely with a pinkish flush, sometimes reddening from the base upward). In smaller specimens, the branches are usually thin, tubular, and upright like a candelabra, but in larger specimens the branches may be flattened or compressed and grow in rosettes.

FAMILY	Thelephoraceae
DISTRIBUTION	North America, Europe, northern Asia
HABITAT	In woodland
ASSOCIATION	Ectomycorrhizal, with conifers
GROWTH FORM	On ground at base of trees, among roots
ABUNDANCE	Locally common
SPORE COLOR	Brown
EDIBILITY	Not edible

HEIGHT
Up to 4 in
(100 mm)

DIAMETER
Up to 3 in
(75 mm)

THELEPHORA PALMATA

STINKING EARTHFAN

(SCOPOLI) FRIES

505

With names like the Stinking Earthfan and the Fetid False Coral, it is no surprise to discover that this conifer-associated species has a rather unpleasant smell. Some have likened it to old cabbage water, others to rotting garlic or overripe cheese. Although it resembles a coral fungus in shape, it is a close relative of several bracket-like fungi, including the ordinary Earthfan (*Thelephora terrestris*) and the Carnation Earthfan (*T. caryophyllea*), and a more distant relative of bolete-like species, such as *Boletopsis grisea*, and tooth fungi, such as *Phellodon niger*.

SIMILAR SPECIES

Thelephora anthocephala is a very similar species most often found in broadleaf woodland and lacking the distinctive unpleasant smell of *T. palmata*. Some of the darker *Ramaria* species may be similarly colored, but they are not leathery and have branches with pointed tips.

Actual size

The Stinking Earthfan has leathery fruitbodies with branches that are narrow at the base, widen out into a fan, and then split into several flattened prongs. The tips are wedge-like, never pointed. The colors are typically purplish brown with whitish branch tips when young, darkening to a grayish brown when old.

PUFFBALLS & EARTHSTARS, BIRD'S NESTS & STINKHORNS

The puffballs and earthstars, together with the bird's nest fungi and stinkhorns, were all once artificially classed together as gasteromycetes—literally "stomach fungi"—since all produce their spores inside their fruitbodies, not on the outer surfaces.

The puffballs and many similar-looking species are actually closely related to agarics—some even having the remains of gills inside their closed caps. Many are adapted to desert conditions, where ordinary fruitbodies would shrivel and die. Some, like the false truffles, have gone underground and rely on animals to spread their spores. The extraordinary earthstars have spores puffed out by raindrops.

The miniature bird's nest fungi are also related to agarics, though they hardly look like it. They, too, rely on rain—the drops in a heavy shower splashing out tiny, egglike packets of spores from their nestlike cups. Stinkhorns are a group all on their own and include some of the most bizarre fruitbodies in the fungal world. Their spores are formed inside gelatinous "eggs," and are then lifted up into the air on a variety of odd receptacles—many looking like strange sea creatures. Stinkhorn spores are spread by flies and all species emit a memorable stench.

FAMILY	Diplocystidiaceae
DISTRIBUTION	North America, Europe, Africa, Central and South America, Asia, Australia
HABITAT	In woodland
ASSOCIATION	Ectomycorrhizal, with broadleaf trees and conifers
GROWTH FORM	On ground, singly or in troops
ABUNDANCE	Common
SPORE COLOR	Brown
EDIBILITY	Not edible

HEIGHT
Up to 2 in
(50 mm)

DIAMETER
Up to 4 in
(100 mm)

508

ASTRAEUS HYGROMETRICUS
BAROMETER EARTHSTAR
(PERSOON) MORGAN

The Barometer Earthstar produces fruitbodies that are spherical at first. At maturity the thick outer skin splits and (if the weather is damp) peels back to form 6–12 rays or arms, revealing the puffball-like spore sack at the center. The rays are strongly hygroscopic and in dry weather curl back over the spore sack.

Despite its English name and its appearance, the Barometer Earthstar is not actually an earthstar, being completely unrelated to the true earthstars in the genus *Geastrum*. It is a curious case of parallel evolution. Both groups of fungi have developed the same method of dispersing their spores—using the pressure of falling raindrops to puff them out through the hole in the fruitbody top. The Barometer Earthstar has developed the additional ability to extend its leathery "arms" in wet weather (ready for the raindrops) and fold them back over the fruitbody for protection when it is dry.

SIMILAR SPECIES

Astraeus hygrometricus is cosmopolitan, but related species (best distinguished microscopically) occur in Southeast Asia. Most *Geastrum* species have rays that are not hygroscopic and remain extended in dry weather (though in a few species the rays may partly curl upward).

Actual size

FAMILY	Agaricaceae
DISTRIBUTION	North America, Europe, Africa, Central and South America, Asia, Australia
HABITAT	In dry woodland, scrub, and desert
ASSOCIATION	With broadleaf trees and conifers
GROWTH FORM	On ground, singly or in small groups
ABUNDANCE	Locally common
SPORE COLOR	Brown
EDIBILITY	Edible (in "egg" stage)

HEIGHT
Up to 24 in
(600 mm)
CAP DIAMETER
Up to 3 in
(75 mm)

BATTARREA PHALLOIDES

SANDY STILTBALL

(DICKSON) PERSOON

509

The Sandy Stiltball is a typical fungus of arid lands and deserts, its fruitbodies having a tough stalk and well-protected spore mass, enabling it to withstand the driest conditions. It may be surprising, therefore, to find that it was first described from England in 1785—though it is a rare species in the British Isles, occurring mainly in dry, sandy hedgerows. It appears to be cosmopolitan, however, and can be locally common elsewhere. In Cyprus, where it is known as the Donkey Fungus, it is even eaten in its immature "egg" stage.

SIMILAR SPECIES

Battarrea stevenii is sometimes considered a separate, larger species occurring in southern Europe and elsewhere, but analysis of DNA sequencing suggests it is not distinct and the two are treated here as a single species. The Desert Shaggy Mane (*Podaxis pistillaris*) grows in similar arid places, but has a shaggy, elongated cap or head.

The Sandy Stiltball emerges from a whitish, buried "egg" that may remain at the stem base or disintegrate. The cap or head is covered by a white, membranous skin at first, but this later splits apart to reveal a rusty brown spore mass. The stem is hard, dry, shaggy-scaly, and pale brown.

Actual size

FAMILY	Agaricaceae
DISTRIBUTION	Europe, western Asia
HABITAT	In grassland and woodland
ASSOCIATION	With grass and broadleaf trees
GROWTH FORM	On ground, singly or in small groups
ABUNDANCE	Common
SPORE COLOR	Brown
EDIBILITY	Edible (when young)

HEIGHT
Up to 2½ in
(60 mm)

DIAMETER
Up to 2½ in
(60 mm)

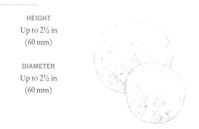

510

BOVISTA NIGRESCENS
BROWN PUFFBALL
PERSOON

The Brown Puffball is almost spherical, smooth, and whitish to cream at first. The white outer surface is shed at maturity to reveal the dark brown, papery, slightly shiny, inner surface. This in turn splits to uncover the woolly-powdery, dark brown spore mass inside.

Like its smaller relation *Bovista plumbea*, the Brown Puffball forms stemless fruitbodies that are initially covered in a soft, white skin. This outer skin is shed once the spores are mature to reveal the papery, inner skin—dark brown in *B. nigrescens*, lead-gray in *B. plumbea*—which splits open at the top for spore release. The loss of the outer skin also releases the fruitbodies from their point of attachment to the soil. As a result, mature Brown and Gray Puffballs are free to roll around in the wind, distributing their spores as they go.

SIMILAR SPECIES
Bovista pila is a look-alike North American species. The Gray Puffball (*B. plumbea*) occurs in both America and Europe and is a smaller species of calcareous grassland. *Bovista graveolens* is another similar, but uncommon, continental European species with an unusual preference for disturbed ground.

Actual size

FAMILY	Calostomataceae
DISTRIBUTION	North America, Central and northern South America
HABITAT	In woodland
ASSOCIATION	Ectomycorrhizal, with oak
GROWTH FORM	On ground, singly or in small groups
ABUNDANCE	Occasional
SPORE COLOR	Yellow-buff
EDIBILITY	Not edible

HEIGHT
Up to 3 in
(80 mm)

DIAMETER
Up to 1 in
(25 mm)

CALOSTOMA CINNABARINUM
RED ASPIC-PUFFBALL
CORDA

511

Calostoma species look like outlandish puffballs, but are, in fact, more closely related to the earthballs and the boletes than to the true puffballs. The fruitbodies seem to be preserved in aspic and it has been suggested that this gelatinous outer coating may be a protective layer, helping the fungus withstand desiccation or damage by invertebrate predators. The name *Calostoma* means "pretty mouth," referring to the red, ridged opening at the top of the spore sack. The bright orange-red coloring comes from a distinct pigment called calostomal, which has been isolated from the fungus itself.

SIMILAR SPECIES

The Red Aspic-Puffball is restricted to the Americas, but other species occur in Asia and Australasia. In North America, the Yellow Aspic-Puffball (*Calostoma lutescens*) is similar, but has a yellowish stem and spore sack (though the ridged cross at the top is red). *Calostoma ravenelii* is also yellowish, but lacks the gelatinous outer layer.

The Red Aspic-Puffball looks like a gelatinous ball at first, but as it matures the gelatinous outer layer (often containing reddish fragments) sloughs off, exposing the puffball-like, inner spore sack. This has a ridged, red cross at the top that opens to release the spores. The spore sack is raised from the ground by a thick, reddish, coarsely netted, spongy, gelatinous stem.

Actual size

FAMILY	Agaricaceae
DISTRIBUTION	Eastern North America, Europe, Central America, northern Asia, Australia, New Zealand
HABITAT	In rich grassland and scrub, sometimes in gardens
ASSOCIATION	With grass or broadleaf trees
GROWTH FORM	On ground, singly or in troops and rings
ABUNDANCE	Common
SPORE COLOR	Olive-brown
EDIBILITY	Edible when young

HEIGHT
Up to 30 in
(750 mm)

DIAMETER
Up to 30 in
(750 mm)

CALVATIA GIGANTEA

GIANT PUFFBALL

(BATSCH) LLOYD

512

Actual size

Though generally the size of a soccerball, fruitbodies of the Giant Puffball can occasionally reach spectacular dimensions, the largest recorded being over 5 ft (1.5 m) in diameter and weighing over 40 lb (20 kg). What's more, they often grow in fairy rings, though there is little about them that is fairylike. The fruitbodies contain vast numbers of spores—around 15 trillion to the pound (half kilo)—which are released when the old fruitbodies break up and weather away. When young and white throughout, before the spores mature, the Giant Puffball is edible and is sometimes offered for sale in local markets.

SIMILAR SPECIES

In western North America, *Calvatia booniana* can be a similar size, but its surface breaks up into polygonal scales. The widespread *Lycoperdon utriforme* also has a scaly surface and may reach 8 in (200 mm) across, though it has a wide, sterile base. *Calvatia cyathiformis* is similar, but has a smooth surface and purple-brown spores.

The Giant Puffball produces rounded, flattened-spherical fruitbodies without any stem. The surface is smooth, slightly velvety, whitish to cream, peeling easily when young. Old fruitbodies become papery and brown, sometimes drying out and persisting for months, before disintegrating to release the olive-brown spores inside.

FAMILY	Agaricaceae
DISTRIBUTION	North America, continental Europe, northern Asia
HABITAT	In dry grassland, lawns, and roadsides
ASSOCIATION	With grass
GROWTH FORM	On ground, singly or clustered
ABUNDANCE	Common
SPORE COLOR	Pale green to ocher-brown
EDIBILITY	Probably poisonous

HEIGHT	Up to 5 in (125 mm)
CAP DIAMETER	Up to 4 in (100 mm)

CHLOROPHYLLUM AGARICOIDES

PUFFBALL PARASOL

(CZERNAJEW) VELLINGA

513

Half-puffball, half-agaric—the Puffball Parasol is an example of a secotioid fungus, an agaric in which the cap remains closed, the spores maturing inside to be released as the fruitbody weathers away. This is an adaptation to dry climates; in the wild the Puffball Parasol is a fungus of the steppes and other arid grasslands, though it has also found a home in dry roadsides and gardens. It was formerly referred to its own genus, *Endoptychum*, but DNA research reveals that it is related to the False Parasol (*Chlorophyllum molybdites*) and may be equally poisonous.

SIMILAR SPECIES

Agaricus inapertus was formerly called *Endoptychum depressum* and thought to be related to the Puffball Parasol, but is actually closer to the Horse Mushroom (*A. arvensis*). It has a similar shape, but the mature spore mass (and spores) are chocolate-brown and it has an almond smell. The Texan Desert Mushroom (*Longula texensis*) is similar.

Actual size

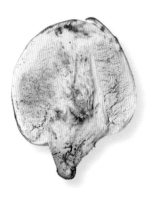

The Puffball Parasol produces a puffball-like fruitbody with a half-internal stem. The cap surface is smooth at first, then scaly, and white to cream, becoming buff to brownish. The inner spore mass is white at first, becoming yellowish (see photo left) to brown. The short stem is cap-colored with an indistinct ring joined to the base of the cap.

FAMILY	Gallaceaceae
DISTRIBUTION	New Zealand
HABITAT	In woodland
ASSOCIATION	Ectomycorrhizal, with southern beech
GROWTH FORM	Half-embedded in ground, singly or in small groups
ABUNDANCE	Common
SPORE COLOR	Brown
EDIBILITY	Not edible

HEIGHT
Up to 1½ in
(40 mm)

DIAMETER
Up to 4 in
(100 mm)

514

GALLACEA SCLERODERMA
VIOLET POTATO FUNGUS
(COOKE) LLOYD

This New Zealand specialty must be one of the most handsome and striking of the truffle-like fungi, but unfortunately is not an edible species. It is ectomycorrhizal, forming an association with the roots of living southern beech trees (*Nothofagus* species) and is common in native New Zealand forests. Oddly, DNA research has shown it to be a distant relative of coral fungi (*Ramaria*) and stinkhorns. The name *Gallacea* comes from the Latin for "oak apple," from its supposed resemblance to such galls, and *scleroderma* from its supposed resemblance to earthballs, though neither oak apples nor earthballs are ever bright violet.

SIMILAR SPECIES

The striking color of the Violet Potato Fungus is unique. Other *Gallacea* species are whitish to pale pink and are not likely to be confused with this species. *Cortinarius porphyroideus* is another New Zealand fungus with equally bright colors, but though the violet cap is enclosed and truffle-like, it has a distinct stem.

The Violet Potato Fungus forms truffle-like fruitbodies that are partly embedded in surface soil and leaf litter. They are irregularly ball-shaped, with a surface that is finely hairy or scaly, and strikingly purple to bright violet, turning brown where bruised. When cut, the interior is olive brown to dark grayish brown (see photo below right).

Actual size

FAMILY	Geastraceae
DISTRIBUTION	North America, Europe, Africa, Central and South America, Asia, Australia
HABITAT	In woodland, scrub, and hedgerows
ASSOCIATION	With broadleaf trees and conifers
GROWTH FORM	On ground, singly or in troops
ABUNDANCE	Occasional
SPORE COLOR	Brown
EDIBILITY	Not edible

GEASTRUM FORNICATUM

ARCHED EARTHSTAR

(HUDSON) HOOKER

HEIGHT
Up to 4 in
(100 mm)

DIAMETER
Up to 3 in
(80 mm)

515

The Arched Earthstar has one of the most remarkable and highly evolved fruitbodies in the fungal kingdom. Starting as a ball, it splits open into starlike rays or arms which peel back to reveal the puffball-like spore sack at the center. Each ray then splits again into two layers attached at the tips. The lower layer remains in the soil and leaf litter, the upper layer rises up, cantilevering the spore sack upward, where its spores are puffed out by the action of falling raindrops. The Arched Earthstar was once thought to resemble a manikin, and was even illustrated with a human face in a book published in 1695.

SIMILAR SPECIES

Most other earthstars lack the arched or cantilevered fruitbodies of *Geastrum fornicatum,* and so lack rays that are folded cage-like underneath. *Geastrum quadrifidum*, however, does have cantilevered rays, but is generally smaller and the opening at the top of the spore sack has a pale ring around it.

The Arched Earthstar has fruitbodies that are almost spherical at first. At maturity the thick outer skin splits and peels back to form 3–5 rays or arms. The rays then separate into two layers. The lower layer remains cuplike in the earth or litter, while the upper layer arches upward lifting the central spore sack with it.

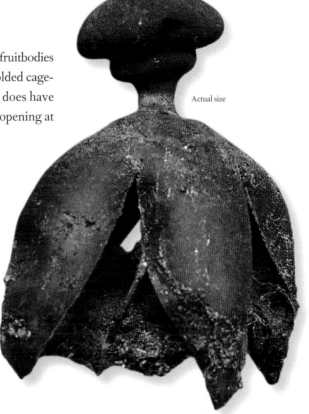

Actual size

FAMILY	Geastraceae
DISTRIBUTION	North America, Europe, Africa, Central and South America, Asia, Australia, New Zealand
HABITAT	In woodland, scrub, hedgerows, and dunes
ASSOCIATION	With broadleaf trees and conifers
GROWTH FORM	On ground, singly or in troops
ABUNDANCE	Common
SPORE COLOR	Brown
EDIBILITY	Not edible

HEIGHT
Up to 2½ in
(60 mm)

DIAMETER
Up to 5 in
(120 mm)

GEASTRUM TRIPLEX
COLLARED EARTHSTAR
JUNGHUHN

516

This is one of the commonest and most widespread earthstars and also one of the largest. Like many other *Geastrum* species it is weakly hygroscopic with rays that tend to open slightly in wet weather and curl inward again when dry. Traditionally, like puffballs, the Collared Earthstar and other *Geastrum* species were used as styptics to staunch wounds. The Collared Earthstar was also used in folk medicine by the Cherokee to treat the umbilical cord of newborns. In traditional Chinese medicine it is still used to reduce inflammation in the respiratory tract, being taken as a weak tea.

SIMILAR SPECIES

Typical specimens are easily distinguished from other earthstars by the conspicuous collar around the puffball-like spore sack. Otherwise the species is very similar to the rarer *Geastrum lageniforme* which is almost identical, but lacks the collar. Further research is required to see if the two are really distinct, or just forms of the same fungus.

Actual size

The Collared Earthstar produces fruitbodies that are onion-shaped at first, with a pointed tip. At maturity the thick outer skin splits and peels back to form 4–7 rays or arms, revealing the puffball-like spore sack at the center. In the Collared Earthstar, the rays are brittle and tend to split, leaving a diagnostic ringlike collar or cup around the spore sack.

FAMILY	Strophariaceae
DISTRIBUTION	Australia, New Zealand
HABITAT	In woodland
ASSOCIATION	With broadleaf trees
GROWTH FORM	On ground or decayed fallen wood
ABUNDANCE	Occasional
SPORE COLOR	Brown
EDIBILITY	Not edible

HEIGHT
Up to 1½ in
(40 mm)

CAP DIAMETER
Up to 2½ in
(60 mm)

LERATIOMYCES ERYTHROCEPHALUS

RED POUCH FUNGUS

(TULASNE & C. TULASNE) BEEVER & D.-C. PARK

517

The Red Pouch Fungus looks like a brightly colored button-mushroom that has not yet opened up to reveal its gills. But in this peculiar species, the cap never opens and the gills inside are reduced to a honeycomb-like structure. The spores may be spread by birds, since the cap resembles a large red berry, or by small mammals in Australia. Recent DNA research has shown that the Red Pouch Fungus is closely related to ordinary agarics with normal gills—including the Redlead Roundhead (*Leratiomyces ceres*)—which suggests that the non-opening cap is a comparatively recent evolutionary development.

SIMILAR SPECIES

The unrelated Scarlet Berry Truffle (*Paurocotylis pila*) also grows in Australia and New Zealand and is similarly colored, but lacks a stem. The related *Leratiomyces ceres* has a bright orange cap and is also found in the same area, but is a conventional agaric with gills.

Actual size

The Red Pouch Fungus forms puffball-like fruitbodies, with a spherical to egg-shaped cap and long stem. The cap is smooth, often lobed or creased, and curled inward at the base. The surface is shiny to slightly sticky and bright scarlet. The stem is cylindrical and white to yellowish. When cut, the interior of the cap is brown.

FAMILY	Agaricaceae
DISTRIBUTION	Southern and western North America, Central America
HABITAT	In desert and arid ground
ASSOCIATION	With xerophytic desert scrub vegetation
GROWTH FORM	On ground, singly or in small groups
ABUNDANCE	Occasional
SPORE COLOR	Chocolate-brown
EDIBILITY	Not edible

HEIGHT
Up to 4 in
(100 mm)

CAP DIAMETER
Up to 3 in
(80 mm)

518

LONGULA TEXENSIS
TEXAN DESERT MUSHROOM
(BERKELEY & M. A. CURTIS) ZELLER

Longula texensis looks like a true mushroom (*Agaricus* species) that has not opened its cap, and recent molecular research has confirmed that this is precisely the case. The species has been transferred to the genus *Agaricus*, but illegitimately since the name *A. texensis* already exists for a completely different species. It seems that the closed cap of the Texan Desert Mushroom has evolved in response to arid conditions, allowing the spores to mature safe from sun and wind. They are eventually released as the cap weathers away. The species is not restricted to Texas, but occurs from Mexico north to Oregon.

SIMILAR SPECIES

Other desert and dryland species have evolved similar fruitbodies. *Podaxis pistillaris* has a closed cap shaped like an elongated egg. *Phellorinia herculeana* has broadly club-shaped fruitbodies. Immature, unopened fruitbodies of the larger *Agaricus* species may also look similar, but show developing pallid or pinkish gills when the cap is cut through.

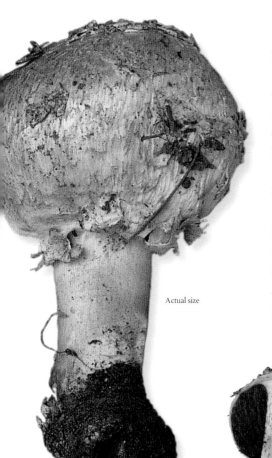

Actual size

The Texan Desert Mushroom looks like an unopened *Agaricus* species. The cap is more or less round, white at first, becoming brownish with age, smooth then coarsely scaly. It does not open, but contains a spore mass that is chocolate-brown to blackish when mature (see photo near left). The cap-colored stem has a coarse ring immediately under the cap, and gradually becomes woody with age.

FAMILY	Agaricaceae
DISTRIBUTION	North America, Europe, Africa, Central America, Asia
HABITAT	In woodland
ASSOCIATION	With broadleaf trees on calcareous (basic) soil
GROWTH FORM	On ground, singly, in small clusters, or in troops
ABUNDANCE	Occasional
SPORE COLOR	Brown
EDIBILITY	Edible when young

HEIGHT
Up to 4 in
(100 mm)

DIAMETER
Up to 2½ in
(60 mm)

LYCOPERDON ECHINATUM
SPINY PUFFBALL
PERSOON

519

Surprisingly, recent DNA research has shown that puffballs belong in the same family as ordinary cultivated mushrooms. Instead of producing spores on gills, however, puffballs have spores that develop inside their enclosed caps. When it is time to release the spores, puffballs have evolved a very elegant method of dispersal: they use raindrops. A hole forms at the top of the fruitbody and the spores are puffed out every time a drop hits. Elastic tissue inside the puffball ensures that it springs back into shape. Evidence from Sweden suggests that the Spiny Puffball may be a useful environmental indicator, since the species declines with acidification.

SIMILAR SPECIES
American collections have sometimes been referred to a separate species, *Lycoperdon americanum*, but further research is required to see if this is really distinct. A second American species, *L. pulcherrimum*, is very similar but is said to have stouter spines that never turn brown with age.

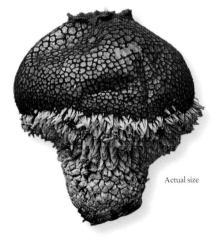

The Spiny Puffball is distinguished by long, dense spines that are white at first, but quickly turn brown (see photo right). They are shed with age, leaving behind a netlike pattern on the puffball surface. At maturity, a round hole forms at the apex of the fruitbody, allowing the brown spores to puff out.

Actual size

FAMILY	Agaricaceae
DISTRIBUTION	North America, Europe, northern Asia
HABITAT	In woodland
ASSOCIATION	With broadleaf trees or conifers
GROWTH FORM	On ground, singly, in small clusters, or in troops
ABUNDANCE	Very common
SPORE COLOR	Brown
EDIBILITY	Edible when young

HEIGHT
Up to 3 in
(80 mm)

DIAMETER
Up to 2 in
(50 mm)

520

LYCOPERDON PERLATUM
COMMON PUFFBALL
PERSOON

The Common Puffball or Devil's Snuff Box is edible when young, though care should be taken not to confuse them with poisonous earthballs. In the past, they were valued as styptics to staunch wounds and treat burns, as tinder for lighting fires, and as a means of smoking out and stupefying bees. Some indigenous cultures, however, treated puffballs with caution, since their spores were thought to cause blindness. Local names included Blindman's Bellows and No-Eyes. The spores can irritate the eyes and nose and, if inhaled in quantity, may even cause an allergic reaction in the lungs called lycoperdonosis.

SIMILAR SPECIES
Other puffball species may look similar. *Lycoperdon excipuliforme* is larger, grayer, and, when mature, the whole upper part disintegrates to release its spores. *Lycoperdon nigrescens* has blackish spines when young, turns dark brown when old, and prefers acidic woodland. *Lycoperdon pyriforme* has almost smooth fruitbodies that grow in dense clusters on rotting or buried wood.

The Common Puffball is a familiar woodland species, whitish to cream at first, and powdered with granular, conical spines or warts. With age it becomes browner, and the spines are shed to leave a netlike pattern on the surface. At maturity, a round hole forms at the apex of the fruitbody allowing the brown spores to puff out.

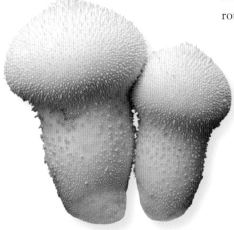

Actual size

FAMILY	Agaricaceae
DISTRIBUTION	North America, Europe, Africa, Central America, Asia
HABITAT	In woodland
ASSOCIATION	With broadleaf trees and conifers
GROWTH FORM	On rotting wood, typically in dense clusters
ABUNDANCE	Very common
SPORE COLOR	Brown
EDIBILITY	Edible when young

HEIGHT
Up to 2½ in
(60 mm)

DIAMETER
Up to 1½ in
(40 mm)

LYCOPERDON PYRIFORME

STUMP PUFFBALL

SCHAEFFER

521

The Stump Puffball grows on rotten wood, often on buried wood as well as stumps, and frequently appears in huge swarms. Recent molecular research has shown that it is not all that closely related to other puffballs, though still close enough to be included in the same genus. The epithet *pyriforme* means "pear-shaped," and the fruitbodies can indeed take the form of elongated, inverted pears—hence the alternative common name of the Pear-shaped Puffball. The genus name *Lycoperdon* is far more curious, since it means (euphemistically) a "wolf breaking wind"—a bizarre reference also found in the French word for puffball, *vesse-de-loup*.

SIMILAR SPECIES

Most other puffballs grow on soil and they lack the root-like, white rhizomorphs of the Stump Puffball. Those few that do grow on wood were formerly placed in the separate genus *Morganella*. These include *Lycoperdon subincarnatum* in eastern North America which has spines that leave a netlike pattern when shed, and a number of tropical species, most of which are darker, smaller, or almost stemless.

Actual size

The Stump Puffball produces cream to pale brown fruitbodies that have a finely granular surface, becoming almost smooth when mature. The stems have conspicuous, white, root-like rhizomorphs at the base. As with most other puffballs, a hole forms at the apex of the fruitbody allowing the brown spores to puff out.

FAMILY	Russulaceae
DISTRIBUTION	Western North America
HABITAT	In woodland
ASSOCIATION	Ectomycorrhizal, with conifers
GROWTH FORM	On ground, singly or in small groups
ABUNDANCE	Occasional
SPORE COLOR	White
EDIBILITY	Not edible

HEIGHT
Up to 1½ in
(35 mm)

CAP DIAMETER
Up to 1½ in
(35 mm)

MACOWANITES LUTEOLUS
YELLOW BRITTLEBALL
A. H. SMITH & TRAPPE

522

Macowanites luteolus is a fungus caught halfway between being a brittlegill agaric (*Russula* species) and a puffball. It has a cap and stem like an agaric, but the cap never opens, the gills are poorly formed, and the spores mature inside like the spores of a puffball. This group of fungi was first discovered in South Africa and named after pioneer local mycologist, Peter MacOwan—but later research has shown that they are particularly common in the Pacific Northwest of America, where several different species have been collected in conifer forest.

SIMILAR SPECIES

The cream to pale, dull yellow colors should distinguish *Macowanites luteolus* from related species, together with its slightly acrid taste. *Macowanites iodiolens* occurs in the same area and is similarly colored, but is mild-tasting with a distinctive smell of disinfectant.

Actual size

The Yellow Brittleball looks like an unopened *Russula* species. The cap is more-or-less round, smooth, and cream to pale dull yellow. It does not open, but contains a spore mass (sometimes intermixed with gill-like plates) which is cream to pale dull yellow when mature. The short cap-colored stem extends into the spore mass.

FAMILY	Agaricaceae
DISTRIBUTION	Southern North America, continental Europe, Africa, Central and South America, Asia, Australia
HABITAT	In desert, steppe, and dunes
ASSOCIATION	With dryland and dune vegetation
GROWTH FORM	On ground, singly or in small groups
ABUNDANCE	Occasional
SPORE COLOR	Black
EDIBILITY	Not edible

HEIGHT
Up to 12 in
(300 mm)

CAP DIAMETER
Up to 2 in
(50 mm)

MONTAGNEA ARENARIA
DESERT INKCAP
(DE CANDOLLE) ZELLER

523

The Desert Inkcap is another dryland specialist, widely distributed around the globe not only in deserts and arid lands, but also in coastal sand dunes. It is related to the familiar inkcap *Coprinus comatus*, but is much more woody and does not actively release its spores. Instead, these mature rapidly on the gills and remain there until the gills disintegrate and are gradually blown away. A number of additional *Montagnea* species have been described from around the world, mainly based on differences in spore size, but recent research suggests that they are just variations of the single species *M. arenaria*.

SIMILAR SPECIES

Montagnea arenaria could easily be passed over as an old, dried-up specimen of a conventional inkcap, such as *Coprinus comatus*. The latter species, however, lacks a woody stem or a basal volva and is altogether softer and more delicate, normally collapsing in dry weather.

Actual size

The Desert Inkcap has a rather ragged, weatherbeaten look. Its cap is flat and dull brown, the margins often irregular. The gills are black, crisped, and twisted, typically curling back over the cap. The stem is shaggy, woody-tough, and pale brownish. At its base is a brownish volva, embedded in the earth or sand.

FAMILY	Geastraceae
DISTRIBUTION	North America, Europe, Africa, Central and South America, Asia; introduced in Australia
HABITAT	In woodland, scrub, hedgerows, and dunes
ASSOCIATION	With broadleaf trees and conifers
GROWTH FORM	On ground, singly or in troops
ABUNDANCE	Occasional to rare
SPORE COLOR	Brown
EDIBILITY	Not edible

HEIGHT
Up to 3 in
(75 mm)

DIAMETER
Up to 6 in
(150 mm)

524

MYRIOSTOMA COLIFORME
PEPPER POT
(WITHERING) CORDA

The Pepper Pot is primarily a dryland species, quite common and widespread in semi-desert areas but rare elsewhere. It looks like an earthstar (*Geastrum* species), but rather than having one hole for spore release, the Pepper Pot has several—hence its common name. Oddly for a semi-desert species, it was first described from England, where it was long thought to have become extinct (not having been seen since 1880) until rediscovered in 2006. It is still on the national Red Lists of many European countries, however, and is one of 33 fungi proposed for international protection under the Bern Convention.

SIMILAR SPECIES
No very similar species are known. Earthstars (*Geastrum* species) not only have a single opening at the top (more like a salt-shaker than a pepper pot), but also have their puffball-like heads supported by a single column, not several columns as in *Myriostoma coliforme*.

The Pepper Pot has fruitbodies that are almost spherical at first. At maturity the thick outer skin splits and peels back to form 5–12 rays or arms, revealing the puffball-like spore sack at the center. The spore sack is supported by several small columns and is pierced by holes, through which the spores are released.

Actual size

FAMILY	Sclerodermataceae
DISTRIBUTION	North America, Europe, North and East Africa, northern Asia
HABITAT	In dry woodland and scrub
ASSOCIATION	Ectomycorrhizal, with pine and more rarely oak
GROWTH FORM	On ground, singly or in small groups
ABUNDANCE	Locally common
SPORE COLOR	Brown
EDIBILITY	Not edible

HEIGHT
Up to 12 in
(300 mm)

DIAMETER
Up to 8 in
(200 mm)

PISOLITHUS ARHIZUS

DYEBALL

(SCOPOLI) RAUSCHERT

525

The poor Dyeball is not one of the world's most attractive fungi, its fruitbodies often being mistaken for horse dung—even at close quarters. It was formerly known as *Pisolithus tinctorius*, the epithet (and the English name) referring to its traditional use in dyeing, where it produces a range of yellow and purple colors. The spores are formed in pea-size peridioles that can be seen studding the interior, if younger fruitbodies are cut open. These disintegrate on maturity, as does the outer surface, so that old fruitbodies are little more than a dusty mass of brown spores.

SIMILAR SPECIES

The Dyeball was once thought to be cosmopolitan, but DNA research has shown it is a complex of different species—some associating with eucalypts in Australia. The true Dyeball is a northern hemisphere species, locally common in dry, sandy soil (it is rare in the rain-soaked British Isles), but introduced elsewhere in pine plantations.

Actual size

The Dyeball resembles a large puffball when young, with a wide, often irregular, often half-buried stem. The surface is smooth, pale ocher-brown, becoming blackish brown, brittle, and disintegrating. If cut when young, the interior is dark brown, marbled with pale, pea-size peridioles (in which the spores are formed). The whole fungus becomes reddish brown and powdery when mature.

FAMILY	Agaricaceae
DISTRIBUTION	North America, Africa, Central and South America, Asia, Australia
HABITAT	In desert and semi-desert
ASSOCIATION	With desert vegetation, often with termite mounds
GROWTH FORM	On ground, singly or in small groups
ABUNDANCE	Locally common
SPORE COLOR	Reddish brown
EDIBILITY	Edible when young

HEIGHT
Up to 6 in
(150 mm)

CAP DIAMETER
Up to 1½ in
(40 mm)

526

PODAXIS PISTILLARIS
DESERT SHAGGY MANE
(LINNAEUS) FRIES

This is one of the most widespread and conspicuous fungi of desert and semi-desert lands, found in arid tropical and subtropical areas around the globe. It is in the same family as ordinary cultivated mushrooms and the Shaggy Ink Cap, which it resembles when young, but its fruitbodies are tough and their caps never open. Despite this toughness, young fruitbodies are widely eaten in Arabia and are even cultivated for food in northern Pakistan and India, where they are known as *khumbi*. In southwestern Africa and Australia the powdery spore mass has been used as a cosmetic by indigenous peoples.

SIMILAR SPECIES
Several other desert species have evolved fruitbodies with caps that never open, protecting their spores from desiccation. Those with shaggy, whitish fruitbodies include *Longula texensis*, which has more rounded, ball-like caps, and *Phellorinia herculeana*, which has similar but broadly club-shaped fruitbodies.

Actual size

The Desert Shaggy Mane looks rather like the Shaggy Ink Cap when young, but is tougher and woodier. The cap is elongated egg-shaped, scaly, and whitish cream. It never opens up, but is fused to the woody-tough, whitish stem. The reddish brown spores mature inside the cap, and are only released when the cap surface turns brown and weathers away.

FAMILY	Rhizopogonaceae
DISTRIBUTION	North America, Europe, northern Asia; also with planted pine in Africa, South America, Australia, New Zealand
HABITAT	In woodland
ASSOCIATION	Ectomycorrhizal, with pine
GROWTH FORM	In soil and leaf litter
ABUNDANCE	Locally common
SPORE COLOR	Pale brown
EDIBILITY	Not edible

HEIGHT
Up to 2 in
(50 mm)

DIAMETER
Up to 2 in
(50 mm)

RHIZOPOGON LUTEOLUS
YELLOW FALSE TRUFFLE
FRIES & NOORDHOLM

527

Rhizopogon species are truffle-like relatives of the boletes and (like *Suillus* species) only associate with conifers. The fruitbodies of *R. luteolus* can be surprisingly conspicuous, partly because of their color and size, but mainly because they normally grow half-embedded in the ground and half-exposed, rather than hiding deep in needle litter. The species has spread around the world in pine plantations. In some areas, it has deliberately been introduced as a beneficial ectomycorrhizal associate, helping the trees establish themselves on poor soils or on reclaimed land such as old spoil heaps.

SIMILAR SPECIES

Other *Rhizopogon* species are similar, though many are whitish or associated with conifers other than pine. *Rhizopogon vulgaris* and *R. ochraceorubens* are both yellowish pine associates, but bruise red on handling. The Common Earthball (*Scleroderma citrinum*) can also look similar, but is scaly, is blackish when cut, and has an unpleasant rubbery smell.

Actual size

The Yellow False Truffle produces solid, potato-like fruitbodies (see photo above) that are sordid yellow-ocher and may have some darker, finely threadlike, mycelial cords attached. The interior is spongy, whitish yellow at first, becoming dingy olive-brown on maturity.

FAMILY	Sclerodermataceae
DISTRIBUTION	North America, Europe, North Africa, northern Asia
HABITAT	In acidic woodland
ASSOCIATION	Ectomycorrhizal, with broadleaf trees and conifers
GROWTH FORM	On ground, singly or in small groups and clusters
ABUNDANCE	Very common
SPORE COLOR	Black
EDIBILITY	Poisonous

HEIGHT
Up to 2 in
(50 mm)

DIAMETER
Up to 4 in
(100 mm)

SCLERODERMA CITRINUM
COMMON EARTHBALL
PERSOON

528

Earthballs are very common ectomycorrhizal associates of trees, producing a mass of blackish spores that are released as the fruitbodies split open at the top—the edges sometimes peeling back in a starlike manner. The Common Earthball is particularly fond of acid woodlands and heaths. If cut, it has a very distinctive "earthball smell"—rather like perished rubber. Fruitbodies were apparently once used to adulterate truffle products, but are in fact poisonous, causing gastroenteritic symptoms if eaten. They are occasionally host to the curious Parasitic Bolete (*Pseudoboletus parasiticus*).

SIMILAR SPECIES

The Scaly Earthball (*Scleroderma verrucosum*) favors less acid woodland, has a thinner skin with smaller scales, and often has a wide, stemlike base. Some other earthballs may be distinguished by their scaleless surface, but most need microscopic examination to identify to species. *Rhizopogon* species may also look similar.

Actual size

The Common Earthball forms almost spherical fruitbodies. The bright ocher to buff surface breaks up into coarse warts or scales. There is no stem, but root-like rhizomorphs at the base. When cut, the skin is up to ¼ in (5 mm) thick, whitish, but weakly reddening. The spore mass inside is white at first, then marbled purplish black, finally powdery and dark gray (see photo near left).

FAMILY	Stephanosporaceae
DISTRIBUTION	Europe
HABITAT	In woodland
ASSOCIATION	With conifers, especially yew
GROWTH FORM	On ground
ABUNDANCE	Occasional
SPORE COLOR	Yellowish
EDIBILITY	Not edible

HEIGHT
Up to 1½ in
(40 mm)

DIAMETER
Up to 1½ in
(40 mm)

STEPHANOSPORA CAROTICOLOR
CARROT-COLORED TRUFFLE
(BERKELEY) PATOUILLARD

529

Most truffle-like fungi have fruitbodies that are whitish, brown, or black—but the Carrot-Colored Truffle is a colorful exception, if it can be spotted half-buried in woodland litter. The color comes from stephanosporin, a compound that has been isolated from fruitbodies. Stephanosporin is a precursor to a natural insecticide (also found in the fruitbodies), so it seems that the orange pigment helps keep the Carrot-Colored Truffle insect-free. The species is restricted to calcareous woodland in Europe and in the British Isles is most often found under yew.

SIMILAR SPECIES
The orange to red colors of *Stephanospora caroticolor* are distinctive. The truffle-like milkcap, *Lactarius stephensii*, also occurs in Europe, but has a duller, orange to red-brown outer surface and exudes a white latex when cut.

Actual size

The Carrot-Colored Truffle forms spherical to irregular, soft and fleshy, truffle-like fruitbodies. The smooth surface is fragile and evanescent, pale orange-yellow at first, becoming carrot-red and bruising blackish. The interior is yellow to orange with fine, honeycomb-like chambers in which the spores are produced.

FAMILY	Agaricaceae
DISTRIBUTION	North America, Europe, Africa, South America, Asia, Australia
HABITAT	In drylands and dunes
ASSOCIATION	With dryland and dune vegetation, often with mosses
GROWTH FORM	In soil and sand
ABUNDANCE	Occasional
SPORE COLOR	Brown
EDIBILITY	Not edible

HEIGHT
Up to 2½ in
(60 mm)

DIAMETER
Up to ½ in
(15 mm)

530

TULOSTOMA BRUMALE
WINTER STALKBALL
PERSOON

Stalkballs are relatives of the puffballs (*Lycoperdon* species) that have evolved to survive arid conditions. They typically grow in deserts, steppes, and drylands and generally favor calcareous sites. The Winter Stalkball, also known as the Common Stalked Puffball, is one of the most frequently encountered species in north temperate regions. It typically produces fruitbodies late in the year and is often found in coastal dunes, where the woody stalk may be half-buried in sand. It can occur in dry or sandy places inland. Before cement became commonplace, they sometimes grew in the mortar of old garden walls.

SIMILAR SPECIES
Many similar *Tulostoma* species occur worldwide. Commoner ones include *T. squamosum*, which has a shaggy stem, and *T. fimbriatum*, which has a slightly scaly stem and an irregular hole at the top of the spore sack, without a neat, raised rim.

The Winter Stalkball resembles a miniature puffball on a stick. The round, ball-like spore sack is smooth, buff at first, becoming gray. At the top is a small hole with a raised rim from which the spores are released (see photo left). The spore sack is lifted from the ground by a smooth to slightly scaly, woody, brownish stalk.

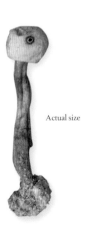

Actual size

FAMILY	Strophariaceae
DISTRIBUTION	New Zealand
HABITAT	In woodland
ASSOCIATION	With broadleaf trees
GROWTH FORM	On ground
ABUNDANCE	Occasional
SPORE COLOR	Brown
EDIBILITY	Not edible

HEIGHT	Up to 3 in (75 mm)
CAP DIAMETER	Up to 1½ in (40 mm)

WERAROA VIRESCENS

BLUE POUCH FUNGUS

(MASSEE) SINGER & A. H. SMITH

531

The Blue Pouch Fungus—a New Zealand specialty—is another peculiar species that is halfway between being an agaric and a puffball. If cut open, honeycomb-like remains of gills can be seen—but the cap never opens and the spores mature inside. It has currently been left stranded in *Weraroa*, since DNA sequencing has shown that it is not closely related to the reputedly hallucinogenic type species (*W. novae-ʒealandiae*), which has been transferred to *Psilocybe*, nor to its erstwhile companion the Red Pouch Fungus (*W. erythrocephala*), which has been transferred to *Leratiomyces*.

SIMILAR SPECIES

Weraroa novae-ʒealandiae (now *Psilocybe weraroa*) looks similar, but grows on very rotten wood, is blue-staining, and (when cut) has a gray-brown rather than reddish brown interior. The Verdigris Agaric (*Stropharia aeruginosa*), which also occurs in New Zealand and may be related, is similarly colored but has a normal cap and gills with a scaly stem.

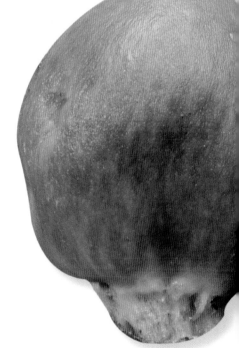

The Blue Pouch Fungus forms puffball-like fruitbodies. The cap is conical and smooth, becoming wrinkled. The surface is slightly sticky and pale blue to greenish blue when damp, polished and dull green when dry. The stem is cylindrical, continuing into the cap interior, and white to bright yellow. When cut, the interior of the cap is reddish brown.

Actual size

FAMILY	Agaricaceae
DISTRIBUTION	North America, Europe, Africa, Central and South America, Asia, Australia, New Zealand
HABITAT	In open ground, field edges, exposed garden mulch, and dunes
ASSOCIATION	On straw, rotten wood, and plant debris
GROWTH FORM	In small or large groups
ABUNDANCE	Common
SPORE COLOR	White
EDIBILITY	Not edible

HEIGHT
Up to ½ in
(15 mm)

DIAMETER
Up to ½ in
(15 mm)

CYATHUS OLLA
FIELD BIRD'S NEST
(BATSCH) PERSOON

532

Just like miniature nests, complete with eggs, the bird's nest fungi have evolved a remarkable method of spore dispersal involving raindrops. Young fruitbodies are drum-shaped, but on maturity the drumskin ruptures to reveal the cup or "nest" below. The "eggs" inside are packets of spores (peridioles) attached to the base of the cup by a coiled thread. When a raindrop splashes into the open cup, the coil is released and the peridiole is catapulted into the air. It can land as much as a yard (1 m) away, leaving the spores to disperse gradually as the peridiole breaks down.

SIMILAR SPECIES

The less common *Cyathus stercoreus* is similar to the Field Bird's Nest but often grows on dung. It can be distinguished microscopically by its much larger spores. *Cyathus striatus* is common, but prefers damper sites and has a hairy outer and fluted inner surface. In the tropics and elsewhere, there are 30–40 additional species, all of similar "bird's nest" form.

Actual size

The Field Bird's Nest forms fruitbodies that are drum-shaped at first, the whitish to ocher "drumskin" rupturing on maturity to reveal the gray, egglike peridioles below (see photo left). The mature fruitbodies typically develop a distinct, flared margin. Outer and inner surfaces are smooth and silvery gray.

FAMILY	Agaricaceae
DISTRIBUTION	North America, Europe, Central and South America, Asia, New Zealand
HABITAT	In damp woodland, shady gardens, and woodchip mulch
ASSOCIATION	On rotten, often mossy, wood or plant debris
GROWTH FORM	In small or large groups
ABUNDANCE	Common
SPORE COLOR	White
EDIBILITY	Not edible

HEIGHT
Up to ½ in
(15 mm)

DIAMETER
Up to ¼ in
(8 mm)

CYATHUS STRIATUS
FLUTED BIRD'S NEST
(HUDSON) PERSOON

533

The Fluted Bird's Nest—also known as the Splash Cup—prefers mossy, fallen branches in damp, shady areas, whereas the equally common Field Bird's Nest (*Cyathus olla*) prefers open ground. Their resemblance to miniature bird's nests is remarkable, but local names also include Fairy Goblets and Pixies' Purses, with the peridioles seen as coins instead of eggs. In Scotland, finding them on the way to work was once considered a lucky omen. They may also bring good fortune in medicine. Antibiotics called striatins have been isolated from *Cyathus striatus*, as well as an extract that appears to have potential as a cancer therapeutic.

Actual size

SIMILAR SPECIES

On open ground, *Cyathus olla*, with a smooth outer surface and cup more like a wide-rimmed dish, is a common, cosmopolitan species. In the tropics and elsewhere, there are many additional bird's nests with fluted inner and shaggy outer cups, including *C. limbatus*, *C. poeppigii*, and *C. novae-ʒeelandiae*. They are differentiated mainly by microscopic characters.

The Fluted Bird's Nest forms fruitbodies that at first look like a tiny, shaggy, brown goblet with a smooth, whitish top. This top surface ruptures at maturity to reveal the gray, egglike peridioles below. The inner surfaces of the goblet are strongly fluted and silvery gray.

FAMILY	Agaricaceae
DISTRIBUTION	North America, Central and South America, Eastern Asia, Australia, New Zealand
HABITAT	In woodland
ASSOCIATION	On rotten wood and plant debris, especially bracken
GROWTH FORM	In small or large groups
ABUNDANCE	Locally common
SPORE COLOR	White
EDIBILITY	Not edible

HEIGHT
Less than ¼ in
(6 mm)

DIAMETER
Less than ¼ in
(6 mm)

534

NIDULA NIVEOTOMENTOSA
WOOLLY BIRD'S NEST
(HENNINGS) LLOYD

Actual size

Nidula species differ from other bird's nest fungi in having peridioles (the egglike packets containing the spores) that are not attached to the base of the cup, but instead are embedded in a sticky gel. Raindrops falling into the cup dissolve the gel, allowing the peridioles to splash out when conditions are damp and ideal for spore germination. The Woolly Bird's Nest is a small but locally common species, especially in western North America where it seems to have a particular fondness for old, dead stems of bracken.

SIMILAR SPECIES

Nidula candida is a related North American species with substantially larger, gray-brown fruitbodies. The widespread Fluted Bird's Nest (*Cyathus striatus*) has a shaggy, brown outer surface, but is conspicuously fluted or ridged inside the cup. The Field Bird's Nest (*C. olla*) is of similar shape to the Woolly Bird's Nest, but smooth.

The Woolly Bird's Nest forms fruitbodies that are cylindrical, flaring slightly toward the top, covered with a whitish veil that ruptures on maturity to reveal red-brown, egglike peridioles in a sticky gel below. The margin and outer surfaces are white and woolly-hairy, the inner suface tan and smooth.

FAMILY	Geastraceae
DISTRIBUTION	North America, Europe, Africa, Central and South America, Asia, Australia, New Zealand
HABITAT	In woodland, gardens, dunes
ASSOCIATION	On decaying wood and vegetation, garden mulch, and dung
GROWTH FORM	In troops or swarms
ABUNDANCE	Common
SPORE COLOR	White
EDIBILITY	Not edible

SPHAEROBOLUS STELLATUS

SHOOTING STAR

TODE

HEIGHT
Less than ⅛ in
(2 mm)

DIAMETER
Up to ⅛ in
(3 mm)

535

The fruitbodies of the Shooting Star may be tiny, but they have been dubbed the "Big Berthas" of the fungal world. When mature they open in a star-like manner to reveal a ball of spores sitting in a cup. Osmotic pressure below the cup builds up until it is suddenly released and the cup everts (turns inside-out) explosively—hence the alternative English name of the Cannonball Fungus. The spore ball is shot as much as 6 ft (2 m) into the air and as far as 20 ft (6 m) horizontally. It is sticky, so can adhere to any vegetation in its flight path, or indeed to parked cars and painted surfaces, which can sometimes become peppered with spore balls.

Actual size

SIMILAR SPECIES

Two very similar species, *Sphaerobolus ingoldii* and *S. iowensis*, have been distinguished by DNA analysis and are known to occur in North America (the former also in Japan), but may be more widespread. Both can only be separated from *S. stellatus* by microscopic examination.

The Shooting Star is a tiny fungus, but grows in dense groups. Individual fruitbodies may arise directly from the substrate, but more frequently from a cream to buff sheet of tissue. Each is a half-embedded sphere, opening in a star shape when mature. When the spore ball has been shot out, the everted inner surface of the fruitbody remains like a miniature bubble in a yellow to orange, star-shaped cup.

FAMILY	Phallaceae
DISTRIBUTION	Southern North America, Africa, Central and South America, southern Asia (and Japan), Australia, New Zealand; naturalized in England
HABITAT	In woodland and gardens
ASSOCIATION	On rich soil or very decayed woody remains
GROWTH FORM	On ground, singly or in groups
ABUNDANCE	Occasional
SPORE COLOR	Olive-brown
EDIBILITY	Edible (in "egg" stage)

HEIGHT
Up to 4 in
(100 mm)

DIAMETER
Up to 4 in
(100 mm)

536

ASEROË RUBRA
STARFISH FUNGUS
LABILLARDIÈRE

The Starfish Fungus, which is also known as the Anemone Stinkhorn, was originally described from Tasmania, but has a widespread distribution in the tropics and subtropics, as well as Australasia and Asia north to Japan. Curiously, it has appeared for many years in a woodland near London—presumably as an exotic introduction, since it is otherwise unknown from Europe. Like the stinkhorns, the Starfish Fungus produces its spores in an evil-smelling slime that attracts flies, the agents of spore dispersal. Fruitbodies are variable in shape and color, some forms being orange, yellowish, or even white. They are all currently considered to belong to a single, widespread species, but further research may prove otherwise.

The Starfish Fungus emerges from a gelatinous, white "egg," the remains of which persist at the stem base. The mature fruitbody is usually red, but rather variable, some forms having a short stem and 14–22 narrow, wispy "arms," while the more typical form has a longish stem and 5–9 arms, each of which branches into two. The spore slime is in the central disc.

SIMILAR SPECIES
The Devil's Fingers (*Clathrus archeri*) is similarly colored, but has fewer, longer arms on a reduced stalk with the spore slime on the inner part of each arm. The African and Asian *Aseroë arachnoidea* is similar to the Starfish Fungus, but whitish. The recently described South American *A. floriformis* forms a strange, pale yellow, sunflower-like fruitbody.

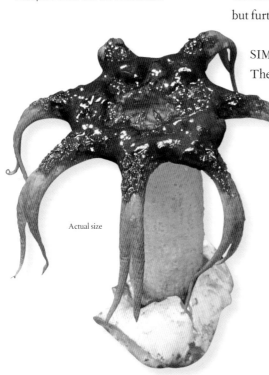

Actual size

FAMILY	Phallaceae
DISTRIBUTION	Australia, New Zealand, Africa; naturalized in Europe and western North America (California)
HABITAT	In woodland and gardens
ASSOCIATION	On rich soil or very decayed woody remains
GROWTH FORM	On ground, singly or in groups
ABUNDANCE	Occasional
SPORE COLOR	Olive-brown
EDIBILITY	Edible (in "egg" stage)

HEIGHT
Up to 2½ in
(60 mm)

DIAMETER
Up to 8 in
(200 mm)

CLATHRUS ARCHERI
DEVIL'S FINGERS
(BERKELEY) DRING

537

Originally described from Tasmania, the Devil's Fingers—
or the Octopus Stinkhorn—is said to have been shipped into
continental Europe with straw for ANZAC cavalry during
World War I. More prosaically, the fungus has also been
introduced with exotic garden plants, and has now become
widely naturalized in southern England and, more recently, in
California. The inner parts of the tentacle-like arms are covered
in a sweet, but fetid, olive-brown slime that attracts flies, which
subsequently distribute the spores. As a fly attractant, it may
therefore be no coincidence that the fruitbody itself resembles
some grotesque, carrionlike flower.

SIMILAR SPECIES
The Starfish Fungus (*Aseroë rubra*) is similarly colored, but
produces its arms on a more distinct stalk with the spore slime
in a central mass. Other species of *Clathrus* either have the arms
united at the tip, or have branching and united arms, forming a
complete or partial cage, as in *C. ruber*.

The Devil's Fingers has fruitbodies that
emerge from a gelatinous, white "egg" similar
to those of stinkhorns, but slightly smaller and
often formed in clusters. The remains persist at
the base of the short stem. The spore-bearing
part of the fruitbody has 4–8 radiating "arms,"
variously colored pink to red.

Actual size

FAMILY	Phallaceae
DISTRIBUTION	Europe, North Africa, southwestern Asia; naturalized in California and Mexico
HABITAT	In woodland and gardens
ASSOCIATION	On rich soil or very decayed woody remains
GROWTH FORM	On ground, singly or in groups
ABUNDANCE	Occasional
SPORE COLOR	Olive-brown
EDIBILITY	Edible (in "egg" stage), but best avoided

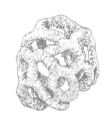

HEIGHT
Up to 5 in
(120 mm)

DIAMETER
Up to 3½ in
(90 mm)

538

CLATHRUS RUBER
RED CAGE
P. MICHELI EX PERSOON

Most representatives of the clathroid fungi are tropical or subtropical, but the Red Cage is a north-temperate species, common in the Mediterranean area but also known from milder, coastal regions as far north as the British Isles. Perhaps not surprisingly, the species has been regarded with deep suspicion in European folklore. In parts of France it was believed to cause convulsions, eruptions of the skin, and even cancer. One old Italian report described finding it growing on a human skull in a ruined church. In fact, it is said to be edible in the "egg" stage, though hardly tempting given the foul-smelling slime it later produces. An alternative common name is the Lattice Stinkhorn.

SIMILAR SPECIES

In the American subtropics and tropics, *Clathrus crispus* is similarly colored, but the net-forming branches are thicker, so that the spaces between are smaller and resemble pierced holes. The widespread *Colus hirudinosus*, known from southern Europe, and the similar Australian *C. pusillus*, have arms which only form a network near the top of the fruitbody.

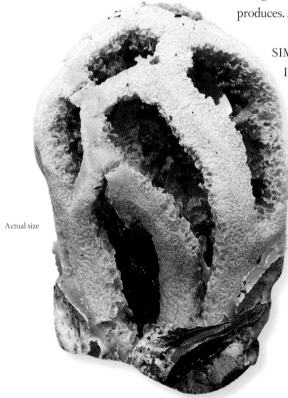

Actual size

The Red Cage develops from a gelatinous, white "egg," the remains of which persist at the base. The fruitbody is salmon-pink to scarlet, the branching arms joining together to form a lattice-like cage. The inner side of the arms is covered with an olive-brown spore slime. The fruitbody is quite fragile and collapses when old.

FAMILY	Phallaceae
DISTRIBUTION	Southern South America, Australia, New Zealand; naturalized in southeastern England and East Africa
HABITAT	In woodland and gardens
ASSOCIATION	On rich soil or very decayed woody remains
GROWTH FORM	On ground, singly or in groups
ABUNDANCE	Occasional
SPORE COLOR	Olive-brown
EDIBILITY	Edible (in "egg" stage)

HEIGHT
Up to 10 in
(250 mm)

DIAMETER
Up to 10 in
(250 mm)

ILEODICTYON CIBARIUM

BASKET FUNGUS

TULASNE

539

Ileodictyon species resemble the cage fungi, but the fruitbodies become completely detached at maturity and show radial symmetry, with no distinction between top and bottom. Apparently, they are released suddenly from their "eggs," rather like a jack-in-the-box. The fruitbodies may tumble around in the wind, helping spore dispersal, though like other members of the family their spores are normally spread by flies. The Basket Fungus was originally described from New Zealand and was said to have been formerly eaten by Maoris in its "egg" stage (*cibarium* means "edible"), though since the Maori name for it translates as "thunder excrement," this may be doubtful.

SIMILAR SPECIES

A related species, *Ileodictyon gracile*, is found in Australasia, Africa, Japan, and southern Europe. It has thinner, flatter arms without a crumpled appearance. Several of the cage-like *Clathrus* species are white, including the African *C. preussii*, but in *Clathrus* the cages have a distinct base and do not normally become detached.

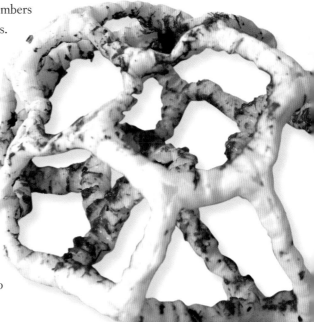

Actual size

The Basket Fungus develops from a gelatinous, white "egg," but on maturity the fruitbody detaches itself, leaving the remains of the egg behind. The detached fruitbody has no distinct base or upperside, but forms a large, white, cage-like network. The arms of the net have a crinkled or pleated appearance, with the inner side covered in a brownish spore slime.

FAMILY	Phallaceae
DISTRIBUTION	Sub-Saharan Africa
HABITAT	In woodland and gardens
ASSOCIATION	On rich soil or very decayed woody remains
GROWTH FORM	On ground, singly or in groups
ABUNDANCE	Occasional
SPORE COLOR	Olive-brown
EDIBILITY	Not edible

HEIGHT
Up to 5 in
(120 mm)

DIAMETER
Up to 1½ in
(40 mm)

540

LYSURUS CORALLOCEPHALUS
CORALHEAD STINKHORN
WELWITSCH & CURREY

The Coralhead Stinkhorn was formerly placed in its own genus, *Kalchbrennera*, because of its unusual, coralloid head with the slimy spore mass on the outer, rather than the inner, parts of the branches. Like other stinkhorns, the spore mass smells of carrion and attracts flies, which subsequently spread the spores. The species was first collected in Angola by the Austrian explorer and botanist Friedrich Welwitsch, and is restricted to sub-Saharan Africa. It is said to grow with or close to very rotten wood and it seems that, like other members of the family, it is a late-stage wood-rotting fungus.

SIMILAR SPECIES

The related and more widespread *Lysurus periphragmoides* is similarly colored, but has a larger head with a well-formed cage or net without coralloid protuberances. A recently described Asian species, *L. pakistanicus*, has a yellowish stem and a still larger, pinkish, cage-like head.

Actual size

The Coralhead Stinkhorn emerges from a gelatinous "egg," the remains of which persist at the stem base. The mature fruitbody has a long, hollow, reddish to cream stem. The fertile head consists of narrow, red branches that typically form a mesh with small coralloid protruberances. When fresh, the outer parts of the branches are covered in an olive-brown spore slime.

FAMILY	Phallaceae
DISTRIBUTION	Asia; naturalized in North America, southern Europe, Australia
HABITAT	In woodland and gardens
ASSOCIATION	On rich soil or very decayed woody remains
GROWTH FORM	On ground, singly or in groups
ABUNDANCE	Occasional
SPORE COLOR	Olive-brown
EDIBILITY	Edible (in "egg" stage)

HEIGHT
Up to 6 in
(150 mm)

DIAMETER
Up to 1 in
(25 mm)

LYSURUS MOKUSIN

RIBBED LIZARD'S CLAW

(LINNAEUS) FRIES

541

The Ribbed Lizard's Claw or Lantern Stinkhorn was originally described from China where it is apparently eaten in its "egg" stage, though mainly for its reputed medicinal properties (it is said to help cure gangrenous ulcers). Like many other phalloids, it has since established itself in suitable climates elsewhere and has now become fairly common in parts of Australia and the southern United States. The "claws" are interspersed with an evil-smelling spore slime that attracts flies. As a late-stage wood-rotter, it has a liking for woodchip garden mulch, where it can often appear in quantity, much to the consternation of suburban garden owners.

SIMILAR SPECIES

Lysurus gardneri is a similar African-Asian species but has a round, not ridged, stem. The Lizard's Claw (*L. cruciatus*), is a more widespread species, occasionally found as an alien in Europe, that also has a round, not ridged, stem and fertile arms that typically break free at the top.

The Ribbed Lizard's Claw emerges from a gelatinous "egg," the remains of which persist at the stem base. The mature fruitbody has a distinctly ridged stem that is pallid to reddish. The fertile head consists of 4–6 short, pink to orange-red arms that remain joined at the pointed top, giving the head a compact, fluted appearance. The olive-brown spore-slime appears between the arms.

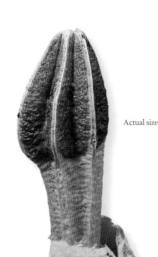

Actual size

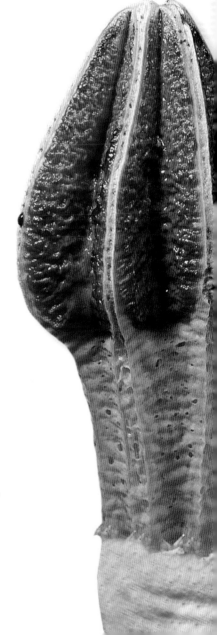

FAMILY	Phallaceae
DISTRIBUTION	Southeast Asia, Australia, New Zealand
HABITAT	In woodland and gardens
ASSOCIATION	On rich soil or decayed woody remains
GROWTH FORM	On ground or stumps, singly or in groups
ABUNDANCE	Occasional
SPORE COLOR	Olive-brown
EDIBILITY	Not edible

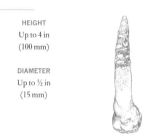

HEIGHT
Up to 4 in
(100 mm)

DIAMETER
Up to ½ in
(15 mm)

542

MUTINUS BORNEENSIS
YELLOW DOG STINKHORN
CESATI

The Yellow Dog Stinkhorn was originally described from the island of Borneo, but extends into Australia and New Zealand. As in other stinkhorns, the spores are formed inside an egglike receptacle and are surrounded by a gelatinous matrix. When mature, the eggs rupture and the foul-smelling, slimy spore mass is raised above the ground on a hollow, fragile stem that expands rapidly, possibly using the water stored in the jelly of the "egg." In the Yellow Dog Stinkhorn, the spore-slime often appears banded—left in a series of tidemarks as the stem expands.

SIMILAR SPECIES
Mutinus elegans is similar but is more brightly colored, with an orange to reddish pink, tapered stem. The Dog Stinkhorn (*M. caninus*) has a more distinct head and an orange-flushed stem. *Mutinus ravenelii* is similar, but reddish pink.

The Yellow Dog Stinkhorn emerges from a small gelatinous "egg" that persists at the stem base. The mature fruitbody has a spongy, tapering stem, which is white but flushed yellow to orange toward the tip. There is no distinct head, but the upper part of the stem is covered by olive-brown spore slime.

Actual size

FAMILY	Phallaceae
DISTRIBUTION	North America, Europe, Central America, northern Asia, New Zealand
HABITAT	In woodland and gardens
ASSOCIATION	On rich soil or decayed woody remains
GROWTH FORM	On ground or stumps, singly or in groups
ABUNDANCE	Common
SPORE COLOR	Olive-brown
EDIBILITY	Said to be edible (in "egg" stage)

HEIGHT
Up to 5 in
(120 mm)

DIAMETER
Up to ½ in
(15 mm)

MUTINUS CANINUS

DOG STINKHORN

(HUDSON) FRIES

543

This small stinkhorn is surprisingly easy to miss when it grows among leaves in woodland. The fly-attracting smell may indicate its presence, though the odor is not so strong as in the Common Stinkhorn. The miniature gelatinous "eggs" from which the fruitbody arises often occur in clusters, usually on or near stumps or on buried wood, though occasionally it can fruit quite high up on the rotting remains of trees. The species was originally described from Shrewsbury, England in 1778, but is widespread and quite common throughout the northern hemisphere and possibly introduced elsewhere.

SIMILAR SPECIES

Mutinus elegans (common in eastern North America, rare in Europe) is similar but is more brightly colored, usually reddish pink, and tapered, lacking a distinct head. The American *M. ravenelii* is also reddish, but shaped more like the Dog Stinkhorn. The purplish red *M. bambusinus* is widespread in the tropics as far north as Japan.

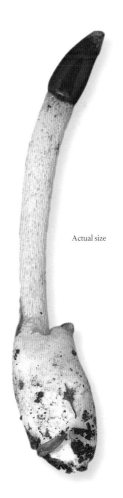

Actual size

The Dog Stinkhorn emerges from a small gelatinous "egg," the remains of which persist at the stem base. The mature fruitbody has a spongy stem, pale at the base and flushed bright orange toward the smooth, fertile head, which, when fresh, is covered with a cap of olive-brown spore slime.

FAMILY	Phallaceae
DISTRIBUTION	North America, Europe, northern Asia
HABITAT	In woodland and gardens
ASSOCIATION	In rich soil and very rotten woody material
GROWTH FORM	Singly or in troops
ABUNDANCE	Common
SPORE COLOR	Olive-brown
EDIBILITY	Edible (in "egg" stage)

HEIGHT
Up to 8 in
(200 mm)

DIAMETER
Up to 1½ in
(40 mm)

544

PHALLUS IMPUDICUS
COMMON STINKHORN
LINNAEUS

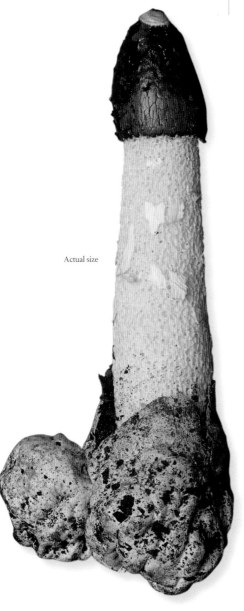

Actual size

Not surprisingly, this phallic fungus (*impudicus* means "shameless") has attracted a wealth of folklore. In Europe the immature fruitbody was locally known as "devil's egg" or "witch's egg," while the mature fungus was called "Satan's member." The fungus was believed to have aphrodisiac qualities. In Victorian England, the illustrator Beatrix Potter "could not find courage to draw it," while Charles Darwin's daughter Etty collected and burnt all the stinkhorns she could find, lest they corrupt the morals of her maidservants. The species is actually edible in its "egg" stage, is said to have a pleasant nutty flavor, and in Germany was once used to flavor sausages.

SIMILAR SPECIES
Phallus hadrianus is a similar north-temperate stinkhorn, typically growing in dunes, that differs in having pinkish "eggs." Specimens of the Common Stinkhorn with a short netlike veil have been mistaken for the tropical *P. indusiatus*, which has a much larger and more conspicuous veil.

The Common Stinkhorn produces fruitbodies from a gelatinous, white "egg" that remains at the base of the stem. The stem is white, hollow, and spongy. The fertile head is corrugated and covered in an olive-brown, sweet, and sickly smelling spore slime when fresh. Occasional specimens may produce a short netlike veil, hanging from the base of the fertile head.

FAMILY	Phallaceae
DISTRIBUTION	Africa, Central and South America, southern Asia (including China and Japan), Australia
HABITAT	In woodland and gardens
ASSOCIATION	In rich soil and very rotten woody material
GROWTH FORM	Singly or in troops
ABUNDANCE	Occasional
SPORE COLOR	Olive-brown
EDIBILITY	Edible

PHALLUS INDUSIATUS
VEILED LADY
SCHLECHTENDAL

HEIGHT
Up to 12 in
(300 mm)

DIAMETER
(including veil)
Up to 6 in
(150 mm)

545

Stinkhorns are not usually considered attractive, but this extraordinary tropical species is surely an exception. Unlike most stinkhorns, *Phallus indusiatus* unfurls a delicate veil-like net, or indusium, that reaches almost to the ground. Because of this, it was formerly referred to a separate genus, *Dictyophora*. In China it is often found growing in bamboo forests as its alternative name of the Bamboo Fungus suggests. Surprisingly, this strange fungus is cultivated in eastern Asia to be sold, fresh or dried, in "egg" or mature form as a delicacy and (because of its shape) as a purported aphrodisiac.

SIMILAR SPECIES

There are several similar tropical species, including *Phallus multicolor* which has a yellow-orange net, and *P. cinnabarinus* which has a reddish net. The Common Stinkhorn (*P. impudicus*) occasionally produces smaller and less delicate nets (a form called *P. impudicus* var. *togatus*) and such fruitbodies have been mistaken for the true Veiled Lady.

The Veiled Lady produces fruitbodies similar to those of the Common Stinkhorn (*Phallus impudicus*), with a white, spongy, hollow stem and wrinkled fertile head covered in olive-brown spore slime. But, additionally, it produces a delicate, white, veil-like net or indusium, which falls skirtlike from the base of the fertile head.

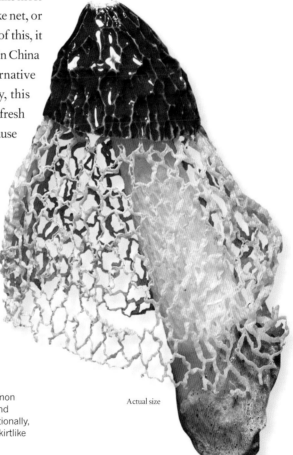

Actual size

FAMILY	Phallaceae
DISTRIBUTION	Eastern North America, Eastern Asia, Australia, New Zealand
HABITAT	In woodland and gardens
ASSOCIATION	On rich soil or very decayed woody remains
GROWTH FORM	On ground, singly or in groups
ABUNDANCE	Occasional
SPORE COLOR	Olive-brown
EDIBILITY	Not edible

HEIGHT
Up to 3 in
(75 mm)

DIAMETER
Up to 1 in
(25 mm)

PSEUDOCOLUS FUSIFORMIS
STINKY SQUID
(E. FISCHER) LLOYD

Like most phalloids, the sticky spore mass of the Stinky Squid emits a fetid smell—likened to that of pig slurry—which attracts flies. The flies then spread its spores. It is a diminutive but colorful species, originally described from the island of Réunion and since found in East Asia as far north as Japan, as well as Australia, New Zealand, and Hawaii. It was first seen in North America in 1915—where it is presumably an exotic introduction—and is now one of the many fungi spreading through gardens and parks in woodchip mulch.

SIMILAR SPECIES
The widespread Devil's Fingers (*Clathrus archeri*) is larger and has arms that are almost always free (not joined) at the top. The Ribbed Lizard's Claw (*Lysurus mokusin*) has a ribbed stem and short, stubby arms. Other similar species occur in the tropics.

The Stinky Squid has fruitbodies that emerge from a gelatinous, whitish to gray-brown "egg," the remains persisting at the stem base. The short, hollow stem divides into 3–5 "arms," which taper to the tip where they are initially joined, but may become detached. The arms are pink to orange or red, and the stem base is whitish. The olive-black spore slime adheres to the inner surface of the arms.

Actual size

FAMILY	Phallaceae
DISTRIBUTION	Central and South America
HABITAT	In woodland
ASSOCIATION	In rich soil and leaf litter
GROWTH FORM	Singly or in troops
ABUNDANCE	Occasional
SPORE COLOR	Olive-brown
EDIBILITY	Not edible

HEIGHT
Up to 6 in
(150 mm)

DIAMETER
Up to 1 in
(25 mm)

STAHELIOMYCES CINCTUS
CUMMERBUND STINKHORN
E. FISCHER

547

Ordinary stinkhorns produce peculiar fruitbodies, but the Cummerbund Stinkhorn is in a bizarre class all of its own. Restricted to the neotropics, it emerges from colored gelatinous "eggs" that are attached to rotting wood by threadlike rhizomorphs. Normal stinkhorn stems are hollow and often semiperforated, but in this species the holes are as big as those in a Swiss cheese. Strangest of all, the evil-smelling spore slime is not carried on the head or tip of the stem—but in a constricting cummerbund-like band below the top.

SIMILAR SPECIES

No other fungus closely resembles the fruitbodies of this eccentric species. The Borneo Stinkhorn (*Mutinus borneensis*) often has spore slime in one or more ill-defined bands near the tip of the stem, but the stem is not pierced, nor is the slime in a single, constricting ring.

Actual size

The Cummerbund Stinkhorn produces fruitbodies from a purplish, gelatinous "egg" that remains at the stem base. The stem itself is white, hollow, cylindrical, and pierced with roundish holes. The sticky, olive-brown mass of spores is formed in a band around the stem about three-quarters of the way up.

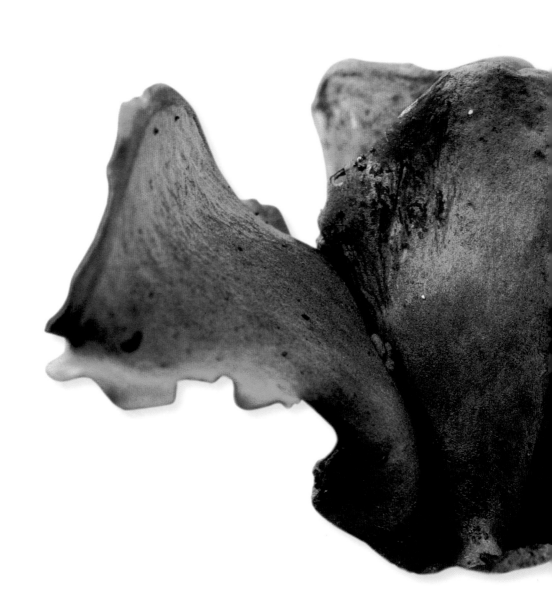

CUP FUNGI, MORELS, TRUFFLES, FLASK FUNGI & LICHENS

This group of species all belong in the *Ascomycota*. In terms of species, they are the largest group in the kingdom Fungi—but most, including the yeasts and molds, are too small to identify without a microscope.

The cup fungi, however, contain many conspicuous species, most but not all of them with cup- or disc-shaped fruitbodies. The morels and the true truffles are close relatives. The morels' honeycomb heads are, in effect, complex cups turned inside out, while the compacted folds inside truffles are the remains of cups.

Individual fruitbodies of the flask fungi are usually very small, frequently no more than black spots on decaying wood or leaves. Some species, however, produce these tiny fruitbodies in colonies immersed in stroma—sterile tissue that may resemble a single large fruitbody. They include some peculiar parasites, like the caterpillar fungi.

Lichens are a diverse group of fungi that form mutually beneficial associations with algae and cyanobacteria. Their partners live among the sterile hyphae and they need light to photosynthesize, so the whole fungus is on display, rather than just a fruitbody. When produced, the true, spore-producing fruitbodies are often disc-shaped—though many lichens spread by releasing ready-mixed propagules of hyphae and algal cells.

FAMILY	Pyrenomenataceae
DISTRIBUTION	North America, Europe, North Africa, Central and South America, Asia, Australia, New Zealand
HABITAT	In woodland and scrub
ASSOCIATION	On bare ground, especially disturbed and compacted clay
GROWTH FORM	On ground, in groups and clusters
ABUNDANCE	Common
SPORE COLOR	White
EDIBILITY	Edible

HEIGHT
Up to 2 in
(50 mm)

DIAMETER
Up to 4 in
(100 mm)

ALEURIA AURANTIA
ORANGE PEEL FUNGUS
(PERSOON) FUCKEL

550

The Orange Peel Fungus is cup-shaped at first, with a smooth, bright orange inner surface and an outer surface that is covered in a fine, whitish down, making it seem pale orange. With age, the fungus opens up and expands to become disc-shaped, often irregularly so (sometimes splitting or breaking) when growing close together in a cluster.

The Orange Peel Fungus is a common, widely distributed, and very conspicuous species with a preference for growing in clusters on bare, clayey, compacted ground, especially ground that has previously been disturbed. It is very brittle and thin, but is said to be edible, though perhaps more as a colorful embellishment than as a meal. A lectin (protein) extracted from the fungus (*Aleuria aurantia* lectin, or AAL) specifically binds to the carbohydrate fucose and has been widely used in a range of analytical tests and procedures. Research suggests that it may, for example, help detect certain forms of cancer.

SIMILAR SPECIES

A related species, *Aleuria rhenana*, is bright orange-yellow but has a distinct stalk. *Caloscypha fulgens* is also orange-yellow, but with blue-greenish tints on the outer surface. Most other bright orange cup fungi are much smaller.

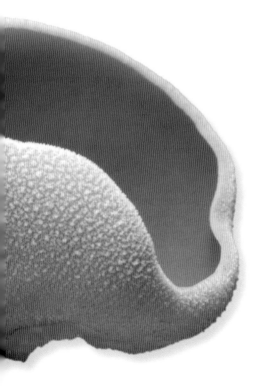

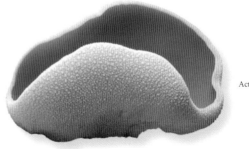

Actual size

FAMILY	Pyronemataceae
DISTRIBUTION	North America, continental Europe, North Africa, Central and South America, northern Asia, Australia, New Zealand
HABITAT	In woodland
ASSOCIATION	With conifers, less commonly broadleaf trees
GROWTH FORM	On ground or in moss, in clusters
ABUNDANCE	Locally common
SPORE COLOR	White
EDIBILITY	Not edible

HEIGHT
Up to 2 in
(50 mm)

DIAMETER
Up to 1 in
(25 mm)

ALEURIA RHENANA

STALKED ORANGE PEEL FUNGUS

FUCKEL

551

The Stalked Orange Peel Fungus is a rather cumbersome name for this small, but attractive, cup fungus that surely deserves a better one. Its fruitbodies are as bright as those of the more familiar Orange Peel Fungus (*Aleuria aurantia*), but are typically goblet-shaped. The two may not be as closely related as their names suggest, since the Stalked Orange Peel Fungus is often referred to the genus *Sowerbyella* and may not be a true *Aleuria* species at all. It is generally rare in Europe (and absent from the British Isles), but is perhaps more common in western North America.

SIMILAR SPECIES

The Orange Peel Fungus (*Aleuria aurantia*) is similarly colored, but is larger and lacks a stalk. The Rosy Goblet (*Microstoma protractum*) is similarly shaped and can be orange-red, but is typically more scarlet with a ragged edge to the cup margin.

The Stalked Orange Peel Fungus is cup-shaped, with a smooth, bright yellow-orange to orange inner surface, and an outer surface that is pale yellow and finely scurfy. The cup is distinctly stalked, the stalk pale yellow, but covered with a whitish mycelium toward the base.

Actual size

FAMILY	Helotiaceae
DISTRIBUTION	North America, Europe, South America, Asia, New Zealand
HABITAT	In woodland
ASSOCIATION	With broadleaf trees and conifers
GROWTH FORM	On rotten stumps, fallen logs, and branches
ABUNDANCE	Common
SPORE COLOR	White
EDIBILITY	Not edible

HEIGHT
Less than ⅛ in
(1 mm)

DIAMETER
Up to 1 in
(25 mm)

552

ASCOCORYNE CYLICHNIUM
LARGE PURPLE JELLYDISC
(TULASNE) KORF

Ascocoryne cylichnium and its close relative, *A. sarcoides*, are both common and widespread in woodland, where they are often mistaken for species of the true jelly fungi, such as *Exidia recisa*, though actually belonging to the cup fungi. Both are wood-rotters and, like many other wood-rotters, contain enzymes—in this case ascocorynin—that inhibit bacterial growth and may have some potential use in medicine. It is also possible that the presence of *Ascocoryne* species in wood may help to prevent colonization by more harmful wood-destroying fungi.

SIMILAR SPECIES

The equally common Purple Jellydisc (*Ascocoryne sarcoides*) is generally smaller and less often disc-shaped, but is best distinguished microscopically. It is often accompanied by irregularly lobed and clustered fruitbodies of similar color that produce only conidia (asexual spores). *Ascotremella faginea* is gelatinous and reddish purple, but forms fruitbodies that are brainlike, rather than disc-shaped.

The Large Purple Jellydisc typically produces fruitbodies in dense clusters or troops. Individual fruitbodies start as pale reddish purple to lilac-purple, firmly gelatinous blobs, which gradually become button-like with age. When mature, they are generally thin and disc-shaped, often rather pleated and wavy, and attached to wood at the base or by an abbreviated stem.

Actual size

FAMILY	Helotiaceae
DISTRIBUTION	North America, Europe, North Africa, Central and South America, Asia
HABITAT	In woodland
ASSOCIATION	On broadleaf wood
GROWTH FORM	On fallen branches and twigs, in dense swarms
ABUNDANCE	Very common
SPORE COLOR	White
EDIBILITY	Not edible

HEIGHT	DIAMETER
Less than ⅛ in (1 mm)	Up to ⅛ in (3 mm)

BISPORELLA CITRINA

LEMON DISCO

(BATSCH) KORF & S. E. CARPENTER

553

This is one of the commonest and, thanks to its color, one of the more conspicuous small discos or discomycetes—an old but still useful term for disc and cup fungi. It is particularly common on beech logs and fallen branches, though it will happily grow on all kinds of broadleaf wood. *Bisporella citrina* was first described in 1789 by the German naturalist and mycologist Dr. August Batsch, but has since been found to be widespread, occurring from Asia to South America.

SIMILAR SPECIES

The related *Bisporella sulfurina* is similarly colored, but even smaller and grows in clusters on old, blackened, fungal stroma on wood. Yellow *Hymenoscyphus* species may look superficially similar, but are always clearly stalked when observed under a hand lens. Many other small, yellow discos have fringed or hairy margins to the discs.

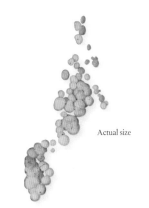

Actual size

The Lemon Disco forms tiny, disc-shaped fruitbodies, typically in dense swarms. The upper surface is smooth and shallowly cup-shaped at first, becoming disc-shaped or even slightly rounded when mature. The undersurface is also smooth and normally attached to the wood at the center, sometimes by a very short stem. All parts are bright lemon-yellow, becoming more golden-yellow when old.

FAMILY	Bulgariaceae
DISTRIBUTION	North America, Europe, Asia
HABITAT	In woodland
ASSOCIATION	With broadleaf trees, particularly oak
GROWTH FORM	On dead limbs and recently fallen logs and branches
ABUNDANCE	Common
SPORE COLOR	Black
EDIBILITY	Not edible

HEIGHT
Up to ½ in
(15 mm)

DIAMETER
Up to 1½ in
(40 mm)

554

BULGARIA INQUINANS
BLACK BULGAR
(PERSOON) FRIES

The Black Bulgar—or the Poor Man's Liquorice as it is also known—is often found growing in large quantities on recently fallen trunks and limbs of oaks. It seems probable that the fungus is an endophyte, meaning that it exists in some form in the wood of the living tree. It bides its time, waiting for a bough to break, and when this eventually happens it is ready to become the first colonizer of the newly dead wood. It produces abundant blackish brown spores that can stain the hands and will leave an impressive spore print if fruitbodies are left overnight on white paper. Not unsurprisingly it has been used to produce a blackish natural dye.

Actual size

SIMILAR SPECIES
The Black Bulgar is often confused with the completely unrelated *Exidia glandulosa* that is also common on oak. The latter species can, however, be distinguished by its sparsely warted upper surface, and by producing a white, not black, spore print.

The Black Bulgar forms densely gelatinous, rubbery fruitbodies in clusters or large troops. Each fruitbody is shaped like a button or an inverted cone. The outer surface is scurfy and brownish to blackish brown. The inner surface is smooth and black with a distinct, often inrolled margin that may make the fruitbody look cup-shaped (see photo left). With age, the fruitbodies expand and become flatter.

FAMILY	Caloscyphaceae
DISTRIBUTION	North America, Europe, northern Asia
HABITAT	In woodland
ASSOCIATION	With conifers
GROWTH FORM	On soil and leaf litter
ABUNDANCE	Occasional
SPORE COLOR	White
EDIBILITY	Not edible

HEIGHT
Up to 1 in
(25 mm)

DIAMETER
Up to 2 in
(50 mm)

CALOSCYPHA FULGENS

GOLDEN CUP

(PERSOON) BOUDIER

555

In upland conifer forests in North America, the Golden Cup or Blue-Staining Cup is known as a snow-melt fungus, the fruitbodies appearing in spring as the winter snows start to melt away. It is not only colorful, thanks to its remarkable blue-staining reaction when bruised, but is also unique. Based on molecular research, it has been placed in its own single-species family. The Golden Cup also occurs in Europe, but is generally uncommon, except in alpine areas. The species was not recorded from the British Isles until the 1960s and may have been introduced with exotic conifers.

SIMILAR SPECIES

The green-blue bruising reaction is unique among yellow cup fungi. In North America, however, *Caloscypha fulgens* has also been called the Spring Orange Peel Fungus, though the true Orange Peel Fungus (*Aleuria aurantia*) fruits later in the year, does not change color when bruised, and is normally a bright orange without yellowish tones. *Sowerbyella radicata* has a distinct, rooting stem.

Actual size

The Golden Cup forms fruitbodies that are cup-shaped at first, often becoming lobed or irregular when they expand. Old specimens may be almost flat and irregularly disc-shaped. The inner surface is smooth, and bright yellow-orange to orange. The outer surface is matt and slightly duller, turning olive to blue-green, especially at the margin, with age or when bruised. A very short stem may be present.

FAMILY	Dermateaceae
DISTRIBUTION	North America, Europe, Asia
HABITAT	In woodland
ASSOCIATION	With broadleaf trees
GROWTH FORM	On underside of very rotten, damp, fallen wood
ABUNDANCE	Occasional
SPORE COLOR	Brown
EDIBILITY	Not edible

HEIGHT
Less than ⅛ in
(1 mm)

DIAMETER
Up to ½ in
(15 mm)

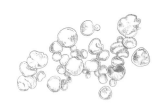

556

CATINELLA OLIVACEA
OLIVE SALVER
(BATSCH) BOUDIER

This handsome species grows in troops on the undersides of damp, fallen logs and decayed wood, so is seldom seen unless searched for. The hidden habitat is rather odd for normal spore dispersal by air currents, and recent research has shown that most *Catinella* spores become trapped in a slimy layer at the surface of the disc, and are almost certainly spread by small insects crawling over the fruitbodies. The same research has also shown by DNA analysis that the Olive Salver, though superficially resembling other disc and cup fungi, belongs in a quite different class, though its family placement is as yet uncertain.

SIMILAR SPECIES
The shape and color of the Olive Salver should be distinctive. *Rutstroemia bulgarioides* is similarly colored, but has a short stalk and grows on spruce cones. Several *Claussenomyces* species on rotten wood are olive or brighter green, but all have much smaller discs without a neatly differentiated margin.

Actual size

The Olive Salver produces clusters or troops of disc-shaped fruitbodies. The upper surface is smooth and dark olive-green to blackish green. The rim of the disc is raised, neatly fluted, or ribbed, and ocher to yellowish olive. The undersurface is dark brown and slightly scurfy.

FAMILY	Dermateaceae
DISTRIBUTION	North America, Europe, Asia, Australia
HABITAT	In woodland
ASSOCIATION	On rotten broadleaf wood, especially oak
GROWTH FORM	On fallen branches and woody fragments
ABUNDANCE	Common
SPORE COLOR	White
EDIBILITY	Not edible

HEIGHT
Up to ⅜ in
(8 mm)

DIAMETER
Up to ¼ in
(5 mm)

CHLOROCIBORIA AERUGINASCENS

GREEN ELFCUP

(NYLANDER) KANOUSE EX C. S. RAMAMURTHI ET AL

557

The Green Elfcup is a common and widespread species, remarkable not so much for its deep blue-green fruitbodies but for its ability to stain the wood that it grows on the same color—it is also known as the Green Stain Fungus. This stained wood can frequently be found in woodland, even though fruitbodies may not always be present. Oak is a favorite substrate for the Green Elfcup and pieces of this "green oak" were once collected in England and used in Tunbridge Ware, a popular form of decorative marquetry which employed inlaid woods of different colors. It was earlier used for the same purpose in Italy, providing blue-green inlays for Renaissance intarsia paneling.

SIMILAR SPECIES

An equally common species, *Chlorociboria aeruginosa*, produces similarly stained wood and can only be distinguished microscopically. In New Zealand (where *C. aeruginascens* is not known to occur) no less than 15 species have been recognized, and similar research elsewhere may show equal diversity at the microscopic and molecular level.

Actual size

The Green Elfcup produces thin, shallowly cup-shaped, turquoise (blue-green) fruitbodies in small troops or clusters. The cups are normally stalked, but the stalk is not always central and may be attached to the side. With age, the cups become flat and irregularly disc-shaped, curling up in dry weather, and eventually develop discolored, pale yellowish patches.

FAMILY	Vibrisseaceae
DISTRIBUTION	New Zealand
HABITAT	In wet woodland
ASSOCIATION	With broadleaf trees
GROWTH FORM	On wet, rotten wood, in clusters
ABUNDANCE	Occasional
SPORE COLOR	White
EDIBILITY	Not edible

HEIGHT
Up to 1 in
(25 mm)

DIAMETER
Up to ¼ in
(5 mm)

558

CHLOROVIBRISSEA PHIALOPHORA
GREEN PINBALL
SAMUELS & L. M. KOHN

Vibrissea species typically grow in or alongside rivers and streams on submerged or water-sodden wood. Their long, threadlike spores are adapted to water dispersal, germinating when they settle on a branch caught up in the current. They are a cosmopolitan group of fungi, but related *Chlorovibrissea* species—also with water-borne spores—are confined to Australasia where there are just four rather similar-looking species. The Green Pinball is as yet known only from New Zealand, growing in clustered troops on very wet wood in temperate rain forests.

SIMILAR SPECIES
Chlorovibrissea melanochlora and *C. bicolor* are similar Australian species, but have contrastingly colored (yellow and dark green) heads and stems. *Chlorovibrissea tasmanica* is known from both Australia and New Zealand and is very similar to the Green Pinball, but is said to have a slightly hairier stem. It is best distinguished microscopically.

Actual size

The Green Pinball typically produces fruitbodies in clusters or troops. Each has a long, smooth to finely velvety, green stem, with an irregularly spherical, green to blackish green, fertile head that becomes stickily shiny when damp.

FAMILY	Sarcoscyphaceae
DISTRIBUTION	Southern North America (Florida), Africa, Central and South America, southern Asia, Australia
HABITAT	In woodland
ASSOCIATION	On broadleaf wood
GROWTH FORM	On logs and fallen wood
ABUNDANCE	Very common
SPORE COLOR	White
EDIBILITY	Said to be edible

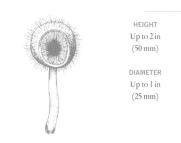

HEIGHT
Up to 2 in
(50 mm)

DIAMETER
Up to 1 in
(25 mm)

COOKEINA TRICHOLOMA

HAIRY TROPICAL GOBLET

(MONTAGNE) KUNTZE

559

Cookeina species are very common and conspicuous throughout the tropics, often growing in small troops on fallen trunks and logs. They belong in the same family as the temperate Scarlet Elf Cup and most are brightly colored. The rather deep and well-formed cups of the tropical goblets catch rainwater, causing the spore-containing cells that line the inner surface to swell. When the cups dry out, the water-filled cells rupture under pressure and the spores are shot out. *Cookeina tricholoma* is said to be eaten by some indigenous peoples in Malaysia and Mexico.

SIMILAR SPECIES

The equally common Smooth Tropical Goblet (*Cookeina sulcipes*) can be similarly colored, but has a smooth outer surface with only a fringe of small white hairs around the margin of the cup. *Cookeina sinensis* is a recently described Chinese species very similar to *C. tricholoma*, but distinguished microscopically.

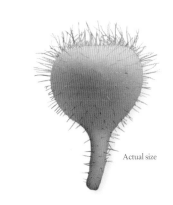

Actual size

The Hairy Tropical Goblet has a very distinct cup and stem. The inner surface of the cup is smooth, and pale pink to pinkish orange or pinkish red. The outer surface is similarly colored, and is sparsely covered in long, whitish to brownish, bristly hairs. The stem is paler and sparsely hairy.

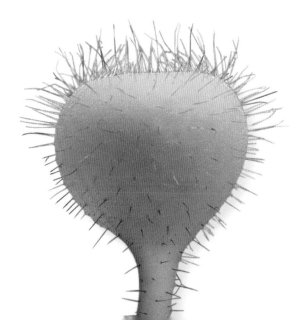

FAMILY	Cyttariaceae
DISTRIBUTION	Southern South America
HABITAT	In woodland
ASSOCIATION	On southern beech
GROWTH FORM	On trunks and attached branches, in clusters
ABUNDANCE	Occasional
SPORE COLOR	White
EDIBILITY	Edible

HEIGHT
Up to 2 in
(50 mm)

DIAMETER
Up to 2 in
(50 mm)

560

CYTTARIA DARWINII
DARWIN'S GOLFBALL FUNGUS
BERKELEY

Charles Darwin collected specimens of this species in 1832 when visiting Tierra del Fuego on the voyage of the *Beagle*. They were examined and named in his honor by the Rev. Miles Berkeley, the leading British mycologist of his day, and are still preserved in the herbarium at Kew Gardens in the UK. Darwin noted that the local indigenous people ate the fungus raw as a staple item of food, the Spanish name for it being *Pan del Indio* (Indian Bread). *Cyttaria darwinii* and related species continue to be eaten and sold at markets today, though the fruitbodies are typically turned into pickles and chutneys.

SIMILAR SPECIES

Several related species grow on southern beech in Chile and Argentina. *Cyttaria espinosae*, *C. berteroi*, and *C. johowii* are all of similar shape and color, and are best distinguished microscopically. Other species, including *C. gunnii*, occur in Australia and New Zealand.

The Darwin's Golfball Fungus produces fruitbodies which are golfball-like, smooth and pallid at first, becoming pale yellow with a pitted honeycomb- like surface when mature. They are sticky when cut. The fruitbodies grow in clusters on trees, often associated with large, gall-like conks in the wood. When fully mature, the fruitbodies fall to the ground.

Actual size

FAMILY	Cyttariaceae
DISTRIBUTION	Southern Australia, New Zealand
HABITAT	In woodland
ASSOCIATION	On southern beech
GROWTH FORM	On trunks and attached branches, in clusters
ABUNDANCE	Occasional
SPORE COLOR	White
EDIBILITY	Said to be edible

CYTTARIA GUNNII

ORANGE GOLFBALL FUNGUS

BERKELEY

HEIGHT
Up to 4 in
(100 mm)

DIAMETER
Up to 4 in
(100 mm)

561

Like all *Cyttaria* species, the Orange Golfball Fungus grows only on southern beech (*Nothofagus*) and is restricted to myrtle beech in Australia and silver beech in New Zealand. It is also known as the Beech Strawberry. Together with their hosts, golfball fungi are relics of the old Gondwana supercontinent that brought together South America, Antarctica, and Australasia. No trees now remain in Antarctica, but *Nothofagus* and *Cyttaria* species are still found in Chile and Argentina and in Australia and New Zealand, though both trees and fungi have separated into different species in each area. The Orange Golfball Fungus was once eaten by aboriginal peoples in Australia.

The Orange Golfball Fungus produces fruitbodies that, as the common name suggests, are golfball-like, smooth and pallid at first, becoming yellow to orange with a deeply pitted or dimpled surface when mature. They have a pale or whitish sterile base, and are mostly hollow when cut. Fruitbodies grow in clusters, often associated with large, gall-like conks in the wood.

SIMILAR SPECIES

Cyttaria septentrionalis is a very similar Australian species, but only grows on Antarctic Beech. *Cyttaria pallida* is a similar, but whitish species restricted to New Zealand. Other species, including *C. darwinii*, occur in the southern beech forests of Chile and Argentina.

Actual size

FAMILY	Morchellaceae
DISTRIBUTION	North America, Europe
HABITAT	In woodland and scrub
ASSOCIATION	With broadleaf trees
GROWTH FORM	On soil, singly or in small groups
ABUNDANCE	Occasional
SPORE COLOR	White
EDIBILITY	Edible (if cooked)

HEIGHT
Up to ½ in
(10 mm)

DIAMETER
Up to 8 in
(200 mm)

562

DISCIOTIS VENOSA
BLEACH CUP
(PERSOON) ARNOULD

Though it may resemble a very large cup fungus, *Disciotis venosa* is actually more closely related to the morels than to most other cup fungi. It occurs at much the same time, in spring, and—like morels—is edible if well-cooked, but poisonous if raw or undercooked. The chlorine-like smell which gives it the name the Bleach Cup is hardly tempting, however. The epithet *venosa* means "veined"—hence the alternative English name, the Veined Cup. These shallow veins or irregular ridges on the inner surface of the cup are related to the much more pronounced lobes and folds found in the morels and many *Gyromitra* species.

SIMILAR SPECIES

Several species of *Discina* form very similar fruitbodies, notably *D. ancilis* (which is also known as *Gyromitra ancilis*), which lacks the bleach smell and is normally found in conifer forests. Like all *Discina* and *Gyromitra* species, it can be dangerously poisonous. Some larger *Peziza* species may also look similar, but usually lack the veining found in *Disciotis* and *Discina* species.

Actual size

The Bleach Cup is cup-shaped at first, but expands with age to become irregularly disc-shaped. The inner surface is brown and, when mature, develops irregular, and sometimes quite prominent, veins or ridges. It may also become puckered and distorted. The outer surface is sordid whitish to pale brown, often flecked with small brownish scales.

FAMILY	Sclerotiniaceae
DISTRIBUTION	North America, Europe, northern Asia
HABITAT	In woodland
ASSOCIATION	With wood anemone and related species
GROWTH FORM	On soil, arising from sclerotia
ABUNDANCE	Occasional
SPORE COLOR	White
EDIBILITY	Not edible

HEIGHT
Up to 4 in
(100 mm)

DIAMETER
Up to 1¼ in
(30 mm)

DUMONTINIA TUBEROSA

ANEMONE CUP

(BULLIARD) L. M. KOHN

563

Dumontinia tuberosa is a curious little fungus that is exclusively associated with *Anemone* species. It is a parasite on the tubers or rhizomes of the plant, and at the end of the year produces an underground sclerotium, a dense mass of fungal tissue, that overwinters. In the spring, fruitbodies arise from the sclerotia on long stalks, opening up into cups at, or just above, the surface. It therefore fruits at much the same time as the anemones flower. A related species, *Sclerotinia sclerotiorum*, has a wide range of hosts and is a potentially serious pathogen of many crop species.

SIMILAR SPECIES

Very similar-looking fruitbodies arising from sclerotia are formed by other species in the genera *Dumontinia* and *Sclerotinia*, but are not associated with anemones. *Dumontinia ulmariae*, for example, occurs with meadowsweet (*Filipendula ulmaria*). Similar brown, though generally shorter-stalked, fruitbodies belonging to the genus *Rutstroemia* are found on dead sticks, fallen leaves, old seed cases, and decaying vegetation.

Actual size

The Anemone Cup forms its fruitbody on a long, often crooked stem that rises out of the soil. The fertile cup is almost ball-shaped at first, but opens up and expands to become cup-shaped, then flat and disc-shaped (see photo left). All surfaces are smooth, and pale to dark brown.

FAMILY	Sarcosomataceae
DISTRIBUTION	Eastern North America
HABITAT	In woodland
ASSOCIATION	With broadleaf trees
GROWTH FORM	On sticks and fallen branches
ABUNDANCE	Common
SPORE COLOR	White
EDIBILITY	Not edible

HEIGHT
Up to 1 in
(25 mm)

DIAMETER
Up to 2 in
(50 mm)

564

GALIELLA RUFA
HAIRY RUBBER CUP
(SCHWEINITZ) NANNFELDT & KORF

The Hairy Rubber Cup was originally described in the same genus as the Black Bulgar (*Bulgaria inquinans*), which it rather resembles in terms of its rubbery-gelatinous texture. It is, however, more closely related to the grossly gelatinous Bombmurkla (*Sarcosoma globosum*) that also grows in eastern North America. Like its relative, the Hairy Rubber Cup is typically found in late spring and summer, and can be common in some areas. A compound called galiellalactone has been isolated from fruitbodies and it may have some potential in treating prostate cancer.

SIMILAR SPECIES
Several other cup fungi have an orange inner surface and a brown to black outer surface, but most are small, often found on soil or dung rather than wood, and are not so rubbery-gelatinous as *Galiella rufa*.

The Hairy Rubber Cup forms rubbery-gelatinous, shallowly cup-shaped fruitbodies in clusters or troops. The outer surface is woolly-hairy and brownish to blackish brown. The inner, fertile surface is smooth and dull orange to reddish brown, with a toothed, often incurved, margin.

Actual size

FAMILY	Pyronemataceae
DISTRIBUTION	North Africa, Asia; introduced in Europe
HABITAT	In woodland and parkland
ASSOCIATION	Ectomycorrhizal, with cedar
GROWTH FORM	Singly or in troops
ABUNDANCE	Occasional
SPORE COLOR	White
EDIBILITY	Poisonous

HEIGHT
Up to 2 in
(50 mm)

DIAMETER
Up to 3 in
(80 mm)

GEOPORA SUMNERIANA
CEDAR CUP
(COOKE) M. TORRE

565

This is a spring-fruiting fungus that can be searched for under cedars in parks and gardens. It naturally follows the distribution of cedar species in North Africa and Asia, but has long established itself as an exotic species with planted trees in Europe, where it is widespread and not uncommon if deliberately looked for. It was formerly known as *Sepultaria sumneriana*, but is related to other later-fruiting *Geopora* species, which are ectomycorrhizal with a range of different plants. All of them seem to prefer sandy, alkaline soils. The species is hardly likely to be eaten, but is said to be poisonous.

SIMILAR SPECIES

Other *Geopora* species produce similar half-buried fruitbodies, but they typically appear later in the year and are not associated with cedars. *Peziza ammophila* is also similar, but occurs in sand dunes and has a brown interior surface. *Sarcosphaera coronaria* has a purplish interior.

The Cedar Cup develops truffle-like fruitbodies near the soil surface. At maturity, the top of the fruitbody splits, sometimes in a starlike manner, to reveal a deep cup, sunk into the soil. With age the cup opens up more widely. The interior is smooth and whitish, the exterior brown and scurfy.

Actual size

FAMILY	Glaziellaceae
DISTRIBUTION	Central and South America, Southeast Asia, Pacific islands
HABITAT	In woodland
ASSOCIATION	Ectomycorrhizal, with broadleaf trees
GROWTH FORM	In soil or leaf litter
ABUNDANCE	Occasional
SPORE COLOR	White
EDIBILITY	Not edible

HEIGHT
Up to 2 in
(50 mm)

DIAMETER
Up to 2 in
(50 mm)

566

GLAZIELLA AURANTIACA
ORANGE BLADDER
(BERKELEY & M. A. CURTIS) SACCARDO

Like the Orange Peel Fungus (*Aleuria aurantia*), fruitbodies of the Orange Bladder may be overlooked as discarded fruit— or even brightly colored plastic. If collected, they may still not resemble fungi, since their curious, bladderlike hollowness does not suggest any well-known group of species. Up until the 1980s it was generally thought *Glaziella aurantiaca* belonged to the Zygomycota—a fungal phylum that has a few species with truffle-like fruitbodies—but subsequent research shows it is actually a strange cup-fungus with gigantic spores. There is just one subtropical species worldwide.

SIMILAR SPECIES

The brightly colored, hollow fruitbodies of the Orange Bladder should be distinctive, though in Australia and New Zealand the Scarlet Berry Truffle (*Paurocotylis pila*) forms rather similar bright red fruitbodies that are sometimes partly hollow.

Actual size

The Orange Bladder forms bladderlike fruitbodies of irregular shape. Its outer surface is smooth, bright yellow-orange to orange or orange-red. When cut, the interior is hollow, the spores being produced within the thin, gelatinous fruitbody wall.

FAMILY	Pyronemataceae
DISTRIBUTION	North America, Europe, Asia
HABITAT	In woodland
ASSOCIATION	Ectomycorrhizal, with broadleaf trees and conifers
GROWTH FORM	On soil, more rarely very rotten fallen wood
ABUNDANCE	Common
SPORE COLOR	White
EDIBILITY	Not edible

HEIGHT
Up to ½ in
(15 mm)

DIAMETER
Up to 1¼ in
(30 mm)

HUMARIA HEMISPHAERICA
GLAZED CUP
(F. H. WIGGERS) FUCKEL

567

Though small, the Glazed Cup is an attractive little species with an inner surface like fine bone-china. It forms a mutually beneficial relationship with the roots of living trees, including both conifers (such as pine) and broadleaf trees (such as birch). It is a common species in the northern hemisphere, typically found in small troops on bare soil alongside paths, more rarely on very rotten, fallen wood. The species epithet *hemisphaerica* means "like half a sphere," which precisely describes its neat and regular shape. It is sometimes known as the Brown-Haired Fairy Cup.

SIMILAR SPECIES
Similar cup-shaped fruitbodies are formed on soil by species in the genus *Tarzetta*, including *T. catinus*. They tend to be cream, buff, or pale brown throughout, however, and lack the contrasting colors and textures of the Glazed Cup. In North America, some *Jafnea* species may also look similar, but are typically much larger.

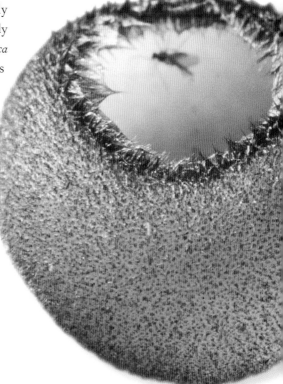

Actual size

The Glazed Cup forms fruitbodies that are almost globose when young with a small opening at the top, but become neatly cup-shaped to bowl-shaped when mature. The inner surface is smooth and bone-white, like porcelain. The margin and outer surface is densely covered in fine brown hairs.

FAMILY	Hyaloscyphaceae
DISTRIBUTION	Europe, Asia; introduced in North America
HABITAT	In woodland
ASSOCIATION	With larch
GROWTH FORM	On canker calluses and bark of infected trees
ABUNDANCE	Occasional
SPORE COLOR	White
EDIBILITY	Not edible

HEIGHT	Less than ⅛ in (1 mm)
DIAMETER	Up to ¼ in (5 mm)

568

LACHNELLULA WILLKOMMII
LARCH CANKER DISCO
(HARTIG) DENNIS

This is one of several attractive, orange-and-white *Lachnellula* species. Most are wood-rotters, but *L. willkommii* is a wound parasite that causes a canker of larches, making them worthless as timber. It was first described from Germany and is particularly prevalent on the European Larch, but can attack other conifer species. It was introduced into North America in the 1920s, but has only caused serious problems since the 1980s when it was found in eastern Canada. It appears to spread rapidly in damper climates, especially among closely packed plantation trees. "Disco," short for discomycete, is the old name for a large group of species with disc-shaped fruitbodies.

SIMILAR SPECIES
Several very similar *Lachnellula* species can occur on larch, notably the common *L. occidentalis*, which is a harmless decayer of dead wood and does not cause cankers. Additional species are found on other conifers. All are bright yellow-orange, and are only distinguishable microscopically.

Actual size

The Larch Canker Disco produces fruitbodies that are cup-shaped at first, but expand when they are mature. The upper surface is smooth and bright yellow-orange in color, with a conspicuous margin of white hairs that also cover the lower surface. The fruitbodies are centrally attached by a short stem.

FAMILY	Hyaloscyphaceae
DISTRIBUTION	North America, Europe, North Africa, Central and South America, northern Asia, Australia, New Zealand
HABITAT	In woodland and scrub
ASSOCIATION	With plants
GROWTH FORM	On dead twigs, wood, and plant stems
ABUNDANCE	Very common
SPORE COLOR	White
EDIBILITY	Not edible

HEIGHT
Less than ⅛ in
(1 mm)

CAP DIAMETER
Less than ⅛ in
(1 mm)

LACHNUM VIRGINEUM

SNOWY DISCO

(BATSCH) P. KARSTEN

569

Individual fruitbodies of *Lachnum virgineum* (formerly known as *Dascyscyphus virgineus*) are so small and delicate, that they would hardly be noticeable if they did not grow in swarms. The fungus is extremely common and widespread, but is often passed by unless fallen wood is turned over and dead stems examined. It can fruit at any time, but is most frequently found in damp spring weather when its miniature fruitbodies appear on almost anything, from old herbaceous stems to dead brambles, fallen twigs, nutshells, cones, and other woody debris.

SIMILAR SPECIES

Many similar species are known with tiny, hairy, cup-shaped fruitbodies, most of them colored, but some of them white. They are best distinguished microscopically, but include *Lachnum tenuissimum* on dead grass stems, *L. rhytismatis* on old sycamore leaves, and *Dasyscyphella nivea* on oak and beech wood.

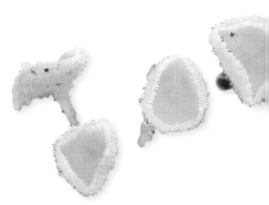

The Snowy Disco produces swarms of tiny fruitbodies. Each is stalked and goblet-shaped at first, the cup expanding with age to become flat and disc-shaped. The outer surface is white and densely hairy, the hairs forming a thick and conspicuous margin around the cup or disc. The inner surface is smooth, white to cream.

Actual size

FAMILY	Rutstroemiaceae
DISTRIBUTION	Southeastern North America, Europe
HABITAT	In woodland
ASSOCIATION	With chestnut
GROWTH FORM	On fallen chestnut cupules
ABUNDANCE	Common
SPORE COLOR	White
EDIBILITY	Not edible

HEIGHT
Up to ½ in
(15 mm)

DIAMETER
Up to ½ in
(10 mm)

570

LANZIA ECHINOPHILA
CHESTNUT CUP
(BULLIARD) KORF

Chestnut trees share most of their fungi, such as the Beefsteak Fungus (*Fistulina hepatica*), with oaks, but *Lanzia echinophila* (formerly known as *Rutstroemia echinophila*) is a real specialist, growing only on the inside surfaces of the spiny cupules that contain the nuts. It appears toward the end of the year, when the fallen cupules have become brown, and arises in small groups within each cup. Other fungi in this group have evolved to take advantage of similar highly specific niches—some species occurring only on fallen catkins of alder, others on hazel catkins, still others on scales of fallen fir cones.

SIMILAR SPECIES
Many other brown, stalked, cup fungi occur, but none is found on old chestnut cupules. *Ciboria batschiana* is a similar-looking species, but occurs on old, fallen acorns. *Rutstroemia firma* is common on fallen oak twigs. *Rutstroemia petiolorum* is another common species on old beech and oak leaves.

Actual size

The Chestnut Cup produces fruitbodies that are cup-shaped at first, but expand when mature. The upper surface is smooth and brown to reddish brown, with a brighter, finely toothed margin. The undersurface is smooth and ocher-brown, as is the narrow, centrally attached stem.

FAMILY	Leotiaceae
DISTRIBUTION	North America, Europe, North Africa, Central America, Asia, Australia, New Zealand
HABITAT	In woodland
ASSOCIATION	With broadleaf trees
GROWTH FORM	On soil and leaf litter, often in clusters or troops
ABUNDANCE	Common
SPORE COLOR	White
EDIBILITY	Not edible

HEIGHT
Up to 3 in
(80 mm)

DIAMETER
Up to 1½ in
(40 mm)

LEOTIA LUBRICA

JELLYBABY

(SCOPOLI) PERSOON

571

The fruitbodies of *Leotia lubrica* have been dubbed "jellybabies," thanks more to their rubbery-gelatinous texture than to their drumstick appearance. They are common in broadleaf woodlands, but easy to overlook because of their ocher-olive colors. The Jellybaby appears to be a very widespread fungus, but recent molecular studies have suggested that at least four species of *Leotia* exist, not all of which are yet characterized or named. Unfortunately, it seems that neither fruitbody colors nor microscopic details may provide a sure guide to their eventual identification.

SIMILAR SPECIES

In North America, *Leotia viscosa* is a common species with a deep green head and yellowish stem. The wholly olive-green *Coryne atrovirens* looks like a *Leotia* species (and has even been given the name *L. atrovirens*), but is actually the imperfect (asexual) stage of an unrelated fungus. *Cudonia* species are similarly shaped, but not gelatinous.

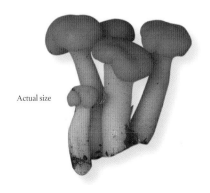

Actual size

The Jellybaby produces gelationous, drumstick-like fruitbodies. The head is smooth and slippery to sticky when moist, cartilaginous-gelatinous, often lobed or irregular, and ocher to olive or brown. The undersurface and stem are equally gelatinous but scurfy or scaly, the same color as the head, or more yellow to yellow-orange.

FAMILY	Leotiaceae
DISTRIBUTION	North America, Central America
HABITAT	In woodland
ASSOCIATION	With broadleaf trees and conifers
GROWTH FORM	On soil and leaf litter, often in clusters or troops
ABUNDANCE	Common
SPORE COLOR	White
EDIBILITY	Not edible

HEIGHT
Up to 3 in
(75 mm)

DIAMETER
Up to 1 in
(25 mm)

572

LEOTIA VISCOSA
GREENCAP JELLYBABY

FRIES

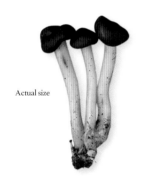

Actual size

The Greencap Jellybaby forms gelatinous fruitbodies with a distinct head and stalk. The head is sticky or slimy when damp, cartilaginous-gelatinous, often lobed or irregular, and olive to deep green. The stem is gelatinous, finely scurfy, and whitish to yellowish or buff, sometimes with small green dots.

This is a rather more attractive, two-tone version of the widespread Jellybaby (*Leotia lubrica*) with a cap that can be a striking shade of jade or malachite-green. It is a common species in North America, where it grows in groups or clusters in woodland litter or occasionally on very rotten wood. A few texts suggest it is edible (and it is certainly not known to be poisonous), but it seems improbable that anyone would ever willingly collect and eat such a small, slimy, gelatinous fungus.

SIMILAR SPECIES

The common Jellybaby (*Leotia lubrica*) has a duller, more yellowish head that often has olive tints but is never deep green. *Coryne atrovirens* (or *L. atrovirens*) has similar-looking fruitbodies that are entirely olive-green.

FAMILY	Geoglossaceae
DISTRIBUTION	North America, Europe, northern Asia, New Zealand
HABITAT	In grassland, occasionally in woodland
ASSOCIATION	With mosses
GROWTH FORM	On soil and in grass
ABUNDANCE	Occasional
SPORE COLOR	White
EDIBILITY	Not edible

HEIGHT
Up to 3 in
(80 mm)

DIAMETER
Up to ½ in
(15 mm)

MICROGLOSSUM OLIVACEUM

OLIVE EARTHTONGUE

(PERSOON) GILLET

573

Apart from its distinctive color and white (not black) spores, the Olive Earthtongue looks pretty much like the commoner black earthtongues such as *Trichoglossum hirsutum*. Recent molecular research, however, indicates that it is more closely related to species such as the Jellybaby (*Leotia lubrica*) than the true earthtongues. In Europe, *Microglossum olivaceum* is a species of unimproved grasslands, a habitat that has declined drastically over the last 50 years. In Sweden, the population of the Olive Earthtongue is estimated to have fallen by 95 percent. For that reason it is now on the Red List of threatened fungal species in several different countries.

SIMILAR SPECIES

Microglossum viride is a woodland species, deeper green, and with a rough or scurfy stem. The North American *M. rufum* is an orange to yellow species. The true earthtongues, including *Trichoglossum hirsutum*, are predominantly black with occasional olive or brownish tones.

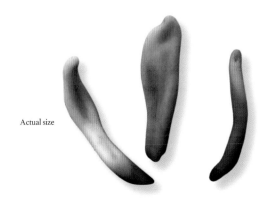

Actual size

The Olive Earthtongue forms stalked, club-shaped fruitbodies. The smooth, fertile head is of variable shape, sometimes narrow, sometimes swollen, but is usually compressed and furrowed. It is typically blue-green to olive-brown or occasionally pinkish to purple-brown, fading with age. The cylindrical stem is smooth, sometimes glossy, olive to brown, or occasionally blue-green.

FAMILY	Geoglossaceae
DISTRIBUTION	North America, northern Asia, New Zealand
HABITAT	In woodland
ASSOCIATION	With mosses
GROWTH FORM	On soil and very rotten wood, clustered in moss
ABUNDANCE	Occasional
SPORE COLOR	White
EDIBILITY	Not edible

HEIGHT
Up to 3 in
(75 mm)

DIAMETER
Up to ½ in
(15 mm)

574

MICROGLOSSUM RUFUM

ORANGE EARTHTONGUE

(SCHWEINITZ) UNDERWOOD

This colorful earthtongue was first described by American mycologist L. D. von Schweinitz in 1834. Curiously he gave his new species the epithet *rufum*, which means "red," despite the fact that *Microglossum rufum* is actually yellow to orange. The species is locally common in North America, but is additionally found in New Zealand, Japan, and parts of Eastern Asia. It has even been featured on a set of stamps issued by Bhutan in the Himalayas. Recent research has indicated that the Orange Earthtongue, like other species of *Microglossum*, is not closely related to the true earthtongues, all of which are black-spored.

SIMILAR SPECIES

Microglossum viride is a deep green species, while the smooth-stemmed *M. olivaceum* is olive-green to brown. The Yellow Fan (*Spathularia flavida*) is similarly colored, but the head is always flared and fanlike. The unrelated *Cordyceps militaris* grows on insect pupae and is bright vermilion-orange.

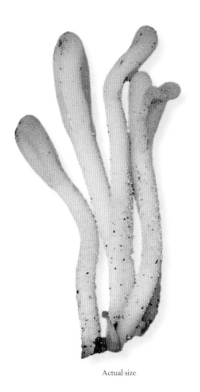

Actual size

The Orange Earthtongue forms stalked, club-shaped fruitbodies. The smooth fertile head is of variable shape, sometimes narrow, sometimes swollen, but is usually compressed and furrowed. It is typically bright yellow to yellow-orange, with a cylindrical stem that is normally distinctly scurfy, but occasionally smooth, especially when older.

FAMILY	Sarcoscyphaceae
DISTRIBUTION	North America, Europe, northern Asia
HABITAT	In woodland
ASSOCIATION	With broadleaf trees
GROWTH FORM	On or alongside rotten, sometimes buried, wood
ABUNDANCE	Rare
SPORE COLOR	White
EDIBILITY	Not edible

HEIGHT
Up to 1½ in
(40 mm)

DIAMETER
Up to 1 in
(25 mm)

MICROSTOMA PROTRACTUM
ROSY GOBLET
(FRIES) KANOUSE

575

This is a spring-fruiting fungus, with the typically bright colors that are often found in the family Sarcoscyphaceae. It appears to be primarily an alpine-arctic species and typically grows in calcareous woodland. It is rare throughout much of its range, but becomes somewhat more frequent in the far north. The Rosy Goblet was collected in Scotland in the nineteenth century, but has not been seen in the British Isles since then and is presumed to be locally extinct. In several European countries it is of conservation concern and has been placed on their Red Lists of endangered fungal species.

Actual size

SIMILAR SPECIES
The related *Microstoma floccosum* is very similar, but the stalked cups have a conspicuously hairy outer surface. The Scarlet Elfcup (*Sarcoscypha coccinea*) and related species are similarly colored, and young, stalked fruitbodies could be confused with the Rosy Goblet. The cup margins, however, are not torn or ragged.

The Rosy Goblet produces clusters of long-stalked, cup-shaped fruitbodies. The stalk is slender, whitish, and finely downy. The cup is ball-shaped at first, with a small opening at the top. With age, the cup expands and eventually becomes almost disc-shaped with a ragged margin. The inner surface is smooth and bright orange-red to scarlet, the outer surface paler.

FAMILY	Helotiaceae
DISTRIBUTION	Europe, northern Asia
HABITAT	In woodland mires, ditches, and bogs
ASSOCIATION	With conifers and broadleaf trees, often with sphagnum moss
GROWTH FORM	On wet litter and plant debris, in troops
ABUNDANCE	Occasional
SPORE COLOR	White
EDIBILITY	Not edible

HEIGHT
Up to 4 in
(100 mm)

DIAMETER
Up to ½ in
(15 mm)

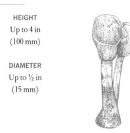

576

MITRULA PALUDOSA
BOG BEACON
FRIES

When growing in large troops, the brightly colored Bog Beacon can be a cheering sight in a dank, gloomy woodland mire. The fungus grows on decaying vegetation, but only when it is completely waterlogged in bogs, marshes, ditches, and mires. The Bog Beacon can even produce fruitbodies under water, so that part of the stem is often submerged. It is an early-fruiting species, typically appearing in late spring or early summer. *Mitrula* means a "little miter or turban" (a good description of the fertile head), while *paludosa* means "of marshes."

SIMILAR SPECIES

In North America, *Mitrula paludosa* is replaced by a look-alike species (or species complex) called *M. elegans* (the Swamp Beacon), that is barely distinct even by DNA analysis. A second, less common look-alike, *M. borealis*, occurs in both North America and Europe and can be distinguished microscopically.

Actual size

The Bog Beacon typically produces fruitbodies in troops. Each has a long, smooth, whitish to slightly translucent stem, with an irregularly shaped, bright shiny yellow to yellow-orange, fertile head. This head can be elongated, egg-shaped, or simply round, and is smooth to somewhat furrowed.

FAMILY	Helotiaceae
DISTRIBUTION	North America, Europe, northern Asia
HABITAT	In woodland
ASSOCIATION	On broadleaf wood, particularly beech
GROWTH FORM	On logs, stumps, and dead branches
ABUNDANCE	Common
SPORE COLOR	White
EDIBILITY	Not edible

HEIGHT
Up to 2 in
(50 mm)

DIAMETER
Up to 2 in
(50 mm)

NEOBULGARIA PURA

BEECH JELLYDISC

(PERSOON) PETRAK

577

The Beech Jellydisc often grows in dense clusters composed of multiple fruitbodies. It is a highly gelatinous species, the jelly-like flesh retaining rainwater. This prevents it from drying out when growing on exposed wood and gives the fungus extra time to produce and release its spores. The Beech Jellydisc was once placed in the genus *Bulgaria* alongside the equally gelatinous (but black) *B. inquinans*, but the two species are now known to be unrelated. Several new compounds called neobulgarones have recently been isolated from the fungus that may have some use in combating or inhibiting plant diseases.

SIMILAR SPECIES

Large clusters of the Beech Jellydisc might be mistaken for unrelated *Tremella* species, but the pink color and presence of disc-like surfaces should be distinctive. *Ascotremella* and *Ascoryne* species are more closely related and can look very similar, though their fruitbodies are usually more purple than pink. They can be distinguished microscopically.

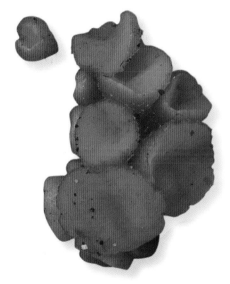

Actual size

The Beech Jellydisc produces gelatinous, button-shaped fruitbodies that often coalesce in large clumps. The upper surface is pale pinkish, sometimes with a purplish tint, smooth and disc-shaped at first, but often becoming irregular and swollen when older. The outer surface is similarly colored, but finely scurfy.

FAMILY	Pyronemataceae
DISTRIBUTION	North America, Europe, Asia
HABITAT	In woodland
ASSOCIATION	Ectomycorrhizal, with broadleaf trees and conifers
GROWTH FORM	On soil, in small but dense clusters
ABUNDANCE	Occasional
SPORE COLOR	White
EDIBILITY	Poisonous

HEIGHT
Up to 4 in
(100 mm)

DIAMETER
Up to 2½ in
(60 mm)

578

OTIDEA ONOTICA
HARE'S EAR
(PERSOON) FUCKEL

Actual size

The Hare's Ear is one of the larger and more attractive *Otidea* species, a group of woodland fungi that often grow in dense clusters, rising out of the leaf litter. Recent research suggests that they are probably ectomycorrhizal, forming an association with living trees. A few other *Otidea* species are similarly colored, but most are some shade of brown. The majority are ear-shaped, though one recently described species, *O. subterranea*, is truffle-like. The Hare's Ear is sometimes listed as edible, but fruitbodies contain the toxin gyromitrin and are therefore potentially poisonous, especially if eaten raw.

SIMILAR SPECIES
Other similarly colored *Otidea* species include *O. concinna*, which is a brighter yellow and lacks pinkish tints, and *O. leporina*, which is ocher. Neither grow as tall as *O. onotica*. *Caloscypha fulgens* and *Sowerbyella radicata* are differently shaped, the former also having blue-green tints on the outer surface, the latter having a root-like stem.

The Hare's Ear, as the name suggests, typically forms fruitbodies that are tall and irregularly ear-shaped or, less typically, shorter and almost cup-shaped. They are, however, always slit or open on one side. The incurved inner surface is smooth, and ocher, with a pinkish or apricot-orange flush. The outer surface is finely scurfy and ocher. A very short, whitish stem may be present.

FAMILY	Pezizaceae
DISTRIBUTION	North America, Europe, South America, Asia, New Zealand
HABITAT	In sand dunes
ASSOCIATION	With marram grass
GROWTH FORM	In sand, half-buried, singly or in small troops
ABUNDANCE	Occasional
SPORE COLOR	White
EDIBILITY	Not edible

HEIGHT
Up to 1 in
(25 mm)

DIAMETER
Up to 1½ in
(40 mm)

PEZIZA AMMOPHILA

DUNE CUP

DURIEU & MONTAGNE

579

As with plants, the fungi that grow in dunes are often highly specialized, coping not only with sand but also with salt. The Dune Cup is one of these halophilic (salt-loving) species and is often found with the first tussocks of marram grass (*Ammophila arenaria*) above the shoreline. It grows on the dead roots of the grass that are buried beneath the sand and produces its fruitbodies from a root-like tube of mixed sand and fungal tissue that extends upward, eventually giving rise to a half-buried, cup-like fruitbody at the surface.

SIMILAR SPECIES

Within the large genus *Peziza*, this is an easy species to distinguish because of its dune habitat. However, two species of *Geopora*, *G. arenicola* and *G. arenosa*, produce similar fruitbodies in sandy soil, sometimes in dune-slacks (damp, often marshy depressions between the dunes). Both can be distinguished by the white inner surface of their cups.

Actual size

The Dune Cup forms fruitbodies that are entirely hidden in sand at first, but gradually split open from the top to reveal quite a deep inner cup, still half-buried in sand. When old, they may become irregularly disc-shaped. If dug up, they have a stemlike base of mixed sand and fungal tissue. All surfaces are buff to dark brown.

FAMILY	Pezizaceae
DISTRIBUTION	Eastern North America, Europe
HABITAT	In woodland
ASSOCIATION	With broadleaf trees and conifers
GROWTH FORM	On ground or litter
ABUNDANCE	Rare
SPORE COLOR	White
EDIBILITY	Not edible

HEIGHT
Up to 1 in
(25 mm)

DIAMETER
Up to 2 in
(50 mm)

580

PEZIZA AZUREOIDES
AZURE CUP
DONADINI

Most *Peziza* species have rather dull-colored fruitbodies in various shades of cream, buff, and brown, but a few have more distinctive bluish, violet, or purple tints. The Azure Cup belongs to this small group, but is not a common species and can be identified with certainty only by microscopic examination of its spores. *Peziza azureoides* (the epithet means "azure-like") was first described from France as recently as the 1980s and has subsequently been found a very few times elsewhere in Europe and in northeastern America.

SIMILAR SPECIES

The Purple Cup (*Peziza praetervisa*) and the Violet Cup (*P. violacea*) are two commoner species with variable, but similarly colored, fruitbodies. Both, however, are fire-site fungi—occurring on burned ground or charred wood. The Violet Crown Cup (*Sarcosphaera coronaria*) is a much larger species with a whitish outer surface.

The Azure Cup forms fruitbodies that are initially cup-shaped, but may expand with age and become more irregular. The inner surface is smooth and bluish to violet. The outer surface is scurfy or granular and similarly colored.

Actual size

FAMILY	Pezizaceae
DISTRIBUTION	North America, Europe, North Africa, Central and South America, northern Asia, New Zealand
HABITAT	In woodland
ASSOCIATION	With broadleaf trees and conifers
GROWTH FORM	Typically clustered
ABUNDANCE	Common
SPORE COLOR	White
EDIBILITY	Edible (if cooked)

HEIGHT
Up to 2 in
(50 mm)

DIAMETER
Up to 4 in
(100 mm)

PEZIZA BADIA

BAY CUP

PERSOON

581

In Europe at least, the Bay Cup is one of the most commonly encountered *Peziza* species, often growing in troops and clusters on embankments and alongside paths in conifer plantations. It seems to like poor, sandy soil and damp, bare ground. The contrast between the olive-brown interior and more reddish brown exterior may help to make the species recognizable in the field—though *Peziza* species are never easy fungi to identify. The Bay Cup is said to be poisonous raw, but edible if it is well-cooked. It is very thin-fleshed, however, and no one seems to think it worthwhile.

SIMILAR SPECIES

Many other *Peziza* species are brown and grow on soil. They are best distinguished microscopically. *Peziza phyllogena* is perhaps closest in size and color to the Bay Cup, but typically grows on rotten wood or woody litter and fruits in the spring.

The Bay Cup forms fruitbodies that are cup-shaped when young, but more irregular with age, especially when growing in clusters. The inner surface is smooth and dark brown, usually with an olive tint. The outer surface is scurfy or granular, and more reddish brown or tan-brown.

Actual size

FAMILY	Pezizaceae
DISTRIBUTION	North America, Europe, western Asia
HABITAT	On old bonfire sites and other burned ground
ASSOCIATION	In woodland and scrub
GROWTH FORM	On burnt soil
ABUNDANCE	Occasional
SPORE COLOR	White
EDIBILITY	Edible when cooked

HEIGHT
Up to 10 in
(250 mm)

DIAMETER
Up to 12 in
(300 mm)

582

PEZIZA PROTEANA
BONFIRE CAULIFLOWER
(BOUDIER) SEAVER

Peziza proteana normally forms whitish, cup-shaped fruitbodies, but occasionally produces extraordinary, cauliflower-like, convoluted masses that are often referred to as forma *sparassoidea*, the Bonfire Cauliflower or Cabbage-Head Fungus. When examined closely, these masses consist of ordinary fruitbodies growing so densely together that the cups are completely distorted. The species in either form is an example of a specialist fire-site fungus, which in the natural world might appear after forest fires, but are now mostly found on old bonfire sites. Such fungi often have a high tolerance to alkaline soils (wood ash is typically alkaline) or are deep-growing and only stimulated to produce fruitbodies by heat.

SIMILAR SPECIES

The "cauliflower" form resembles a pallid, distorted species of morel or *Gyromitra*, but these are normally brownish and have distinct, whitish stems. The unrelated Cauliflower Fungus (*Sparassis crispa*) has seaweedlike fronds and grows at the base of trees. The cup-shaped form is best distinguished from similar *Peziza* species microscopically.

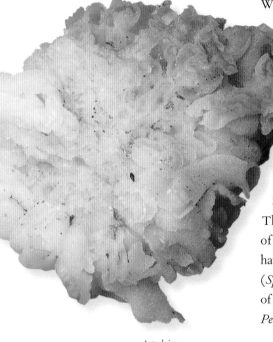

Actual size

The Bonfire Cauliflower can form ordinary cup-shaped fruitbodies with a smooth, ivory-white inner surface and scurfy outer surface. In its "cauliflower" form, however, it produces large, distorted, folded, and chambered masses that are similarly colored, but may be flushed pinkish, lilac, or ocher with age.

FAMILY	Pezizaceae
DISTRIBUTION	North America, Europe, Africa, Central and South America, Asia, Australia, New Zealand
HABITAT	On dung, compost heaps, mulch
ASSOCIATION	On manured substrates
GROWTH FORM	Singly or more typically clustered, often densely so
ABUNDANCE	Common
SPORE COLOR	White
EDIBILITY	Poisonous unless well cooked

HEIGHT	Up to 2 in (50 mm)
DIAMETER	Up to 3 in (80 mm)

PEZIZA VESICULOSA

BLISTERED CUP

BULLIARD

583

The Blistered Cup, also known as the Bladder Cup, is a common species of manure heaps and dungy ground, now becoming increasingly frequent in enriched mulch beds. When happy with its habitat it can often run riot, producing thousands of clustered fruitbodies. These fruitbodies often grow so compactly that they become distorted. They are also quite brittle and break easily under pressure. As a result, the inner and outer surfaces sometimes become detached, leading to the formation of bladder-like blisters, making the fruitbodies even more irregular. The epithet *vesiculosa* means "blister-forming." *Peziza vesiculosa* contains metabolites which show antitumor activity and has been used in Japan to treat tumors and boost immune function.

SIMILAR SPECIES

The color, large size, habitat, and tendency to blister usually distinguish this species. The common *Peziza cerea* is of similar color and size, but typically grows in old mortar (sometimes between paving stones or brickwork) and damp plaster in buildings. Many other *Peziza* species grow on soil, dung, and rotten wood, but most are smaller or more deeply colored.

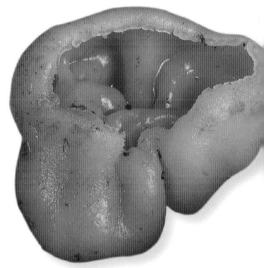

Actual size

The Blistered Cup produces comparatively large, cup-shaped fruitbodies that often become distorted, especially when growing in dense clusters (see photo above). The inner surface is smooth and pale yellowish brown to buff, the outer surface similar but scurfy or granular. Margins usually remain incurved. With age, the inner and outer surfaces may separate and become blistered.

FAMILY	Sarcoscyphaceae
DISTRIBUTION	Southeastern North America (Florida), Africa, Central and South America, southern Asia (including China and Japan)
HABITAT	In woodland
ASSOCIATION	With broadleaf trees
GROWTH FORM	On fallen logs and branches
ABUNDANCE	Occasional
SPORE COLOR	White
EDIBILITY	Not edible

HEIGHT
Up to ½ in (15 mm)

DIAMETER
Up to 4 in (100 mm)

584

PHILLIPSIA DOMINGENSIS

MAUVE ELF CUP

BERKELEY

This is a large, and often strikingly colored, tropical cup fungus which is common and widespread on logs and dead wood. It is related to the tropical goblets (*Cookeina* species) and, like them, can be highly variable in color. Bright pinkish violet or mauve seems typical, but recent molecular research has shown that specimens with colors ranging from bright yellow to reddish brown are too closely related to characterize as different species. Occasionally, fruitbodies with different colors can even appear on the same log, suggesting that the carotenoid pigment phillipsiaxanthin, isolated from *Phillipsia* fruitbodies, may be very unstable.

SIMILAR SPECIES

The wide color variation of *Phillipsia domingensis* can make it hard to distinguish without microscopic examination. A related but much less common tropical species, *P. carnicolor*, normally has orange to salmon-pink fruitbodies, while *P. crispata* is typically orange to brownish red. Scarlet specimens may appear similar to fruitbodies of *Sarcoscypha coccinea*.

Actual size

The Mauve Elf Cup produces fruitbodies that are flask- or funnel-shaped when young, but expand to become shallowly cup-shaped or disc-shaped (see photo above), with a very short, central stalk. The outer surface is smooth and whitish, the inner surface smooth and variously colored, from dull to bright mauve, pink to red or reddish brown, and even orange to yellow.

FAMILY	Rhizinaceae
DISTRIBUTION	North America, Europe, northern Asia; introduced in southern Africa
HABITAT	In conifer woodland
ASSOCIATION	With conifers
GROWTH FORM	On soil, singly or in small groups
ABUNDANCE	Occasional
SPORE COLOR	White
EDIBILITY	Not edible

HEIGHT
Less than ⅛ in
(2 mm)

DIAMETER
Up to 2½ in
(60 mm)

RHIZINA UNDULATA

PINE FIREFUNGUS

FRIES

585

The Pine Firefungus can be a serious pathogen of conifers (not just pine), attacking the roots and causing "group dying" of mature trees and newly planted seedlings. Spores in the soil are stimulated to germinate at high temperatures (95–115°F / 35–45°C) and do so during natural forest fires or brash-burning by foresters. Fruitbodies may appear within three months of a fire and continue for several years until gradually disappearing. Younger fruitbodies sometimes rise at the center like an inverted bowl, giving them a puffed-up look that presumably explains the alternative American name of the Doughnut Fungus.

SIMILAR SPECIES

Some *Discina* species, such as *D. ancilis*, are superficially similar and are also found in conifer forests. Their undersurfaces are quite different, however, being more or less centrally attached to the ground and lacking the rhizoids of the Pine Firefungus. The Bleach Cup (*Disciotis venosa*) has similar blister-like wrinkles, but smells of bleach and grows in a different habitat.

Actual size

The Pine Firefungus produces flat, not cup-shaped, fruitbodies that are roughly circular at first, but may coalesce. The upper surface is smooth but irregularly undulating (sometimes rising at the center), dark brown to blackish brown, and with a distinctly paler, whitish to yellowish margin. The buff to ocher under-suface is attached to the ground by numerous root-like rhizoids.

FAMILY	Sarcoscyphaceae
DISTRIBUTION	Western North America, Europe
HABITAT	In woodland
ASSOCIATION	With broadleaf trees
GROWTH FORM	On mossy fallen branches
ABUNDANCE	Common
SPORE COLOR	White
EDIBILITY	Not edible

HEIGHT
Up to 2 in
(50 mm)

DIAMETER
Up to 2 in
(50 mm)

586

SARCOSCYPHA COCCINEA
SCARLET ELFCUP
(JACQUIN) SACCARDO

The closely related group of species known as Scarlet Elfcups are among the most spectacularly colored north-temperate fungi, especially since fruitbodies are normally produced in midwinter or very early spring. In the British Isles *Sarcoscypha* species have a distinctly western Atlantic distribution, and elsewhere they seem to prefer mild, damp climates, often fruiting on mossy fallen branches in sheltered river valleys. Like their tropical relatives, *Phillipsia* species, they contain bright carotenoid pigments. Very occasionally, fruitbodies are found that are bright yellow, or even unpigmented and white.

SIMILAR SPECIES
The Scarlet Elfcups are a complex of very similar species that can be distinguished only microscopically. Among them are *Sarcoscypha austriaca*, common in eastern North America and Europe, *S. dudleyi* and the smaller *S. occidentalis*, also in eastern North America, *S. jurana* in central Europe, and *S. macronesica* in Madeira and the Canary Islands. Additional species occur in Asia and Africa.

Actual size

The Scarlet Elfcup produces cup-shaped fruitbodies that are often distinctly stalked when young, but tend to lose the stalk when they expand. Old fruitbodies become flat and irregularly disc-shaped. The interior surface is smooth and normally bright scarlet, the outer surface similarly colored but appearing whitish from its covering of fine hairs, which are straight under the microscope.

FAMILY	Sarcosomataceae
DISTRIBUTION	Eastern North America, continental Europe
HABITAT	In woodland
ASSOCIATION	With spruce
GROWTH FORM	On ground, in needle litter
ABUNDANCE	Rare
SPORE COLOR	Brown
EDIBILITY	Not edible

HEIGHT
Up to 4 in
(100 mm)

DIAMETER
Up to 4 in
(100 mm)

SARCOSOMA GLOBOSUM

BOMBMURKLA

(SCHMIDEL) REHM

587

This strange-looking species typically occurs in early spring, half-buried in deep moss and needle litter in old, undisturbed spruce forests. It is basically a cup fungus, but the stem below the cup is gelatinous and becomes grossly swollen with water. This store of water helps the fruitbody to develop, even in dry winter weather. It is called Bombmurkla in Sweden, its European stronghold, where the fungus is protected by law, and is also known as the Charred-Pancake Cup. In other Scandinavian and eastern European countries, as old forests have been cut down, the Bombmurkla has become endangered or even gone extinct. It has now been proposed for international protection under the Bern Convention.

The Bombmurkla forms fruitbodies that are almost globose, often half-buried in moss and needle litter. The upper surface is a smooth, shiny, blackish brown disc with a distinct margin. The grossly swollen stem below is velvety and blackish brown, often wrinkled or folded, and contains a semi-gelatinous watery fluid when cut.

SIMILAR SPECIES

There are two related species in North America, *Sarcosoma latahense* and *S. mexicanum*, but both (though somewhat gelatinized) are more typically cup-shaped and lack the grossly swollen stem of *S. globosum*. Black species of *Plectania* and *Pseudoplectania* are also cup-shaped, but not gelatinized.

Actual size

FAMILY	Pezizaceae
DISTRIBUTION	North America, Europe, North Africa, western Asia
HABITAT	In woodland, usually on calcareous soil
ASSOCIATION	Ectomycorrhizal, with broadleaf trees and conifers
GROWTH FORM	On or in soil, normally half-buried
ABUNDANCE	Occasional
SPORE COLOR	White
EDIBILITY	Poisonous

HEIGHT	Up to 3 in (75 mm)
DIAMETER	Up to 6 in (150 mm)

588

SARCOSPHAERA CORONARIA

VIOLET CROWN CUP

(JACQUIN) J. SCHRÖTER

Actual size

This is an attractive and distinctive species, producing half-buried fruitbodies that are almost truffle-like at first, but which split open to release their spores like a cup fungus. In Europe, the species is on the Red Lists of threatened fungal species in over a dozen countries and is one of the fungi proposed for international protection under the Bern Convention. It appears to be less rare in North America. Though sometimes claimed to be edible if cooked, the Violet Crown Cup contains gyromitrin, a potentially lethal poison also found in the false morels, and is therefore best avoided. It has an alternative common name of the Pink Crown Fungus.

SIMILAR SPECIES

Among the cup fungi, several *Peziza* species have violet-colored fruitbodies, including *P. violacea* and *P. praetervisa*. Both normally occur on burned ground, however, and are more regularly cup-shaped. *Geopora* species have half-buried fruitbodies similar to those of the Violet Crown Cup, but with white to cream interior surfaces.

The Violet Crown Cup has fruitbodies that are initially sordid whitish, smooth, and truffle-like, and half-buried in soil. When mature, the brittle upper surface splits, often irregularly but sometimes in a starlike manner, to reveal a hollow cup. The smooth inner surface of the cup is pinkish lilac to violet in color, and sometimes has gray or brownish tones. Fruitbodies growing close together often coalesce.

FAMILY	Pyronemataceae
DISTRIBUTION	North America, Europe, North Africa, Central and South America, Asia, Australia, New Zealand
HABITAT	In woodland
ASSOCIATION	On damp rotten wood or wood-enriched soil
GROWTH FORM	Singly or in troops
ABUNDANCE	Common
SPORE COLOR	White
EDIBILITY	Not edible

HEIGHT
Less than ⅛ in
(1 mm)

DIAMETER
Up to ¼ in
(20 mm)

SCUTELLINIA SCUTELLATA
COMMON EYELASH
(LINNAEUS) LAMBOTTE

589

The Common Eyelash—or Eyelash Cup—is an attractive little fungus, frequently found on damp, rotten wood where it can sometimes grow in small troops. Though individual fruitbodies are small, the eyelash-like hairs around the margin of the disc are usually long enough and dark enough to see without needing a magnifying lens. These hairs may help protect the developing fungus from grazing by invertebrates, such as mites, and may also help retain the moisture needed for spore release. The bright color of the spore-bearing disc comes from a mixture of carotene pigments, also found in some other red and orange fungi.

SIMILAR SPECIES
Scutellinia scutellata is the commonest of several species of eyelash fungi that are indistinguishable in the field, but can be separated by microscopic examination. *Anthracobia* species grow in swarms on burned ground, are duller red to orange, and have very short, brown, marginal hairs. *Cheilymenia* species growing in swarms on dung are similar to *Anthracobia*.

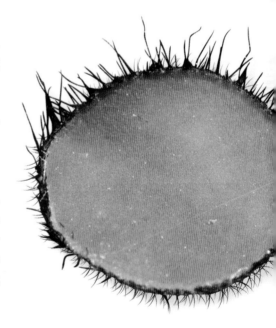

The Common Eyelash forms small fruitbodies that are cup-shaped at first, but quickly expand to disc-shaped. The inner surface is smooth and bright red to orange-red. The outer surface is similar colored, but sparsely covered in brown to blackish hairs which give an eyelash-like fringe to the margin of the disc.

Actual size

FAMILY	Cudoniaceae
DISTRIBUTION	North America, Europe, northern Asia
HABITAT	In conifer woodland
ASSOCIATION	With conifers
GROWTH FORM	On soil or needle litter, in troops
ABUNDANCE	Occasional
SPORE COLOR	White
EDIBILITY	Not edible

HEIGHT
Up to 3 in
(80 mm)

DIAMETER
Up to 1¼ in
(30 mm)

590

SPATHULARIA FLAVIDA
YELLOW FAN
PERSOON

Looking rather like a miniature kayak paddle or an African fan, *Spathularia flavida* is a small, but brightly colored, and distinctive fungus found in conifer forests throughout the northern hemisphere. It appears to be a litter-rotting species, breaking down needles and other plant litter and gradually turning them into humus. An odd piece of research has shown that the species has a defense mechanism against fungus-eating invertebrates (springtails). If a fruitbody is damaged, for example by biting, the springtails move away from it, suggesting that the Yellow Fan releases some kind of repellent chemical or smell.

SIMILAR SPECIES

In North America, *Spathulariopsis velutipes* is similarly shaped, but has a cream fertile head and a reddish brown, slightly velvety stem. The common and widespread Jellybaby (*Leotia lubrica*) is less brightly colored, often greenish, and has a rounded head. *Dacryopinax* species are spatula-shaped, but always grow on wood.

Actual size

The Yellow Fan forms stalked fruitbodies that resemble flattened clubs at first, but are fan-shaped or spatula-shaped when mature. The fertile, fan-shaped, pale yellow head surrounds the top part of the stem, and is usually wrinkled or veined. The stem is round, smooth, and similarly colored or paler.

FAMILY	Pyronemataceae
DISTRIBUTION	North America, Europe, Asia
HABITAT	In woodland
ASSOCIATION	Possibly ectomycorrhizal, with broadleaf trees and conifers
GROWTH FORM	On soil
ABUNDANCE	Common
SPORE COLOR	White
EDIBILITY	Not edible

HEIGHT
Up to 2½ in
(60 mm)

DIAMETER
Up to 2 in
(50 mm)

TARZETTA CATINUS
GREATER TOOTHED CUP
(HOLMSKJOLD) KORF & J. K. ROGERS

591

Tarzetta is Italian for a "little cup" and *catinus* is Latin for a "basin," so it is no surprise to discover that *Tarzetta catinus* (sometimes spelt *Tarzetta catinus*) is a distinctly cup-shaped fungus. It is quite common in woodlands, though easily overlooked, and recent research has indicated that it may be ectomycorrhizal, forming an association with the roots of living trees. The Greater Toothed Cup was one of 52 new species first described by the naturalist Theodor Holmskjold in the 1790s. His beautifully illustrated book was called (in Latin) *Happy Resting Periods in the Country Studying Danish Fungi*—a curious title for an important scientific reference work.

SIMILAR SPECIES
Tarzetta spurcata is a very similar species that can only be distinguished microscopically. The Toothed Cup (*T. cupularis*) and *T. scotica* are both smaller, not exceeding ¾ in (20 mm) in diameter. The Glazed Cup (*Humaria hemisphaerica*) is similarly shaped, but the interior surface is white.

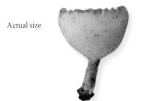

Actual size

The Greater Toothed Cup forms fruitbodies that are almost globose when they are young, but become cup-shaped when mature, often with a short, central stem embedded in the soil. The inner surface is smooth and pale cream to ocher-brown in color (see photos above), with a toothed or serrated margin. The outer surface is similarly colored and scurfy or felted.

FAMILY	Geoglossaceae
DISTRIBUTION	North America, Europe, northern Asia, New Zealand
HABITAT	In grassland or woodland
ASSOCIATION	With mosses
GROWTH FORM	On soil or mossy grass, singly or scattered
ABUNDANCE	Common
SPORE COLOR	Black
EDIBILITY	Not edible

HEIGHT
Up to 3 in
(80 mm)

DIAMETER
Up to ⅜ in
(8 mm)

592

TRICHOGLOSSUM HIRSUTUM
HAIRY EARTHTONGUE
(PERSOON) BOUDIER

In Europe, the earthtongues are typical fungi of unimproved pastures, old lawns, and coastal turf. Along with the waxcaps (*Hygrocybe* species), they are good indicator species of undisturbed, species-rich grasslands. Elsewhere, however, they can be found in mossy woodlands. The Hairy Earthtongue is one of the commonest and most widespread species. Under a good hand lens the fine hairs are seen to be comparatively large, blackish brown, and very pointed. They perhaps help protect the spore-producing surface from fungus-eating mites and other small invertebrates. The genus name *Trichoglossum* actually means "hairy tongue."

SIMILAR SPECIES

Several less common *Trichoglossum* species, such as *T. walteri*, are very similar and can only be distinguished microscopically. Closely related earthtongues in the genus *Geoglossum* may look similar, but are smooth-stemmed (not finely hairy) under a magnifying lens.

The Hairy Earthtongue forms black, stalked, club-shaped fruitbodies. The fertile head can be narrowly club-shaped but is often swollen, resembling a paddle or pointed spade, and is usually compressed and furrowed. Under a magnifying lens it can be seen to be covered in short hairs. The cylindrical stem is deep black and visibly hairy to velvety.

Actual size

FAMILY	Sarcosomataceae
DISTRIBUTION	Eastern North America, Europe, northern Asia
HABITAT	In woodland
ASSOCIATION	With broadleaf trees
GROWTH FORM	On or alongside rotten, sometimes buried, wood
ABUNDANCE	Occasional
SPORE COLOR	White
EDIBILITY	Not edible

HEIGHT
Up to 5 in
(120 mm)

DIAMETER
Up to 4 in
(100 mm)

URNULA CRATERIUM
DEVIL'S URN
(SCHWEINITZ) FRIES

593

The Devil's Urn or Crater Cup is a spring-fruiting fungus, fairly common in eastern North America but much less so elsewhere. It normally fruits on rotten, fallen broadleaf branches that may be half-buried in moss or leaf litter, but the fungus is actually present in the wood before it falls. On living trees, particularly oaks, it is quite a serious pathogen, causing a disease called strumella canker. The name comes from the synonym *Strumella coryneoidea*, which is now known to be an asexual stage in the life cycle of the Devil's Urn. Blackish pustules form on infected bark, and trees may be killed or severely damaged, leading to substantial economic losses in forestry stands.

SIMILAR SPECIES
The blackish *Urnula hiemalis* is similar but smaller and rarer, and is known only from Alaska and Scandinavia. The paler, purplish *Neournula pouchetii* is also smaller, grows with conifers, and is uncommon in western North America and Europe. The related, but rare, *Sarcosoma globosum* is a much fleshier, gelatinous species.

The Devil's Urn forms stalked, urn- or goblet-shaped fruitbodies. Immature fruitbodies are club-shaped, but soon tear open at the top to reveal a deep, cup-shaped interior with a ragged, rolled-back margin. The inner surface is smooth, and blackish to blackish brown. The outer surface is pale pinkish gray or brownish gray, and initially scurfy, becoming darker when mature.

Actual size

FAMILY	Discinaceae
DISTRIBUTION	North America, Europe, North Africa, Central America, Asia
HABITAT	In woodland
ASSOCIATION	Ectomycorrhizal, with conifers
GROWTH FORM	On soil and leaf litter
ABUNDANCE	Common
SPORE COLOR	Yellowish
EDIBILITY	Poisonous, potentially lethal

HEIGHT
Up to 6 in
(150 mm)

DIAMETER
Up to 6 in
(150 mm)

594

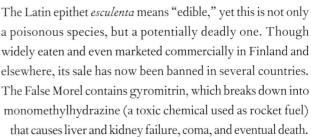

GYROMITRA ESCULENTA

FALSE MOREL

(PERSOON) FRIES

The Latin epithet *esculenta* means "edible," yet this is not only a poisonous species, but a potentially deadly one. Though widely eaten and even marketed commercially in Finland and elsewhere, its sale has now been banned in several countries. The False Morel contains gyromitrin, which breaks down into monomethylhydrazine (a toxic chemical used as rocket fuel) that causes liver and kidney failure, coma, and eventual death. Much of the toxin can be removed by cooking (though the fumes may be poisonous) with two changes of water. Deaths have nonetheless occurred among people who have eaten the fungus unharmed for years, so common sense suggests that the False Morel is a species to avoid.

SIMILAR SPECIES

Many other *Gyromitra* species exist and are similarly dangerous. All lack the honeycomb-like heads of the true morels, but instead have brainlike folds and lobes. *Gyromitra infula* is a common species, with a weakly lobed, brown cap resembling species of saddle fungi (*Helvella*).

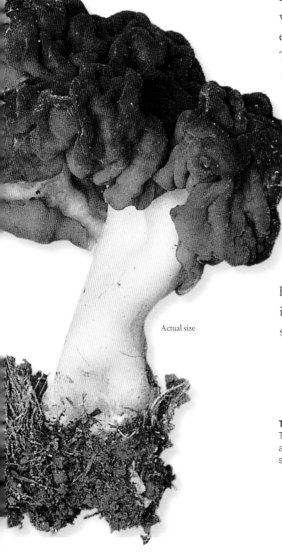

Actual size

The False Morel forms fruitbodies with a brainlike head and a paler stem. The fertile head is brittle, becoming deeply folded and convoluted with age, and pale to deep reddish or purplish brown. The stem is whitish to ocher, sometimes with brown tints, smooth or slightly felted.

FAMILY	Helvellaceae
DISTRIBUTION	North America, Europe, Central America, Asia
HABITAT	In woodland
ASSOCIATION	Ectomycorrhizal, with broadleaf trees and conifers
GROWTH FORM	On soil and leaf litter, singly or in small groups
ABUNDANCE	Occasional
SPORE COLOR	White
EDIBILITY	Not edible

HEIGHT
Up to 4 in
(100 mm)

DIAMETER
Up to 1 in
(25 mm)

HELVELLA ATRA

DARK SADDLE

J. KÖNIG

595

The Dark Saddle is one of several *Helvella* species where the fertile, upper surface, instead of being cup-shaped, has twisted inside out. It may end up looking something like a saddle, but frequently becomes lobed and irregular. Though the smaller species are often difficult to distinguish, *H. atra* is generally recognizable by its dark, smoky colors and smooth stem. It is widespread in the northern hemisphere, but is nowhere common and is even on national Red Lists of threatened fungal species in some European countries.

SIMILAR SPECIES

The common Elfin Saddle (*Helvella lacunosa*) has a smilarly colored head, but is much larger and has a stem that is deeply chambered and furrowed. *Helvella leucopus* has a smooth but white stem. *Helvella pezizoides* is very similar, but somewhat larger, with the cap margin inrolled and the undersurface distinctly felted or hairy.

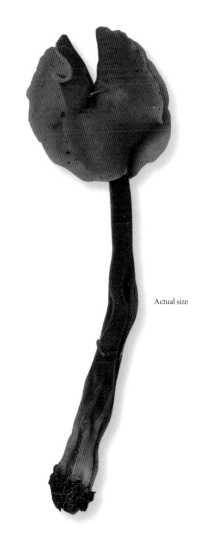

Actual size

The Dark Saddle forms fruitbodies with a lobed or saddle-shaped head and a cylindrical stem. The fertile head is thin and deeply folded or lobed. The upper surface is smooth to wrinkled and dark gray to brownish black, the undersurface paler and smooth to finely felted. The stem is similarly colored, smooth or sparsely grooved, and finely hairy.

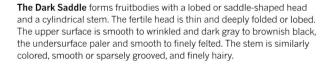

FAMILY	Helvellaceae
DISTRIBUTION	North America, Europe, North Africa, Central America, Asia, New Zealand
HABITAT	In woodland
ASSOCIATION	Ectomycorrhizal, with broadleaf trees, more rarely conifers
GROWTH FORM	On soil and leaf litter
ABUNDANCE	Common
SPORE COLOR	White
EDIBILITY	Not edible

HEIGHT
Up to 6 in
(150 mm)

DIAMETER
Up to 2 in
(50 mm)

596

HELVELLA CRISPA
WHITE SADDLE
(SCOPOLI) FRIES

The White Saddle is more typically cream to pale buff, but is certainly a pallid species, and one of the commonest of the saddle-fungi or false morels, occurring mainly in broadleaf woodland from late summer to early winter. The species is often listed as edible and is widely consumed in eastern Europe and Central America (where it is even sold in markets). It does, however, contain toxins similar to those found in *Gyromitra* species and—though some of the poisons may be broken down by thorough cooking—is best avoided.

SIMILAR SPECIES
The Elfin Saddle (*Helvella lacunosa*) is similarly shaped, but gray. The uncommon *H. lactea* is very similar to the White Saddle, but has a white (rather than cream) head with a smooth (not finely hairy) undersurface. Edible morels (*Morchella* species) have brown, honeycomb-like caps.

Actual size

The White Saddle forms fruitbodies with an irregularly saddle-shaped head and a deeply furrowed stem. The fertile head is thin, brittle, and cartilaginous, cream or buff. The margins are free (not attached to the stem), and the undersurface is minutely hairy and cap-colored. The stem is deeply incised, with irregular, honeycomb-like hollows (see photo right), and is cap-colored or whiter.

FAMILY	Helvellaceae
DISTRIBUTION	North America, Europe, Africa, Central America, Asia
HABITAT	In woodland
ASSOCIATION	Ectomycorrhizal, with broadleaf trees and conifers
GROWTH FORM	On soil and leaf litter
ABUNDANCE	Common
SPORE COLOR	White
EDIBILITY	Not edible

HEIGHT
Up to 6 in
(150 mm)

DIAMETER
Up to 2 in
(50 mm)

HELVELLA LACUNOSA

ELFIN SADDLE

AFZELIUS

597

It is hard to think of the Elfin Saddle as a cup fungus, but many closely related *Helvella* species do have cup-shaped heads. In the Elfin Saddle, however, the cup seems to have melted and collapsed, since it hangs down from the top of the stem in contorted folds and blisters. Any self-respecting elf would surely avoid it. The species has been considered edible by some, but since it belongs in the large group of false morels, it is probably best avoided. It would certainly need to be well-cooked to remove any gyromitrin-like toxins.

SIMILAR SPECIES

The White Saddle (*Helvella crispa*) is similarly shaped, but whitish to cream or buff. The less common *H. atra* is similarly colored, but has a cylindrical, smooth stem. Some "species" of uncertain status, such as *H. sulcata* and *H. palustris*, are almost identical to the Elfin Saddle and may be only variant forms of it.

Actual size

The Elfin Saddle forms fruitbodies with an irregular, gray head and a paler stem. The fertile head is thin, brittle, and cartilaginous, pale gray to almost black, sometimes vaguely saddle-shaped, but more frequently lobed and variously contorted (see photo right). The margins are free (not attached to the stem), and the undersurface is a paler gray. The stem is deeply incised, with irregular, honeycomb-like hollows, and is pale to deep gray.

FAMILY	Helvellaceae
DISTRIBUTION	North America, Europe, Central America, Asia
HABITAT	In woodland
ASSOCIATION	Ectomycorrhizal, with broadleaf trees and conifers
GROWTH FORM	On soil and leaf litter
ABUNDANCE	Occasional
SPORE COLOR	White
EDIBILITY	Not edible

HEIGHT
Up to 3 in
(80 mm)

DIAMETER
Up to 2 in
(50 mm)

598

HELVELLA MACROPUS
FELT SADDLE
(PERSOON) P. KARSTEN

Helvella macropus is an example of a saddle fungus that still retains a cup-shaped fruiting body. In many other species, such as the Elfin Saddle (*Helvella lacunosa*), the cup has become so highly distorted that it is hardly recognizable. In the past, these various shapes led to the saddle fungi being split between different genera, but more recent research has shown that they all belong together in the genus *Helvella*. The Felt Saddle is not considered edible and, like other false morels, may well be poisonous, especially if eaten uncooked.

SIMILAR SPECIES
Helvella villosa is similar but usually smaller and is best distinguished microscopically. *Helvella cupuliformis* is also similar, though the cups have a tendency to open completely when mature. The commoner and larger Elfin Saddle and White Saddle (*H. crispa*) both have highly irregular caps and stems that are deeply chambered and furrowed.

Actual size

The Felt Saddle forms cup-shaped fruitbodies with a long, cylindrical stem. The cup is thin and typically incurved so that it appears half-folded. The upper surface is smooth and brown to grayish brown (see photo left), the undersurface paler and scurfy or felted. The stem is similarly colored, smooth (not ridged), and scurfy or felted.

FAMILY	Morchellaceae
DISTRIBUTION	North America, Europe, Asia
HABITAT	In woodland and scrub
ASSOCIATION	Possibly ectomycorrhizal, with broadleaf trees
GROWTH FORM	In soil or leaf litter, often in troops
ABUNDANCE	Occasional
SPORE COLOR	Cream
EDIBILITY	Edible (if cooked)

HEIGHT
Up to 6 in
(150 mm)

DIAMETER
Up to 2½ in
(60 mm)

MITROPHORA SEMILIBERA

SEMIFREE MOREL

(DE CANDOLLE) LÉVEILLÉ

599

The Semifree Morel—or Half-Free Morel—is the least favored of the edible morels, with a taste often said to be "disappointing." Like other morels, it can only be safely eaten if well-cooked, a procedure that breaks down the toxins present in the raw fungus. These can be quite unpleasant. No fewer than 77 guests at a North American banquet a few years ago were hospitalized as a result of consuming raw morels, tastefully sliced in a salad. *Mitrophora* means "bearing a miter or turban," which aptly described the shape of the fertile head, though the species is closely related to the true morels and is frequently referred to as *Morchella semilibera*.

SIMILAR SPECIES

Morchella elata and *M. esculenta* both have larger heads (compared to stem length) that are fully attached to their stems, not free at the margin. False morels, including *Gyromitra* and *Verpa* species, have heads that are wrinkled, folded, or lobed, rather than honeycomb-like.

The Semifree Morel produces fruitbodies with a comparatively small, fertile head and long, contrasting stem. The head is brownish and honeycomb-like, attached to the stem for about half to two-thirds of its length, hanging freely at the margin. The stem is white to cream, cylindrical, and finely scurfy (see photo far right).

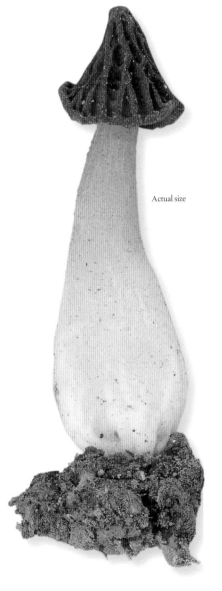

Actual size

FAMILY	Morchellaceae
DISTRIBUTION	North America, Europe, Africa, Central and South America, Asia, Australia, New Zealand
HABITAT	In woodland and scrub, often on burned ground
ASSOCIATION	Possibly ectomycorrhizal, with conifers
GROWTH FORM	In soil or leaf litter, often in troops
ABUNDANCE	Locally common
SPORE COLOR	Cream
EDIBILITY	Edible (if cooked)

HEIGHT
Up to 6 in
(150 mm)

DIAMETER
Up to 2½ in
(60 mm)

600

MORCHELLA ELATA
BLACK MOREL
FRIES

Actual size

The Black Morel is celebrated as one of the finest of edible fungi, though it should be noted that (like all morels) it is poisonous if eaten raw or undercooked. It is widely gathered and sold commercially and is also now cultivated. In North America, the spring morel season is a big business in itself, attracting thousands of tourists to favorite forest areas and local morel festivals. *Morchella elata* is particularly associated with burned ground, where it can sometimes fruit in vast numbers. Recent DNA research, however, indicates that the Black Morel is a complex of closely related species (including *M. conica*), not all of which may be fire-site fungi.

SIMILAR SPECIES

Members of the *Morchella elata–M. conica* species complex can be distinguished from the similar and equally edible *M. esculenta* complex by their darker colors and more conical heads. False morels, including *Gyromitra* and *Verpa* species, have heads that are wrinkled, folded, or lobed, rather than honeycomb-like.

The Black Morel has fruitbodies with a dark, conical, fertile head and whitish stem. The head is honeycomb-like or pitted, rather than wrinkled, in shades of dark brown, and normally narrows toward the top (see photo right). It is attached to the stem (not loose), which is whitish, sometimes flushed pinkish to brown or blackish, finely scurfy, and smooth to wrinkled.

FAMILY	Morchellaceae
DISTRIBUTION	North America, Europe, North Africa, Central and South America, northern Asia, New Zealand
HABITAT	In calcareous woodland and scrub
ASSOCIATION	Possibly ectomycorrhizal, with broadleaf trees
GROWTH FORM	In soil or leaf litter, often in troops
ABUNDANCE	Locally common
SPORE COLOR	Cream
EDIBILITY	Edible (if cooked)

HEIGHT
Up to 12 in
(300 mm)

DIAMETER
Up to 6 in
(150 mm)

MORCHELLA ESCULENTA

MOREL

(LINNAEUS) PERSOON

601

The Morel (or Yellow Morel) is another classic edible species—commercially collected and marketed all over the world. As with the Black Morel (*Morchella elata*), it appears to represent a species complex, DNA research showing that at least three genetically distinct species (*M. esculenta*, *M. crassipes*, and *M. spongiola*) occur in central Europe, though distinguishing them by sight may be difficult, if not impossible. Fruitbodies typically appear in spring and have a preference for calcareous soil—including dunes (which makes cleaning the honeycomb fruitbodies a nightmare)—and slightly disturbed sites.

SIMILAR SPECIES

The Morel can be distinguished from the Black Morel (*Morchella elata*) by its paler, often yellowish brown, color, its typically less conical head, and its frequently larger size. The poisonous False Morel (*Gyromitra esculenta*) has a head that is folded and convoluted, rather than honeycomb-like.

Actual size

The Morel forms fruitbodies with a typically pale brownish, fertile head and whitish stem. The head is honeycomb-like or pitted in shades of ocher, honey-brown, or yellowish brown (or more rarely grayish brown), and is often, but not always, rounded at the top. It is attached to the stem (not loose), which is whitish to pale ocher, finely scurfy, and smooth to wrinkled.

FAMILY	Morchellaceae
DISTRIBUTION	North America, continental Europe
HABITAT	In woodland and scrub
ASSOCIATION	Possibly ectomycorrhizal, with broadleaf trees
GROWTH FORM	In soil
ABUNDANCE	Occasional
SPORE COLOR	Yellowish
EDIBILITY	Poisonous

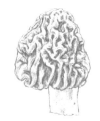

HEIGHT
Up to 5 in
(125 mm)

DIAMETER
Up to 1½ in
(40 mm)

602

VERPA BOHEMICA
EARLY FALSE MOREL
(KROMBHOLZ) J. SCHRÖTER

In North America, *Verpa bohemica* is one of the first morel-like fungi to appear in the spring, but it continues to produces fruit bodies throughout the morel season. It is eaten by some and even sold commercially, but contains gyromitrin, a dangerous and potentially lethal poison with rather unpredictable effects. Best advice is therefore to avoid consuming any of the false morels, since they are hardly worth the gamble. Microscopically, *V. bohemica* is noted for its exceptionally large spores, a useful, additional identification feature for the mycologist.

SIMILAR SPECIES

True morels, such as *Morchella elata* and *M. esculenta*, have fertile heads that are completely attached to the stem, not just attached at the top. As its name suggests, the similar Semifree Morel, *Mitrophora semilibera*, has a fertile head that is partly attached to the stem, but is free at the base. The widespread *Verpa conica* has a free, but smooth, thimble-like head.

Actual size

The Early False Morel forms fruitbodies that look very like the true morels, but the fertile head is attached only at the top of the stem and hangs loose, like an inverted cup. The head itself is yellowish to reddish brown, rubbery to cartilaginous, and deeply folded and wrinkled. The stem is cream to white, smooth to granular, and cylindrical (narrowing toward the top).

FAMILY	Elaphomycetaceae
DISTRIBUTION	North America, Europe, Asia
HABITAT	In woodland
ASSOCIATION	Ectomycorrhizal, with broadleaf trees and conifers
GROWTH FORM	In soil or leaf litter
ABUNDANCE	Very common
SPORE COLOR	White
EDIBILITY	Not edible

HEIGHT
Up to 2 in
(50 mm)

DIAMETER
Up to 2 in
(50 mm)

ELAPHOMYCES MURICATUS

MARBLED HART'S TRUFFLE

FRIES

603

Elaphomyces means "deer fungi," and these false truffles can often be found at the edge of deer scrapes in woodland—if the deer have failed to eat them all. Squirrels and mice also dig up fruitbodies for food, and presumably spread the spores in their droppings. They were once used as an ingredient in herbal medicine for women about to give birth, and in the early nineteenth century were sold in London's Covent Garden market as "Lycoperdon nuts." It was also believed that they grew where deer had rutted and, possibly for this reason, were considered to be of value as an aphrodisiac.

SIMILAR SPECIES

The equally common Hart's Truffle (*Elaphomyces granulatus*) has a preference for conifers and, when cut, lacks the marbling in the rind which gives the Marbled Hart's Truffle its name. Other *Elaphomyces* species are much less common, and some have a smooth, not warted, outer surface.

Actual size

The Marbled Hart's Truffle produces almost spherical fruitbodies (see photo above) in soil or under leaf litter. The fruitbodies are quite hard, densely but finely warted, and ocher to orange-brown, becoming darker and duller when old. When cut, they have a thick, marbled, purplish brown rind enclosing a central spore mass that is whitish when young (see photo left), black and powdery when mature.

FAMILY	Discinaceae
DISTRIBUTION	North America, Europe, Central America, Asia
HABITAT	In woodland
ASSOCIATION	Ectomycorrhizal, with broadleaf trees and conifers
GROWTH FORM	In soil or leaf litter
ABUNDANCE	Occasional
SPORE COLOR	White
EDIBILITY	Said to be edible (if cooked)

HEIGHT
Up to 2½ in
(60 mm)

DIAMETER
Up to 2½ in
(60 mm)

604

HYDNOTRYA TULASNEI
COMMON FOLD-TRUFFLE
(BERKELEY) BERKELEY & BROOME

Actual size

This is one of the commonest truffle-like fungi, though it still needs to be carefully searched for under leaf litter in woodland. It has a distinct smell when fresh, variously described as musty or like caramel, and is said to be edible if thoroughly cooked, though worthless. The smell does attract animals, however, and the spores are probably spread in their droppings. It is readily eaten by red squirrels in Scotland, and probably elsewhere. The Common Fold-Truffle is a relative of cup-shaped *Discina* species and morel-like *Gyromitra* species, but the spore-bearing surface remains densely folded inside the fruitbody and never opens up.

SIMILAR SPECIES

Many similar truffle-like species occur and they are best separated microscopically, since their spores are usually large and distinctive. Several less-common species of *Hydnotrya* are almost hollow, resembling a cup fungus that never expands. The true truffles (*Tuber* species) are much denser inside, and rarely have open chambers.

The Common Fold-Truffle produces truffle-like fruitbodies in soil or under leaf litter. The fruitbodies are almost spherical to irregularly lobed, smooth to slightly downy or wrinkled, and reddish brown. When cut, the whitish to pink interior consists of dense folds with open chambers and cavities (see photo bottom left).

FAMILY	Pyronemataceae
DISTRIBUTION	Australia, New Zealand; introduced in Great Britain
HABITAT	In woodland and scrub
ASSOCIATION	With broadleaf trees
GROWTH FORM	In soil
ABUNDANCE	Occasional
SPORE COLOR	White
EDIBILITY	Not edible

HEIGHT
Up to 1 in
(20 mm)

DIAMETER
Up to 1 in
(20 mm)

PAUROCOTYLIS PILA

SCARLET BERRY TRUFFLE

BERKELEY

605

The bright color of the Scarlet Berry Truffle and its habit
of growing on the surface, rather than underground, suggest
that the fruitbodies may have evolved to attract birds in its native
New Zealand. The fungus even grows under podocarp trees
with bright red berries. The birds eat the truffles along with the
berries, and spread the spores in their droppings. Curiously, the
fungus was found fruiting in England in the 1970s and has since
spread into Scotland, turning up in gardens and waste ground.
It was presumably introduced accidentally with exotic plants.

SIMILAR SPECIES

This unusual truffle-like fungus should be quite distinctive.
In New Zealand, *Leratiomyces erythrocephalus* has a fruitbody
of similar shape and color, but is easily distinguished by
its white stem. An uncommon, unrelated, bright orange,
truffle-like species, *Stephanosphora caroticolor*, grows in north-
temperate woodlands.

Actual size

The Scarlet Berry Truffle produces a tuberous fruitbody that is
smooth and round at first, but becomes dimpled, wrinkled, and
irregular with age (see photo right). The surface is bright red to
reddish brown. The texture is comparatively soft and rubbery,
white when cut, becoming partly hollow.

FAMILY	Pezizaceae
DISTRIBUTION	Southern Europe, North Africa
HABITAT	In deserts and drylands
ASSOCIATION	Ectomycorrhizal, with the rockrose *Helianthemum guttatum*
GROWTH FORM	In soil
ABUNDANCE	Occasional
SPORE COLOR	White
EDIBILITY	Edible

HEIGHT
Up to 4 in
(100 mm)

DIAMETER
Up to 4 in
(100 mm)

606

TERFEZIA ARENARIA
MOROCCAN DESERT TRUFFLE
(MORIS) TRAPPE

Terfezia species, including the Moroccan Desert Truffle or Terfez, have long been eaten in North Africa, Arabia, and the Middle East, even though their appearance was considered a mystery, and was once though to be connected with thunder. The fact that they grow underground in deserts (and hence are seldom seen) may have led to the suggestion that desert truffles were the "manna" on which the Israelites fed as mentioned in the Bible. They were certainly highly valued by the ancient Romans, who had them shipped into Italy from Egypt and Libya. Today, they are still regularly collected to be sold in local markets or exported. They are not closely related to the true truffles and their taste is said to be subtler.

SIMILAR SPECIES
Several similar-looking, edible *Terfezia* and *Tirmania* species grow in the Mediterranean area, as well as in Arabia and the Middle East. They are best distinguished microscopically, as are the true truffles (*Tuber* species), though these are normally associated with trees.

Actual size

The Moroccan Desert Truffle produces a tuberous, potato-like fruitbody. The surface is irregular and somewhat rough. Young specimens are whitish, but become pinkish to brown with age. Inside they have a dense, veined texture, which is white at first and then often flushed pinkish (see photo right) to wine-red.

FAMILY	Tuberaceae
DISTRIBUTION	Europe, North Africa, western Asia
HABITAT	In woodland
ASSOCIATION	Ectomycorrhizal, with broadleaf trees
GROWTH FORM	In soil or leaf litter
ABUNDANCE	Occasional
SPORE COLOR	Brown
EDIBILITY	Edible

HEIGHT
Up to 4 in
(100 mm)

DIAMETER
Up to 6 in
(150 mm)

TUBER AESTIVUM

SUMMER TRUFFLE

VITTADINI

607

The Summer Truffle is more widespread than most other commercially harvested species, extending into northern as well as southern Europe. It is less valued than the Black or White Truffles, but was traditionally hunted in England until the 1930s—using a poodle-like "truffle dog" to sniff out the fruitbodies. The distinctive and valued aroma of truffles has evolved to attract animals (such as voles and squirrels) that feed on the fruitbodies and then spread the spores in their droppings. Curiously, the main component of the Summer Truffle's odor is thiobismethane, which (on its own) is usually considered putrid.

SIMILAR SPECIES

The Burgundy Truffle (*Tuber unciniatum*) was thought to be a closely related species—considered of superior flavor by gourmets—but recent molecular analysis has shown that it is identical to the Summer Truffle. The Black Truffle (*T. melanosporum*) looks similar, but is purplish black inside, and has a more Mediterranean distribution.

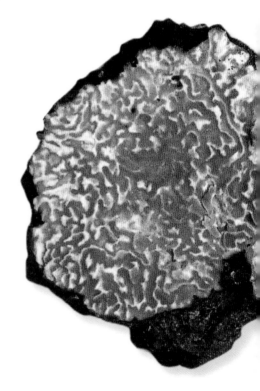

Actual size

The Summer Truffle forms subterranean fruitbodies that are spherical to irregularly lobed. The surface is almost crustlike, blackish brown to black, and covered in polygonal warts. The inner flesh is whitish at first, becoming pinkish or pale brown (see photo above), with both darker and paler marbling.

FAMILY	Tuberaceae
DISTRIBUTION	Continental Europe (Croatia and Italy)
HABITAT	In woodland
ASSOCIATION	Ectomycorrhizal, with broadleaf trees
GROWTH FORM	In soil or leaf litter
ABUNDANCE	Rare
SPORE COLOR	Brown
EDIBILITY	Edible

HEIGHT
Up to 6 in
(150 mm)

DIAMETER
Up to 6 in
(150 mm)

608

TUBER MAGNATUM
WHITE TRUFFLE
PICO

The White Truffle—or Tartufo di Alba—has a very restricted distribution, being found mainly in the Piedmont region of northern Italy, in an area centered around the town of Alba, with a separate population in Croatia. Its rarity and its intense aroma make it the most sought-after and highly valued truffle of them all. In 2007 a single (but exceptionally large) fruitbody fetched an astonishing US$330,000 at a charity auction, though the normal commercial price is considerably lower at around US$2,000 per pound. The fungus is hunted using trained dogs, typically small spaniels, that sniff out and dig up the underground fruitbodies.

SIMILAR SPECIES

Among commercial species, *Tuber borchii* (the Whitish Truffle) is similar, but fruitbodies are typically smaller and lack the intense aroma and flavor of the true White Truffle. Around a dozen similar, whitish species of truffle exist worldwide, but require microscopic examination for precise identification. Many unrelated fungi also produce pallid, truffle-like fruitbodies.

Actual size

The White Truffle forms subterranean, potato-like fruitbodies that are sometimes almost spherical, but more frequently lobed and irregular. The surface is whitish to cream or pale brown, and more or less smooth. When cut, the flesh is pinkish to pale reddish brown with white marbling (see photo above left).

FAMILY	Tuberaceae
DISTRIBUTION	Continental Europe. Cultivated in North America, southern Africa, Australia, New Zealand
HABITAT	In woodland or scrub
ASSOCIATION	Ectomycorrhizal, with broadleaf trees, particularly oak and hazel
GROWTH FORM	In soil or leaf litter
ABUNDANCE	Rare
SPORE COLOR	Brown
EDIBILITY	Edible

HEIGHT
Up to 4 in
(100 mm)

DIAMETER
Up to 4 in
(100 mm)

TUBER MELANOSPORUM

BLACK TRUFFLE

VITTADINI

609

The Black Truffle—or Truffe du Périgord—is one of the most highly esteemed culinary species, especially valued in French cuisine for its aroma and flavor. It has been semi-cultivated in France for centuries, with groves of trees planted in suitable places and impregnated with truffle mycelium. With luck, after some years, these *truffières* produced valuable crops. Today, young saplings (principally oak and hazel) are routinely inoculated with truffle mycelium and the cultivation of the Black Truffle has spread around the globe. The scent is close to boar pheromone, which is why sows were once used to hunt truffles, though separating sow and truffle was always a problem.

SIMILAR SPECIES

Other commercial truffles with a black, warted surface include the Summer Truffle (*Tuber aestivum*), which has much paler, pallid to pinkish flesh and is substantially less aromatic, the Winter Truffle (*T. brumale*), with gray-brown flesh, and the Bagnoli Truffle (*T. mesentericum*), which has fruitbodies with a distinct cavity at the base.

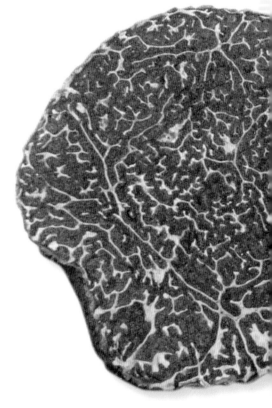

Actual size

The Black Truffle forms subterranean fruitbodies that are spherical to irregularly lobed. The surface is almost crustlike, dark gray to black, and covered in polygonal warts. The inner flesh is purplish black with whitish marbling.

FAMILY	Clavicipitaceae
DISTRIBUTION	North America, Europe, Africa, Central and South America, Asia, Australia, New Zealand
HABITAT	In grassland
ASSOCIATION	Parasitic, on grasses, especially rye
GROWTH FORM	Arising from fallen sclerotia
ABUNDANCE	Common
SPORE COLOR	White
EDIBILITY	Poisonous

HEIGHT
Up to ½ in
(15 mm)

DIAMETER
Less than ⅛ in
(3 mm)

610

CLAVICEPS PURPUREA
ERGOT
(FRIES) TULASNE

Claviceps purpurea has a complex life-cycle intimately linked to that of its grass hosts. It is most frequently seen in its ergot stage—the ergots being small, purplish black propagules that form among the grass seeds. These fall to earth, overwinter, and produce miniature, drumstick-like fruitbodies in late spring, to reinfect the grasses as they begin to flower. Ergots contain lysergic acid—a precursor of LSD—and ergotamine, which constricts blood vessels. Eating infected grain caused epidemics of madness, convulsions, and gangrene in the Middle Ages, but in smaller doses ergot has long been used medically in childbirth and to treat migraine.

SIMILAR SPECIES

A genetically distinct variety, *Claviceps purpurea* var. *spartinae*, grows on saltmarsh grasses and has evolved ergots that can float in saltwater, aiding dispersal. Related species of *Claviceps* include the Horse's Tooth (*C. gigantea*) which infects maize in Central America, and has cream to grayish ergots as large as both the Latin and common names suggest.

The Ergot produces miniature, ocher to reddish brown, drumstick-like "fruitbodies," the heads of which are actually sterile stroma in which the true fruitbodies (looking like tiny pimples under a magnifying lens) are immersed. These fruitbodies arise from banana-shaped, purplish black ergots (or sclerotia)—propagules that formed in the ears of grain, were shed, and have overwintered on the ground.

Actual size

FAMILY	Cordycipitaceae
DISTRIBUTION	North America, Europe, Asia
HABITAT	In grassland and woodland
ASSOCIATION	Parasitic, on moths
GROWTH FORM	Arising from buried pupae
ABUNDANCE	Common
SPORE COLOR	White
EDIBILITY	Edible

HEIGHT
Up to 3 in
(80 mm)

DIAMETER
Up to ¼ in
(5 mm)

CORDYCEPS MILITARIS
SCARLET CATERPILLAR-CLUB
(LINNAEUS) LINK

611

This is the most commonly encountered *Cordyceps* species in north temperate regions, probably because of its eye-catching color. Like all *Cordyceps* species, *C. militaris* is a parasite of insects, infecting and then completely consuming the body of its host. If a fruitbody is carefully unearthed, the host from which it arises will be found at the base. For the Scarlet Caterpillar-Club, this is a buried lepidopteran pupa, usually presumed to be that of a moth. Perhaps surprisingly, *C. militaris* has been used in traditional Chinese medicine (and cuisine) and is now cultivated as a more readily available alternative to the better-known *C. sinensis*.

SIMILAR SPECIES
The Scarlet Caterpillar-Club typically grows in moss and grass where its shape and color may superficially resemble species of *Clavulinopsis*, such as the bright yellow-orange *C. luteoalba*. The heads of *Clavulinopsis* species are smooth, however, and never finely pimpled.

The Scarlet Caterpillar-Club produces club-shaped "fruitbodies." The head is elongated and slightly swollen, bright orange to orange-scarlet. It is actually a sterile stroma in which the true fruitbodies, looking like tiny pimples under a magnifying lens, are immersed. The stem is similarly colored, but paler toward the base, which is attached to the remains of its host.

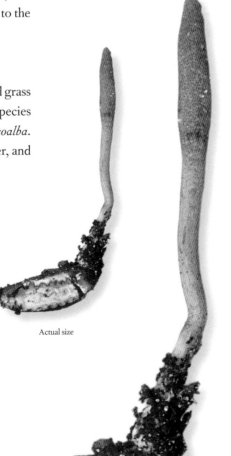

Actual size

FAMILY	Xylariaceae
DISTRIBUTION	Europe
HABITAT	In woodland
ASSOCIATION	On ash, rarely other broadleaf trees
GROWTH FORM	On dead trunks, logs, and branches
ABUNDANCE	Very common
SPORE COLOR	Dark brown
EDIBILITY	Not edible

HEIGHT
Up to 1½ in
(40 mm)

DIAMETER
Up to 3 in
(80 mm)

612

DALDINIA CONCENTRICA
CRAMP BALL
(BOLTON) CESATI & DE NOTARIS

Cramp Balls are common on ash trees, where the conspicuous fruitbodies persist all year round. The name comes from a local English belief that carrying the fungus would prevent cramp. Its alternative name of King Alfred's Cake refers to the ninth-century English King Alfred, who was once supposedly scolded for letting cakes burn, an apt description of the cinder-like fruitbodies. Though they may look dry, Cramp Balls actually store large amounts of water, enabling the fungus to produce and release spores even during long periods of dry weather. Cramp Balls have been used as a fungal dye to produce a range of brown to grayish greens.

SIMILAR SPECIES
Many similar species occur worldwide on different hosts. In North America and elsewhere, *Daldinia childiae* has long been erroneously called *D. concentrica*, but the latter is known only from Europe. *Daldinia childiae* grows on a variety of different hosts, and has yellowish (rather than purplish) pigments in alkali. *Daldinia loculata* is similar, but has a rather shiny surface and a preference for birch.

Actual size

The Cramp Ball forms hard, almost spherical "fruitbodies." The "fruitbody" is actually a stroma of sterile tissue in which the real fruitbodies, sometimes visible as shallow mounds under a magnifying lens, are immersed. The stroma is initially reddish brown, becoming black when mature, smooth, and often finely cracked under a lens. If cut, the hard context is dark brown to black and marked by a series of paler concentric rings (see photo right).

Actual size

FAMILY	Ophiocordycipitaceae
DISTRIBUTION	North America, Europe, Asia
HABITAT	In woodland
ASSOCIATION	Parasitic, on fruitbodies of *Elaphomyces* species
GROWTH FORM	Arising from buried fruitbodies
ABUNDANCE	Occasional
SPORE COLOR	White
EDIBILITY	Not edible

HEIGHT
Up to 5 in
(120 mm)

DIAMETER
Up to ¼ in
(20 mm)

ELAPHOCORDYCEPS CAPITATA
DRUMSTICK TRUFFLE-CLUB
(HOLMSKJOLD.) G. H. SUNG, J. M. SUNG & SPATAFORA

613

Most *Cordyceps* species are parasites of insects, often emerging (like *C. militaris*) from buried pupae. A few, however, grow on Hart's Truffles (*Elaphomyces* species) and recent DNA research has shown that these truffle-eating species belong in their own separate genus. Their hosts are very common in woodlands, but are seldom seen unless deliberately searched for. The Drumstick Truffle-Club—which is also known as the Truffle Eater—takes over the Hart's Truffle fruitbodies and produces its own, which rise up out of the ground. If dug up carefully, the remains of the truffle-like host will still be attached to the bottom of the stem.

SIMILAR SPECIES

Elaphocordyceps longisegmentis (often misnamed *Corydyceps canadensis*) is very similar, differing microscopically in its longer spore segments. The Snaketongue Truffle-Club (*E. ophioglossoides*) also parasitizes Hart's Truffles, but is blackish olive and club-shaped.

The Drumstick Truffle-Club produces drumstick-like fruitbodies arising from the buried remains of Hart's Truffles. The head is more or less oval (like the head of a matchstick), and ocher to brown. It is actually a stroma in which the individual fruitbodies of the fungus are immersed, visible under a magnifying lens as tiny pimples. The stem is cylindrical, smooth or slightly furrowed, and yellow becoming paler near the base. The cut flesh is whitish to cream (see photo top right).

Actual size

FAMILY	Ophiocordycipitaceae
DISTRIBUTION	North America, Europe, Asia
HABITAT	In woodland
ASSOCIATION	Parasitic, on fruitbodies of *Elaphomyces* species
GROWTH FORM	Arising from buried fruitbodies
ABUNDANCE	Occasional
SPORE COLOR	White
EDIBILITY	Not edible

HEIGHT
Up to 3 in
(80 mm)

DIAMETER
Up to ½ in
(10 mm)

614

ELAPHOCORDYCEPS OPHIOGLOSSOIDES
SNAKETONGUE TRUFFLE-CLUB
(EHRHART) G. H. SUNG, J. M. SUNG & SPATAFORA

This is another fungus that parasitizes Hart's Truffles (*Elaphomyces* species), the Snaketongue Truffle-Club rising out of the ground where the host fruitbodies are buried. The species has been used in traditional herbal medicine in China and Japan, and recent research has shown that it may contain several interesting compounds. These include an antifungal antibiotic named ophiocordin, polysaccharides that show antitumor activity, and extracts that might afford protection against Alzheimer's disease. The Snaketongue Truffle-Club is now commercially cultured and an extract is currently available as one of the ingredients in a dietary supplement for athletes and bodybuilders.

SIMILAR SPECIES

The Drumstick Truffle-Club (*Elaphocordyceps capitata*) also parasitizes Hart's Truffles, but is yellow-brown and differently shaped. Earthtongues (*Geoglossum*, *Microglossum*, and *Trichoglossum* species) are similarly shaped, but are not yellow toward the base, and have heads that are smooth or finely hairy, not pimpled under a magnifying lens.

Actual size

The Snaketongue Truffle-Club produces club-shaped "fruitbodies." The head is elongated and slightly swollen, dark red-brown to black. It is actually a sterile stroma in which the true fruitbodies, looking like tiny pimples under a magnifying lens, are immersed. The stem is blackish brown, but yellowish toward the base, which is attached to the remains of its host, often covered in yellow strands.

FAMILY	Hypocreaceae
DISTRIBUTION	North America, Europe, Asia
HABITAT	In damp woodland
ASSOCIATION	On broadleaf trees, particularly willow, with *Hymenochaete tabacina*
GROWTH FORM	On dead, attached branches
ABUNDANCE	Rare
SPORE COLOR	Yellowish
EDIBILITY	Not edible

THICKNESS
Up to ¼ in
(5 mm)

DIAMETER
Up to 4 in
(100 mm)

HYPOCREOPSIS LICHENOIDES

WILLOW GLOVES

(TODE) SEAVER

615

The lobes of *Hypocreopsis lichenoides* often become raised and elongated, looking like a gloved hand clasping the branch on which it is growing. In Sweden, the species is known as "trollhand." The lobed fingers are stromatic, composed of sterile tissue in which the tiny, individual fruitbodies (visible as dots under a magnifying lens) are formed. The *Hypocreopsis* does not grow on the wood itself, but is a parasite on *Hymenochaete tabacina*, a wood-rotting fungus that forms a brownish crust with bracket-like margins. In Europe, the Willow Gloves is recognized as a rare species and is on the Red Lists of threatened fungal species in several countries.

SIMILAR SPECIES

A closely related species, the Hazel Gloves (*Hypocreopsis rhododendri*), occurs with *Hymenochaete corrugata* on hazel and other broadleaf branches. In Australia and New Zealand, the recently discovered *Hypocreopsis amplectens* has been found on tea-tree (*Leptospermum scoparium*) and southern beech.

Actual size

The Willow Gloves forms a soft, effused fruitbody on the upper surface of branches. The surface is smooth at first, later wrinkled, and is divided into long, fingerlike lobes, yellow-brown to orange-brown with a lighter margin. This "fruitbody" is actually a sterile stroma, in which the tiny, individual, dotlike fruitbodies are immersed at maturity (they are visible with a magnifying lens).

FAMILY	Hypocreaceae
DISTRIBUTION	North America, Central America
HABITAT	In woodland
ASSOCIATION	Parasitizing *Russula* and *Lactarius* species
GROWTH FORM	Covering host fruitbodies
ABUNDANCE	Common
SPORE COLOR	White
EDIBILITY	Edible

THICKNESS
Less than ⅛ in
(0.5 mm)

DIAMETER
(of individual fruitbody)
Less than ⅛ in
(0.5 mm)

616

HYPOMYCES LACTIFLUORUM
LOBSTER FUNGUS
(SCHWEINITZ) TULASNE & C. TULASNE

The brightly colored Lobster Fungus is a strange-looking object that is actually produced by one fungus, *Hypomyces lactifluorum*, completely engulfing the fruitbody of another. The hosts are species of *Lactarius* and *Russula*, particularly *L. piperatus* and *R. brevipes*. Even more remarkable is that the Lobster Fungus, both parasite and host, is eaten and widely relished in North America, where there is a commercial trade in the species. It is claimed that it actually tastes like lobster. There is, however, no certainty that the host species is always edible, and older fruitbodies may be infected with bacteria.

SIMILAR SPECIES

Other *Hypomyces* species are less colorful or have different habits. *Hypomyces luteovirens* also parasitizes *Russula* species in North America, but is yellow-green and confines itself to the stem and gills. *Hypomyces hyalinus* parasitizes *Amanita* species, but is whitish.

Actual size

The Lobster Fungus covers all surfaces of its host fruitbody with a sterile, bright orange stroma in which the tiny, individual fruitbodies develop. These are half-immersed, but resemble small, raised pimples when examined under a magnifying lens. The color of the stroma becomes darker with age. The gills of the host are reduced to no more than furrows by the Lobster Fungus (see photo right).

FAMILY	Hypocreaceae
DISTRIBUTION	North America, Europe, Central America, northern Asia
HABITAT	In woodland
ASSOCIATION	Parasitizing *Russula* and *Lactarius* species
GROWTH FORM	On stem and gills of host fruitbodies
ABUNDANCE	Common
SPORE COLOR	White
EDIBILITY	Not edible

THICKNESS	Less than ⅛ in (0.5 mm)
DIAMETER	(of individual fruitbody) Less than ⅛ in (0.5 mm)

HYPOMYCES LUTEOVIRENS

GREENGILL FUNGUS

(FRIES) TULASNE & C. TULASNE

617

Unlike the related Lobster Fungus (*Hypomyces lactifluorum*), the Greengill Fungus is not considered a gourmet's treat—and the greenish yellow color is perhaps less tempting. It is a widespread species, originally described from Sweden, that also parasitizes agarics in the genera *Lactarius* and *Russula*. It normally only forms its crustlike stroma on the undersurface of the cap and sometimes also the stems. This means that the parasitized agaric may look quite healthy from above, but distinctly green around the gills when turned over.

SIMILAR SPECIES

Hypomyces lateritius is a related species on the gills of *Lactarius* fruitbodies, but is yellowish (without green tints), becoming orange to brick-red at maturity. In eastern North America, *Hypomyces banningiae* is also similar, but is yellow to buff.

Actual size

The Greengill Fungus covers the gills and often the stem of its host fruitbody with a sterile stroma in which the tiny, individual fruitbodies develop. The stroma is whitish at first, becoming yellowish (see photo left), then green. Individual fruitbodies resemble small, raised pimples when examined under a magnifying lens.

FAMILY	Xylariaceae
DISTRIBUTION	North America, Europe, western Asia
HABITAT	In woodland
ASSOCIATION	On broadleaf wood, particularly beech
GROWTH FORM	On dead branches and logs
ABUNDANCE	Very common
SPORE COLOR	Dark brown
EDIBILITY	Not edible

HEIGHT Up to ¼ in (7 mm)
DIAMETER Up to ½ in (10 mm)

618

HYPOXYLON FRAGIFORME

BEECH WOODWART

(PERSOON) J. KICKX FILS

Actual size

The Beech Woodwart forms troops of hard, half-spherical cushions that often coalesce and become irregular. Each cushion is composed of sterile tissue in which the small, individual fruitbodies are formed, projecting like pimples from the surface, and giving the cushions a warty appearance. The cushions are hard and rather brittle, pinkish red at first, becoming dull brick-red at maturity, and blackening in old age.

The Latin name *fragiforme* means "strawberry-like," and, when mature, the Beech Woodwart does bear some fanciful resemblance to the fruit, though its "strawberries" are hard, crusty, and quite inedible. As with closely related *Xylaria* species, the fruitbodies are actually stroma, growths of sterile tissue in which the true fruitbodies (looking like raised pimples) are immersed. Each "strawberry" is therefore a cluster of tiny fruitbodies. The Beech Woodwart is one of the first fungi to colonize dead beech wood, and research suggests that it may be latently present in healthy wood, waiting for a branch to die or a limb to fall.

SIMILAR SPECIES

Several other *Hypoxylon* species form half-spherical cushions that have reddish tints when young or mature, but these are rarely found on beech. The cushions of *H. fuscum* are more purplish and almost smooth, and are most frequently found on hazel. *Hypoxylon howeanum* is another hazel associate and *H. intermedium* is normally found on ash.

FAMILY	Nectriaceae
DISTRIBUTION	North America, Europe, North Africa, Central America, Asia; introduced in Australia, New Zealand
HABITAT	In woodland and gardens
ASSOCIATION	On broadleaf trees and shrubs
GROWTH FORM	On branches and twigs
ABUNDANCE	Very common
SPORE COLOR	White
EDIBILITY	Not edible

THICKNESS
Less than ⅛ in
(0.5 mm)

DIAMETER
Less than ⅛ in
(0.5 mm)

NECTRIA CINNABARINA

CORAL SPOT

(TODE) FRIES

619

The Coral Spot is a very common species and, since it typically grows in swarms, is more conspicuous than might be expected for such a tiny fungus. It not only produces reddish fruitbodies, clustered together like miniature raspberries, but also pink, cushionlike structures (sometimes referred to as the *Tubercularia vulgaris* form) that contain asexual spores. The latter form usually appears first, but both the asexual and sexual stages can occur intermixed on the same branch. The Coral Spot is typically found on dead attached or fallen branches (it has a particular fondness for beech and sycamore), but it can be a weak wound parasite, infecting damaged branches and causing Nectria canker.

The Coral Spot initially forms swarms of smooth, miniature, pink to pale red cushions that break through the outer layer of host bark. Later, these are gradually replaced by the true fruitbodies, which are even smaller (best seen under a magnifying lens), deeper red, spherical, minutely warted, and bunched together in clusters.

SIMILAR SPECIES

Many other *Nectria* species produce fruitbodies of similar size and color, but they are not conspicuously distributed in swarms along branches in the manner typical of the Coral Spot. *Nectria galligena* can be common on broadleaf trees, forming fruitbodies on cankerous growths. *Nectria fuckeliana* is a cause of cankers on conifers.

Actual size

FAMILY	Onygenaceae
DISTRIBUTION	North America, Europe
HABITAT	In pastures and woodland
ASSOCIATION	With animal remains
GROWTH FORM	On rotting horns and hooves, in troops
ABUNDANCE	Occasional
SPORE COLOR	White
EDIBILITY	Not edible

HEIGHT
Up to ½ in
(10 mm)

DIAMETER
Up to ¼ in
(5 mm)

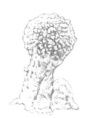

620

ONYGENA EQUINA
HORN STALKBALL
(WILLDENOW) PERSOON

Actual size

Wood-rotting fungi are commonplace, but some fungi are able to rot keratin, a substance found in hair, horns, nails, hooves, feathers, and claws. Most of these keratin-rotters are microscopic and are found in the soil. Some are even found in house-dust and several can cause unpleasant infections if they get into skin, hair, or nails. The Horn Stalkball, however, forms comparatively large and perfectly visible, drumstick-like fruitbodies. These fruitbodies can occasionally be found on old, shed sheep or cattle horns and similar animal remains—not the usual sort of place to look for interesting fungi.

The Horn Stalkball produces fruitbodies like miniature puffballs, with a globose head and cylindrical stem. The head is whitish to cream and minutely warted when young, becoming brownish and smooth. It disintegrates at maturity to release the spores. The stem is smooth and similarly colored.

SIMILAR SPECIES
A related species, the Feather Stalkball (*Onygena corvina*), grows on old feathers, owl pellets, and tufts of animal hair. The unrelated *Phleogena faginea* has fruitbodies that look rather similar, but grow on wood and have a distinct curry smell.

FAMILY	Ophiocordycipitaceae
DISTRIBUTION	Asia (Himalayas)
HABITAT	In grassland
ASSOCIATION	Parasitic, on ghost moths
GROWTH FORM	Arising from buried larvae
ABUNDANCE	Occasional
SPORE COLOR	White
EDIBILITY	Edible

HEIGHT
Up to 6 in
(150 mm)

DIAMETER
Up to ½ in
(10 mm)

OPHIOCORDYCEPS SINENSIS

CHINESE CATERPILLAR FUNGUS

(BERKELEY) G. H. SUNG ET AL

621

Since at least the fifteenth century, *Ophiocordyceps sinensis* has been used in Tibet and China as an aphrodisiac and tonic. The fungus is a parasite on the underground larvae of ghost moths, and occurs mainly in the Himalayan foothills and the vast grasslands of the Tibetan plateau. Though caterpillar fungi have always been scarce and valuable, in recent years interest in alternative medicines in the West, together with increasing wealth in China, has meant that collecting them has become a major local source of income—good specimens being worth their weight in gold.

SIMILAR SPECIES

A related and rather similar-looking species, *Ophiocordyceps robertsii*, occurs on buried moth larvae in New Zealand. Other *Ophiocordyceps* species parasitize a variety of insects—including ants, beetles, and wasps—but are typically smaller and drumstick-shaped, or thin and hairlike.

Actual size

The Chinese Caterpillar Fungus produces cylindrical to narrowly club-shaped "fruitbodies." The head is elongated, tapering toward the tip, slightly swollen, and dark reddish brown. It is actually a sterile stroma in which the true fruitbodies, looking like tiny pimples under a magnifying lens, are immersed. The stem is similarly colored or paler, and extends underground where it is attached to the mummified host.

FAMILY	Hypocreaceae
DISTRIBUTION	Eastern Asia
HABITAT	In woodland
ASSOCIATION	With broadleaf trees
GROWTH FORM	On rotten wood
ABUNDANCE	Occasional
SPORE COLOR	White
EDIBILITY	Poisonous

HEIGHT Up to 4 in (100 mm)
DIAMETER Up to 3 in (80 mm)

622

PODOSTROMA CORNU-DAMAE

POISON FIRE CORAL

(PATOUILLARD) BOEDIJN

Red is usually a danger signal in the natural world, but it is not a signal that normally applies to fungi. *Podostroma cornu-damae* is an exception, however, since this flame-red fungus is extremely poisonous and has recently caused the deaths of several people in Japan. Research has shown that the Poison Fire Coral contains six different trichothecene toxins, causing spontaneous bleeding, brain atrophy, and other unpleasant symptoms. The toxins are similar to those used in chemical warfare. Fortunately, *P. cornu-damae* appears to be a rather uncommon species confined to eastern Asia. The epithet *cornu-damae* means nothing more sinister than "deer-horn," referring to its typical shape.

SIMILAR SPECIES

The poisonings in Japan were apparently caused by confusion with the similarly colored, edible club fungus *Clavulinopsis miyabeana*, which is soft-textured. The Scarlet Caterpillar-Club (*Cordyceps militaris*) is also similar and sometimes eaten in Asia, but it is never highly branched and always arises from buried moth pupae.

The Poison Fire Coral produces erect "fruitbodies" of variable shape, from simple to branched and coral-like to antler-like. These are actually composed of hard, stromatic tissue in which the true fruitbodies, visible as tiny dots under a magnifying lens, are immersed. The interior flesh is white.

Actual size

FAMILY	Xylariaceae
DISTRIBUTION	Europe
HABITAT	In pasture
ASSOCIATION	With horses
GROWTH FORM	On dung
ABUNDANCE	Occasional to rare
SPORE COLOR	Blackish brown
EDIBILITY	Not edible

HEIGHT
Up to ¼ in
(7 mm)

DIAMETER
Up to ½ in
(15 mm)

PORONIA PUNCTATA

NAIL FUNGUS

(LINNAEUS) FRIES

623

This odd relative of *Xylaria* species is a coprophilous or dung-loving fungus. In particular, it likes old, dried horse dung—and this commodity has become increasingly rare in Europe. Not only are almost all the old working horses long gone, but modern horse-keeping practices interfere with the natural grazing-dunging cycle on which the fungus relies. In England, it is still quite common in the New Forest, which is grazed by semi-wild ponies, but in most other parts of Europe it has declined drastically, to the point of becoming locally extinct.

SIMILAR SPECIES

A similar species, *Poronia erici*, occurs on marsupial, rabbit, and other dung in Australia and is also known on rabbit dung in Europe. It typically forms slightly smaller discs, but is best distinguished microscopically. *Poronia oedipus* is a widespread tropical species, also found in Australia and New Zealand, with stems up to 1 in (25 mm) tall.

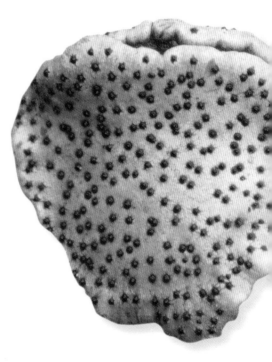

Actual size

The Nail Fungus forms nail-like "fruitbodies" with the stem half-buried in dung. The hard, pale buff disc is actually a stroma—sterile tissue in which the true fruitbodies, which are visible as black dots, are immersed. The undersurface is smooth and grayish white, becoming brown to black with age.

FAMILY	Xylariaceae
DISTRIBUTION	Western North America, Europe, North Africa, Asia
HABITAT	In woodland
ASSOCIATION	On broadleaf wood
GROWTH FORM	On rotten, often buried, wood, in clusters
ABUNDANCE	Very common
SPORE COLOR	Black
EDIBILITY	Not edible

HEIGHT
Up to 3 in
(80 mm)

DIAMETER
Up to ½ in
(10 mm)

624

XYLARIA HYPOXYLON
CANDLESNUFF FUNGUS
(LINNAEUS) GREVILLE

The Candlesnuff Fungus often looks like the wick of a candle that has blackened while burning, and then been snuffed out. Like *Xylaria polymorpha*, the "fruitbody" is actually a sterile stroma in which lots of tiny, individual fruitbodies are embedded. When the fungus is mature and entirely black, these can be seen under a magnifying lens looking like little raised pimples. Before they are developed, however, the fungus produces large numbers of asexual spores that color the heads white (this is the "candlesnuff" stage). Once these are dispersed, the heads turn first gray and eventually black, as the sexual spores are formed.

SIMILAR SPECIES

In eastern North America, *Xylaria longiana* is a very similar species, which is only distinguishable microscopically. *Xylaria carpophila*, *X. magnoliae*, and *X. oxyacanthae* are also very similar, but have unusually restricted host preferences: they grow only on fallen beech cupules, fallen magnolia pods, and fallen hawthorn berries respectively.

The Candlesnuff Fungus forms erect, straplike, or clublike fruitbodies. The stems are tough, black, finely hairy, and often rather flattened and straplike. The fertile head may be a simple pointed club, hard and black, as if burned, or it may be a flattened club, whitish at first (see photo left), then gray, then black, simple or branched like an antler.

Actual size

FAMILY	Xylariaceae
DISTRIBUTION	North America, Europe, Asia
HABITAT	In woodland
ASSOCIATION	On broadleaf wood
GROWTH FORM	On rotten, often buried, wood, in clusters
ABUNDANCE	Very common
SPORE COLOR	Black
EDIBILITY	Not edible

HEIGHT
Up to 4 in
(100 mm)

DIAMETER
Up to 1 in
(25 mm)

XYLARIA POLYMORPHA
DEAD MAN'S FINGERS
(PERSOON) GREVILLE

625

When growing in clusters, especially from buried wood, *Xylaria polymorpha* is aptly, if gruesomely, named, the Dead Man's Fingers. Each finger is in fact a sterile stroma of fungal tissue in which multiple, tiny, individual fruitbodies are formed. If a finger is cut in half, these individual fruitbodies can be seen as little, black, toothlike pits or indentations in the surface crust. A few smaller *Xylaria* species have specialized habitats, such as *X. oxyacanthae* on fallen hawthorn berries, or *X. carpophila* on fallen beech cupules. *Xylaria polymorpha*, however, grows on a wide range of broadleaf wood and is consequently a common and widespread species.

SIMILAR SPECIES

Many *Xylaria* species, especially in the tropics, produce similar stromatic fruitbodies and are best distinguished microscopically. *Xylaria longipes* is a common north-temperate species forming similar, but slightly narrower, fingers and is typically associated with sycamore. *Xylaria hypoxylon* is much smaller.

Actual size

The Dead Man's Fingers produces black, club-shaped fruitbodies with short, cylindrical stems. The outer surface is hard and appears to be smooth and matt, but under a magnifying lens is finely granular and wrinkled, with shallow raised warts when mature. When cut, the flesh is white and tough, the outer surface showing as a thin, black crust with toothlike indentations.

FAMILY	Xylariaceae
DISTRIBUTION	Eastern North America
HABITAT	In woodland
ASSOCIATION	On broadleaf wood
GROWTH FORM	On fallen fragments of wood in litter
ABUNDANCE	Common
SPORE COLOR	Black
EDIBILITY	Not edible

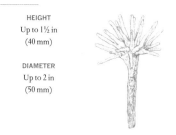

HEIGHT
Up to 1½ in
(40 mm)

DIAMETER
Up to 2 in
(50 mm)

626

XYLARIA TENTACULATA
FAIRY SPARKLER
RAVENEL EX BERKELEY

In its mature state, the Fairy Sparkler is just another small *Xylaria* species with a black, slightly club-shaped fruitbody—but in its immature state it develops a firework-like explosion of arms at the top of its stem that gradually lengthen and twist like miniature tentacles. This is the asexual stage of the fungus, the spores developing on the arms and giving them a powdery, whitish appearance—just like the snuffed candlewicks of *Xylaria hypoxylon*. The blackish sexual spores develop later, but by then the brittle little tentacles have disappeared.

SIMILAR SPECIES
The widespread Candlesnuff Fungus (*Xylaria hypoxylon*) often develops a few projections, but these are usually irregular and give the fruitbodies an antler-like appearance. Other *Xylaria* species with branchlike projections occur in the tropics.

The Fairy Sparkler forms erect stromatic fruitbodies with a stem and head. The stem is tough, black, and slightly rough. The fertile head of the sexual state is simple, swollen, hard, and black. In the asexual state, it forms a crown of 8–20 pale gray to whitish, armlike projections, that taper toward the tips, and gradually become elongated, fragile, and twisted.

Actual size

FAMILY	Parmeliaceae
DISTRIBUTION	Western North America, northern Europe, northern Asia
HABITAT	On conifers, more rarely broadleaf trees
ASSOCIATION	Lichenized, with algae
GROWTH FORM	Pendant from branches
ABUNDANCE	Locally common
SPORE COLOR	White
EDIBILITY	Said to be edible (if cooked)

LENGTH
Up to 36 in
(900 mm)

DIAMETER
Less than ⅛ in
(0.5 mm)

BRYORIA FREMONTII

WILA

(TUCKERMAN) BRODO & D. HAWKSWORTH

627

Wila is the name given to this lichen by the Shuswap of British Columbia, one of many North American native peoples who once collected and ate the species, which is also known as the Bear Hair Lichen. Specimens that were yellowish were avoided as being very bitter, and it has since been found that these contain higher-than-normal levels of vulpinic acid, a potentially dangerous poison. Good Wila, when cleaned and cooked by steaming for several days in a pit, is said to resemble bland, gelatinous liquorice. It was a staple winter food for some indigenous peoples and an occasional famine food for others. Perhaps not surprisingly, it is seldom eaten today.

SIMILAR SPECIES

Many other *Bryoria* species are filamentous and look similar to *B. fremontii*. Most have narrower filaments, however, and are typically less dark than the Wila. Some of the larger *Usnea* species form similar hanging growths, but are gray-greenish.

The Wila forms long, filamentous thalli that hang down from branches. The filaments are highly branched, often becoming entangled, and are smooth, cylindrical to compressed, soft when wet and wiry when dry. Main branches are yellowish to reddish brown or chocolate-brown. Fruitbodies are uncommon, but bright yellow.

Actual size

FAMILY	Cladoniaceae
DISTRIBUTION	North America, Europe, Central and South America, Asia, Australia, New Zealand
HABITAT	On soil, peat, rotten wood
ASSOCIATION	Lichenized, with algae
GROWTH FORM	On ground and rotten wood, singly or in troops
ABUNDANCE	Very common
SPORE COLOR	White
EDIBILITY	Not edible

HEIGHT
Up to 2½ in
(60 mm)

DIAMETER
Less than ⅛ in
(2 mm)

628

CLADONIA FLOERKEANA

DEVIL'S MATCHSTICK

(FRIES) FLÖRKE

Cladonia floerkeana has an uncanny resemblance to an old-fashioned, red-tipped matchstick, though the flaky gray stems would make it exceedingly difficult to strike. Individuals are small, but they often grow in large numbers on heathy or peaty ground, looking like some miniature garden display in scarlet and gray. It is also quite frequent on old, rotten, fallen wood in open ground. The species is very widespread and can be found in similar habitats around the world. It was given its peculiar Latin name in honor of Gustav Heinrich Flörke, a German lichenologist of the early nineteenth century.

SIMILAR SPECIES

Many similar species of *Cladonia* produce red fruitbodies on top of stems, though in some species, such as *C. diversa*, the stems are more yellowish green than gray. *Cladonia macilenta*, sometimes called the British Soldier, has unbranched, gray stems.

The Devil's Matchstick arises from a thin, gray mat. The upright stems are simple or sparsely branched, gray, and covered with small flakes and granules. The fruitbodies on top of the stems are smooth, rounded (like the head of a matchstick), sometimes coalescing, and bright pinkish red to red.

Actual size

FAMILY	Cladoniaceae
DISTRIBUTION	North America, Europe, southern South America, Antarctica, Asia
HABITAT	On ground, on soil, fallen wood, and stone
ASSOCIATION	Lichenized, with algae
GROWTH FORM	In large patches
ABUNDANCE	Common
SPORE COLOR	White
EDIBILITY	Said to be edible (if cooked)

CLADONIA RANGIFERINA

REINDEER LICHEN

(LINNAEUS) WEBER EX F. H. WIGGERS

HEIGHT
Up to 4 in
(100 mm)

DIAMETER
Less than ⅛ in
(2 mm)

629

This lichen takes both its Latin and English names from the reindeer or caribou (*Rangifer tarandus*). In winter, when leaves and grasses disappear, reindeer graze on *Cladonia rangiferina* and similar lichens, which in the past were often called "reindeer moss." Unlike mosses and other plants, however, lichens are slow-growing and it may take between five and 15 years for the fungi to recover from grazing. This is one of the reasons why reindeer herds (and reindeer herders) are necessarily nomadic. The Reindeer Lichen was once boiled and eaten by the Dena'ina people of Alaska, but it contains a mixture of acids that may cause stomach problems.

SIMILAR SPECIES

Cladonia rangiferina is one of a group of related species with a similar branching habit. These include *C. portentosa*, which is rather more delicate with a wider angle of branching, and *C. arbuscula*, which has strongly recurved branches

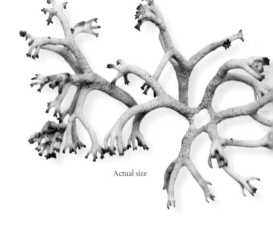

Actual size

The Reindeer Lichen forms upright, finely branched, shrubby growths arising from small, crustose primary thalli. The pale, whitish gray, branched outgrowths are tinted purplish brown toward the tips, and grow densely interwoven, forming extensive mats.

FAMILY	Cladoniaceae
DISTRIBUTION	North America, continental Europe, northern Asia
HABITAT	On ground, soil, fallen wood, and stone
ASSOCIATION	Lichenized, with algae
GROWTH FORM	In large patches
ABUNDANCE	Common
SPORE COLOR	White
EDIBILITY	Not edible

HEIGHT
Up to 6 in
(150 mm)

DIAMETER
Up to 3 in
(75 mm)

630

CLADONIA STELLARIS
STAR REINDEER LICHEN
(OPIZ) POUZAR & VEZDA

Cladonia stellaris is a species of "reindeer moss," grazed by these animals in Scandinavia and the far north. Unlike its relative, *C. rangiferina*, it contains usnic acid—a compound with antibiotic properties. At one time, it was even commercially collected to create an antibiotic ointment called Usno. Today, the lichen is still harvested, but mainly for decorative purposes. Being long-lasting, it is used in wreaths, particularly in Germany, and occasionally in flower decorations—or even to create miniature bushes and trees for architects and model-railway enthusiasts.

SIMILAR SPECIES

Cladonia stellaris is similar to the Reindeer Lichen (*C. rangiferina*) and related species, but is much paler and has a more finely branched, compact habit. It is also a species with a preference for open sites and drier, more continental climates.

The Star Reindeer Lichen forms erect, shrubby growths, typically growing gregariously, arising from small, crustose primary thalli. The growths are compactly branched, and pale yellowish green to gray-green. The tips are very fine and often starlike.

Actual size

FAMILY	Collemataceae
DISTRIBUTION	North America, Europe, Africa, Central and South America, Asia
HABITAT	On damp trees, less commonly on damp rocks
ASSOCIATION	Lichenized, with cyanobacteria
GROWTH FORM	In groups
ABUNDANCE	Occasional
SPORE COLOR	White
EDIBILITY	Not edible

THICKNESS
Up to ¼ in
(5 mm)

DIAMETER
Up to 3 in
(80 mm)

COLLEMA FURFURACEUM
BLISTERED JELLY LICHEN
DU RIETZ

631

Most naturalists know that lichens are fungi that form a mutually beneficial association with various species of algae. These algae are usually called photobionts, since their role in the partnership is to produce sugars from sunlight. But for some lichens, the photobiont partner is not an alga, but a cyanobacterium. Cyanobacteria were once called "blue-green algae," but, although they may look similar, they are not remotely related to the true algae. Larger species of cyanobacteria tend to be gelatinous and grow in damp or wet places. As a result many of the lichens that partner cyanobacteria are called jelly lichens and also favor damp spots, in wet woodlands or on rocks near streams and waterfalls.

The Blistered Jelly Lichen forms a flat, rubbery, almost disc-shaped thallus comprised of large, leaflike lobes that may partly curl up when dry. The upper surface is conspicuously ridged and often covered in small, simple or branched propagules (isidia). The whole lichen is dark green-brown to blackish.

SIMILAR SPECIES
Several other species of *Collema* are similar, though some become much more gelatinous in wet weather. The rare River Jelly Lichen (*C. dichotomum*) actually grows submerged on rocks in streams. Rock tripe (*Umbilicaria* species) is similarly shaped, but is less rubbery, and has distinct hairlike fringes.

Actual size

FAMILY	Pannariaceae
DISTRIBUTION	North America, East Africa, Central and South America, Eastern and southern Asia, Australia, New Zealand
HABITAT	On living trees
ASSOCIATION	Lichenized, with cyanobacteria
GROWTH FORM	In patches
ABUNDANCE	Occasional
SPORE COLOR	White
EDIBILITY	Not edible

THICKNESS	Up to ¼ in (5 mm)
DIAMETER	Up to 2 in (50 mm)

ERIODERMA SOREDIATUM

SOREDIATE FELT LICHEN

D. J. GALLOWAY & P. M. JØRGENSEN

632

Erioderma means "woolly skin," and the Sorediate Felt Lichen and its relatives are distinguished by having a finely woolly surface texture. Their partners are gelatinous cyanobacteria rather than algae, which means that they tend to prefer damp habitats. The Sorediate Felt Lichen, first described from New Zealand, is a widespread but uncommon species of moist lowland forests. The related Boreal Felt Lichen (*E. pedicellatum*) is far rarer and is now restricted to just a few relic populations in Labrador and Newfoundland. The latter species is one of only two fungi on the IUCN's global Red List of Threatened Species.

SIMILAR SPECIES

The Sorediate Felt Lichen is distinguished from most other *Erioderma* species by producing soredia—powdery propagules composed of both fungal hyphae and cyanobacterial cells—on its lower surface. *Parmelia* species, like the Gray Crottle (*P. saxatilis*), are foliose but non-felty, the undersurface dark and with rhizines (rootlike strands that anchor the lichen to the surface).

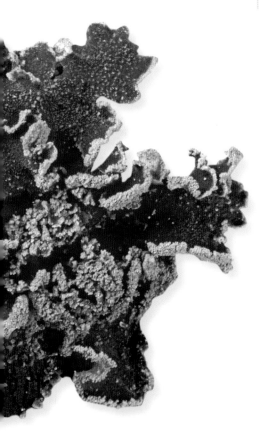

The Sorediate Felt Lichen forms widely lobed, foliose thalli. The upper surface is felted to finely hairy, gray-brown to green-gray, the undersurface whitish with bluish soralia (areas where the soredia are formed).

Actual size

FAMILY	Parmeliaceae
DISTRIBUTION	North America, Europe, North Africa, Asia
HABITAT	On living broadleaf trees, more rarely on rocks
ASSOCIATION	Lichenized, with algae
GROWTH FORM	On branches and trunks
ABUNDANCE	Very common
SPORE COLOR	White
EDIBILITY	Not edible

HEIGHT
Up to 1½ in
(40 mm)

DIAMETER
Up to 1½ in
(40 mm)

EVERNIA PRUNASTRI

OAKMOSS LICHEN

(LINNAEUS) ACHARIUS

633

Perfumes and fungi may not seem to go together, but *Evernia prunastri* was, and surprisingly still is, extensively used as a fixative to retain and prolong the scents of fine perfumes. The Oakmoss Lichen also has a distinct scent of its own and is one of the basic fragrances used in chypre and fougères perfumes. "Cyprus powder," containing the lichen, was once used to perfume wigs. Until recently, several thousand tons of the fungus were collected each year, mainly in France, Italy, Morocco, and the Balkans. Concern that *E. prunastri* can sometimes provoke allergic reactions may, however, have reduced this curious trade.

SIMILAR SPECIES

Despite its name, the Oakmoss Lichen is not restricted to oak trees. It can be confused with *Pseudevernia furfuracea*, coincidentally also used in perfumes, which is more rigid with an undersurface that becomes blackish with maturity. *Ramalina* species may also look similar, but upper and under surfaces are similarly colored.

Actual size

The Oakmoss Lichen forms shrubby, branching growths that hang from trunks and branches. The straps or branches are fairly soft (not rigid), flattened, smooth, yellowish to gray-green on the upper surface, and whitish on the underside.

FAMILY	Parmeliaceae
DISTRIBUTION	Western North America, continental Europe, North Africa, Central America, western Asia
HABITAT	On conifers, rarely on broadleaf trees or rocks
ASSOCIATION	Lichenized, with algae
GROWTH FORM	In tufts, from branches
ABUNDANCE	Common
SPORE COLOR	White
EDIBILITY	Poisonous

HEIGHT
Up to 3 in
(75 mm)

DIAMETER
Up to 3 in
(75 mm)

634

LETHARIA VULPINA
WOLF LICHEN
(LINNAEUS) HUE

Actual size

The Wolf Lichen forms shrubby, and densely branched thalli on branches. The whole lichen is a bright yellow-green when fresh. Fruitbodies are rare, but brown, smooth, and disc-shaped when they occur.

The Latin *vulpina* means "of wolves," and the Wolf Lichen derives its name from its former use in Scandinavia for killing wolves. The lichen contains a poison called vulpinic acid and animal carcasses stuffed full of the lichen were left out as bait. In North America, the Achomawi of California used it to poison arrow tips. The species was also widely collected as a dyestuff, for wool in Scandinavia and for porcupine quills (used in basket-making) in North America. It produces a bright greenish yellow dye. The Apache used the Wolf Lichen to paint yellow crosses on their feet, believing that this allowed them to pass their enemies unseen.

SIMILAR SPECIES

In North America, *Letharia columbiana* is a very similar species, but more frequently produces brown, disc-shaped fruitbodies. Recent molecular research suggests that a second, genetically distinct species also occurs in western North America and Morocco, though it may not be distinguishable by sight.

FAMILY	Lobariaceae
DISTRIBUTION	North America, Europe, Africa, Asia
HABITAT	On broadleaf trees, more rarely rocks
ASSOCIATION	Lichenized, with algae and cyanobacteria
GROWTH FORM	In patches
ABUNDANCE	Occasional
SPORE COLOR	White
EDIBILITY	Not edible

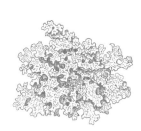

LOBARIA PULMONARIA

LUNGWORT

(LINNAEUS) HOFFMANN

THICKNESS
Up to ¼ in
(5 mm)

DIAMETER
Up to 10 in
(250 mm)

635

Lobaria pulmonaria is unusual in simultaneously forming an association with an alga and a cyanobacterium, the latter capable of fixing nitrogen and thus increasing the lichen's supply of nutrients. It needs clean, damp air for this to work, however, and the Lungwort only grows in wetter, pollution-free climates. It is often considered an indicator species of old woodland and forest. The shape and veining of the lobes was once thought to resemble lungs, a sure sign for medieval herbalists that it was divinely created to cure lung diseases, though this has not been supported by modern research.

The Lungwort forms large, foliose thalli with flattened, notched, leafy lobes. The upper surface is bright green and shiny when wet, gray-green when dry, and is wrinkled or ridged and netlike. The undersurface is pale tan. Fruitbodies are infrequent, but disc-shaped and orange-brown.

SIMILAR SPECIES

Other *Lobaria* species are similar, but often grayer, even when wet. In western North America, *Lobaria oregana* is a very similar, greenish species found mainly on conifers. The more widespread *L. virens* is also green, but typically has a smooth upper surface.

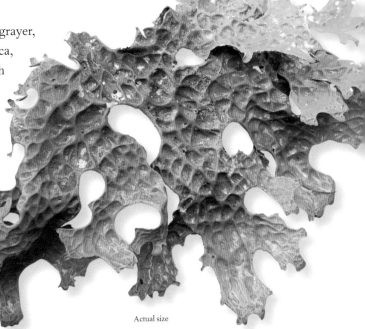

Actual size

FAMILY	Parmeliaceae
DISTRIBUTION	North America, Europe, Africa, Central and South America, Antarctica, Asia
HABITAT	On trees, rocks, and walls
ASSOCIATION	Lichenized, with algae
GROWTH FORM	In patches
ABUNDANCE	Common
SPORE COLOR	White
EDIBILITY	Not edible

THICKNESS
Up to ¼ in
(5 mm)

DIAMETER
Up to 2 in
(50 mm)

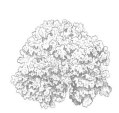

636

PARMELIA SAXATILIS
GRAY CROTTLE
(LINNAEUS) ACHARIUS

Lichens were once frequently used as dyestuffs. In Scotland, they were known as "crottles," and the common Gray Crottle was collected by local people in the Hebrides to dye Harris tweed, as well as their own homespun clothing. The lichen gave the wool a reddish brown to purple-brown color (as well as a distinctive smell). The same or similar lichens were also used for dyeing in Ireland and Scandinavia. It has been claimed that in medieval Europe *Parmelia saxtilis* was considered to be a cure for epilepsy, but only if it were collected from an old human skull, preferably that of a hanged man.

SIMILAR SPECIES

Many species of *Parmelia* and associated genera are gray-green, foliose, and superficially similar to the Gray Crottle. *Parmelia sulcata* is particularly common, but is distinguished by having a network of whitish ridges on its upper surfaces.

The Gray Crottle forms foliose thalli with flattened lobes that widen to the tips. The upper surface is pale gray to green-gray, the undersurface blackish, and attached to rocks or wood by root-like "rhizines." Fruitbodies are infrequent, but disc-shaped with a smooth, orange-brown surface and grayish, toothed margin.

Actual size

FAMILY	Peltigeraceae
DISTRIBUTION	North America, Europe, Asia, Australia
HABITAT	On ground, trees, or rocks
ASSOCIATION	Lichenized, with cyanobacteria
GROWTH FORM	In groups
ABUNDANCE	Common
SPORE COLOR	White
EDIBILITY	Not edible

THICKNESS
Up to ¼ in
(5 mm)

DIAMETER
Up to 10 in
(250 mm)

PELTIGERA MEMBRANACEA

MEMBRANOUS DOG-LICHEN

(ACHARIUS) NYLANDER

637

Large leafy lichens are sometimes found growing in mossy turf, even in garden lawns, and *Peltigera membranacea* is one of the commonest species in this habitat. Like all the dog-lichens, as well as the jelly lichens (*Collema* species), it forms a partnership not with an alga, but with a cyanobacterium. *Peltigera* species do not swell up in wet weather as much as some jelly lichens, but the Membranous Dog-Lichen does change from pale gray to brown and become noticeably more rubbery. It probably grows among mosses because they tend to retain the moisture that the cyanobacteria need to function.

SIMILAR SPECIES

The dog-lichens are a large and varied group, and there are many species that may look superficially similar, including *Peltigera lactucifolia*, which also has a fondness for mossy lawns. *Collema furfuraceum* and its allies lack the hairlike rhizines on the undersurface. *Umbilicaria cylindrica* has conspicuous black rhizines.

Actual size

The Membranous Dog-Lichen forms thalli of large, leaflike lobes that partly curl up when dry. The upper surface is brown when wet, and pale gray when dry, and veined or undulating. The undersurface is whitish to pale brown, with conspicuous, hairlike rhizines. Fruitbodies are common and are smooth, elliptical, and reddish brown, typically arising from the margins of the lobes.

FAMILY	Teloschistaceae
DISTRIBUTION	North America, Europe, Africa, Central and South America, Asia, Australia, New Zealand
HABITAT	On living broadleaf trees and conifers
ASSOCIATION	Lichenized, with algae
GROWTH FORM	On branches and twigs
ABUNDANCE	Locally common
SPORE COLOR	White
EDIBILITY	Not edible

HEIGHT
Up to 1 in
(25 mm)

DIAMETER
Up to 2 in
(50 mm)

638

TELOSCHISTES CHRYSOPHTHALMUS
GOLDEN-EYE LICHEN
(LINNAEUS) BELTRAMINI

The Golden-Eye Lichen is a particularly photogenic species looking rather like a miniature bouquet, thanks to its bright orange fruitbodies dotted among the branched thallus lobes. The name *Teloschistes* actually means "split ends," which aptly, but unkindly, describes the hairy branch tips, while *chrysopthalmus* means "golden eye," referring to the eyelash-fringed, disc-shaped fruitbodies. It is a very widespread and locally common species, but becomes increasingly rare northward—especially in Europe, where the Golden-Eye Lichen is on the preliminary international Red List of threatened macrolichens.

SIMILAR SPECIES

The Golden-Hair Lichen (*Teloschistes flavicans*) is similarly colored and branched, but very rarely produces fruitbodies. It also occurs on rocks as well as trees. *Usnea florida* looks similar to the Golden-Eye Lichen, with eyelash-fringed fruitbodies, but is grayish green and typically much larger.

The Golden-Eye Lichen forms shrubby growths on twigs and branches. The lobes are branched and yellow-orange with a grayish undersurface, each branch ending in numerous, hairlike fibrils. Fruitbodies are disc-shaped, up to ¼ in (5 mm) across, smooth, bright orange, with a grayish to orange, fringed margin.

Actual size

FAMILY	Umbilicariaceae
DISTRIBUTION	North America, Europe, Africa, Central and South America, Asia, Australia, New Zealand
HABITAT	On acid rocks
ASSOCIATION	Lichenized, with algae
GROWTH FORM	In patches
ABUNDANCE	Occasional
SPORE COLOR	White
EDIBILITY	Said to be edible (if cooked)

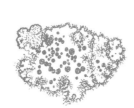

THICKNESS
Up to ¼ in
(5 mm)

DIAMETER
Up to 2 in
(50 mm)

UMBILICARIA CYLINDRICA

FRINGED ROCK TRIPE

(LINNAEUS) DELISE EX DUBY

639

Rock tripe presumably takes its name from its appearance, rather than its taste. But species of rock tripe, including *Umbilicaria cylindrica*, were once used as food by many North America indigenous peoples, including the Huron, Algonquin, Cree, and Inuit. Sir John Franklin and his men, on an ill-fated expedition to discover the Northwest Passage, ate rock tripe and their boot leather in an effort to stay alive. A possibly tastier Japanese species called the Iwatake (*Umbilicaria esculenta*) was once eaten as a delicacy, collectors being lowered down cliffs in baskets to collect the lichen from the rocks.

SIMILAR SPECIES

Other species of rock tripe can be very similar, but most lack the conspicuous marginal hairs of *Umbilicaria cylindrica*. The Netted Rock Tripe (*U. proboscidea*), which may also have been eaten by desperate explorers, has a network of wrinkles or ridges on its upper surface.

The Fringed Rock Tripe forms foliose thalli that are attached to rocks at a single point. Thalli are irregularly spherical or leaflike, pale to dark gray (but brownish when wet), with a smooth upper surface conspicuously fringed with long, stiff, blackish hairs. The margins are often inrolled, and the undersurface is pale gray to buff.

Actual size

FAMILY	Parmeliaceae
DISTRIBUTION	Continental Europe, western Asia
HABITAT	On conifers, more rarely broadleaf trees
ASSOCIATION	Lichenized, with algae
GROWTH FORM	Pendant from branches
ABUNDANCE	Locally common
SPORE COLOR	White
EDIBILITY	Not edible

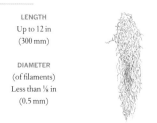

LENGTH
Up to 12 in
(300 mm)

DIAMETER
(of filaments)
Less than ⅛ in
(0.5 mm)

640

USNEA BARBATA
OLD MAN'S BEARD
(LINNAEUS) WEBER EX F. H. WIGGERS

Beard lichens are common in old, unspoilt forests where they festoon the branches of living trees—but they are highly pollution-sensitive and have become rare or extinct in many areas. They have long been used as a folk medicine in various cultures, mainly to treat wounds and infections. This may have been quite effective, since beard lichens contain usnic acid, a bitter compound with antibiotic properties, also found in the Star Reindeer Moss (*Cladonia stellaris*). Nowadays, *Usnea* species (often dubiously identified as *U. barbata*) are commercially collected and marketed for use in homeopathy, aromatherapy, herbal, and other alternative medicines.

SIMILAR SPECIES

Usnea barbata appears to be restricted to continental Europe and Asia. The name, however, has been widely applied to similar species elsewhere—many of which are difficult to distinguish. The Methuselah's Beard (*Dolichousnea longissima*) can produce strands over 9 ft (3 m) long, but is seriously threatened by pollution, logging, and collecting for decorative and herbal use.

Actual size

The Old Man's Beard forms long, hairlike thalli that hang down from branches. The hairlike filaments are branched, the branches of uneven thickness, smooth to ridged, warty, or granular, pale greenish gray, and whitish inside if cut. Fruitbodies are generally absent (common in the related *U. florida*), but are disc-like and pale grayish if they are present.

FAMILY	Teloschistaceae
DISTRIBUTION	North America, Europe, Africa, Central and South America, Antarctica, Asia, New Zealand
HABITAT	On calcareous and siliceous rocks
ASSOCIATION	Lichenized, with algae
GROWTH FORM	In patches
ABUNDANCE	Locally common
SPORE COLOR	White
EDIBILITY	Not edible

THICKNESS
Less than ⅛ in
(2 mm)

DIAMETER
Up to 2 in
(50 mm)

XANTHORIA ELEGANS

ELEGANT SUNBURST LICHEN

(LINK) TH. FRIES

641

The Elegant Sunburst Lichen is an extremely widespread species, occurring in every continent except Australia. It typically grows on rocks, especially those enriched by bird droppings, but is also able to colonize roofs and other man-made structures. The bright coloring comes from carotenoid pigments, and the lichen was once used to make face paint by indigenous peoples in northwestern America. These same pigments may help the lichen, which is often found in alpine areas, to survive high levels of ultraviolet radiation. In a Martian environment simulation, involving irradiation in a vacuum, spores of the Elegant Sunburst Lichen survived and germinated more successfully than those of other tested lichens.

SIMILAR SPECIES

The related *Xanthoria sorediata* is very similar, but lacks disc-shaped fruitbodies. Some *Caloplaca* species, such as the common, yellow *C. flavescens* and the bright orange *C. ignea*, look similar, but the lobes of the *Xanthoria* should peel cleanly from the rock surface, whereas the lobe-like crusts of *Caloplaca* will not.

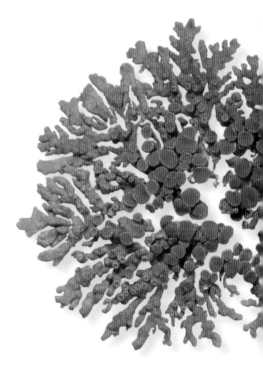

The Elegant Sunburst Lichen forms foliose, almost crustose, thalli that are strikingly bright yellow-orange to deep orange-red. Thalli are typically spherical, with narrow, radiating, straplike lobes. The disc-shaped fruitbodies are common in the center of the thallus and are similarly colored or darker, with a distinct, notched margin.

Actual size

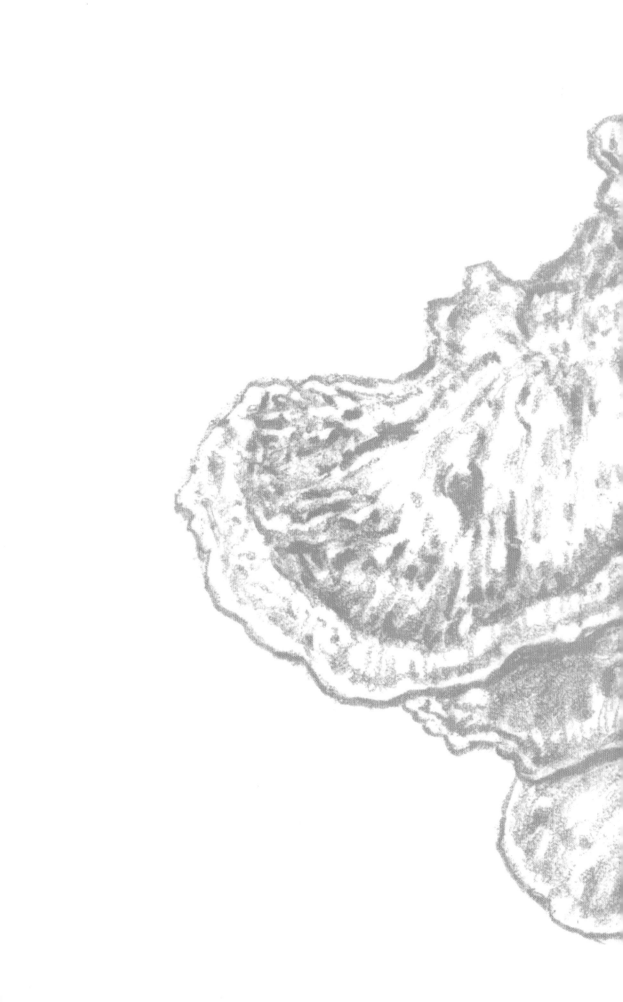

APPENDICES

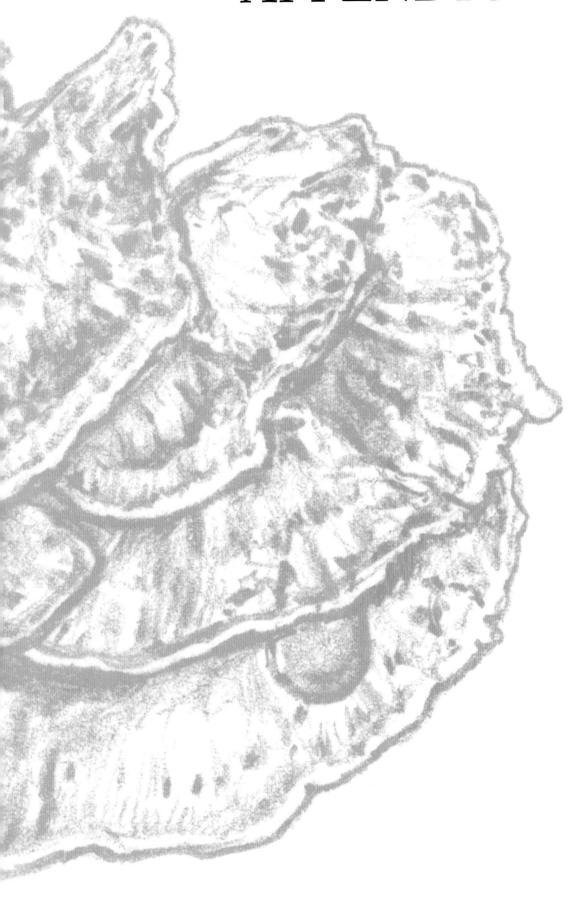

GLOSSARY

Technical terms have been avoided wherever possible or have been glossed where they occur in the text. A certain number of mycological or other scientific terms are difficult to avoid, however, and these are briefly explained in the alphabetical list below.

Ascomycete any fungus belonging to the phylum Ascomycota.

Ascus (pl. asci) a microscopic cell in which spores are formed, typical of cup fungi and other species in the Ascomycota.

Basidiomycete any fungus belonging to the phylum Basidiomycota.

Basidium (pl. basidia) a microscopic cell on which spores are formed externally, typical of agarics and other species in the Basidiomycota.

Bioluminescence the production of light by a living organism.

Bioremediation the removal of environmental pollutants using living organisms.

Calcareous containing chalk or lime.

Cartilaginous like cartilage, gristly.

Concolorous of the same color.

Conk (in American English) a fruitbody of a bracket fungus; (generally) a swollen canker on a living tree produced by a wood-rotting fungus (e.g. *Inonotus obliquus*, p. 396).

Coprophilous dung-loving.

Coralloid branched, like coral.

Cord a visible strand formed by hyphae clumping together.

Cortina a thin, cobwebby, partial veil covering the gills of some agarics (e.g. *Cortinarius* species).

Crustose forming a crust.

Cuticle an outer covering, especially the cap surface of a fruitbody.

Decurrent (of gills, pores, etc.) running down the stem.

Depressed (of a cap) with a central depression or dip.

Ectomycorrhizal forming mycorrhiza in which the hyphae of the fungal partner form a sheath around the root cells of the plant partner.

Effused flat, spread out or skinlike.

Endomycorrhizal forming mycorrhiza in which the hyphae of the fungal partner penetrate the root cells of the plant partner.

Endophyte a fungus (or other organism) that lives within the tissues of a plant.

Epithet (or species epithet) the second word in the scientific name of a species (e.g. "*bisporus*" in "*Agaricus bisporus*").

Evanescent quickly disappearing or fleeting.

Excentric (of a stem) not central.

Fibril a small fiber.

Fibrillose covered in small fibers.

Flocculose/floccular covered in small, soft tufts.

Foliose (of lichens) with leaflike lobes.

Foray a field trip to collect or record fungi.

Fruitbody a sporocarp; the spore-bearing organ of a fungus (e.g. a mushroom).

Gills lamellae; a spore-bearing surface composed of thin blades, such as those below the cap of an ordinary cultivated mushroom.

Girdle (of a stem) a band of scales encircling the stem, often slightly irregular or incomplete.

Hygrophanous (of caps) changing color and becoming somewhat translucent when damp.

Hygroscopic absorbing moisture (and bending or twisting as a result, as in the "arms" of *Astraeus hygrometricus*, p. 508).

Hypha (pl. hyphae) a microscopic filament out of which fungi (apart from yeasts) are composed; the fungal equivalent of plant and animal cells.

Indusium an enclosing membrane (as in the "net" of *Phallus indusiatus*, p. 545).

Metabolites chemical compounds naturally produced by fungi and other organisms.

Montane upland; a vegetation zone (often damp and cool) below "subalpine."

Mycelium (pl. mycelia) a mass of interconnected hyphae that together form the living fungus from which fruitbodies arise; called "spawn" by mushroom cultivators.

Mycologist one who studies fungi.

Mycorrhiza a mutually beneficial, symbiotic association between fungal hyphae and plant roots, whereby the fungus supplies nutrients to the plant and the plant supplies carbohydrates to the fungus.

Nitrophile a nitrogen-loving organism (growing in enriched or manured soil).

Peridiole a packet of spores (as in the "eggs" of bird's nest fungi, pp. 532–34).

Phalloid resembling or related to the stinkhorns (*Phallus* species, pp. 544–45).

Phenolic relating to a group of chemical compounds that include phenol (carbolic acid).

Polypore alternative name for a bracket fungus (p. 363).

Poroid having a spore-bearing surface made up of pores (as in the boletes, p. 325).

Propagule any part of a fungus that can propagate itself when detached (such as a spore or a sclerotium).

Ramifying branching.

Red List an agreed list of species (local, national, or international) that are under threat and are of conservation concern.

Rhizoid a root-like structure made up of hyphae.

Rhizomorph a visible strand formed by hyphae clumping together.

Ring an annulus; remains of a partial veil forming a ring around the stem of some agarics and other fungi.

Ring zone a ringlike area of scales or other veil fragments around the stem of some agarics and other fungi.

Rust a plant disease caused by microscopic "rust fungi," often leaving rusty-brown lesions on stems and leaves.

Saprotroph an organism that feeds on dead matter (e.g. fallen leaves or branches)

Sclerotium (pl. sclerotia) a hardened pellet or ball of hyphae, usually serving as a propagule.

Scurfy (of a cap or stem) having the surface roughened by small scales.

Smut a plant disease caused by microscopic "smut fungi," often producing powdery, chocolate-brown spores.

Species complex a group of closely related but genetically distinct species that may look so similar to each other that they are difficult or impossible to distinguish by sight.

Sporocarp technical name for a fungal fruitbody.

Striate (of cap margins) finely striped.

Stroma sterile fungal tissue on or in which fruitbodies are formed (as in *Xylaria* species, pp. 624–26).

Thallus (pl. thalli) mycelium, particularly of a lichen where the mycelium is exposed and may be crustlike or frondlike.

Umbo a central boss on a cap, sometimes sharp or point-like, sometimes no more than a bump.

Umbonate (of caps) having a central boss or bump.

Veil a thin, protective covering to a developing fruitbody or (if a partial veil) to its spore-producing surface; the veil typically breaks apart when the fruitbody expands, leaving fragments or scales behind, sometimes a volva or ring.

Volva remains of a veil, leaving a sack-like or baggy receptacle at the base of the stem of some agarics (e.g. *Volvariella* species, pp. 320–21).

645

NOMENCLATURE

Kingdom the highest classification rank (as in the kingdom Fungi).

Phylum (pl. phyla) a classification rank above class and below kingdom (as in the phylum Basidiomycota).

Class a classification rank above order and below phylum (as in the class Agaricomycetes).

Order a classification rank above family and below class (as in the order Agaricales).

Family a classification rank above genus and below order (as in the family Agaricaceae).

Genus (pl. genera) a classification rank above species and below family (as in the genus *Agaricus*).

Section a secondary classification rank sometimes used to divide a genus into groups of related species (as in *Agaricus* section *Bivelares*).

Species a classification rank below genus (as in the species *Agaricus bisporus*).

RESOURCES

The books and web sites listed below are just a selection of the many resources currently available to those with an interest in the larger fungi.

FURTHER READING: GENERAL INTEREST

Bessette, A.R. & Bessette A.E. *The Rainbow Beneath my Feet: a mushroom dyer's field guide.* Syracuse, NY: Syracuse University Press, 2001.

Gilbert, O. *New Naturalist: Lichens.* London: HarperCollins, 2000.

Hall, I.R. et al. *Edible and Poisonous Mushrooms of the World.* Portland, OR: Timber Press, 2003.

Harding, P. *Mushroom Miscellany.* London: HarperCollins, 2008.

Money, N. *Mr. Bloomfield's Orchard.* New York: Oxford University Press, 2002.

Purvis, W. *Lichens.* London: Natural History Museum; Washington: Smithsonian, 2007.

Spooner, B. & Roberts, P. *New Naturalist: Fungi.* London: HarperCollins, 2005.

Stamets, P. *Growing Gourmet and Medicinal Mushrooms* (3rd edn). Berkeley, CA: Ten Speed Press, 2000.

FURTHER READING: REGIONAL FIELD GUIDES

North America

Barron, G. *Mushrooms of Ontario and Eastern Canada* (3rd edn). Edmonton: Lone Pine, 1999.

Bessette, A.E., Bessette, A.B., & Fischer, D.W. *Mushrooms of Northeastern North America.* Syracuse, NY: Syracuse University Press, 1997.

Brodo, I.M., Sharnoff, S.D., & Sharnoff, S. *Lichens of North America.* New Haven, CN: Yale University Press, 2001.

Hemmes, D.E. & Desjardin, D.E. *Mushrooms of Hawai'i.* Berkeley, CA: Ten Speed Press, 2002.

Huffman, D.M. et al. *Mushrooms and other Fungi of the Midcontinental United States* (2nd edn). Iowa City, IA: University Iowa Press, 2008.

Metzler, S. & Metzler, V. *Texas Mushrooms.* Austin, TX: University Texas Press, 1992.

Phillips, R. *Mushrooms of North America.* Boston, MA: Little, Brown & Co., 1991.

Roody, W.C. *Mushrooms of West Virginia and the Central Appalachians.* Lexington, KY: Kentucky University Press, 2003.

Trudell, S. & Ammirati, J. 2009. *Mushrooms of the Pacific Northwest.* Portland, OR: Timber Press, 2009.

British Isles & Europe

Dobson, F.S. *Lichens: An Illustrated Guide to the British and Irish Species* (5th edn). Slough: Richmond Publishing, 2005.

Evans, S. & Kibby, G. *Pocket Nature: Fungi.* London: Dorling Kindersley, 2004.

Phillips, R. *Mushrooms.* London: Macmillan, 2006.

Sterry, P. & Hughes, B. *Collins Complete Guide to British Mushrooms and Toadstools.* London: HarperCollins, 2009.

Australia & New Zealand

Fuhrer, B. *A Field Companion to Australian Fungi*. Melbourne: Bloomings Books, 2001.

Ridley, G.S. & Horne, D. *A Photographic Guide to Mushrooms and other Fungi of New Zealand*. Auckland: New Holland, 2007.

Young, A.M. *A Field Guide to the Fungi of Australia*. Sydney: UNSW Press, 2004.

Southern Africa

Gryzenhout, M. *Pocket Guide: Mushrooms of South Africa*. Struik, Cape Town: Struik, 2010.

Central & South America

Gamundi, I. & Horak, E. *Fungi of the Andean-Patagonian Forests*. Buenos Aires: Vazquez Mazzini, 2007.

Mata, M. *Costa Rica Mushrooms Vol. 1*. INBio, Santo Domingo de Heredia: INBio, 2003.

Mata, M., Halling, R., & Mueller, G.M. *Costa Rica Macrofungi Vol. 2*. Santo Domingo de Heredia, INBio, 2003.

SOME USEFUL WEB SITES

The following web sites offer valuable information and several feature excellent photographs of fungi that may be helpful for identification. Using a search engine to query a species or topic may bring many additional web sites for examination.

British Mycological Society
http://www.britmycolsoc.org.uk/

647

Cybertruffle and **Cyberliber**—wide range of information about fungi
http://www.cybertruffle.org.uk/eng/index.htm

European Mycological Association—includes contacts for local societies worldwide
http://www.euromould.org/links/socs.htm

Fungimap (Australia)
http://www.rbg.vic.gov.au/fungimap/home

Index Fungorum—a freely searchable on-line database
http://www.indefungorum.org/

Landcare Research (New Zealand) — Virtual Mycota
http://virtualmycota.landcareresearch.co.nz/ebforms/vM_home.aspx

MushroomExpert—keys, photos, information (North America)
http://www.mushroomexpert.com/

Mycokey—keys, photos, information (Europe)
http://www.mycokey.com/

North American Mycological Association
http://www.namyco.org/

Tom Volk's Fungi—photos, information
http://botit.botany.wisc.edu/toms_fungi/fotm.html

The CLASSIFICATION *of* FUNGI

As with plants, the scientific classification of fungi dates back to Carl Linnaeus—the great, eighteenth-century Swedish naturalist. Linnaeus and the early naturalists classified fungi by superficial similarities in shape, but after Darwin the goal was to create a more natural classification that brought related species together, whether or not they looked similar.

In the twentieth century, fungal classification still took account of fruitbody shape, but also used microscopic and other details to determine relationships. Since the 1990s, however, DNA analysis has substantially altered traditional concepts, showing, for example, that many apparently distinct groups of fungi—such as puffballs and mushrooms—are in fact closely related. Further research will undoubtedly result in additional changes.

The kingdom Fungi is currently divided into seven major divisions called "phyla." Nearly all the larger fungi belong in two of these: the Ascomycota and the Basidiomycota. Each phylum is further divided into "classes," the classes into "orders," and the orders into "families." The chart here includes only those phyla, classes, orders, and families represented in this book.

The family name is given under each species entry. If you look up the Common Earthball (*Scleroderma citrinum*, page 528), for example, you will see that it is in the family Sclerodermataceae. The chart will tell you that the Sclerodermataceae belong in the order Boletales, class Agaricomycetes, phylum Basidiomycota. This shows that the Common Earthball is a distant relative of the boletes (same order) and an even more distant relative of agarics and bracket fungi (same class).

648

ASCOMYCOTA			
EUROTIOMYCETES			
ONYGENALES			
Elaphomycetaceae	Onygenaceae		
LECANOROMYCETES			
LECANORALES			
Cladoniaceae	Parmeliaceae		
PELTIGERALES			
Collemataceae	Lobariaceae	Pannariaceae	Peltigeraceae
TELOSCHISTALES			
Teloschistaceae			
UMBILICARIALES			
Umbilicariaceae			
LEOTIOMYCETES			
CYTTARIALES			
Cyttariaceae			
HELOTIALES			
Dermateaceae	Geoglossaceae	Helotiaceae	Hyaloscyphaceae
Rutstroemiaceae	Sclerotiniaceae	Vibrisseaceae	
LEOTIALES			
Bulgariaceae	Leotiaceae		
RHYTISMATALES			
Cudoniaceae			
PEZIZOMYCETES			
PEZIZALES			
Caloscyphaceae	Discinaceae	Glaziellaceae	Helvellaceae
Morchellaceae	Pezizaceae	Pyronemataceae	Rhizinaceae
Sarcoscyphaceae	Sarcosomataceae	Tuberaceae	
SORDARIOMYCETES			
HYPOCREALES			
Clavicipitaceae	Cordycipitaceae	Hypocreaceae	Nectriaceae
Ophiocordycipitaceae			
XYLARIALES			
Xylariaceae			

BASIDIOMYCOTA			
AGARICOMYCETES			
AGARICALES			
Agaricaceae	Amanitaceae	Bolbitiaceae	Clavariaceae
Cortinariaceae	Cyphellaceae	Entolomataceae	Fistulinaceae
Hydnangiaceae	Hygrophoraceae	Inocybaceae	Lyophyllaceae
Marasmiaceae	Mycenaceae	Niaceae	Physalacriaceae
Pleurotaceae	Pluteaceae	Psathyrellaceae	Pterulaceae
Schizophyllaceae	Strophariaceae	Tricholomataceae	Typhulaceae
AURICULARIALES			
Auriculariaceae			
BOLETALES			
Amylocorticiaceae	Boletaceae	Calostomataceae	Coniophoraceae
Diplocystidiaceae	Gomphidiaceae	Gyroporaceae	Hygrophoropsidaceae
Paxillaceae	Rhizopogonaceae	Sclerodermataceae	Serpulaceae
Suillaceae	Tapinellaceae		
CANTHARELLALES			
Cantharellaceae	Clavulinaceae	Hydnaceae	
CORTICIALES			
Corticiaceae			
GEASTRALES			
Geastraceae			
GLOEOPHYLLALES			
Gloeophyllaceae			
GOMPHALES			
Clavariadelphaceae	Gomphaceae		
HYMENOCHAETALES			
Hymenochaetaceae	Repetobasidiaceae	Schizoporaceae	
HYSTERANGIALES			
Gallaceaceae			
PHALLALES			
Phallaceae			
POLYPORALES			
Fomitopsidaceae	Ganodermataceae	Meripilaceae	Meruliaceae
Phanerochaetaceae	Polyporaceae	Sparassidaceae	
RUSSULALES			
Albatrellaceae	Auriscalpiaceae	Bondarzewiaceae	Echinodontiaceae
Lachnocladiaceae	Russulaceae	Stephanosporaceae	Stereaceae
SEBACINALES			
Sebacinaceae			
THELEPHORALES			
Bankeraceae	Thelephoraceae		
DACRYMYCETES			
DACRYMYCETALES			
Dacrymycetaceae			
TREMELLOMYCETES			
TREMELLALES			
Carcinomycetaceae	Tremellaceae		

649

LATIN AND ENGLISH NAMES

Every species has a Latin two-part name: genus (e.g. *Amanita*) plus species epithet (e.g. *muscaria*). The resulting species name (*A. muscaria*) is internationally recognized in all languages. A name may only change as a result of new research. The rules for creating or changing a name are governed by an international code. Not every species has a common name, however, presumably because the English paid fungi little heed. The few genuine old names, like "mushroom," "toadstool," or "puffball," were applied indiscriminately to many different species. Modern English names have almost all been invented in the last two hundred years by natural history writers. They vary from book to book, but a list of recommended English names for some of the larger fungi has now been published and is used here where appropriate.

AUTHOR CITATIONS

It is common practice to follow the scientific name of a fungus with the name of the person who originally described it and the latter is frequently abbreviated. For example, many species were first described by the celebrated Swedish mycologist Elias Magnus Fries, whose name is usually shortened to Fr. In this book, however, we have given the surname of the author rather than the abbreviation, for ease of reference. When a species has been transferred to another genus, it is the convention to place the original author's name in brackets followed by the author who made the transfer. Thus the Destroying Angel (page 58) was originally described as *Agaricus virosus* Fries, but was later transferred to the genus *Amanita* by Bertillon, as *Amanita virosa* (Fries) Bertillon.

INDEX *by* COMMON NAME

651

INDEX *by* SCIENTIFIC NAME

653

654

655

ACKNOWLEDGMENTS

DR. PETER ROBERTS & SHELLEY EVANS

The scientific names of fungi and their classification have largely been based on the on-line database Index Fungorum (http://www.indexfungorum.org/). Thanks to Dr. Paul Kirk for answering queries on current nomenclature.

English names, where appropriate, have been derived from "Recommended English names for fungi in the UK" (http://www.plantlife.org.uk/uploads/documents/recommended-english-names-for-fungi.pdf) or have been sourced from regional guides and on-line references.

Thanks to the editorial team at Ivy Press, especially Lorraine Turner, Stephanie Evans, Katie Greenwood, Jamie Pumfrey, and Kim Davies, for their patience and help.

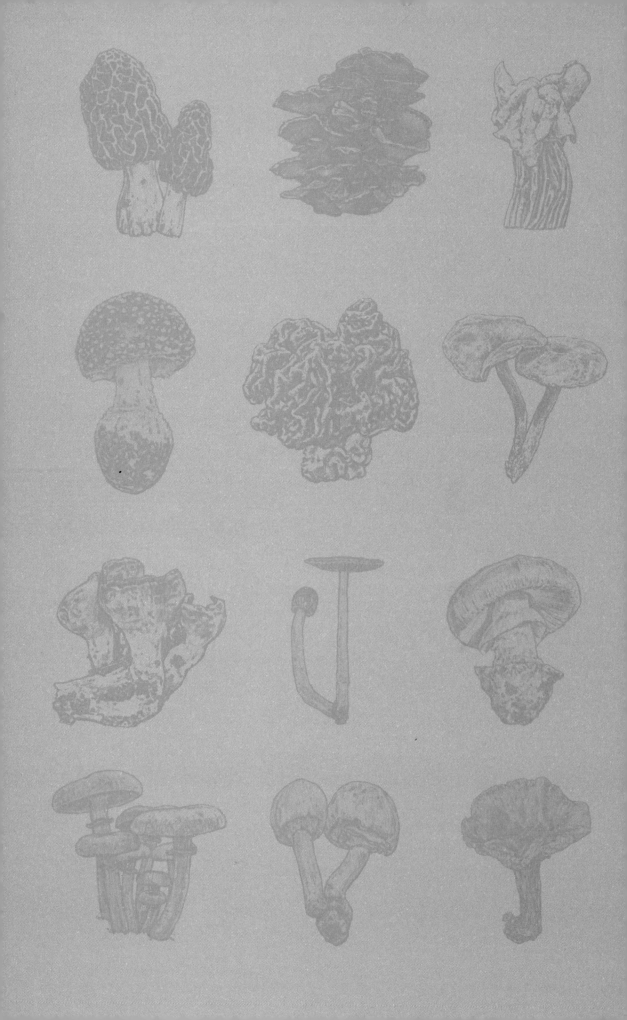